Conquering Complexity

Lessons for defence systems acquisition

Conquering Complexity

Lessons for defence systems acquisition

by

The Defence Engineering Group
University College London

Professor Ken Hambleton
Professor David Kirkpatrick
Mr Ian Holder
Mr David Kimberley
Lt Col (retd) Mike Bragg
Dr Steve McInally
Dr Alex Weiss
Dr Tim Williams

Edited by Dr Alex Weiss

ISBN 0 11 773034 3

Published by TSO (The Stationery Office) and available from:

Online
www.tso.co.uk/bookshop

Mail, Telephone, Fax & E-mail
TSO
PO Box 29, Norwich NR3 1GN
Telephone orders/General enquiries: 0870 600 5522
Fax orders: 0870 600 5533
E-mail: book.orders@tso.co.uk
Textphone: 0870 240 3701

TSO Shops
123 Kingsway, London WC2B 6PQ
020 7242 6393 Fax 020 7242 6394
68–69 Bull Street, Birmingham B4 6AD
0121 236 9696 Fax 0121 236 9699
9–21 Princess Street, Manchester M60 8AS
0161 834 7201 Fax 0161 833 0634
16 Arthur Street, Belfast BT1 4GD
028 9023 8451 Fax 028 9023 5401
18–19 High Street, Cardiff CF10 1PT
029 2039 5548 Fax 029 2038 4347
71 Lothian Road, Edinburgh EH3 9AZ
0870 606 5566 Fax 0870 606 5588

TSO Accredited Agents
See Yellow Pages

Also available through good booksellers

Contents

The front and back cover photographs were kindly provided by BAe Systems.

All royalties from this edition of *Conquering Complexity* are being given to SSAFA (the Soldiers', Sailors' and Airmens' Families Association).

Foreword

Foreword by Vice Admiral Sir Jeremy Blackham KCB BA RN (retd)

During my years serving in the Royal Navy, in command of HM ships and of task groups, I have always appreciated the critical contribution of high-performance, reliable equipment to the effectiveness of the UK's armed forces. In my later post as Deputy Chief of Defence Staff (Equipment Capability), I came to recognise the major problems involved in acquiring large defence systems. Since I joined the defence industry and looked up the other end of the telescope, it has become just as clear to me that industry shares these concerns. I was therefore delighted to learn that, at last, a book is available that will help defence systems engineers, both those serving in the Ministry of Defence as well as those working in industry, to provide more effective equipment solutions for our armed forces.

I am particularly pleased that as well as engineering, the text also stresses the importance of management and analysis in providing equipment that will have to operate successfully in war, that most testing of environments. To me, the people aspect of defence systems has always been of the greatest importance and I am delighted that this volume spends time dealing with this issue.

The task of defence acquisition has probably never been more difficult. With political pressure to minimise defence expenditure and the imperative of getting best value for money with shrinking resources, it is essential that people involved today in equipping our forces understand the wide range of often-conflicting issues and interests which affect equipment acquisition and that they are professionally trained to do their jobs. For the first time, a comprehensive text is available that can be used by the student and experienced defence systems engineer alike to improve their understanding of the wide range of issues involved in fulfilling the equipment needs of the three branches of the armed forces.

Preface

The cost-effective procurement and support of defence systems is crucial to the effectiveness of a nation's armed forces, and can be achieved by the principles of defence systems engineering (DSE). This topic was taught for several years in an MSc course at University College London (UCL), which forms the basis of this book. A brief description is given of the contents of the book, indicating those who will find it useful and outlining the contributions of the various authors.

1 Requirements

Requirements for defence systems stem from the foreign policy of a nation, in this case the United Kingdom, and its perceived role on the world stage. The nature and numbers of defence systems bought are constrained by their cost, and their performance is a compromise between what capability is required, when it is required, what can be afforded, and what is technologically feasible for the nation and/or is available on the international market. Thus the acquisition of new defence systems is a complex and challenging process, blending military doctrine and planning with scientific and engineering expertise. It requires a detailed understanding of the political, industrial and economic environments within which acquisition must achieve best value for money.

No nation can isolate itself from the rest of the world. Every country's security, its prosperity and its resources can be affected profoundly by what happens beyond its borders. The UK is no exception. The government's aim is for the UK to act as an influential power, almost always working with others, to deliver prosperity and stability in an unstable world. There are times when diplomacy is not enough, and force or the threat of force is needed either to defend the UK and its allies or to act in a chivalrous role to defend the weak and oppressed anywhere in the world. At such times, the government and the country rely on the professionalism of the armed forces and the effectiveness of their defence equipment.

2 Acquisition

The acquisition of cost-effective equipment demands the integration of the various different disciplines and processes used by personnel with the technical, managerial and analytical expertise to create, acquire, supply and operate complex systems. A philosophical approach, rather than a process, is required when dealing with large integrated systems. Such an approach can provide a structured way of dealing with the:

- Identification of the system requirement and the associated challenges.
- Analysis of the total life cycle and hierarchy of the system.

- Development of approaches and solutions to solve problems.
- Implementation of the optimum acquisition and operational strategies.

The philosophy of DSE involves the integration of engineering, management and analytical disciplines that are necessary for the acquisition and operation of large and complex systems, and for the achievement of demanding performance, cost and timescale targets despite the uncertainties of rapidly advancing technology, changing national and international policies, and evolving requirements. This philosophy stresses the need to 'look upwards and outwards', an emphasis on the recognition of the complex interactions between systems and sub-systems, a broad outlook based on many disciplines, and recognition that people are one of the most important elements in the design, management and operation of any complex system.

3 Book contents

The contents of this book derive directly from the MSc course in DSE, which was taught to students at the Defence Engineering Group (DEG) of UCL between 1991 and 2004. This course has illuminated the many problems of defence acquisition and has shown how DSE can help to overcome them. This book encapsulates the key principles of DSE within a single volume. In order to keep it to an acceptable length, the text provides only an introduction to several of the disciplines, competences and processes which form part of DSE and omits entirely the war studies, accounting, economics, law, contracts and organisation theory which were ably provided to the MSc course by the staff of King's College London. These topics form important parts of the knowledge base of a defence systems engineer but they are amply covered by existing books and published papers. A selection of further reading is cited at the end of each chapter.

This book is divided into an introduction to DSE, ten chapters describing the constituent disciplines, and some brief conclusions. The first two chapters introduce the subject of DSE, and deal with the UK defence environment and with the challenges of systems acquisition. The subsequent six chapters look in detail at a number of aspects of defence systems acquisition, with separate chapters covering the acquisition process and strategy, finance, analysis, supplier issues, test and evaluation and management. Chapter 9 considers how DSE can help to conquer the challenges of defence systems acquisition. It describes the concept of DSE as it has been taught by the DEG, providing a list of 'lessons' and noting how each contributes to the understanding and resolution of the various defence systems acquisition challenges. The final chapter considers the future and examines the outlook for defence systems acquisition and engineering in the twenty-first century. After a short set of conclusions, four appendices follow; these cover education in DSE, its origins as a new multidisciplinary philosophy, a glossary of the terms and abbreviations that are used throughout the book, and background CVs of the contributing authors. Finally, there is an index of the major entries in the book.

Although anyone concerned with complex systems will find this book useful, it is aimed principally at people working in the defence sectors of both government and industry, who want to understand the interactions of multidisciplinary activities, and need to develop their ability to use systems engineering, management and analysis skills. It is essential reading for those who work in the specification, acquisition and supply of complex defence equipment. The philosophy is equally applicable to other domains that also require the integration of many sub-systems, involve multiple stakeholders and have lengthy timescales; these include industries such as aerospace, information technology, public utilities, telecommunications and transport. For the reader whose work involves a single piece in the large defence-acquisition jigsaw puzzle, this book helps in the understanding of the finished puzzle, and how the pieces fit together to achieve the emergent properties of the system that meet the military requirement.

4 Authors

The authors of the book have each had successful careers in government service or industry where they have used and implemented engineering, management and analytical practices. They joined the DEG at UCL to develop, research and teach DSE as a philosophical approach to achieving success over the life of a complex system. The DSE sections of the book were provided principally by Professor Ken Hambleton and Mr Ian Holder, who together founded the MSc course and established DSE as an academic discipline. These parts have been enriched by significant contributions from Dr Steve McInally. Professor David Kirkpatrick provided the chapters dealing with analysis and finance as well as the chapter covering the challenge of UK defence systems acquisition and the majority of the final part of the book that looks to the future. Lt Col (retd) Mike Bragg contributed the section dealing with the UK armed forces and provided valuable inputs to other sections from a military perspective. Dr Tim Williams produced the section dealing with supply chains and Mr David Kimberley dealt with all aspects of test and evaluation. Dr Alex Weiss covered industrial and supplier issues as well as IT and communications, and acted as managing editor during the final stages of the production of this volume. Most of the book's sections benefited from interactive debate and mutual collaboration between the authors.

The authors would also like to thank Cdre (retd) Peter Tatham, who reviewed the section on the UK armed forces and produced a number of significant insights, and to Miss Debra Shepherd who drew all the illustrations. Thanks also to Mrs Dana Pridie-Sale and Mr Rob Linton, who both provided original information to the authors, and Professor Ron Smith, Mr John Catherall and Ms Lyn Corson who all commented constructively on the text.

The various sections of this book present the views of their authors and do not necessarily reflect a consensus of the DEG or of any other organisation. DSE is not a procrustean dogma but a philosophy within which the most effective approach to managing any particular defence project should evolve through informed debate. DSE has to balance the performance, time and through-life cost of producing novel, complex, high-technology equipment while ensuring that it can readily be integrated with existing and future defence systems. It has to consider the technical feasibility of the perceived requirements and convert them into a coherent set of measurable parameters that can be used to acquire systems to meet the nation's defence objectives at an affordable cost and with an acceptable degree of risk.

This book has been produced with the support of the Defence Science and Technology Laboratory (Dstl) but it should not be taken to represent a Dstl corporate view of systems engineering. Its content is derived from the material used to teach the MSc in DSE at UCL, and as such it represents a substantial body of knowledge relevant to this important subject. One of Dstl's values is 'cherishing knowledge' and Dstl considers it important that such knowledge is not lost, and is made available to inform future discussions and activities in this area critical to decision-making and capability acquisition.

Introduction

to defence systems engineering

The acquisition and implementation of defence systems are both complicated tasks that require a set of unique talents. No single traditional discipline provides the overall skills required to deal with these complex systems – a blend of engineering, management and analysis is required. The new discipline of defence systems engineering (DSE) has been developed since 1991 by the Defence Engineering Group (DEG) at University College London (UCL) and forms the basis of this book.

1 What is defence systems engineering?

Defence systems engineering is the discipline created by the DEG to address the challenges of a complex system's life cycle. In order to understand fully the issues surrounding a defence system, it is necessary to comprehend the political, operational and technical environment in which the system is being acquired and used. For this reason, DSE begins with the defence policy, national economy and available technology, which constitute the environment for acquisition, and then flows down through analysis of requirements for new defence equipment to the interacting activities of design, development, test and evaluation, manufacture, operation and support, with all of the activities being integrated through various strands of analysis. DSE was defined by the DEG in 1995 as follows:

Defence systems engineering is the integration of those engineering, analytical and management activities necessary for the procurement of large and complex defence systems. It uses systems engineering philosophies and procedures to promote the achievement of performance, cost and timescale in the uncertain environment of rapidly advancing technology and evolving industrial and geo-political circumstances.

The DEG was created in response to a requirement defined by the UK Ministry of Defence (MoD) in 1990 for the training and education of its acquisition personnel in systems engineering, defence technologies, management and commercial practices. The aims were:

- To create a centre of excellence in defence systems engineering and acquisition that would develop ideas, knowledge and competences for the benefit of both the MoD and the whole UK.
- To educate a cadre of skilled people able to lead and manage complex defence systems projects in the twenty-first century.

- To increase the professionalism of these skilled defence personnel such that they compare with the best in the world.

DSE is a unique subject that blends the ideas of technology and business, and supports them with systems engineering and analysis. DSE is not a process and it does not prescribe methods. It provides a holistic way of thinking about the totality of problems associated with the acquisition, use and support of a complex defence system, and then helps the practitioner to identify solutions to the problems. DSE is designed to overcome problems through the:

- Application of analysis to identify the true causes of the problem.
- Use of systems engineering and commercial practices to identify solutions.
- Effective use of management and communication skills to plan and lead the implementation of the solution.

DSE may be required at any stage of the defence systems acquisition cycle.

2 Challenges of defence systems acquisition

The House of Commons Defence Committee and the National Audit Office (NAO) have condemned the MoD and its Smart Acquisition initiative as being inefficient and ineffective (respectively), but finding a process to acquire defence systems that provides the required capability faster, cheaper, better and more effectively integrated with existing and future systems is extremely difficult. Smart Acquisition attempts to define a process (intended to

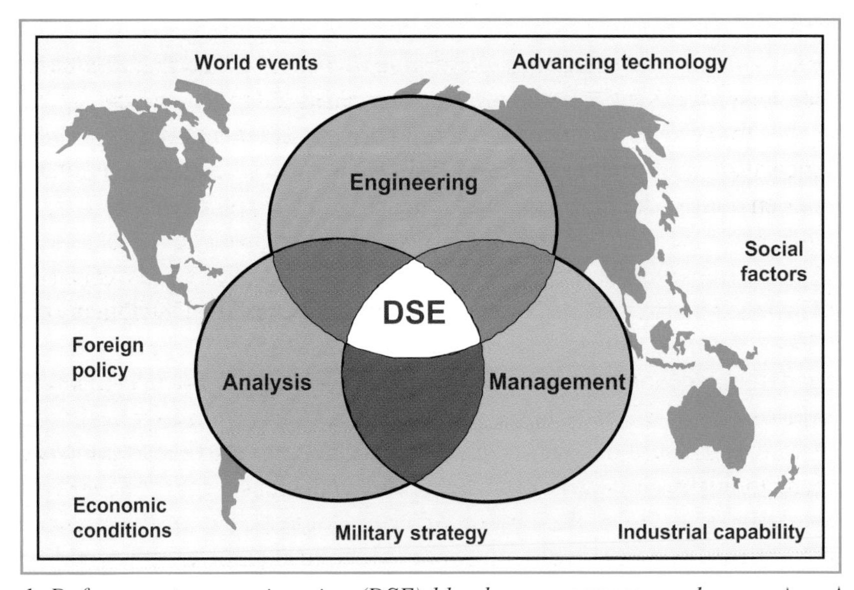

Figure 1. Defence systems engineering (DSE) blends management, analysis and engineering.

be flexible and adaptable) that can be used for all defence acquisitions, whereas DSE supplies the 'big picture' encompassing the multitude of acquisition problems, provides an integrated and disciplined approach to the acquisition of a major defence system, and facilitates selection of the appropriate acquisition process which matches the needs of the project.

DSE needs to be a philosophical approach, rather than a process, because of the diversity of the problems that it addresses. The DEG does not believe that there can be a single process to meet the challenges of acquiring complex defence systems, and has developed DSE to provide 'a way of thinking' that professionals can implement to achieve the best solution. The breadth of the defence systems acquisition challenge is driven by the different technologies used in different defence systems such as ships, submarines, tanks, aircraft, satellites and IT systems, and by their different operational environments. These differences are then magnified by the various acquisition strategies, such as national development, collaborative or commercial off-the-shelf (COTS), and by the various support strategies that may be used. Many of the challenges faced in DSE are similar to those faced by people developing commercial or civil systems, but the issues are broader than in the commercial world. Many complex defence systems exhibit all of the following characteristics:

- The main driver of a defence system's specification and design is the threat the UK faces. This threat is often difficult to define and changes frequently, resulting in requirements that may be expressed vaguely or that may change or evolve.
- The diverse groups of the defence community within the MoD, wider government and industry have different views and responsibilities. These stakeholders, each with distinctive and sometimes conflicting requirements, need to agree and act in a unified manner if the project is to be successful. The personalities of the individuals in the stakeholder community can often play an important part in the decision-making process as well as the interpretation of the individual's post or role.
- Defence systems are used by the armed services and in the UK it is believed that service personnel should have a proactive and influential role in the acquisition process. This adds to the complexity of the stakeholder management issue.
- Defence systems acquisition utilises public funds and there is a need for open and transparent management, decision-making and control processes which an individual or a group cannot manipulate. It is also necessary to allow independent scrutiny. This need for probity in all aspects of a defence system's acquisition can weaken the MoD's hand in negotiations. The forthcoming implementation of the Freedom of Information Act 2000 will have a further effect on the acquisition of defence systems.
- Many defence systems are designed for a 25- or 30-year life cycle, and then have their in-service lives extended. Many have life cycles which approach or exceed 50 years from concept to out of service, during which time the threat may drive users to adopt different mission roles and/or operational profiles for the equipment.
- The extensive use of a wide range of technologies, often at the leading edge of technological advances, adds to the risks of acquiring a defence system. The use of known technologies is often inappropriate as not only would they fail to provide the

required capability, but also defence systems frequently need to be developed in parallel with the technologies they will utilise.

- As the threat is often difficult to identify, the problem of forecasting a system's effectiveness against the threat is a challenge. The performance of a system can often be predicted, but calculating the effectiveness and capability of a system is a much more difficult problem. While data from exercises and operations can be used, the prediction of effectiveness and capability will always be prone to a wide range of uncertainty.
- Defence projects are subject to the vagaries of changing political circumstances, not only within the UK but also internationally. Changes of governments can mean a change of defence policy, and a change in the way the nation's budget is allocated to the various national needs.
- Defence systems are required to be deployable at short notice to varied roles in different environments, and to operate alongside other UK and allied systems. All these factors add to the complexity of the equipment required.

The above list is not definitive, nor is each of the issues unique to defence, but all of these factors are relevant to defence acquisition projects. That these factors tend to be changeable and interdependent makes defence systems acquisition a particularly difficult task – 'a jigsaw puzzle for masochists' as Professor Hambleton put it in his inaugural lecture as a professor.

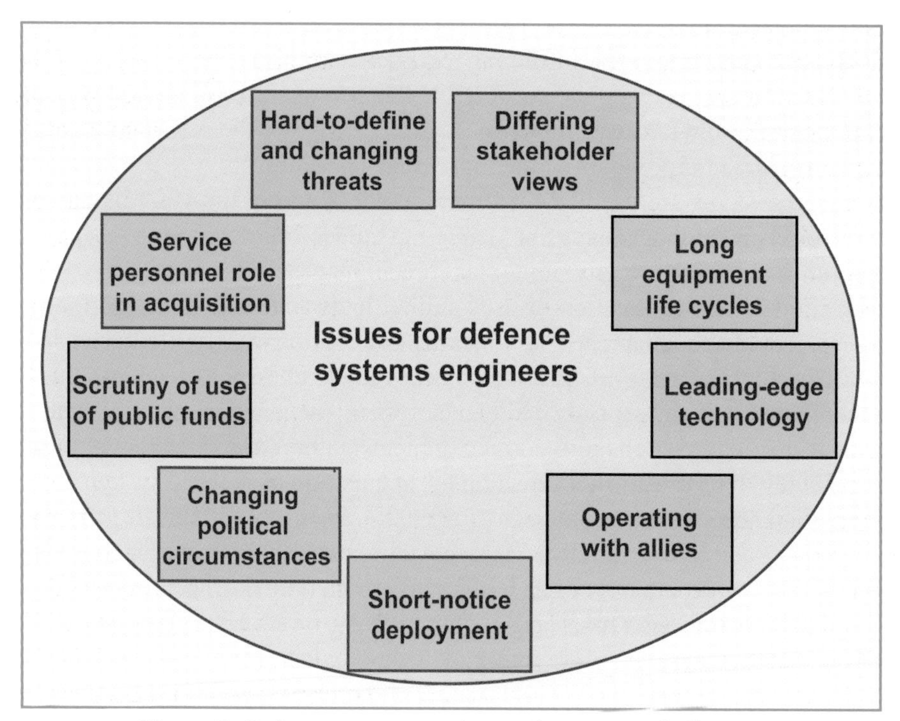

Figure 2. Defence systems engineers face many challenges.

The difficulties that beset the acquisition process, and ultimately affect the success of the equipment acquired, must be overcome as far as possible since the penalties for failure are far more grave than any financial losses a commercial enterprise might suffer. The ability to implement defence policy through the deployment of armed forces is a primary requirement that demands modern, effective, operational defence equipment and systems. Failure of these systems means the loss of lives and the failure of the operation; and both can have major consequences for the nation.

3 Reforms in UK defence systems acquisition

The UK has faced the problems of acquiring complex defence systems for many years, and has tried on a number of occasions to reform the way defence acquisition is undertaken. Since the Second World War, the management of the armed forces and the procurement of their equipment has been progressively centralised by a series of reforms which sought to eliminate duplication in research and development, and to establish logical and traceable requirements for equipment (for example, by the formation of a unified MoD in 1964 with the creation of a Defence Operational Analysis Establishment, and by the institution of the COEIA [combined operational effectiveness and investment appraisal] in 1991). However, these organisational reforms were distracted by the civil/military interface and by the often-unfulfilled aspirations that military research (e.g. in aircraft technologies and electronics) could be exploited to create successful commercial industries; these hopes led to the temporary ministries of Aviation, of Technology and of Aviation Supply in which these dual-use technologies were separated from the purely military technologies. In the early 1970s, the MoD Procurement Executive (PE) merged the three service procurement organisations in the hope that the unified PE could improve the management of defence equipment projects.

In parallel there was a series of procedural reforms intended to provide better control of military research and development. The Gibb-Zuckerman report in 1961 proposed that any equipment project should have three phases (feasibility, project study and development) with check points between each phase to ensure that accurate forecasts of performance, cost and timescale would be available to support the final decision to proceed to full development. The 1966 Downey study concluded that the Gibb-Zuckerman recommendations had not been implemented, and introduced an additional phase by dividing project support into project definition (PD) 1 and 2. Downey also argued that 15% of the estimated development cost should be spent before starting full development. In 1988, the *Learning from Experience* report by Jordan, Lee and Cawsey noted the continuing failure of projects to undertake sufficient planning and experimentation to reduce risks to an acceptable level before starting full development. They proposed that the early project stages should include more detailed technical analysis and demonstration (particularly those involving new technology or software).

In the late 1980s, the MoD decided that it needed to enhance the knowledge and skills of the people who designed and managed the acquisition programmes. While previous changes had been made to processes and organisations, and to the recruitment and training of specialist staff, the new idea was to create, through multidisciplinary education, a cadre of people with the combination of skills needed to tackle the increasing complexity of defence systems. The MoD, with great foresight, realised that the problems of complexity, integration and technology would get more challenging, not easier, and that people with a blend of commercial, technical and analytical skills would be better placed to deal with the complex issues. It developed the appropriate syllabus, competed the requirement amongst the academic community, and announced the foundation of the DEG in 1991. The Group began with the legacy of the previous reforms and processes, and developed new ideas to promote improved acquisition by the MoD; these new ideas were sufficiently robust to absorb the changes in MoD processes that would occur in the 1990s.

The DEG was created shortly after the collapse of the Berlin Wall and the end of the Cold War. The MoD has since undergone two major changes: *Front Line First* (1994) and the *Strategic Defence Review* (1998). The former addressed the need for the efficient use of service manpower, and the increased likelihood of joint operations after the reduction in the major threat faced by the UK, while the latter addressed the issue of what the new threats were and how the UK armed forces would respond to these new threats. The two studies dramatically altered defence strategies in the UK as the threats and potential operations changed. The forces' personnel were redistributed, the need for some particular types of equipment was challenged, and the resulting force structures were optimised for smaller, deployed operations rather than being structured for the single major threat faced by the UK less than a decade before. Despite these changes, there was no need to alter the fundamental principles of DSE, since it is based on a high-level view of the problem. The DEG was able to address each change as modifications rather than fundamental changes. As an example, the fundamental principles are equally applicable to the Downey procurement cycle and the CADMID (concept, assessment, demonstration, manufacture, in-service and disposal) cycle; no major change was required to DSE to cope with the CADMID cycle, and yet the MoD had to change many of its own procurement processes by the introduction of Smart Acquisition (see Chapter 3, Section 1).

4 Origins of defence systems engineering

As stated on page 1, DSE was created by the DEG in the early 1990s (see Appendix 2 for more details) in response to an MoD defined requirement driven by the problems which had been encountered during the acquisition of increasingly complex systems in the 1980s. The most infamous of these problems was the Nimrod AEW aircraft and radar project which was plagued by problems with systems integration, changing requirements, immature technology, a lack of management co-ordination and poor risk mitigation. The Nimrod AEW was not the only project to suffer these problems and together they stimulated the MoD decision to create a cadre of professional systems engineers to lead future projects.

The MoD determined that it needed people with a variety of skills to meet the challenges of future projects. By the late 1980s, information systems and the linking of different systems by computers had begun introducing additional problems of interoperability and interaction, sometimes across very different generations of technologies. The MoD, perceiving future problems of networked-enabled capability (NEC), and the increased use of data links and information technology systems, decided it required people with a blend of skills that no single traditional discipline could provide. The skills required are shown in Figure 3.

- **Project management** – to plan and organise projects.
- **Engineering and technologies** – to understand the systems being acquired.
- **Systems engineering** – to deal with the interfaces and interactions.
- **Leadership and management** – to co-ordinate the teams doing the work.
- **Commercial and business skills** – to partner those in industry.
- **Military operations** – to interface with the service customer.

Figure 3. A wide range of specialist skills are needed by the MoD to meet future project challenges.

The MoD requirement for a skilled group of people was to be achieved via a specialist Master of Science degree. The students would be taught the skills needed to manage complex defence acquisition projects, taking a whole-systems approach. The course would be, in essence, a cross between an MBA and an MSc; it would consist of taught modules, course work, a group project and an individual project. The Chair of Defence Engineering was announced in Parliament (Hansard 26 March 1991) as follows:

> *My Department has decided to create a chair in defence engineering. Following a competition among a number of universities, we have awarded the chair on the basis of a joint bid by University College London (UCL) and King's College London. The chair will have three objectives: to establish a centre of excellence in engineering and procurement matters relating to defence; to raise further the public profile and professional standards of civilian engineers in the Ministry of Defence; and to provide further education and training for MoD engineers. The chair will conduct research in engineering issues of particular interest to the MoD, and intends to provide, from October 1991, a one-year MSc course in the management of defence engineering. The MoD will send about 10 of its brightest young civilian engineers to attend the course, and it is hoped that additional students will be attracted from the United Kingdom and overseas.*

The overall subjects of the course are defined in Figure 4 which lists the MSc degree's main topics.

- International defence environment and politics.
- Commercial and business practices.
- Systems, engineering and technology.
- Analysis.
- Management of people and programmes.

Figure 4. The key subject areas taught during the MSc course on defence systems engineering.

All complex system projects, and this includes defence systems, require both engineering and systems engineering skills to complete them successfully. Within DSE, there is a vital need for engineering, scientific and technical skills to deal with the wide range of complex technical and technological issues that exist both within a system and within its interfaces with other systems.

Management, business and commercial skills are required when implementing complex systems in order to provide the means of planning and integrating people, money and other resources in the most effective way. These skills are also used to examine the external environment in which the new system will have to operate.

Analytical skills are essential when designing complex systems – it is important to understand the causes of any problems that arise. It is also essential that project-team members understand how to use the various tools to analyse the wide range of available data and information.

While individuals with specialist skills are essential to any systems engineering team, major projects demand individuals with many different skills that must be effectively integrated. Members of a successful systems engineering team require a blend of engineering, management and analysis skills – with this mix they will be able to see and understand the complexities of complicated systems and the world in which they will have to operate.

5 Systems engineering

The term 'systems engineering' describes the process of defining and synthesising highly complex engineering systems. Systems engineering is specifically concerned with delivering a whole rather than a partial system, and as such subsumes all the technical disciplines and processes (that deliver sub-systems) necessary to ensure that the desired 'system' is delivered.

The activities commonly associated with systems engineering are not new, even though the term itself has been coined only relatively recently. All large successful projects undertaken by humankind have applied what have come to be referred to as principles of systems engineering, although it is unlikely that people involved in projects undertaken before the last century would recognise the term.

The Egyptians clearly practised many of the processes now believed to be a fundamental part of systems engineering when building the pyramids, including planning, design and the management of manpower and materials, as did the builders of major defensive systems such Hadrian's Wall and medieval castles. The nineteenth century saw the success of the great industrial engineers and designers such as Stephenson and Brunel, who could individually manage the design, construction and application of what were at the time leading-edge technological designs. As the technical content, scale and diversity of projects increased it became more difficult for a single person to acquire, manage and analyse the relevant data and information.

By the late 1940s aircraft had become too complex for a single chief designer. There are no modern-day equivalents of Mitchell, Camm and Chadwick, each of whom had the ability to understand the total system and to know sufficient about each sub-system to control and delegate authority as required. At the same time the first mega-project, the Manhattan Project

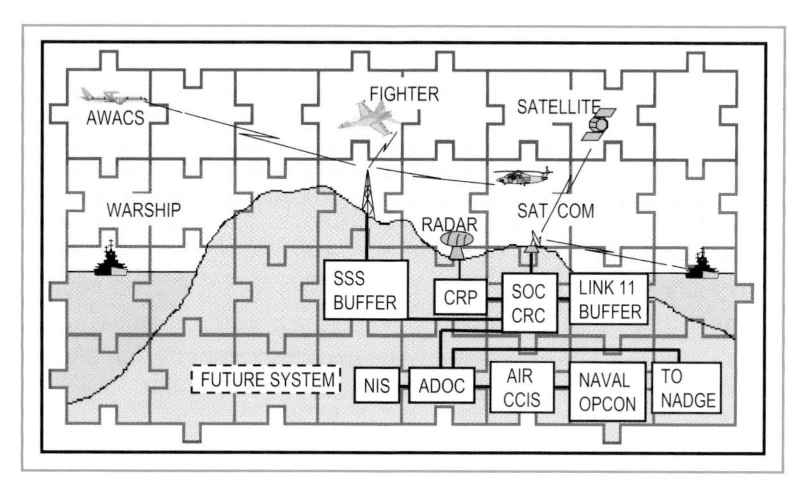

Figure 5. Any NATO member's air defence system is a jigsaw for masochists.

to develop the first atomic bomb, required the integration of a number of different teams and workstreams, and required an integrated management process. This was followed by other complex projects that required high-level integration of separate elements such as ballistic missile programmes and manned space flight, all of which called for a volume of understanding and information well in excess of 'one person's headful' as Professor Hambleton described in his inaugural paper as Chairman of the Electronics Board of the Institute of Electrical Engineers. Similar growth in complexity can be seen in other areas, with products that could once be managed by one person now requiring large integrated teams of people with different skills and the use of systems engineering to knit the whole process together.

Complexity is compounded by the need for systems to work together to achieve a desired defensive goal, either as force elements in a battlegroup or as an integrated set of assets. The UK Air Defence System illustrated diagrammatically in Figure 5 is a good example. The individual elements are all complex systems in their own right, developed by different contractors at different times to separate requirement specifications. To provide the desired emergent properties, they need to be coupled effectively together by secure, robust, wideband communication links under an overall management plan. The integration process could be likened to that of completing a jigsaw, in which each element is a pre-existing piece with its own peculiar interface issues to be solved, often by complex information technology. The system has evolved and been improved over many years and there is no way that such a 'system of systems' (see Chapter 9, Section 3) could be produced by a single fixed-price competitive contract.

There are many definitions for the term 'systems engineering', each with its own emphasis and some of these are presented in the following sections.

5.1 INCOSE

The International Council on Systems Engineering (INCOSE) is the professional organisation for systems engineers. It defines systems engineering as follows:

An interdisciplinary approach is essential to enable the realization of successful systems. It focuses on defining customer needs and the required functionality early in the development cycle, documenting requirements, then proceeding with design synthesis and system validation while considering the complete problem: operations, performance, test, manufacturing, cost and schedule, training and support, and disposal.

This definition emphasises consideration of the system under development as a complete problem and sets the scope of the design challenge according to activities that occur in different phases of the system's life cycle. The definition does not emphasise the use of engineering per se, but takes a broader view in proposing an interdisciplinary approach.

5.2 Ramo

Simon Ramo, who was involved in missile programmes in the 1950s, is sometimes thought of as a founder of modern systems engineering. He defines systems engineering as:

... a branch of engineering which concentrates on the design and application of the whole as distinct from the parts, looking at a problem in its entirety, taking account of all the facets and all the variables and linking the social to the technological.

This definition again emphasises the importance of considering a system from a holistic point of view, but also stresses a broad analysis of the problem that the designed system will address. It introduces the concept, fundamental to DSE, of linking the people with the technology and engineering.

5.3 NASA (National Space and Aeronautics Administration)

NASA, in its handbook on systems engineering, defines systems engineering as:

... an interdisciplinary approach encompassing the entire technical effort to evolve and verify an integrated and life cycle balanced set of system, people, product and process solutions that satisfy customer needs. Systems engineering encompasses the technical efforts related to the development, manufacturing, verification, deployment, operations including training, support, and disposal of a system. It involves the definition and management of the system configuration, the translation of the system definition into work breakdown structures and development of information for management decision-making.

The NASA definition is perhaps the broadest of those listed here. It emphasises an interdisciplinary approach to addressing the design challenge. As with the other definitions, it uses the life cycle to set the scope of the challenge but it goes further in saying that as well as designing a product, complementary 'people' and 'process' systems must also be developed.

NASA portrays systems engineering as an interdisciplinary but mainly technical activity, embracing all of the activities required during the successful life cycle of a system. The definition shows systems engineering to be capable of providing the means of controlling the design, development, testing and production of large complex systems. This is self-evidently true, as NASA has been completing space-based projects since the 1960s whilst coping with advancing technology and rigorous and demanding missions. NASA has used systems engineering to ensure that projects are undertaken in a way that maximises the chances of mission success.

6 Comparing defence systems engineering and systems engineering

As discussed in Section 2 above, systems engineers in defence acquisition face a different set of challenges to those involved in commercial activities. Threats are uncertain and volatile, making threat definition inevitably subjective. Hence the relative value of alternative systems is difficult to assess and open to question. This challenge is compounded by the lack of a clear bottom line of profit or loss, against which options can be viewed and to which activities can be related. The wide set of disparate stakeholders, the extremely long timescales involved in systems development and the potentially fatal consequences of failure in operation all add to the complexities of the problem domain. The need for public accountability and financial initiatives creates additional pressures, although these are common to all government programmes.

Thus it is suggested that DSE is broader and more challenging than systems engineering as practised in the commercial world, where user requirements or marketing opportunities are somewhat easier to define and understand. Defence systems engineers have to push technology to new limits in order to define and specify systems with significantly better performance than existing equipment against uncertain and evolving threats in a variety of global environments. This inevitably involves risk, yet defence systems engineers and project managers are expected to deliver an agreed system performance within defined budgets and timescales. Technical activities are only one aspect of the problem-solving process and the necessity for a fully integrated approach covering technical, management, financial and political issues is vital to the understanding and successful practice of defence systems acquisition. This integrated approach to the totality of DSE has been central to the thinking and teaching of the DEG over the past decade. The broader scope of DSE is shown in Figure 6 overleaf.

The concept of blending an engineering Master of Science degree and a Master of Business Administration degree is easy to conceive, but the DEG faced the challenge of implementing a solution which delivered that concept. The method adopted was to identify disciplines and subjects that help to achieve the engineering or technological requirements of a project; then to ascertain the management and commercial requirements; and finally to seek a unifying or integrating discipline, in this case systems analysis, that was applicable to both the engineering

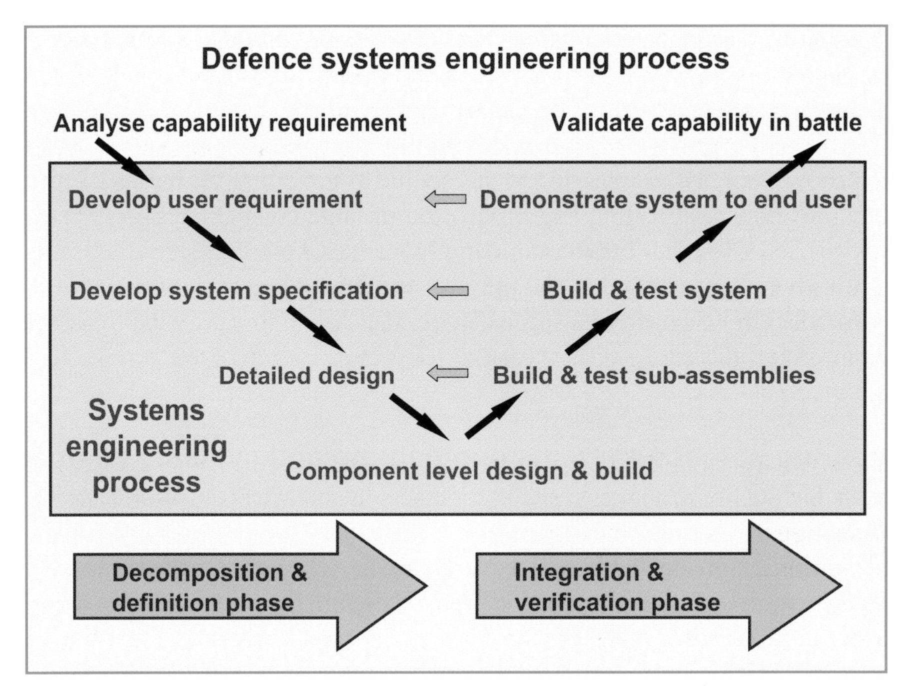

Figure 6. The relationship between defence systems engineering and systems engineering.

and the management elements. The foundation of DSE is therefore a blend of engineering, management and analysis.

- The engineering part of DSE is not exclusively one of the major engineering disciplines but includes elements of systems engineering and the physical sciences. It is related to the knowledge of what type of system will meet the requirement, how to specify the requirement, what current technology can achieve, technological risks and how to overcome them, design, testing, demonstration, manufacture, acceptance, interfaces and interoperability. A deep understanding of an engineering or science discipline is necessary to enable problems to be solved, along with sufficient awareness of experts working in those other areas to allow a transfer of thoughts, ideas and solutions to other disciplines. DSE ranges across aeronautical, electrical, electronic, mechanical and manufacturing engineering, computer science, physics and chemistry.
- The management part of DSE provides the ability to implement the engineering or technological aspects. This element of DSE imparts the knowledge and skill for the acquisition process to be adapted to suit the system being acquired; a process that may differ from system to system. It includes the principles of project management and planning, organising and motivating teams of people, communications skills, organisational development, commercial and legal practices relating to business and contracts, finance and budgeting, financial appraisals and return on investment, and industrial strategy and marketing.

- Analysis provides the link between engineering and management and achieves this through the acquisition, integration and application of data and knowledge. A prime example of an analytical technique that involves engineering and management is the COIEA used to assess projects. DSE analysis begins with international politics and national foreign policy as these lead to the need for the armed forces to implement the UK's foreign policy. It also includes threat assessments, concepts of operation, operational analysis, performance models, systems models, cost models, and the use of robust mathematical and statistical methods to demonstrate and endorse plans and solutions. The linkage between engineering and management achieved by the analytical element of DSE enables much-improved communication between stakeholders and allows cross-stakeholder issues to be rationalised from different perspectives.

An important aspect of DSE is that it emphasises the importance of the customer/supplier relationship in the early stages of the system life cycle. This reflects the innately collaborative and risk-sharing nature of defence projects.

The traditional 'V' model, shown in Figure 6 and now widely quoted in the systems engineering community, has the powerful feature of emphasising the need for planning the verification and validation process as the design progresses. This encourages the discipline of writing requirements and specifications at each stage of design that can be tested and measured. The limitation of the model in respect of defence systems acquisition is that in classic systems engineering it typically starts with a user requirement document (URD). Some relatively blinkered systems engineers accept the user requirement as given and focus exclusively on system specification and design. Given the highly complex and critical nature of defence equipment, the V model for defence systems engineering must be extended upward towards the policy level, increasing the difficulty of defining measures of success. This higher-level perspective necessitates the analysis of the gaps in military capability that will eventually lead to the URD and requires more than just conventional systems engineering.

7 Evolution of defence systems engineering

Over more than a decade of education delivered by the DEG, the discipline of DSE evolved in the collegiate intelligence of the academic staff. This evolution was stimulated by the experience-based inputs of the students themselves (drawn from a range of service and civilian backgrounds), from the research and consultancy work undertaken by the DEG's staff, and from active staff participation in the activities of professional bodies such as INCOSE and advisory groups such as the Department of Trade and Industry's Foresight. Many of the lectures presented established knowledge in the traditional university format, but others covered the scope and complexity of an acquisition case study and encouraged the students to explore and evaluate alternative solutions using their new-found understanding. Many problems that appear intractable can be overcome by avoiding preconceived solutions or by relaxing misunderstood constraints. The integration of the multidisciplinary knowledge of staff and students has provided a unique perspective of the defence acquisition problem, and has generated a set of pragmatic solutions to conquer complexity. Over time the DEG's understanding of the defence acquisition problem has become broader and deeper, and has been refined and tested by 'academic' debate drawing on the practical experiences of staff and students, and of senior visiting speakers from the MoD and industry.

Graduates of the MSc in Defence Systems Engineering have a broad range of skills that enables them to look *upwards and outwards*, as well as *downwards and inwards* to ensure that the solution they propose will solve the problem and not cause additional problems across the boundaries and interfaces of the system with which they are dealing.

8 Summary

DSE is designed to enable professional staff from technical, business and management disciplines to excel in integrated project teams (IPTs) and to develop into team leaders. It is much broader than conventional systems engineering and can be considered to be a culture, or philosophy, that ensures that professional staff use a combination of engineering, management and analysis to ensure that the system life cycle is managed as effectively as possible.

Successful DSE requires the ability to take a holistic view and look outside the immediate boundaries of a project so that factors beyond the boundary are considered as deeply as those within it. This requires an understanding of the location of the boundary and the interfaces, both internal and external. It is the ability to 'think outside the box' which defines defence systems engineers, and makes them stand out from other professionals in an organisation. The role of the defence systems engineer is to optimise the system, not merely to design and provide the sub-systems.

It is this approach, together with the philosophy and discipline of DSE, that enables the effective accomplishment of the acquisition of large and complex defence systems.

Further reading

Aslaken, E and Belcher, R (1992) *Systems Engineering*. Old Tappan, NJ: Prentice-Hall

Blanchard, SB and Fabrycky, WJ (1998) *Systems Engineering and Analysis* (3rd edn). Upper Saddle River, NJ: Prentice-Hall International Inc

Brown, S, Fauvel, J and Finnegan, R (1981) *Conceptions of Inquiry* (Open University Set Book). London: Methuen and Open University Press

Checkland, P (1998) *Systems Thinking, Systems Practice*. Chichester: Wiley

Checkland, P and Howell, S (1998) *Information, Systems and Information Systems*. Chichester: Wiley

DSMC (1991) *Systems Engineering Management Guide*. Fort Belvoir, VA: Defence System Management Centre

Flood, RL and Jackson, MC (1991) *Creative Problem Solving*. Chichester: Wiley

Forsberg, K and Mooz, H (1998) *System Engineering for Faster, Cheaper, Better*. San Jose, CA: International Council on Systems Engineering

Hambleton, KG (1994) How big is a commander's head? Translating data into decisions, *Electronics and Communication Engineering Journal* October: 221–8

Hitchins, DK (1992) *Putting Systems to Work*. Chichester: Wiley
INCOSE (1998) *Systems Engineering Handbook*. Fort Belvoir, VA: International Council on Systems Engineering
MoD (1998) *The Strategic Defence Review* (Cm 3999). London: TSO
Shisko, R (1995) *NASA Systems Engineering Handbook*. Washington, DC: NASA

Websites
www.incose.org/
www.ieee.org/organizations/history-_center/legacies/ramo.html

Chapter 1

UK defence environment

The environment in which defence systems acquisition must be managed is described. The world is ever changing due to factors such as resource shortages, economic developments and the personalities of world leaders. These all contribute to the dynamic interaction between nations and the various alliances that dictate the need for UK national defence, alone or in conjunction with others. There are various different types of conflict in which the UK armed forces may be engaged, and they must plan their organisation and equipment to sustain the capabilities required for those operations. The composition of the UK armed forces is described, outlining the formations of the three services. The capabilities of these forces are being enhanced by digitisation of the battlespace, involving the use of computer hardware and software, together with effective communications, which can provide a battle-winning capability. But force planning and equipment acquisition must be undertaken at the interface of divergent cultures, within and beyond the MoD, that impinge on these activities.

1 International relations

1.1 Introduction

The aim of defence systems engineering (DSE) is to understand and control the procurement, operation and support of complex systems in the defence environment. Defence is an international activity, and DSE is only successful if the highest levels of international activity and politics are included within the analysis of a defence problem. The provision of a useable defence capability starts with the foreign policy of a nation. The definition of a foreign policy and of a national defence policy requires an understanding of international relationships and world politics. The interaction between different nations is shaped by many things such as the length of borders and the distance between countries.

Nations are different; each has its own distinctive features such as people, language(s), laws, land, sea and natural resources that create the individual characteristics of the nation, its culture and nationality. The need for a defence policy is determined by the requirement to protect the citizens, land and transferable resources of a country from threats generated by the actions of one or more nations.

The defence policy of a nation is formed from its foreign policy, which in turn is determined by its relationship with other nations. DSE relies on an understanding of world events, international politics and national relationships, as well as the foreign and defence policies of the nation. The relationships between nations can vary greatly, ranging from relaxed to tense, depending on their respective histories, their foreign policies and their long-term aspirations.

1.2 International tension

The need for defence systems is based on tension, or the prospect of tension, between nations. These tensions are a natural result of their different ways of life, cultures and values. Some of these tensions are fundamental parts of the nation's way of life or culture and are difficult to change; others are less deep-rooted allowing compromises to be reached or settlements to be negotiated. The resolution of tension is difficult because it often means the admission of responsibility, which seems to be problematic for many world political leaders. The admission of errors or failures can result in the reduction or loss of power for a world leader, or at least a loss of popular support, which is often unacceptable. The behaviour and characteristics of world leaders and those involved in national politics is a complex matter. Predicting the behaviour of those with political power is difficult, but successful DSE requires the actions of world leaders to be monitored and considered when taking a long-term or high-level view of the future of a defence system.

1.2.1 The dynamic world

The world is a complex place. There are currently about 200 member states in the United Nations (UN) but the number is not constant and political changes, such as the break-up of the Soviet Union in the early 1990s, often create new nations. Sometimes nations join together to form new larger entities, thereby reducing the total number. This constant state of flux can create tension between nations as any change in borders may introduce a new threat, or alter an existing threat.

1.2.2 Alliances

Area or regional alliances involve the voluntary agreement to certain ideas and principles. Many countries form alliances with other nations, often those with which they share land or maritime borders. The negotiation of an alliance is often a time-consuming activity, but at its conclusion the two nations both have a better understanding of the intention of the other, and each nation has a political framework within which it can work without affecting the other.

Alliances are created to improve stability and to bring mutual benefits to a group of nations, although they often have the effect of creating tension at a higher level, the tension between the Warsaw Pact and the North Atlantic Treaty Organization (NATO) from 1950 until 1990 being an example. The likely benefits include collective defence, free trade and sharing resources such as water from common rivers.

There are alliances based on regions such as the European Union (EU), based on mutual defence and protection such as the NATO, and based on political culture such as the Commonwealth, an association of 53 countries.

The UN provides a forum for all the nations of the world to be represented to discuss matters of international importance, and to decide upon plans of action. The UN charter is to maintain international peace and security, develop friendly relations among nations, co-operate in solving international problems and promoting respect for human rights, and to be the centre for harmonising actions of nations. In conflict situations, the UN Security Council mediates to secure a ceasefire. It may send a peacekeeping force (wearing the distinctive blue berets) to help the parties maintain a truce and keep opposing forces apart. The Security Council can take measures to enforce UN decisions such as imposing economic sanctions or an arms embargo. It can also authorise member states to use individual or collective military action.

1.2.3 National interfaces

Nations are not closed systems that have no interaction with their environments; a closed nation could not exist in the modern world. All nations have open boundaries to a certain extent. The simplest transnational links are natural such as rivers, more complex ones include telecommunications, and very complex ones involve the transfer of people, raw materials and finished goods. Complexity in this case is a measure of the level of human involvement in the process.

A common need for interaction is mutual defence. Any nation may agree to co-operate with another to provide a higher level of defence than either could achieve individually. This might be in a bipartite alliance or as a group such as NATO. Another need that requires interaction between nations is trade. Few nations are self-sufficient in all of the resources needed for stable and continuing development. The negotiation of trade agreements may be at a national level or may be commercial activities undertaken by a non-governmental organisation (NGO). The transfer of resources from one nation to another usually means the reciprocal transfer of other resources or money. A country that has an excess of a scarce and useful resource, such as oil, is in a dominant position when negotiating trade agreements for all kinds of commodities and resources.

A nation in a dominant position – either commercially as a result of a natural resource, physically as a result of its geographical position, or militarily as a result of the armed forces it has acquired – can, depending on the role that it envisages, either be a threat to stability or a stabilising influence in a region.

1.2.4 Threats

All countries desire the opportunity to develop in the manner that they believe is in their best interests. This may not be acceptable to other nations, either because of adverse effects on their own development or because of wider issues such as human rights or religious tolerance.

Geopolitics is of particular importance with reference to territorial problems and issues of state sovereignty. The politics, culture and need of geographically close nations will tend to dominate their foreign policies. However, the increased availability of long-range weapons and the improvements in the logistics of troop movements mean that nations must be aware of what is happening around the world as well as in their own locality – the threat may come from much further away than their immediate neighbours. The increasing sophistication of information technology (IT) and the ability to move data from one nation to another, virtually instantaneously, is creating new information warfare threats.

1.3 Continuous change

There is an old Chinese saying that states: 'May you live in interesting times.' But this was delivered as a curse because the ancient Chinese prized good harvests, dutiful families and consistent administration. It could well be argued that, at the beginning of the twenty-first century, times are very interesting and exciting. The only certainty seems to be that change is continuous with ever varying political and financial demands. An eternal problem facing any government is how much to spend on defence and how much to spend on other priorities such as health, education and social security.

1.3.1 Global defence expenditure

World military expenditure was estimated at $1000 billion at the end of the Cold War in 1989. It then fell steadily for several years by an average of around 4% per annum. This figure conceals a rapid fall in several countries of Western Europe offset by increases in many of the developing nations. The reductions in Europe were the result of economic pressures to spend a higher percentage of government revenues on health, education and social security as well as the ability to reduce manpower due to technical advances in automation and weapon effectiveness. Since 1997, there has been a continuous rise in world military expenditure, particularly fuelled by the United States' 'war on terror' following the 2001 attack on the World Trade Center. The US, as the world's only superpower, dominates world defence markets, with expenditure greater than that of all the countries of Europe combined. No country outside the top fifteen accounts for more than 1% of world defence spending. China continues to increase its defence budget, albeit from a very low starting point, and its actual expenditure may be as much as four times that published. Japan is also

Rank	Country	US$B	%	Rank	Country	US$B	%
1	USA	417.4	47	9	Saudi Arabia	19.1	2
2	Japan	46.9	5	10	South Korea	13.9	1
3	UK	37.1	4	11	Russia	13.0	1
4	France	35.0	4	12	India	12.4	1
5	China	32.8	4	13	Israel	10.0	1
6	Germany	27.2	3	14	Turkey	9.9	1
7	Italy	20.8	2	15	Brazil	9.2	1
8	Iran	19.2	2				

Figure 7. The expenditure of the top fifteen nations in 2003, in US $B (at year 2000 prices) and expressed as a % of the world total. (Information from Stockholm International Peace Research Institute. SIPRI. http://www.sipri.org/contents/webmaster/databases)

Region	1994	2003	1994–2003
Africa	9	11	+ *24%*
Americas	365	451	+ *24%*
Asia/Oceania	120	151	+ *25%*
Europe	200	195	– *2%*
Middle East	47	70	+ *48%*
World	742	879	+ *18%*

Figure 8. There have been real changes in defence expenditure (in year 2000 US$B) since the Cold War ended. (Information from Stockholm International Peace Research Institute. SIPRI. http://www.sipri.org/contents/webmaster/databases)

increasing its spend on defence, having previously been prevented from doing so by law following the end of the Second World War.

Traditionally, governments have increased defence expenditure when the perceived threat level is high and reduced it in periods of supposed peace. A recent example is the 'peace dividend' following the fall of the Berlin Wall, the end of the Cold War and the collapse of the Soviet Union at the end of the last century. Since then the UK defence budget has fallen from just over 4% of GDP to slightly under 2½%.

Unsurprisingly, the UK spends less money on defence than the US, bearing in mind the relative size of its economy. It spends rather less than Japan, a nation with twice the population and booming exports, but more than any other industrialised nation. In proportion to its population, the US spends two and a half times as much as the UK and France and nearly five times as much as the other industrialised nations.

Industrial trends in the defence field have centred around mergers and acquisitions, and a few partnerships, resulting in an increasing globalisation of the defence industry. The

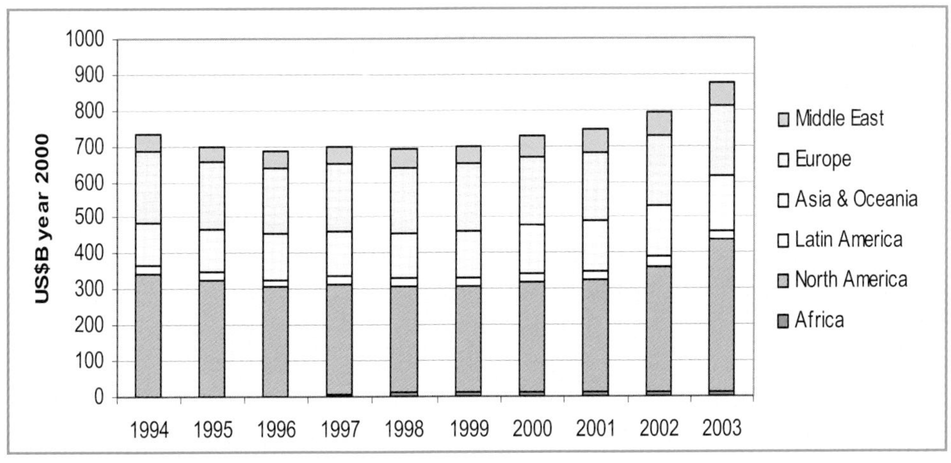

Figure 9. The trend in world defence spending by region over the period 1994–2003. (Information from Stockholm International Peace Research Institute. SIPRI. http://www.sipri.org/contents/webmaster/databases)

result is a few industrial giants in the US and Europe that dominate the market. Well-known names include Boeing, Lockheed, BAE Systems, Thales and EADS (European Aeronautic Defence and Space Company), the largest of which is achieving annual defence sales of more than twenty-five billion US dollars.

Historically, military research has led the development of defence-relevant technologies, but today the development of many of these technologies is driven by global commercial competition and is enabled by private-sector funding of research. As an example, in the middle of the last century, computers were used exclusively by the military for code breaking, artillery trajectory calculations and aircraft stress analysis. The IT field is now dominated by civilian applications with military applications accounting for less than 1% of the market. And this is not the only field where military leadership has waned.

1.3.2 UK government expenditure

For all nations, the amount of government spending is dependent on two factors. The first is the health of the national and international economies together with estimates of their future trends, and second is government revenue, mainly raised from taxes. The problem is always what percentage of government spending should be allocated to defence and how much to such pressing needs as health, education and social security. The difficulties faced by industrialised nations such as Britain come from several sources:

- Health budget demands are growing as the population lives longer and technology produces new drugs, novel treatments and expensive diagnostic and therapeutic equipment.
- Education costs are rising as more of the population complete secondary and enter tertiary education. The present aim of the UK government is for half the population to receive a university education.
- Social security budgets are growing as more younger people are surviving on or helped by state benefits, and the number of long-living retired people increases. Also, of course, unemployment benefit increases dramatically with cyclical rises in the jobless figures; a time too when tax revenues fall.
- Defence spending is only a popular option when there is a serious perceived threat. In times of peace, defence spending has always tended to be allocated a smaller proportion of government spending.

Figure 10 shows a chart of the most recent breakdown of UK government spending and demonstrates that defence spending is around a quarter of that on social security and half of that on health; and this is at a time of low unemployment.

1.3.3 UK defence spending

There has been a steady reduction in UK defence expenditure on equipment in the decade following the end of the Cold War. The total annual spend represents only some 4% of the total world spend on defence. As Figure 11 shows, the UK defence budget has yet to reach

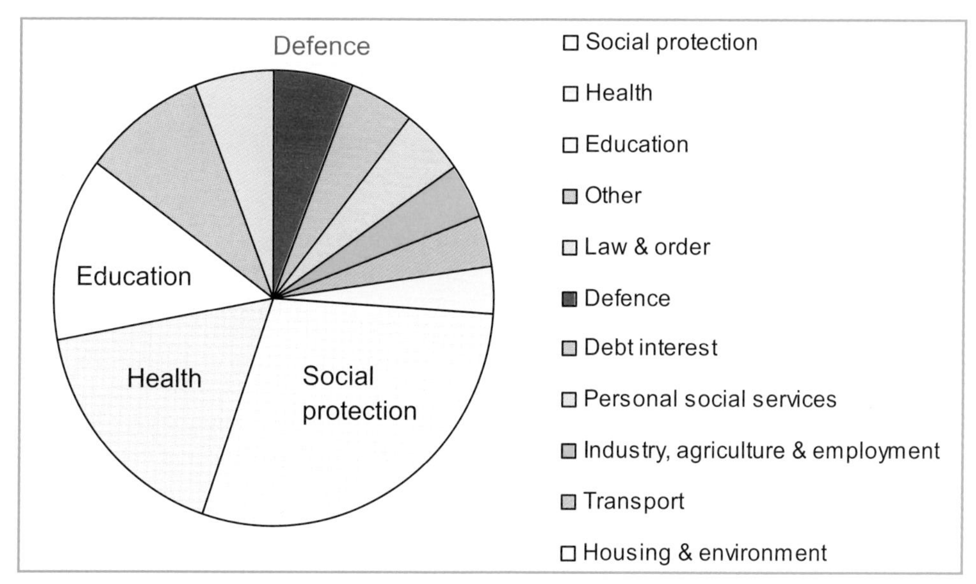

Figure 10. How the UK government divided its expenditure in the year ending April 2004.

the level of spending a decade ago (ignoring the £3B allocated to cover the cost of the second Gulf War in 2003). The defence budget comprises two main parts: the cost of people and the cost of equipment. While the first is important when designing systems, it is the second that is crucial to their funding.

Problems inevitably arise when project costs significantly overrun the allocated budgets, as has recently happened both with the Astute submarine and the Nimrod maritime reconnaissance aircraft upgrades; the total overspend on these two projects amounting to over £1.5B. When this occurs, savings must be found elsewhere in the procurement budget, and this can have a significant financial impact on other major projects.

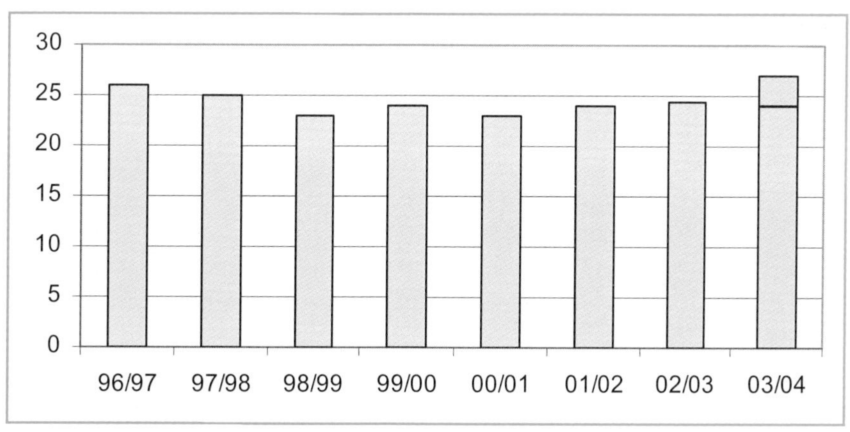

Figure 11. UK defence budget in £B normalised to 2001/02 prices. £3B in 2003/04 was an addition allocated to help cover the expense of the second Gulf War.

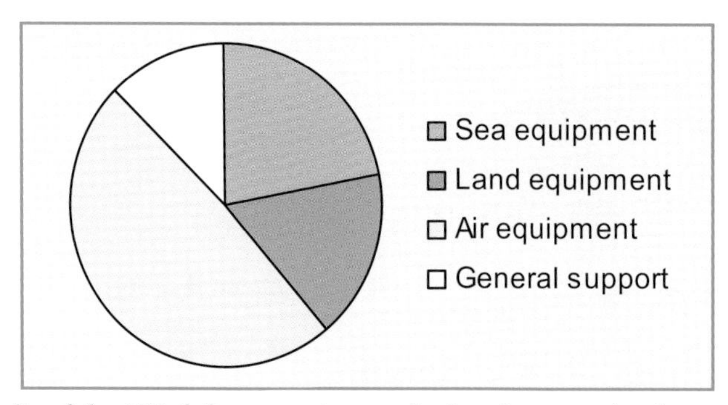

Figure 12. The split of the UK defence equipment budget between land, sea, air and support.

It is interesting to note that at present, expenditure on air systems takes up half the equipment budget, while the other half is roughly split equally between naval equipment, items for the army and support equipment for all three services.

The implementation of Smart Acquisition (see Chapter 3, Section 1) should be helping to increase value for money, but competition policy has also opened up the UK defence market to overseas suppliers to an extent that has not been reciprocated by the other industrialised nations.

Recently, the UK government published its defence industrial policy that considers such issues as security of supply, retention of certain key technologies, export potential, industrial participation, wider MoD policy framework, industrial capabilities and the impact of foreign and security policies. However, this is unlikely to impact on the dramatic decrease in the number of large defence contractors in the UK.

1.3.4 Defence threats and missions

During the 40 years following the end of the Second World War, the threat posed by the Soviet Union was relatively constant, apart from the Cuban missile crisis. However, there were in that period numerous other conflicts involving civil war, end of empire wars, ideological wars like that in Korea, regional conflicts involving two or more nations, as well as counter-terrorism activities of which the fight against the Irish Republican Army (IRA) in the UK has continued over the last 30 years. Since 11 September 2001, both the US and the UK have said that they are 'waging war on terror', but some consider that military actions against Islamic nations such as Afghanistan and Iraq have fomented rather than reduced terrorist activities. Fortunately there has been significant progress in security technology that is helping to combat the continually adapting threat from terrorism. What is clear from past experience is the enormous difficulty in learning the right lessons and predicting what will happen next. The present UK defence mission statement requires the MoD and the armed forces to:

- Make a vital contribution to the UK's security policy and its promotion at home and abroad.
- Direct and provide a defence effort that meets the needs of the present, prepares for the future and insures against the unpredictable.

- Generate modern battle-winning forces and other capabilities necessary to help the UK government to:
    - o Prevent conflicts and build stability.
    - o Resolve crises and respond to emergencies.
    - o Protect and further UK interests.
    - o Meet UK commitments and responsibilities for international security.
- Work with allies and partners to strengthen international security relationships.

1.3.5 The changing and uncertain threat

A recent independent survey by the Stockholm International Peace Research Institute (SIPRI) has shown that on average there have been about 30 wars raging each year. Some 30 countries currently possess ballistic missiles and increasing numbers of these weapons are being traded around the world. Their warheads can be chemical, biological or, for maybe as many as ten nations, nuclear. They can be targeted ruthlessly at cities and their civilian populations.

War may be ideological as well as political; waged by countries with different cultures and morals. Guerrilla warfare always has been and continues to be difficult to counter. There are minority terrorist groups or mercenaries that mix with and usually are indistinguishable from civilians. This asymmetric conflict does not provide a level playing field as terrorists do not feel bound by the Geneva Convention.

1.3.6 Recent operations by UK forces

Looking back over the second half of the twentieth century, the Cold War period from 1945 to 1989 required the near-total commitment of the UK armed forces to supporting NATO against the Soviet Union and its Warsaw Pact allies. This was a relatively stable period when the Royal Navy (RN) used its sea power to control the reinforcement and supply route across the North Atlantic, the Army had considerable land forces based in Western Germany whilst the Royal Air Force (RAF) provided the air defence of the UK and tactical support to the troops in Germany; the RAF also sustained a nuclear strike capability against the USSR, later joined by and then superseded by RN Polaris and Trident submarines.

In the late 1940s, British troops were involved in action in Malaysia, and in 1952 the UK provided part of the UN force which supported South Korea, following its invasion by North Korea with the support of China. In the following decades, the UK armed forces were involved in several low-level campaigns to suppress unrest and/or infiltration in many of its far-flung dependencies.

In 1982, the Falklands War came as a shock to many in the UK. It involved, for the first time in the experience of most service personnel, full-scale conventional warfare against another nation whose forces had some modern equipment. Furthermore, it required the long-range deployment of UK forces (mostly sea and land forces, with restricted air support, essentially limited to carrier-borne Harriers and helicopters), into an inhospitable climate. This conflict illustrated both the importance of technology (exemplified by the Exocet and Sidewinder AIM9L missiles) and the traditional stamina and aggressiveness of the UK infantry.

In 1991, an ad hoc coalition led by the US responded to the Iraqi invasion of Kuwait in the first Gulf War. This conflict essentially used air and land forces deployed to the Arabian peninsula, with the naval role limited mainly to the launch of cruise missiles and mine clearance in the Gulf. From 1992 onwards, air patrols continued over Iraq to enforce an air exclusion zone, with occasional precision strikes against military targets.

Since 1995, UK forces have supported peacemaking and later peacekeeping operations in the Balkans, essentially provided by the use of land forces supported by the threat of air strikes.

In 2002, both the US and the UK engaged in successful operations in Afghanistan to overthrow the Taliban regime. However, they did not succeed in killing or capturing the Al Qaeda leader, Osama bin Laden, who was reputed to be hiding there. In 2005, the armed forces of both countries are still engaged in Afghanistan and, with continuing violence and political instability, there seems to be little likelihood of an early withdrawal.

In 2003, the second Gulf War involved the invasion and occupation of Iraq by the US, supported mainly by the UK, because of the apparent threat from weapons of mass destruction. In the event, no weapons of mass destruction were found, but Saddam Hussein's dictatorial rule was overthrown.

1.3.7 The evolution of UK defence procurement

The present government, like its predecessors, has introduced a number of measures to improve the efficiency of government departments. Recent examples include the private finance initiative (PFI) aimed at getting more industry investment, resource accounting and budgeting (RAB) that endeavours to imitate commercial business practice and the conversion of some government departments to agencies. Defence initiatives aimed at improving the performance of UK armed forces and reducing their cost have been launched by the MoD. The Downey cycle and cardinal points specifications (CPS) have been followed by Smart Acquisition that is now looking for 'better, cheaper, faster and better integrated' equipment acquired by integrated project teams (IPTs).

The PFI is a way of encouraging private-sector capital investment in providing capabilities; projects where the government pays for the use rather than the provision of equipment. It was first used on projects involving buildings but has now been extended to the supply and operation of military equipment. PFI is an excellent example of implementing the through-life approach, since maintenance will be a part of the supply and will need accurate costing. This topic is expanded in Chapter 3.

RAB forces government departments to value and amortise their assets. This involves a switch in the primary focus of financial management from cash expenditure to resource consumption and the need to report on how resources have been consumed, as well as detailing what cash has been spent. In addition, there is a requirement to show all assets on a balance sheet, identify the resource consumption associated with outputs and to budget for outputs rather than inputs. The impact on the MoD is significant since defence has many high-value assets relative to its cash expenditure. RAB is described at length in Chapter 4, Section 3.

In 1988, the Next Steps programme created a number of semi-autonomous government bodies by delegating various government department activities. Established as executive agencies, they aim to improve civil service performance and efficiency by providing a degree of autonomy and self-management. Each has a chief executive reporting to the relevant minister. Individual ministries set up the new agencies with specific objectives and discrete budgets. These agencies now account for two-thirds of civil servant employment. They deliver specific services and are judged by their ability to satisfy their customers. Agency status is sometimes an intermediate step towards privatisation. More than 130 agencies have been created and some have been privatised, such as QinetiQ, formed from part of the earlier Defence Evaluation and Research Agency. The success of agencies in improving efficiency is annually tested by Next Steps reviews.

Agencies in the defence sector tend to differ from most other government agencies because the majority of their customers are internal. The MoD has some fifteen agencies of which the Defence Procurement Agency (DPA), launched on 1 April 1999 as an executive agency of the MoD to replace the Procurement Executive, and the Defence Science and Technology Laboratory (Dstl) are by far the most important to defence systems engineers.

The new management strategy (NMS) has been in place at the MoD since 1991. It provides for stronger central determination of defence policy, plans and resource allocation, with equipment plans being the vehicle for resource allocation. It followed earlier reforms in 1984 that decentralised the management of defence operating costs. The system aligns executive and financial authority to achieve best value for money in meeting agreed tasks within allocated resources. All budget holders have more control of their resources, driving them to take a more commercial approach.

1.3.8 Evolution of UK equipment procurement

In the post Second World War period, equipment procurement was mainly carried out using the so-called Downey cycle – which, incidentally, was a strictly linear process amended but not invented by Downey. It consisted of seven sequential phases: concept, feasibility, project definition, full-scale development, production, in-service and disposal. Formal approval was needed before each phase could commence. This was designed to reduce risk by requiring a thorough appraisal of the previous phase and a detailed technical and financial plan against which to proceed. Each approval process could take several months and the cumulative effect on both project progress and industry planning was demoralising. The current CADMID process (concept, assessment, development, manufacture, in-service, disposal), introduced at the turn of the century, requires only two formal approvals (initial gate and main gate) and was designed to streamline and simplify the procedure.

Meanwhile, in the early 1980s, the MoD focused on open competition for new equipment, providing general requirement statements instead of detailed technical specifications. Industry, with increasing knowledge about the potential products, undertook the system design and bore the financial risk. At about the same time, the RN started using CPS, accepting that existing products, bought commercially off-the-shelf, might satisfy virtually all its needs but that it might have to forgo one or two desirable features. In other words, CPS

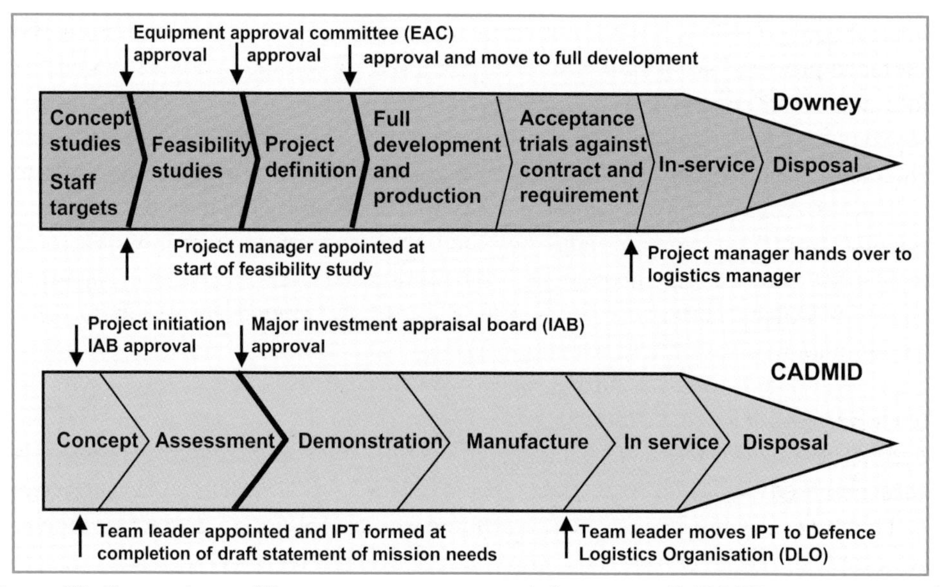

Figure 13. Comparison of Downey procurement and the current CADMID acquisition cycle.

could not be fully mandatory. The aim was to find the most cost-effective and acceptable solution. This worked well in certain areas such as naval radars, where several companies had equipment already developed, but it was less satisfactory when applied to new designs where it was difficult to choose between purely paper products without more detailed requirement criteria. In the competitive era, adjudication usually involved:

- A set of mandatory requirements.
- Get ticks in boxes.
- Pick the cheapest.
- No assessment of whether the company could make what was required.
- Problem of grey areas in the specification.

Weighted scale evaluation was used to compare alternative solutions:

- All stakeholders agreed a list to be scored and the scoring systems to be used.
- Each item was given a relevant weighting.
- Cost was excluded and left to the contracts branch.

Risk and credibility were not built into the scoring system, but were treated as a separate item. Neither Downey's, Levene's (then Chief of Defence Procurement) nor the CPS philosophies proved entirely satisfactory as evidenced by continuing problems with the procurement of military equipment, particularly in protracted timescales, a lack of delegated authority and a failure to balance performance, cost and time. From 1991, the MoD explicitly promoted assessment of the cost effectiveness of alternative bids.

Smart Procurement, launched in 1998 and now called Smart Acquisition, aims to produce new defence projects faster, cheaper, better and more effectively integrated. Key features include acquiring capabilities rather than solutions, taking a through-life approach, improved cost forecasting, the application of systems engineering, the need at times to use incremental acquisition and the necessity for more flexibility in procurement. An important part of Smart Acquisition is 'partnering with industry', where its representatives are included within IPTs (except during the tender process); other parts include simplified approvals, increased early planning and risk reduction, better estimating, well-targeted incentives and more authority delegated to IPT leaders. Smart Acquisition and IPTs are dealt with in more detail in Chapter 3.

1.3.9 Conclusions

Change has been continuous in the defence industry for over a century but in recent years its pace has increased dramatically with mergers, takeovers, and restructuring becoming regular news. This trend has not been confined to industry; radical organisational change is also taking place in government in general and the MoD in particular, with the creation of agencies and the growth of public/private partnerships (PPPs) and PFIs. Thus defence systems

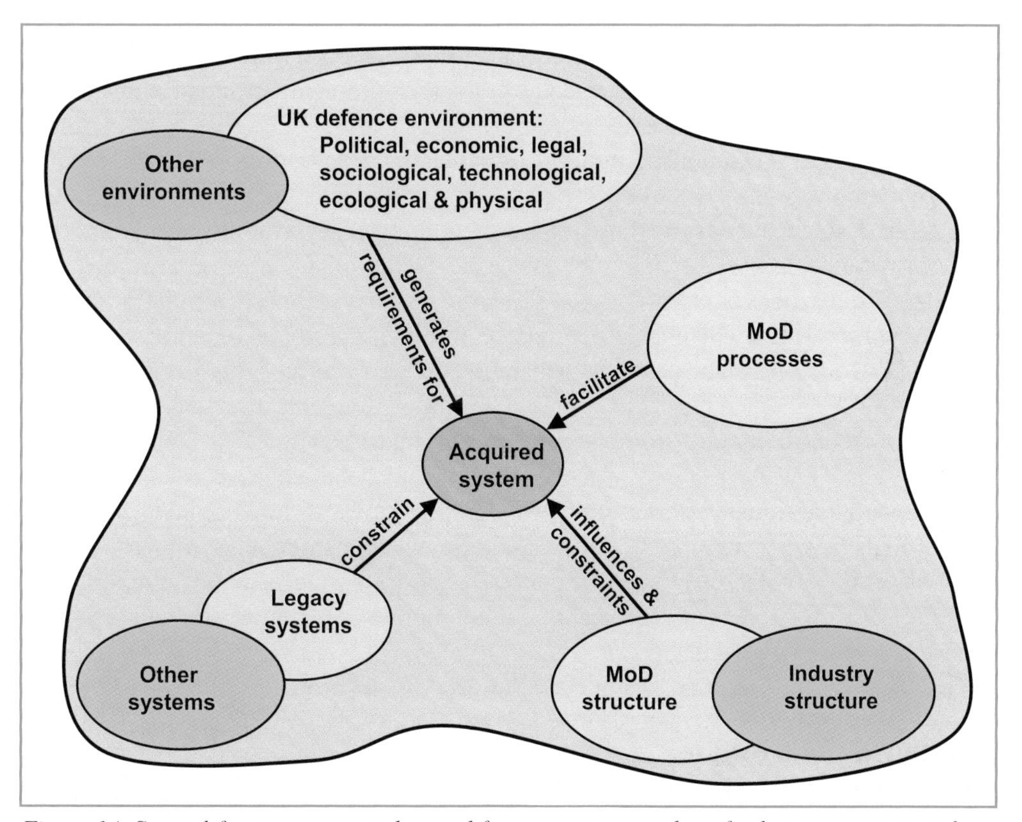

Figure 14. Several factors generate the need for new systems, others facilitate or constrain them.

engineers must learn not only to continue to deal with advancing technology but also to operate in a rapidly evolving environment of organisational change.

It is never easy to forecast the future and yet, with the long development lead times of modern weapon systems, the MoD has to plan for likely wars in future decades and select the most suitable equipment and structure for its armed forces. The threats change as often as politicians and governments. There are no easy answers, but the task of defence systems engineers involved in the acquisition of complex systems is to ensure that their time to market is minimised, they offer best value for money and that their design and architecture are sufficiently flexible to allow rapid updates to combat newly emerging threats.

2 The nature of conflict

Since gunpowder weapons became dominant at the end of the seventeenth century, warfare between developed nations has been fought between opponents armed with similar weapon systems. Intermittently, one nation or another has achieved a temporary superiority by being the first to introduce a new class of combat equipment, such as rifled artillery or armoured fighting vehicles, but invariably the other nations have then exerted themselves to introduce such equipment themselves and thus restore a broad technological parity. The diffusion of the relevant military technologies (via entrepreneurs, spies and traitors) generally enabled the lagging nations to catch up within a decade. But even a short period of military inferiority could expose a laggard country to defeat in war or to the extortion of diplomatic or commercial concessions by better-armed rivals.

During that period of broad technological parity when rival nations deployed similar classes of weapons, some particular weapon systems (such as the Spitfire and the T34 tank) incorporated design features (affecting firepower, mobility or survivability) which conferred significant advantages in combat. In such cases, the successful features were adopted by the designers of rival nations as rapidly as their skills and resources allowed. Similarly, whenever one nation achieved greater combat effectiveness through superior command and control or a better tactical doctrine, and when that greater effectiveness was recognised and understood, the enemy rapidly adopted the same policies and forms of organisation. During periods of warfare, any country's successful design or tactic would be copied or countered by the enemy very rapidly, within a few years or even within a few months, but in peacetime budgetary constraints and traditional customs could delay progress towards re-equipment and reform.

In conflicts between nations with broadly similar weapons – called symmetrical wars – those with the more numerous forces are generally victorious. Occasionally a superiority of numbers can be offset by better leadership, higher morale or better tactics, and the weaker force can win against the odds.

2.1 Three types of warfare

In modern times, the armed forces of developed nations have engaged in three different types of conflict, defined as follows:

1. Regular, symmetric wars were waged against other developed nations using similar weapons and operating under well-established conventions trying to minimise unnecessary casualties and collateral damage. In these wars, commanders manoeuvred to achieve a local superiority of numbers and/or an advantageous position, at which point their opponent would probably withdraw and accept a temporary loss of territory and prestige, hoping to achieve more favourable circumstances for battle in the future.
2. Internal suppression was another form of warfare employed against rebellions by disadvantaged social groups or ethnic minorities whose forces were generally poorly armed and organised. Such conflicts were often brutal and indiscriminate, since the rebels lusted to avenge their many wrongs and the government forces regarded the armed rebels as traitors. More recently, rebellions by dissident groups have been replaced or complemented by political agitation, mass demonstrations and the withdrawal of labour from key industries; these activities often provoke violent or non-violent confrontations with government forces.
3. Asymmetric wars were fought to extend or preserve the frontiers of empire against underdeveloped societies with primitive weapons and organisation. Such wars tended to be savage, even genocidal, in the absence in the opposing forces of any common cultural conventions about the treatment of prisoners and non-combatants. In such warfare, the society with inferior weapons was almost certain to be bloodily defeated if it attempted to fight its better-armed opponent in pitched battles where the latter's weapons could be used effectively (as at the Battle of Omdurman in 1898). The weaker society might succeed only if it adopted the classic guerrilla strategy of evading the enemy's strength and operating against its weakness. In these operations against isolated garrisons and soft economic targets, the weaker society might breach the existing conventions of warfare to achieve surprise by innovative and ruthless tactics. Today, asymmetric warfare is defined as the use of technology, doctrine or tactics designed to deter or defeat a superior enemy by using a different balance of forces and a dissimilar operational approach.

The developed nations' policies for the organisation and equipment of their armed forces always needed to strike a balance between these different types of conflict. Officers appointed on the basis of noble birth or financial wealth were generally more reliable in internal-security conflicts, but might prove too unprofessional for regular warfare. Heavy artillery desirable for regular warfare might be a logistical embarrassment in imperialist and post-imperialist asymmetric wars. During the twentieth century, the intense rivalry between alliances (NATO and Warsaw Pact) of the major military powers encouraged them to give top priority to equipping their forces for regular symmetric war, while hoping that the resulting forces could adapt as required for internal security and imperial policing.

2.2 Current US dominance yields asymmetric warfare

The collapse of the Warsaw Pact at the end of the Cold War created a new situation with the US as the single unchallenged global superpower. Furthermore, the scale of US investment in military technologies (such as stealth, precision guidance, sensors and information transfer) has given it a clear and growing technological advantage over any potential enemy. The scale of this advantage was demonstrated by the decisive success of US-led coalitions in successive symmetric wars against Iraq in 1991 and 2003. The evidence of these conflicts makes it likely that in future an intelligent rogue state or non-state group opposed to US policies would use the tactics of asymmetric warfare (unrestrained by the Geneva Convention) to thwart the operations of the US and its allies. The range of potential tactics extends from propaganda to weapons of mass destruction, as discussed below, and could be used individually or in combination to affect the hearts and minds of US-led nations.

1. Propaganda might seek to convince substantial fractions of coalition nations that they do not have a just cause for war. Campaigns could take advantage of the global proliferation of television channels and Internet sites to carry discouragement, disinformation and disruptive allegations directly to susceptible (and sometimes under-informed) segments of the coalition populations.
2. Operations to distress, damage or destroy the coalition's personnel and equipment in the theatre of operations might convince some of the nations involved that their cause (even if it is clearly just) does not warrant the grief and financial loss incurred. The impact of such operations would be inflated by the pervasive presence of journalists and cameramen, and the worldwide availability of communication facilities. To counteract such asymmetric operations, coalition military personnel must remain imaginatively aware of the wide spectrum of risks presented by an unscrupulous enemy so that they cannot be surprised or discomfited.
3. Action against the homeland infrastructure (e.g. utilities, transport, finance) to cause inconvenience or economic loss to one or more of the coalition nations. Such action would be especially effective in those nations where the utilities, for example, are supplied commercially and consequently tend to economise on countermeasures against service disruption. In extreme cases, a rogue non-state group might use a weapon of mass destruction, whether purpose-built or improvised, against the population of one of the coalition nations in order to discourage the others.

In the UK, the present programme for the acquisition of defence equipment is still driven primarily by the requirements of symmetric warfare against a future unspecified enemy, but since there is no evident symmetrical threat to the UK in the foreseeable future, it is more likely the UK forces will use this equipment in asymmetric warfare. Accordingly it is very important that the acquisition process should take full account of the diverse threats characteristic of asymmetric warfare, and should ensure that the UK's defence equipment does not incorporate any areas of vulnerability (in design or operational doctrine or logistic support) which an intelligent enemy might identify and exploit. Hence acquisition must involve even closer co-operation between the service branches planning future asymmetric operations and other stakeholders in the equipment acquisition process, since the success of equipment in such operations will depend on its overall physical, psychological and public relations effects on the evolving political, economic and security situation in a theatre of peace-making operations. This type of warfare is truly, as Clausewitz (1780–1831) wrote, an extension of politics by other means.

3 The planning of defence

The UK armed forces are required to undertake a diverse range of operations in a wide range of circumstances and different places. In addition, British forces will almost invariably need to deploy jointly and often operate with allied or coalition forces. An important aspect of DSE is to ensure that UK armed forces are given the means to conduct their missions with maximum efficiency. This requires command, structure, equipment and training for single-service or joint-force missions or as part of an international force.

Defence planning involves translating UK government defence policy into high-level missions and defence tasks. In the UK, the armed forces use their military capability to perform these various tasks. The total military capability provided consists of a number of individual capabilities that are needed to perform all the planned defence tasks. There is no direct relationship between tasks and capabilities, as usually each task requires several supporting capabilities and conversely, each capability often has to support several tasks. In

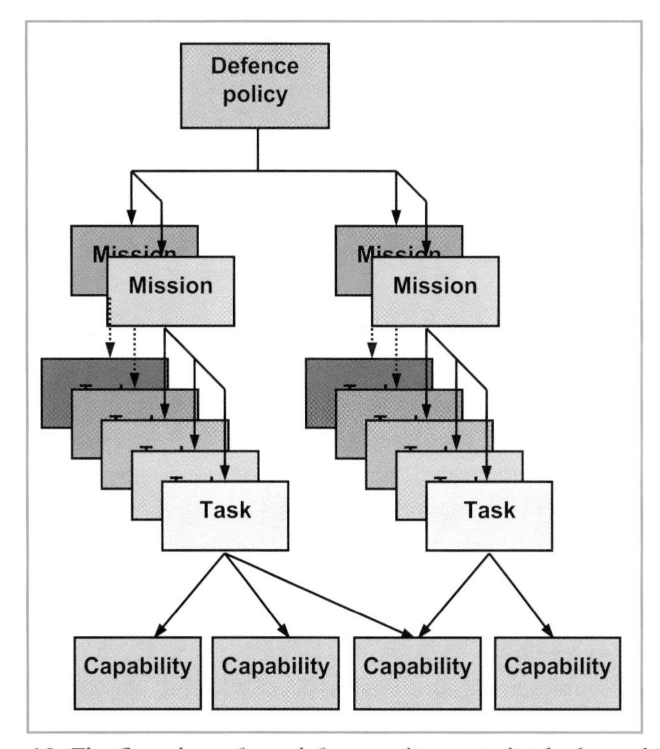

Figure 15. The flow down from defence policy to individual capabilities.

operational terms, it is the current range of military capabilities that determines which tasks can be performed.

UK defence policy specifies national aims and obligations, potential threats to security and the context for UK defence activities. Defence policy is set by the government and expressed by the Secretary of State for Defence. The aim of the defence policy is to:

- Deter any threats to the UK and defend its freedom and territorial integrity and those of its dependant territories. It includes the provision of support to the civil authority in countering terrorism.
- Contribute to the promotion of the UK's wider security interests, including the protection and enhancement of freedom and democratic institutions and the promotion of free trade.
- Promote peace and help maximise the UK's international prestige and influence.

The defence policy has been used to establish a number of defence 'missions' and to provide high-level policies for service co-ordination. The defence missions are further sub-divided into defence 'tasks' for specific planning purposes. Examples of tasks under the 'Regional conflict outside the NATO area' mission include both the Gulf wars and the Falklands conflict. Whilst these aims indicate the macro-level tasks that the armed forces must be equipped and trained to undertake, there is also a requirement to continue to provide lower-level capabilities such as 24-hour peacetime search and rescue facilities, nuclear accident response, defence intelligence, fishery protection, hydrographic and geographic surveying and mapping, supplying military personnel for state ceremonial duties and providing air transport for the royal family and senior members of the government. The eight missions are shown in Figure 16.

3.1 Military capability

British Defence Doctrine (1997) defines capability as: 'the overall potential of the armed forces for combat or other operations'. The more recent second edition (MoD 2001) lists seven fundamental defence capabilities required to deliver fighting power that are considered necessary for an operation to be conducted. These are the ability to command, inform, prepare, project, protect, sustain and operate. The MoD *Acquisition Handbook* defines capability as: 'an operational outcome or effect that users of equipment need to achieve'. It does not provide an indication of how capability is generated.

A weapon system will have effectiveness, but defence capability will only be developed when weapon systems are combined into an operational unit, such as a battery of guns or a platoon of infantry. Some weapon systems, such as combat aircraft or warships, form in themselves an operational unit. The lower-level units are only capable of delivering a single defence capability, or of delivering a single defence capability at any given time. This is an example of single-function defence capability. Only when weapon systems with different capabilities are combined together into combat forces can multi-function defence capability

1. **Peacetime security.** Support against terrorism of all kinds. Assistance in evacuating British (and other) citizens caught up in overseas crises, and specialist support to civil authorities.
2. **Security of the overseas territories.** Reacting to emerging security problems and assisting civil authorities. Providing garrisons and other forms of military presence, including in the Falklands, Cyprus, Gibraltar and the Caribbean, and maintaining the capability to supplement these as needed.
3. **Defence diplomacy.** The creation of a Defence Diplomacy Mission makes conflict-prevention a core activity, linked to the government's broader policy objectives. It includes monitoring arms-control agreements and the Outreach programme (including attachments, training and education) to develop the skills and structures needed by modern democratically accountable forces
4. **Support to wider British interests.** This includes support of Britain's interests and standing overseas, demonstrating UK commitment to international friendships worldwide. It can assist broader national objectives and interests, including training, and support for British exports.
5. **Peace support and humanitarian operations.** Britain will play a full part in international efforts, ranging from disaster-relief logistic or medical support to major combat operations such as were undertaken when NATO's Intervention Force (IFOR) first deployed to Bosnia.
6. **Regional conflict outside the NATO area.** The greatest risks to the UK national economic and political interests, and probably to international stability, remain in the Gulf. The two Gulf wars have shown the need for major combat operations and early deterrent deployments; demanding requirements in relation to strategic transport and to command and control. Regional conflict in North Africa or the Near East could affect UK interests and those of allied nations.
7. **Regional conflict inside the NATO area.** Britain will continue to support NATO's capability for collective defence. NATO must be able to deter and respond to small-scale but militarily demanding regional conflicts, crises or threats to alliance members including the threat or use of nuclear weapons. Britain's military capabilities available to NATO include the UK's leading role in its Rapid Reaction Corps.
8. **Strategic attack on NATO.** No threat on this scale is in prospect but it could reappear, and the conventional forces needed to deter such an attack would take years to create. A long-term insurance is provided through a credible nuclear deterrent and the retention of the essential military capabilities on which the UK could, if necessary, rebuild larger forces over a period.

Figure 16. The eight missions for which the UK armed forces must be prepared.

be developed. Examples of these types of force are all-arms battlegroups and combined air groups, which not only have several capabilities, but can deliver them simultaneously.

The DEG defined defence capability in two ways, first as a single-function defence capability: *the emergent properties from the interaction between a number of similar weapon systems' effectiveness factors, human factors, command structure, maintenance and logistic support to produce an operational unit's sustainable single-function defence capability* and secondly as a multi-function defence capability: *the emergent properties from the interaction between a number of different operational units' single-function defence capabilities, human factors, command structure, maintenance and logistic support to produce a combat force's sustainable multi-function defence capability.* The DEG considered that useable defence capability is created by a combination of factors: environment, enemy, rules of engagement, equipment, personnel, training, maintenance, logistic support, command structure, command and control, defence policy and doctrine.

The performance of systems tends to be expressed as system parameters such as speed, range and payload. These parameters can readily be measured in factories or on test ranges, but the results give little useful information about battlefield performance. It is therefore preferable to consider system effectiveness, which shows a system's ability to perform military actions against competing hostile systems (e.g. kill probability). System effectiveness can be estimated from realistic exercises but is not as easily measured as system parameters. Effectiveness can be converted into system capability by expressing it in terms of battlefield objectives. Capability should be measured against battlefield objectives such as enemy tanks destroyed per battlefield day or infrastructure targets destroyed per sortie.

Both performance and effectiveness refer to individual systems, but for a high-level view it is necessary to consider the capability of the military forces involved in an operation. As previously stated, UK defence doctrine defines military capability as 'the overall potential of the armed forces for combat or other operations'. This is the highest level of military capability and can be considered as the total military capability of the UK. The lowest level of capability, that of an individual system, is probably too small to be significant but can be aggregated into unit capability; the capability of a number of independent systems combined into an operational military unit to perform military actions. Unit capabilities can likewise be aggregated into force capabilities, the sum of all capabilities of all the units comprising the force, and thence into the total military capability. Any deficiency in the total military capability when measured against the requirements derived from the military tasks creates a capability gap.

Associated individual capabilities can be combined to give capability groups such as an underwater battlespace capability or a direct battlefield engagement capability. In turn these groups can further be combined into major capability areas, for example, land, sea and air capability or strategic deployment, manoeuvre and strike capabilities.

3.2 Capability gaps

Once potential capability gaps are identified, analysis is essential to ensure that equipment is selected to fill the gaps in an effective and efficient manner. To achieve this, analysis and planning are conducted to gain an understanding of how best to fill the gaps, what is affordable within the defence budget and to determine priorities for acquisition.

Most major operational capabilities can be provided in a number of different ways. Each alternative will have its own strengths and weaknesses when applied to different situations.

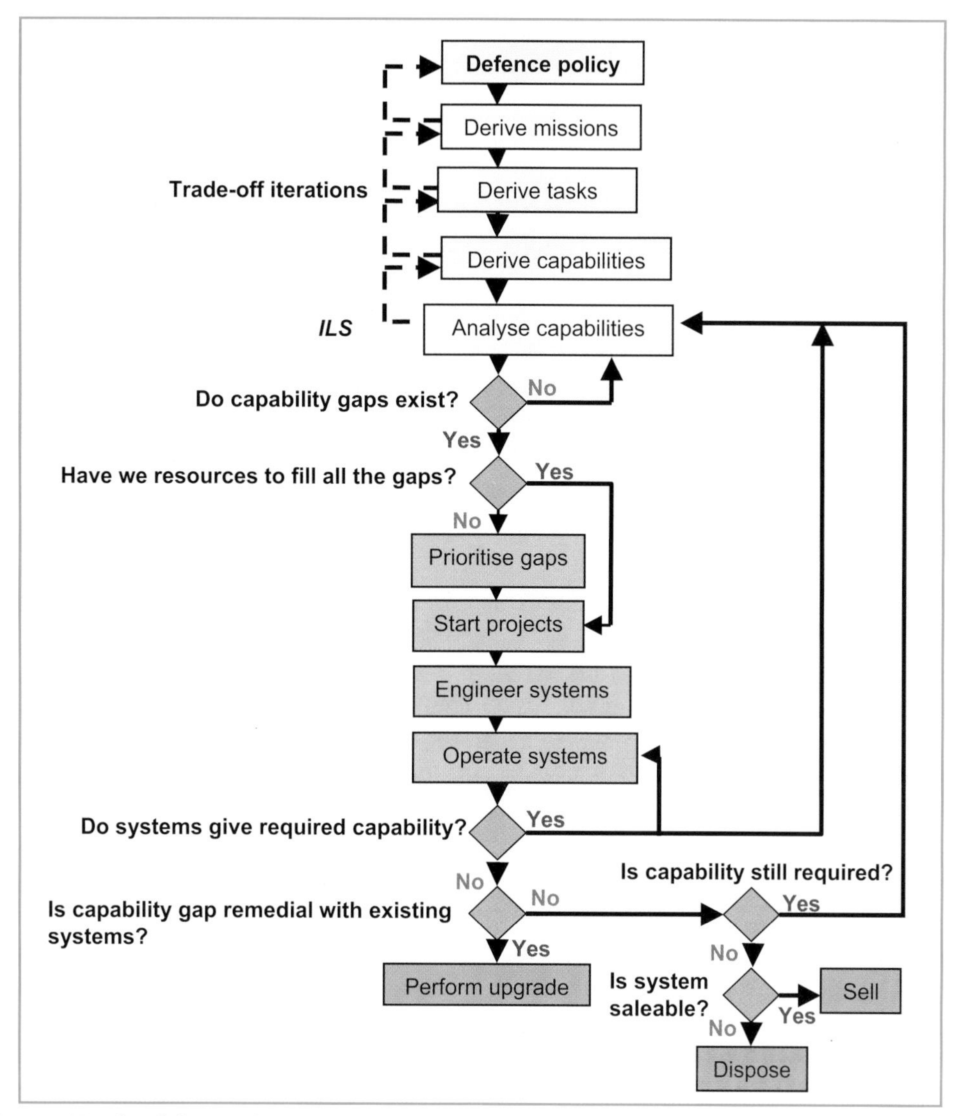

Figure 17. The defence planning flowchart shows the various processes and decisions that are required from initial concept to disposal.

For example, ships, submarines, fixed-wing aircraft and ship-based helicopters can all provide anti-submarine capabilities although some are more suited to particular operational situations than others. To provide operational flexibility in different scenarios, a mix of equipment is usually required and careful analysis is needed to ensure the optimum affordable mix. As more and more platforms are designed for multiple roles, it is crucial to ensure that one capability does not affect the ability of a platform to conduct its other roles. The impact of changes in one capability area must be considered for all other areas to maintain the best capability mix, able to perform the defence tasks and missions. The rapidly changing defence environment

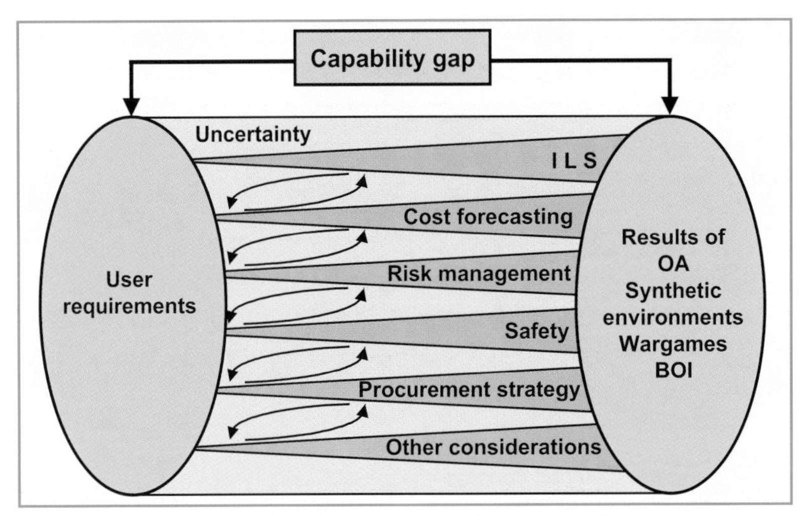

Figure 18. The factors to be considered when moving from capability gap to user requirement.

also places great importance on other considerations such as readiness requirements, force generation processes, deployment of assets and the organisation of support services.

The acquisition of defence equipment requires long-term planning as it often takes many years to bring equipment into service. The planning process starts with a strategic plan which addresses the high-level planning assumptions, lays down the long-term vision, the future force structure and attempts to identify the key drivers for change. The strategic plan provides an overview of the UK defence programme as a whole and drives the equipment plan. The equipment plan is the responsibility of the equipment capability branch and contains the results from the balance of investment studies, the equipment requirements and costed options for each type of required capability.

Balance of investment (BOI) studies determine the best allocation of resources, within a fixed budget, to obtain optimum military effectiveness. High-level BOI studies look at the allocation of resources between capability groups, and thus support the evolution of defence policy. At a more detailed level, BOI studies give consideration to different equipments that can provide an equivalent capability at different performance levels and at different costs. For example, a BOI study might compare long-range strategic lift aircraft against a seaborne solution. BOI analysis is necessary to maintain a coherent and effective defence programme with the available resources. Equipment cost forecasts assist force-mix studies to determine what new equipment is affordable and justifiable within the current force mix. These studies involve a comparison of force effectiveness at equivalent cost, including both direct, indirect and life cycle costs.

3.3 Through-life approach to planning

One of the major findings from the 1998 strategic defence review was the need to adopt a through-life systems approach to improve the assessment of overall equipment costs.

Well-implemented DSE practices can provide increased confidence in the performance, time, cost and effective integration of the system and the right balance of investment between the cost of acquiring new equipment and its in-service support. This should provide the members of the armed forces with the necessary capabilities in a timely manner to undertake successfully the tasks required of them.

Current practice is to record the many aspects of the through-life approach used in DSE in a through-life management plan (TLMP), initiated during the concept phase and continually developed as the project advances. Figure 18 illustrates the through-life approach, showing how a capability gap is refined by operational analysis, followed by the reduction in uncertainty by through-life systems-engineering disciplines that improve accuracy and confidence as the project progresses.

3.3.1 Operational analysis

Various departments of Dstl perform defence equipment operational analysis, starting with help in identifying capability gaps and later providing the evidence to enlighten the decision-making process prior to equipment acquisition.

Operational analysis (OA) is the technical and scientific analysis of the military environment that helps to identify, analyse and provide solutions to problems, such as:

- Strategic threat assessments.
- Planning, mounting, sustaining and supporting military operations.
- Operational effectiveness.
- Tactical operations.
- Supporting operations in wartime.

OA predominantly uses a range of models for defence analysis such as:

- Wargames – using military expertise to fight ‘paper’ wars.
- Simulations – using computer-based techniques.
- Synthetic environments – where models and real equipment can be tested in a range of virtual surroundings, also reducing the need for experiments at different locations.
- Field trials – using real equipment and personnel to validate research.

The tools require an operational context for their use and, most importantly, an agreed and consistent set of assumptions relating to tactics, forces and objectives of the enemy, plus a measure of effectiveness (MoE) to ensure that results can accurately and consistently be compared. Many of these items require military input referred to in studies as ‘military judgement’ in order to create a realistic and viable set of scenarios. The output of OA feeds into a range of project issues such as integrated logistic support (ILS), cost forecasting, risk management, safety and procurement strategy. More details are given in Chapter 5, Section 1.

3.3.2 Cost forecasting

The MoD has a duty to safeguard public money when placing contracts for equipment and services by checking that the prices proposed by industry are fair and that the proposed solution represents value for money. In support of this aim, the MoD uses cost forecasting models in the following three areas:

- Budgetary – time profiles of acquisition expenditure are forecast annually and contribute to the 4- and 10-year spend profiles; the short-term plan (STP) and the equipment plans (EP). The STP/EP process determines whether financial resources can be found for a potential new project and aims to ensure smooth department expenditure. Responsibility for detailed scrutiny and advice to ministers on each major equipment proposal rests with the Investment Approvals Board (IAB).
- High-level studies – Dstl uses equipment cost forecasts in balance of investment studies to identify which new equipments deserve a place in the UK force mix. Each type of equipment's cost effectiveness can be compared either on the basis of common direct and indirect costs or in terms of common effectiveness.
- Selection for acquisition – a particular class of equipment will emerge from the BOI studies that might best fill a future capability need. Several acquisition options may be available to satisfy this capability gap. A combined operational effectiveness and investment appraisal (COEIA) recommends which system should be procured on the basis of cost effectiveness. Arrangements for aspects such as different warranty policies, contractor support or the use of PFI are included in the investment appraisal. A COEIA (see Chapter 5, Section 2) may be necessary at any stage where there is a need to deliberate over a number of options.

Early cost forecasts are based on high-level assumptions that are refined throughout the equipment life cycle as more accurate information becomes available. All the many varied models used to derive cost forecasts depend on the accuracy of available information.

Before cost forecasting begins, each alternative equipment programme must be meticulously defined and recorded in the master data and assumptions list (MDAL). The

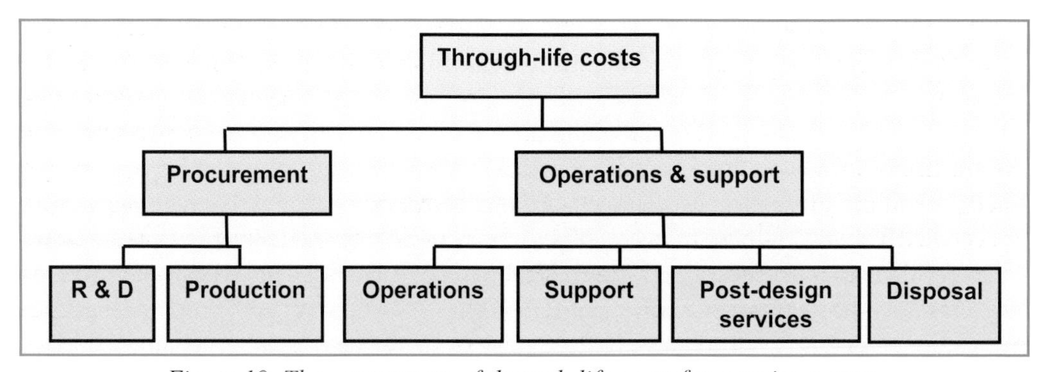

Figure 19. The components of through-life costs for a major system.

MDAL includes all factors affecting cost, including a technical description, definition of the acquisition strategy, training costs, policy on inclusion of indirect costs, the planned delivery schedule, the expected level of operations, the operation level at which the cost forecasts will be made and identification of the economic conditions used in the cost forecast. There is more information on this subject in Chapter 4, Section 1.

3.3.3. Through-life cost

The through-life cost (TLC) of a project is the total expenditure directly associated with it from concept to disposal. The components of TLC are related to the various project phases and are shown in Figure 19. A comprehensive review of all cost elements is important prior to equipment selection since most cost-forecasting errors arise from omission rather than misjudgement.

TLC is complicated by potential variations in operating costs. Typically platforms (ships, main battle tanks and aircraft) have long in-service lives and their high running costs outweigh the initial procurement cost. The TLC of other systems may be dominated by procurement costs, e.g. a guided missile which may be stored in a sealed container until fired, requiring little or no maintenance. The cost of environmentally responsible disposal needs consideration from the outset and can be very high for items such as nuclear submarines. On the other hand, the sale of second-hand ships and aircraft to other nations can generate additional funds.There is more information on TLC in Chapter 3, Section 7.2.

3.3.4 Risk

Project risk has always been a focus for well-trained project managers but the increased focus on TLCs has emphasised the need for formal risk management. A risk manager should be appointed early in a project's life cycle and encouraged to involve all stakeholders in a formal risk identification process. Study groups can look at internal and external risks associated with the project. Any risk that may impact on project success should be identified early so it can be recorded and appropriately managed. Risk is an important cost driver and can have a fundamental impact on the success of the project. Risks need to be recorded in a continually updated risk register.

A risk is an uncertain event that may impact on a project in a positive or negative way and thus may be an opportunity or a threat. For the best chance of success, project risk must attract an appropriate level of management attention. Risks can be avoided, mitigated, accepted or transferred. Avoiding a risk involves changing the direction of the project so that the risk will no longer have an impact. Risk mitigation involves providing contingency resources so that the impact of the risk is reduced to an acceptable level. Some risks which have only a small probability of occurrence, but which would be expensive to avoid or mitigate, should be accepted, acknowledging that additional funding or time may be required in a few cases. Risks should not automatically be transferred, but those risks that cannot be avoided should be managed by the party best placed to manage the risk. Formal procedures for risk management are readily available and the DPA uses a common tool set which aims for a consistent and thorough approach. There is more on risk in Chapter 8, Section 3.

3.3.5 *Incremental acquisition*

Defence systems increasingly rely on a wide range of rapidly changing technologies such as information technology and chemicals. The current complexity level of defence projects makes it increasingly difficult to acquire systems as a single deliverable. Long acquisition timescales and environmental changes lead to equipment entering service that may be obsolete or fails to meet user needs. Incremental acquisition is a strategy that aims to deliver a basic requirement followed by a planned upgrade programme. This means the equipment can enter service rapidly and then is progressively updated to meet changing user needs and remain up to date. Other claimed advantages of planned incremental upgrades are that they can be managed and budgeted more accurately when the relevant technologies have been de-risked, risks can be reduced, state-of-the-art technologies can be inserted and user feedback can be built into future upgrades. Commercial off-the-shelf (COTS) equipment, particularly COTS IT, is often at the forefront of technology as producers strive to maintain a competitive advantage. This can be exploited for applications where state-of–the-art equipment is required and, due to its availability, can be used in an incremental acquisition programme.

Major platforms carrying a wide range of weapon systems and diverse functionality often require ongoing change to their systems and sub-systems. From a through-life approach to the provision of defence capability, it can be more efficient to acquire military capability incrementally for such systems. The baseline requirement can enter service quickly followed by the progressive insertion of more complex functionality, giving more time for trade-offs between performance, time, cost and effective integration of complex parts of the system.

Incremental acquisition requires careful management, particularly through the approvals process. Any incrementally acquired project will have several technical and financial uncertainties when submitted for main gate approval. An overall cost limit must be set for the project with target cost and performance envelopes for each planned improvement. As each increment is achieved, the target cost and these performance envelopes must then be reset for each subsequent increment.

3.3.6 *Integrated logistic support*

ILS is a disciplined management approach, affecting both the MoD and its suppliers, aimed at optimising value for money throughout equipment life cycles. ILS considers all aspects of equipment support and should be used to influence the earliest stages of the acquisition cycle. The MoD is committed to the application of ILS as the business process for achieving reductions in TLCs in association with systems engineering principles. A detailed description of ILS may be found in Chapter 3, Section 7.

4 UK armed forces

4.1 Operations, composition and structure

The formally enunciated aim of the armed forces is: *To deliver security for the people of the United Kingdom and the Overseas Territories by defending them, including against terrorism; and to act as a force for good by strengthening international peace and stability.* Since, ultimately, the work of the defence systems engineer is to support the achievement of the aims of the armed forces, it is important to understand how these forces are organised and what they plan to do with the systems and products procured for them. How the UK armed forces are structured and equipped to carry out the tasks and missions is described at the beginning of Section 3 above. Inevitably their organisation will be subject to change and some details are constrained by the needs of security, but the information provided below is sufficient to help defence systems engineers make an effective contribution.

4.1.1 Military force

The overarching doctrine for the armed forces can be encapsulated in the phrase 'effects-based manoeuvre warfare'. This emphasises that the particular force elements used in any given situation, and the activities that they undertake, will depend on the required effect; the aim being to deploy these effects against identified vulnerabilities in such a way as to shatter the enemy's cohesion and will to fight. It has been described as attacking the moral component of an enemy's fighting power with the intention of causing him to yield before the physical means to resist have been exhausted. This approach can be employed not only in a conventional military way using or threatening combat, but also in a policing role with the minimum of force being used only as a last resort, typically to uphold international law. Additionally, the armed forces can be used in a benign non-combat manner, for example in disaster relief or mountain rescue. These categories are not discrete and, in considering the different types of conflict (general war, limited conflict, regional conflict, civil war, insurgency and terrorism), most feature more than one category; for example, counter-insurgency operations straddle the line between conventional operations and policing.

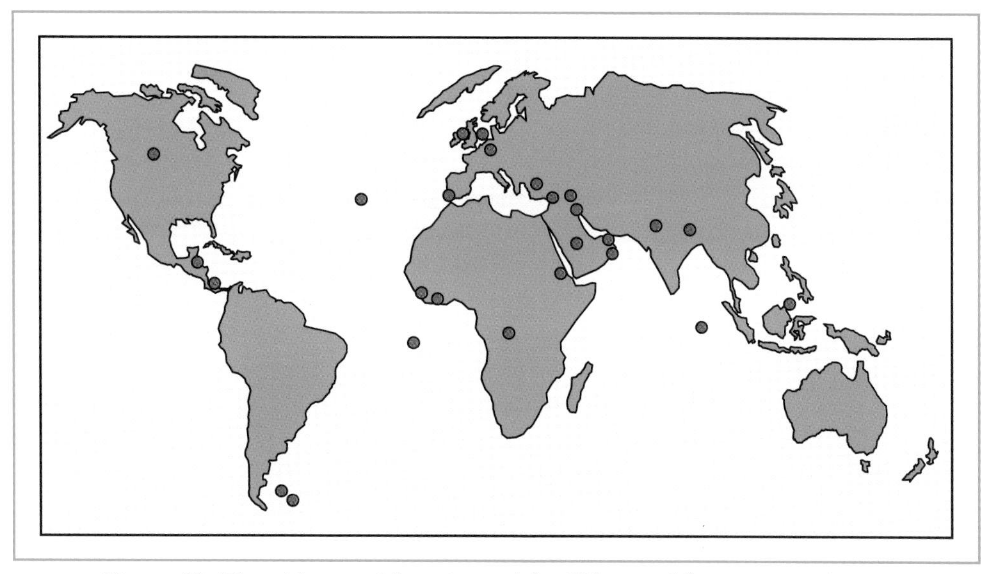

Figure 20. The widespread locations of the UK armed forces in April 2004.

4.1.2 Types of operation

There are ten significantly different types of operation in which the UK armed forces may become involved, and almost all of these require the capability to respond to asymmetric warfare (e.g. suicide bombers or concerted terrorist action).

1. **Nuclear operations** – strategic or sub-strategic.
2. **High-intensity ground operations** – may be strategic or tactical and incorporate armour, artillery, infantry (airborne, airmobile, armoured, mechanised) and combat support (logistics and engineering).
3. **Maritime sea-control operations** – using anti-submarine, anti-air and anti-ship weapons.
4. **Littoral operations** – including amphibious assault, raids, naval air and gunfire support, and land attack from surface and sub-surface platforms.
5. **Air operations** – to win air superiority by destroying enemy aircraft, air bases and missile sites, and to support ground forces by close air support and interdiction, by surveillance and reconnaissance, and by electronic warfare. Note that these are increasingly being conducted by the use of unmanned aerial vehicles (UAVs) that can be 'piloted' from an area of safety.
6. **Special forces operations**.
7. **Space operations** – communications, surveillance and, in the future, weaponry.
8. **Inducement operations** – such as presence and symbolic use, 'showing the flag', as well as precautionary operations, sanctions enforcement, peacekeeping and peacebuilding.
9. **Counter-insurgency and counter-terrorism**.
10. **Humanitarian aid** – food distribution and rescue following natural disasters.

Figure 21. The various types of operation that the UK armed forces must prepare to undertake.

4.1.3 Cultures of the armed forces

Notwithstanding the different historic roots of each branch of the armed forces, there is a strong and increasing emphasis on joint operations and co-operative working. This does not devalue the importance of the individual service ethos with all the benefits to operational effectiveness that this brings; however it does, potentially, mean that both the characteristic style and culture of the operating service, as well as the nature of its potential future operations, should influence a defence systems engineer in creating a cost-effective design and formulating a TLMP.

The RN works in a familiar but often hostile maritime environment, the sea being spoken of as 'the common enemy', and there undoubtedly remains a certain brotherhood between navies even though they may be on opposing sides. The physical constraints of living and operating in a confined space – be it a ship or submarine – tend to drive a ship's crew into working as a close-knit team with all members very much dependent on the skill and professionalism of their colleagues. Given that a ship is a 'system of systems', there is a strong technical and equipment emphasis.

Army culture has evolved from working in a varied and complex environment with the need to hold ground or territory. There is a continuous interface with civilian populations with the need to maintain favourable military/civilian relationships. The discomfort of living and fighting in often unpleasant physical conditions places high demands on leadership and endurance, sustained by a bedrock of regimental tradition, with commanding officers having great autonomy and influence. However, the need to sustain the army in a hostile environment creates a significant logistical challenge, amelioration of which, through the design of increasing reliable equipment, should be one of the goals of the defence systems engineer.

The RAF is focused on its aircrew and has a high degree of professionalism and equipment orientation. Even in war, air safety is of highest importance so there is an inherent attention to risk management and a concomitant focus on compliance with instructions and regulations. Aircrew have to be trained to accept high levels of danger for short periods, usually without the support of comrades, alternating with long periods of comparative safety.

4.1.4 Joint doctrine

Notwithstanding the cultural and environmentally based differences between the branches of the armed forces, almost all operations are carried out on a joint basis. To be effective, this requires conformance with joint doctrine, which aims to provide a common framework of understanding (from the strategic to the tactical level) to aid the effective delivery of military capability. A similar joint doctrine has been developed with key civilian organisations and is now being applied to peace support operations both in the UK and abroad. Whilst, whenever possible, the UK's joint doctrine is aligned with that of likely partners in any future conflict, this cannot always be achieved. Some of the problems of interoperability between allied nations are discussed in Chapter 9, Section 11.

4.1.5 Recent changes

Following the decline of the Soviet Union as a monolithic potential opponent, and the parallel rise of less obvious, but in some cases equally potent, threats, the UK's armed forces are undergoing a period of significant reorganisation. The overall aim is to develop more mobile forces that can be deployed quickly and yet have sufficient offensive and defensive combat power to be effective. This is underpinned by the development of a network-enabled capability (NEC) that aims to link sensors (e.g. satellites and other means of observation) with decision-makers and weapon systems so that information can be translated into synchronised and overwhelmingly rapid effect. This has led to a significant reorganisation and re-balancing of the armed forces based on the principles announced in July 2004, with the detailed implications (e.g. the reorganisation of the infantry regiments) now beginning to emerge.

4.2 Royal Navy

There are currently three aircraft carriers (CVs) that each embark a tailored air group of Harrier VSTOL (vertical/short take-off and landing) aircraft and helicopters. The current primary role of the CV is operations against land targets without dependence on host-nation support, and it is also used as the base for support helicopters to aid amphibious or other operations. The ships are protected by close-in weapons systems that employ a rapid-fire rate to destroy incoming anti-ship missiles. Two replacement carriers (CVFs) are at the early design stage and are due to enter service in the 2015–2020 timeframe. They will be the principal platforms for the short take-off, vertical-landing (STOVL) F35 joint strike fighter. The carrier air group will also include a maritime airborne surveillance and control system to provide warning against air and surface threats, together with command and control for other air operations. The CVF will be able to support anti-submarine warfare as well as littoral operations.

The UK's amphibious capability has been greatly enhanced by the recent additions to the surface fleet of two amphibious assault ships in addition to the single helicopter carrier. These support the Royal Marines and the other elements of the armed forces by providing an extensive capability to sustain operations in littoral areas. This capability will be further enhanced by the four Bay class landing ships, the first two of which are due to enter service in 2005.

The eleven existing Type 42 destroyers (primary role anti-aircraft) are coming to the end of their lives and will be replaced by eight of the new Type 45s, which are planned to enter service before the end of the decade. For the anti-air warfare role, the ships will be fitted with radar, a command and control system and surface-to-air missiles with a prime role of defending the ships in a task force against salvo attacks by anti-ship missiles. Other equipment will include a gun for shore bombardment, an anti-submarine helicopter and a torpedo defence system. A force of up to 60 troops can also be embarked and supported by the ship's aircraft and boats during their operations. The Type 45 at 7,350 tons is large enough to carry vertical-launched cruise missiles should a land attack capability be needed.

There are currently sixteen Type 23 frigates in the fleet. However, as a result of the re-balancing of the armed forces mentioned above, three will be disposed of shortly, leaving a planned destroyer and frigate force totalling 25 vessels. Originally designed for anti-submarine warfare, they are now multi-purpose ships being armed with ship-to-ship and surface-to-air missiles, a shore bombardment gun, anti-submarine torpedo tubes, depth charges and an anti-submarine helicopter.

These ships are complemented by four Type 22 frigates which were also originally designed as anti-submarine vessels but have had anti-surface and anti-aircraft weapons added; more importantly, they have a sophisticated suite of command, control and communications systems and each can, therefore, be used as the lead platform for a small task force. Armament is similar to the Type 23, but with the addition of a close-in anti-missile weapon system. The future surface combatant (FSC), presently at concept stage, is the planned future warship that will eventually replace the Type 22 and Type 23 frigates. FSC may well incorporate the novel features of both a trimaran hull design and all-electric propulsion.

In addition, the surface fleet contains a variety of over 50 other ships – mine counter-measures vessels, survey ships, fishery protection vessels and fast training boats – although again, this total is planned to reduce by six as part of the force re-balancing.

Turning to the sub-surface environment, the four Vanguard nuclear-powered submarines (SSBNs) are armed with the Trident missile to provide the UK's nuclear deterrent. They also carry anti-ship missiles and torpedoes, and are fitted with sophisticated sonar.

A future total of eight Swiftsure and Trafalgar class attack submarines (SSNs) have a wide variety of roles, and are able to be deployed as an integrated layer of defence within a task force. They are armed with torpedoes, anti-ship and cruise missiles and have a comprehensive sonar suite. These boats are capable of co-ordinated high-intensity strike, surveillance and inshore/beach reconnaissance. They are due to be replaced progressively by a smaller number of the Astute class submarines, the first three of which are under construction.

The Fleet Air Arm provides a multi-role aviation combat capability. It has some 200 combat aircraft and 50 support/training aircraft. Principal platforms are the Sea Harrier, a single-seat multi-role day/night all-weather aircraft soon to be replaced, and the Merlin helicopter, which carries four homing torpedoes or depth charges for anti-submarine duties. The Fleet Air Arm also flies Lynx and Gazelle helicopters.

The Royal Marines provide the navy with its own amphibious infantry that can deploy at short notice to mount amphibious assaults. The Royal Marines are capable of operating ashore as a lightly equipped force with specialisations in mountain and cold-weather operations. There are three Commando units, similar in size to an infantry battalion, with integrated artillery, engineer and logistics support units.

The Royal Fleet Auxiliary (RFA) ships form an extremely important element of the integrated maritime force providing logistic support to a task force. These ships are civilian manned and operate as commercial vessels, but at the same time have consistently been found operating in hostile environments alongside their RN counterparts. There is a total of 20 vessels within the RFA including tankers, replenishment ships and landing craft.

4.3 The Army

The Army consists of a number of regiments and corps, each with a specialised role. The Royal Armoured Corps is responsible for battlefield reconnaissance and the destruction of enemy forces by direct fire from its armoured vehicles. Important equipments are the Challenger 2 main battle tank as well as the Scimitar and Sabre combat vehicles reconnaissance and the Army's specialist NBC vehicles.

The infantry comprised, in 2005, 36 battalions of about 800 men each. Typical weapons are the SA 80 rifles, general-purpose machine guns, mortars, anti-tank missiles and man-portable anti-aircraft missiles. The infantry can be deployed in difficult terrain that is unsuitable for vehicles, such as jungle or mountains. They may be employed as:

1. Armoured troops in infantry fighting vehicles.
2. Mechanised infantry in armoured personnel carriers.
3. Air assault troops deployed with helicopters.
4. Light infantry.

The Royal Artillery provides the army's beyond-visual-range guns and surface-to-surface missiles, as well as larger types of surface-to-air missiles. These give general support, providing long-range fire to counter enemy artillery and suppress enemy defensive and command positions. The regiment also furnishes close support for land operations and air defence to counter the threat of low-flying aircraft and pop-up strikes by helicopters. It carries out surveillance and target acquisition using unmanned air vehicles and radar, providing target information of enemy HQ, units, helicopters, concentration areas and mortar positions. Its major items of equipment are the 105mm light gun, AS90 Howitzer and MLRS (multiple launch rocket system).

Described colloquially as 'Sappers', the Royal Engineers' role is to aid the mobility of UK forces using equipment such as track-mounted, amphibious and girder bridges. They also counter enemy mobility using obstacles and craters, destroying bridges and laying anti-tank mines. Additional tasks include mapping, mine clearance and bomb disposal, flood relief, water provision, airfield repair and the erection of buildings.

The Army Air Corps is a helicopter-based force using the Apache, Gazelle and Lynx helicopters for action against enemy tanks using guided weapons or against soft targets using machine guns. They are widely employed to carry out observation and reconnaissance, and the direction of fire for close-support aircraft, naval guns and own artillery. They also have the ability to move a limited numbers of troops and senior commanders.

The Joint Helicopter Command sustains an effective force of battlefield helicopters used for air assault and logistics. It is under the command of HQ Land Command and is responsible for the commando helicopter force, all army aviation units, the RAF support helicopter force that includes the Chinook heavy-lift helicopters, 16th Air Assault Brigade, and the Joint Helicopter Force Northern Ireland.

The Royal Corps of Signals is responsible for communications and information systems including satellites, trunk communications and net radios. The Corps is also responsible for providing the army's electronic warfare (EW) interception, analysis and jamming capability.

The Royal Logistic Corps is responsible for delivering stocks of vehicles, equipment, ammunition, fuel and lubricants, food and other battlefield commodities. It is also responsible for catering and explosive disposal. It employs tank transporters, DROPS (dismountable rack offloading and pick-up system) and various cargo trucks.

The Royal Electrical and Mechanical Engineers (REME) carry out recovery, equipment repair and modifications as well as some maintenance. They are equipped with recovery vehicles, workshop repair vehicles and special tools.

The Intelligence Corps is responsible for operational intelligence, while the Adjutant General's Corps provides police, personnel, legal and education staff services. The Army also has its own chaplaincy, medical, physical training and music services.

4.3.1 Army organisation

On operations, the basic army unit is a battlegroup. This is an ad hoc formation with an appropriate amalgam of armour, infantry, engineers, artillery, signals and army aviation that will be tailored to its planned operational task. It will be based on an infantry battalion or armoured regiment and be around 1,200 personnel strong. A battlegroup can be 'infantry heavy' with one squadron of tanks, 'armour heavy' with three squadrons of tanks, or 'square' with a balance of infantry and armour.

Should it be appropriate to deploy a larger formation, this will normally be a brigade, which will either be armoured or mechanised. The former consists of two armoured infantry battalions, two armoured regiments, one artillery regiment and one engineer regiment. The latter, typically, is formed of one armoured infantry battalion, one armoured regiment, two mechanised-infantry battalions (wheeled) and an artillery regiment and an engineer regiment. In either case the strength is approximately 6,500. The next larger formation is a division, and this is made up of two or more brigades and a significant number of divisional units such as artillery regiments, a reconnaissance regiment, an aviation regiment, a signals regiment, equipment support battalions, a medical regiment, logistics and police regiments. Its total strength is approximately 24,000 personnel. Except in general war, this is likely to be the largest formation deployed.

All but the smallest army operations involve troops from different branches, exploiting the synergies between their respective types of equipment. The necessary co-ordination is achieved by a common doctrine, intensive training and realistic exercises, and is increasingly being facilitated by networked electronic communications. It is vital that all types of equipment engaged in the same operational area should provide a seamless capability of fire and movement, and should be electronically and logistically compatible.

As part of the restructuring of the armed forces mentioned earlier, it is intended to move from the current structure, a force mix of heavy (armoured) and light (e.g. Parachute Regiment/Royal Marines), to one that also includes medium-weight forces. These will offer a high level of deployability (including by air) together with greater levels of mobility and protection that are currently available to light forces. This is being achieved by internal re-balancing of existing forces, but some reductions of overall troop levels have been necessary.

4.4 Royal Air Force

The RAF operates some 500 UK front-line aircraft worldwide. It is organised into three Groups, which are designed to maximise the synergies between similar aircraft types/roles.

No 1 Group comprises all front-line fast-jet aircraft aircraft that provide strike attack, air defence and reconnaissance capabilities which are delivered using variants of the Tornado aircraft. It is also responsible for the operation of the Jaguar aircraft, but these are being phased out (by 2007) as part of the re-balancing mentioned above. No 1 Group also operates the Typhoon that will progressively replace the Tornados and Jaguars.

No 2 Group comprises air transport and air-to-air refuelling aircraft that support front-line operations, whilst No 3 Group provides the battlefield and maritime reconnaissance, intelligence gathering and airborne early warning and control (AWACS). In these roles Sentry aircraft carry out airborne early warning (AEW), Nimrods undertake maritime reconnaissance, Sentinel R conducts battlefield surveillance, Canberra and some Nimrod aircraft undertake intelligence and electronic warfare, while C17 and Hercules aircraft provide tactical air transport, with VC10s and Tristars for air movement/tankers. The RAF Regiment forms a separate element within No 2 Group and provides both airfield security and ground-based air defence with the Rapier surface-to-air missile system.

4.5 Special forces

The special forces are units which have been selected, trained, equipped and designated to conduct unconventional actions to enable or support conventional operations. The characteristics of special forces are rapid response, reach, versatility, precision, discretion, determination and audacity, using small numbers of personnel. The UK special forces comprise the Special Air Service (SAS) with skills in covert and counter-revolutionary operations as well as mountain warfare, and the Special Boat Section (SBS) trained in maritime counter-terrorism, and using swimmers and small boats. Given suitable training, other forces such as paratroops can also carry out special operations should the need arise, but such operations are not their primary role.

4.6 Reserve forces

As the number of full-time UK service personnel diminishes in response to perceived reduced threat levels, the operations of the UK's armed forces are increasingly dependent on the support of territorial/volunteer and reserve forces. In some cases, the reservists provide a similar capability (e.g. infantry, Royal Marines) to their regular counterparts and are, therefore, a means of augmenting and maintaining that capability over longer periods. In other cases (such as medical staff) they provide a capability that either no longer exists or is

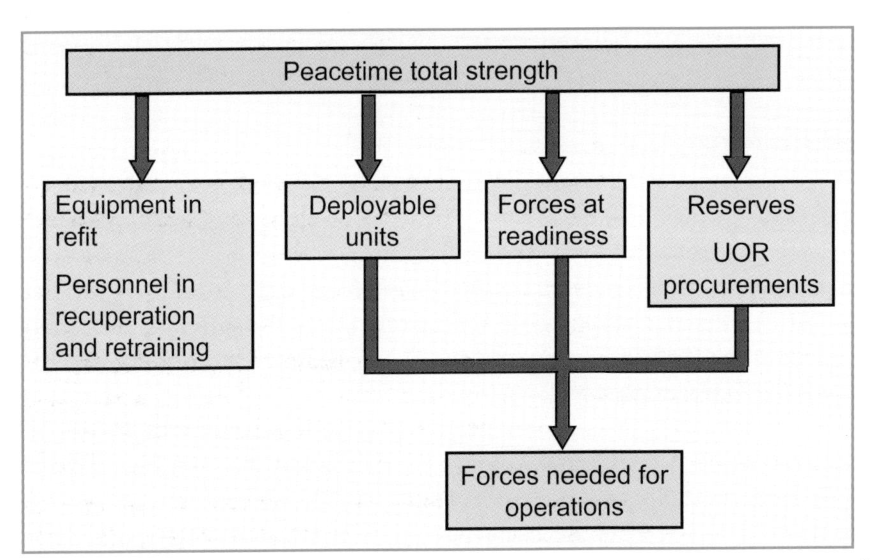

Figure 22. The forces needed for operations are drawn from the total peacetime strength of the armed forces and supported by urgent operation requirement (UOR) procurements.

maintained at a low level within the regular forces. They form an essential part of operations, other than low-level ones, but the need to activate their services can have legal and political implications.

4.7 Planning for operations

The above descriptions intentionally give only indicative information on the armed forces' current size and equipment, for these are inevitably subject to continual change. The strength and shape of the UK armed forces are now determined by the requirement to perform a number of scenarios (e.g. an enduring medium-scale operation or an enduring small-scale operation concurrently with a limited-duration medium-scale operation) at relatively short notice. Unfortunately, in the absence of a reliable crystal ball, it is necessary to base operational preparations for such eventualities on a series of scenarios that model potential future conflicts. Inevitably, there is a mismatch between the prior assumptions and the actual requirements of a given operation. Furthermore, the pre-stocking of equipment and/or retention of personnel 'just in case' is an extremely expensive option. Current policy assumes therefore that, in preparing for operations, reservists can be activated and equipment and sustainability shortfalls can be made up by short-notice procurement action based on urgent operational requirements (UORs). Nevertheless, the total peacetime strength of the UK armed forces must include, in addition to those units at high readiness, sufficient additional equipment to allow for regular maintenance, repair, refit and upgrade programmes as well as to provide for recuperation and retraining of personnel; the latter rotate through the deployed forces to maintain prolonged operational effectiveness without undue strain on the people involved.

5 The digital battlespace

5.1 Introduction

The key transformation in the way future military operations are accomplished is the application of IT to command and control of the armed forces. The resulting NEC should provide a step change in military effectiveness as a result of combining precision weapons and the latest sensor technology into IT networks. Radically improved IT and communications capabilities will enhance situation awareness by combining and rapidly distributing information from many sources, allowing more effective and efficient use of forces. Smart weapons will allow accurate long-range attacks, reducing the risk to own forces and to civilians.

Exploiting these new technologies should provide important enhancements to military capability. The potential of the UK (and other friendly nations) to take advantage of US developments in this field should enable more effective coalition operations, providing political and military advantage. However, the limited availability of some of the latest US technology suggests the need for selective development of these technologies, both in the UK and Europe.

Relevant future UK projects include the ASTOR surveillance system and a range of new smart, long-range, guided weapons as well as the joint battlespace digitisation initiative. The latter should improve operational effectiveness by integrating platforms, weapons, sensors, C^3I (command, control, communications and intelligence) and other IT systems with communications that are compatible with NATO and other potential allies. It also recognises that, within a decade, military operations are likely to merge sea, land and air into a single battlespace where joint and combined operations will become the norm.

The increasing dependence on advanced technology that provides a battle-winning capability may result in some potential enemies implementing unconventional strategies or using alternative approaches such as information warfare. It will be essential to avoid introducing weaknesses that could be readily exploited by hostile nations in the future.

5.2 The IT and communications environment

IT involving computer hardware, software and networks is becoming increasingly prevalent both in military equipment and in everyday life. At virtually every stage of the vertical hierarchy of military systems, IT and its constituent parts are to be found; semiconductors at the material level, integrated circuits at the component level, processors at the sub-assemblies level, work stations as sub-systems and, at the highest level, complete C^3I systems.

Numerous areas of technology have been affected by the growth of IT. There is improved control of existing mechanical devices and automation has made many labour-intensive tasks much simpler. There has been an explosive increase in data quantity, speed and application whilst automated design and production facilities provide improved equipment at reduced cost. On the operational side it is easy to view remote data and images but this has resulted in an overburden of information, unfortunately with little improvement in any automatic précis process.

IT is pervasive in its use by the armed forces. At the systems level, it is found as stand-alone systems such as C^3I and CIS (command information system), and embedded in platforms and weapons, warships, armoured vehicles and aircraft, missiles, smart bombs and torpedoes. At the sub-system level, it has added to the capability of most sensors and is an inherent part of radios and other communications equipment.

So why is IT important to defence systems engineers? First, it does many tasks faster than could be done by a human. It allows straightforward automation of dangerous tasks, such as missile guidance. It is very cost effective for many routine tasks such as messaging. Some tasks are only made possible by the use of IT. An example of this is observation of the nuclear test-ban treaty, where computer simulations of nuclear weapons mean that new devices can be developed without breaking the treaty.

Manpower efficiency improvements have been significant, particularly in areas such as aircrew numbers. A Lancaster bomber needed a pilot, navigator/bomb aimer and flight engineer to do the tasks done by a single person in today's Typhoon. Effective

Figure 23. IT is pervasive, from the displays in the C130 transport aircraft (left) to the joint tactical information distribution systems on a British warship (right). (Photos courtesy BAe Systems.)

logistics management has been transformed by the widespread use of IT to help manage the location, transportation and replenishment of spare parts. Virtual reality has become widespread for training and simulation, providing more cost-effective and environmentally friendly solutions. Finally, IT provides the means by which existing systems can be integrated together into a 'system of systems' (see Chapter 9, Section 3) by providing the 'clever glue' that binds systems together.

It is unfortunate yet perhaps inevitable that, given all the advantages that IT brings, there are many challenges to be overcome. As in any other equipment, there may be hardware faults, but more serious problems can occur in the software, which is difficult to write and which can be corrupted either by user misunderstandings or by external interferences such as viruses. In any case, there is no such thing as fault-free software. Bugs occur, often with undesirable emergent properties, during both initial development and subsequent operation in unforeseen circumstances. Furthermore, information warfare has taken on a new meaning with enemies aiming to distort, corrupt or interfere with IT systems, ideally by covert methods and without having to use direct military force.

Communications are vital for most IT systems and it is important in a military application that the communications are multi-route with a mix of bearers so that they will not cease to work in the event of equipment failure or malfunction. Most military communications also require encryption facilities to maintain security. There are problems with the cost and lack of bandwidth, exacerbated by the rapidly burgeoning growth in information. In addition, some military systems require a mix of voice and data in an electronic warfare environment where data may be corrupted, voices may be distorted and the background noise of battle is often high.

All this raises the question of whether there may be two new classes of war: one fought without IT and other electronics because they have largely been destroyed by the electromagnetic pulse from a nuclear weapon, and the other a more limited and more likely 'information war' fought by an enemy against civilian systems such as financial and public-utility IT systems, which could destroy many of the day-to-day processes essential to normal life in the industrialised nations.

6 Cultures and the MoD

6.1 The three cultures within the MoD

Large organisations in the public and private sectors employ a variety of people with different skills and cultures to staff departments undertaking different functions within the organisation. However, the higher levels of policy-making and management tend to be monocultural and dominated by people who are culturally suited to the particular organisation's mission whether in manufacturing, commerce, arts, or public service. The MoD, an operating organisation as well as a department of state, is distinctive because its highest ranks contain substantial numbers of staff from three very divergent cultures: service officers, scientific civil servants (boffins) and administrative civil servants (mandarins). It thus faces a particular challenge in integrating these diverse groups into a harmonious and effective organisation. Officers, boffins and mandarins (as a result of their diverse education and training) think in different patterns, adhere to different priorities and communicate in different styles; fundamentally they have very different cultural attitudes. These differences in attitude can cause mutual mistrust and misunderstanding, in which the groups grind against each other like ice floes in a heavy swell (with much spray and noise). Senior managers must have sufficient understanding and sympathy for the various cultures if they are to lead their heterogeneous teams effectively.

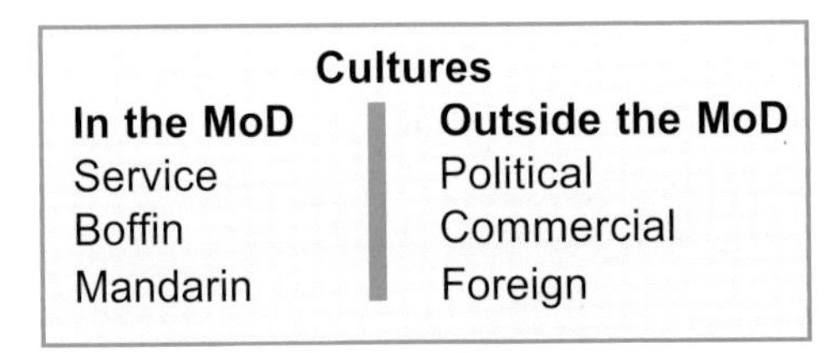

Figure 24. The different cultures that impact on defence systems engineers.

Divergent cultures in the MoD are not a new problem. In the discussions leading to the Dardanelles campaign, RN officers were at a disadvantage because they were not accustomed to argument, whereas the First Lord of the Admiralty (Winston Churchill) could argue the hind leg off a donkey and positively relished the process.

Whenever UK armed forces are involved in a military conflict, all groups in the MoD are driven by the overriding need to overcome the current emergency, and all tribal differences and disputes are waived (at least temporarily). Even in peacetime, relationships within the MoD are now more congenial than formerly, but there remain latent flashpoints which can be triggered by managerial carelessness or insensitivity, and which can cause serious problems.

The different cultures can be viewed as simplified stereotypes, but it must be remembered that most individuals are hybrids who combine the virtues (or vices) of more than one culture, and there are others who occupy an intermediate position between the extremes. The experience of working together on IPTs can help each group to understand the others, particularly if the barriers have already been eroded by appropriate multidisciplinary education.

6.1.1 Acceptance of authority

The training of military officers encourages them to accept as authoritative the judgements of higher-ranking officers. Obedience to orders is vital in combat operations, and it must be inculcated (like physical endurance and weapon skills) by practice in peacetime.

In contrast, boffins are trained to challenge current theories and assumptions, and to scrutinise rigorously any evidence cited to support them. Original research early in their careers gives boffins the knowledge to debate on level terms with their seniors, and those seniors accept that their own views must be modified in the light of the latest results.

Mandarins take respectful note of their seniors' views but rarely make any personal intellectual commitment for or against the policies which they implement. Such commitment by individual mandarins could be stressful, since they may have to execute the contradictory policies of successive governments (e.g. nationalisation, denationalisation, re-nationalisation).

6.1.2 Responsibility

In UK public administration, all key decisions are regarded as the responsibility of the minister, so mandarins expect to delegate difficult decisions upward to their political masters, and to follow the resulting instructions. By contrast, even junior military officers and boffins have always been expected to make independent decisions and to take responsibility for them during training exercises and research activities respectively. When they reach more senior levels, officers and boffins have to manage large numbers of personnel and major capital assets to achieve their allocated objectives, without continual reference to the political head of the MoD. Accordingly officers and boffins who have attained senior ranks are sometimes reluctant to defer to ministerial decisions.

The distinction between the personal qualities needed for administration and management is increasingly recognised in Whitehall, and has stimulated the creation of an increasing number of executive agencies, which have a semi-detached relationship with their parent ministry; these agencies undertake specified functions within agreed guidelines but have freedom to make operational decisions.

6.1.3 Allegiance

Mandarins give their allegiance to the elected government of the day, in accordance with an edict issued by the Cabinet Secretary in the 1980s. He stated that the current government is empowered by its democratic mandate to be the sole judge of the national interest, and hence must have the undivided allegiance of its civil servants. While individual mandarins may have reservations about particular government policies, even private opposition or protest would be deplored by their peers and disapproved of by their seniors.

Military officers have a different status since they are employed by the Crown and are commissioned by the reigning sovereign. Some are content to obey their political masters without demur, but others may feel little respect for a politician who may have only a brief tenure and a limited knowledge of military affairs. Military officers are therefore more inclined to protest (and the heads of each service and the Chief of Defence Staff have the right to go over the heads of their ministers directly to the Prime Minister), even to the point of sacrificing their careers through early retirement, if a politician's decisions are at variance with their own conviction that the national interest is best served by policies which augment the strength and capability of their own service.

Boffins are employed on the same terms as mandarins but are not expected to change their views on the laws of physics when one set of politicians replaces another. Accordingly they develop strong convictions about their specialist areas of expertise and are reluctant to accept decisions which they perceive to be unsound. However, they often lack the political skills and networks, or indeed the commitment, to mount an effective protest.

6.1.4 Communications

Military officers are taught to formulate orders for combat operations with such clarity that they cannot be misunderstood, even amidst extreme confusion, fatigue and fear. Their orders are often illustrated by maps, with overlays and symbols to represent the local terrain and the number and type of opposing combat units deployed. Later, when senior officers have to draft staff papers on the current management and future development of their service, they retain clarity as a primary goal.

Boffins also take great pains to make their reports on complex technical phenomena completely unambiguous. They illustrate their reports with mathematical equations, graphs and charts, and tables of quantitative data. Such illustrations assist debate within the scientific community, but they inhibit communication with military officers and mandarins who are often unfamiliar with that style of presentation and who may react with hostile dismissal of the associated argument.

By contrast, mandarins and their political masters communicate via carefully drafted text, which may deliberately incorporate ambiguity in order to attract the maximum level of support. Their documents include coded references to earlier speeches and manifestos, but they very rarely provide any systematic and quantitative evidence in support of the policies advocated; however, they often include caveats and qualifications (weasel words) which would allow the policy recommendations to be reversed if the political wind changed.

Boffins and mandarins alike pay great attention to their written terms of reference and approved procedures; verbal statements cut no ice. But in the services, the provision of written instructions may be neglected by officers in favour of oral advice and the implicit traditions of the unit involved.

6.2 Three external cultures which impinge on the MoD

6.2.1 Political

All UK departments of state must interact with their political masters, with their commercial suppliers and with a variety of other organisations such as trade unions, pressure groups, and international organisations. Similarly, the MoD's three internal cultures must interface with that of the current government, and those interfaces must address issues on which politicians may hold strong convictions.

One chronic problem at this interface is divergent perspectives on timescales. Politicians tend to have short time horizons; the life of an administration is bounded by the next election a few years ahead, and the tenure of a minister can be even shorter. But a major defence project may be procured over 20 years and may remain in service for several decades. Politicians are understandably reluctant to take 'brave' and unpopular decisions which are sure to damage their own popularity immediately but which might some years later facilitate the tasks of their successors (from their own party or its opposition).

The other major problem is different perspectives on the relative importance of appearance and reality. Since politicians prosper by virtue of the electorate's opinion about their performance, they inevitably pay greater attention to appearance rather than to reality, and to the credibility of an argument (will it convince the man in the street?) rather than to its validity. In the military and scientific cultures, on the other hand, hard facts about the performance of a new weapon are inescapable and may lead to disaster if ignored.

6.2.2 Commercial

The MoD has a particularly close and symbiotic relationship with the defence contractors which manufacture and support high-technology equipment for the armed forces; the terms of the relationship vary with time from co-operative to adversarial and back again, as fashionable strategies in equipment acquisition change.

Defence contractors have a commercial culture, which is primarily aimed at maximising returns to shareholders as required by company law. Their culture can consider all decisions in terms of the balance between financial costs and benefits (in the short and long term). They do not have to take account simultaneously of domestic politics, international diplomacy, service morale and national industrial development, all of which influence decisions in the MoD. Since contractors are in direct competition with their rivals for the approval of their customers and shareholders, their culture prizes realism and ruthlessness and takes little account of tradition or of what onlookers may think. Since they do not rely on budgetary funding, defence contractors must (like all other commercial companies) continuously generate sufficient revenue to maintain their operations; they thus display a sense of urgency which is sometimes lacking in the MoD, except in the face of a clear and present military threat to the UK and its interests.

The commercial culture encourages contractors to take well-considered risks in their operations, rather than be outshone by more enterprising rivals. A favourable outcome can bring rich financial rewards to their companies (and substantial bonuses to the individuals involved), whereas an unfavourable outcome can be blamed on market vagaries and glossed over in the company's annual report. Sometimes this enterprising culture overshoots into technological hubris, particularly when the MoD is prepared to fund a gamble on untried technology. It is also important to remember that some contractors may be multinational or foreign and will therefore exhibit their own national culture that can be very different from that found in the UK.

MoD staff, on the other hand, tend to be risk-averse in peacetime. For these people success would be acknowledged by a trivial incentive payment, perhaps followed many years later by an honour, whereas failure would inevitably result in denunciation by the National Audit Office, public and hostile interrogation by a parliamentary select committee, and abusive headlines in the press. In these circumstances, ministers and mandarins tend to delay decisions while further studies are made, and thus in worst cases succumb to paralysis by analysis.

6.2.3 International armed forces

Politicians have recently stated that it is unlikely in the extreme that the UK would enter a major conflict alone. Historically, the UK joined NATO to counter the Soviet threat of the second half of the twentieth century. Recent conflicts and peacekeeping in the Middle East and former Yugoslavia have always involved UK forces in coalition operations with forces from such diverse countries as the US, Russia and Egypt.

Armed forces from different nations differ culturally in several ways. First, their training may differ dramatically from the UK model. For example, the American 'honor code' taught at US officer cadet academies is very different from the 'all for one and one for all' loyalty bred into UK officer cadets. Secondly, peacekeeping operations in Northern Ireland have resulted in British troops taking the 'win the hearts and minds' approach, rather than the more self-protective American approach, sometimes perceived as 'shoot first and ask questions later' approach to the same problems. In addition, each nation will bring something of its own national culture to its way of doing business.

6.2.4 Foreign nationals in commercial organisations and coalition forces

Variations in national cultures can be very marked and depend on a number of factors such as geography, actual and perceived nationality, politics, history and religion. It is important to be aware of national sensitivities and also the fact that ethics vary considerably, particularly between the industrialised and some of the developing nations.

The growing strength and size of the EU has brought together nations with fairly similar cultures and a plethora of different languages, while the euro struggles to become a universal currency within the region. The Middle East is predominantly Islamic with a universally understood Arabic script and language. It is a male-dominated society with a history of conflict. The wealthy nations owe their position to their reserves of oil.

There is a tendency in the UK to treat people from the USA almost as if they were British, but the language is different and a major trap for the unwary. With their enormous investment in technology in general and their armed forces in particular, they view the quality of their equipment as unbeatable. But for all that, they are relatively open-minded.

The important factor is to recognise national differences and to try to understand them. This necessitates attempting to deal sympathetically and to communicate effectively with foreigners regardless of whether they are coalition members, customers or contractors.

6.3 Conclusions

The three cultures within the MoD, and the three principal external cultures with which the MoD interacts, all have very different values and priorities. It is essential that defence systems engineers find ways of dealing with the wide range of diverse cultures with which they will inevitably come into contact during their work. It is the recognition of the variety of customs and traditions that will enable them to communicate more effectively with system stakeholders; an essential step towards improving the quality of defence equipment.

Further reading

DEG (2002) *The Defence Systems Engineering Handbook*. London: UCL
MoD (1998) *The Strategic Defence Review* (Cm 3999). London: TSO
—— (2001) *British Defence Doctrine* (Joint Warfare Publication 0-01). Swindon: MoD (JDCC)
—— (2002) *The Strategic Defence Review: New Chapter* (Cm 5566). London: TSO
—— (2004) *Delivering Security in a Changing World: Future Capabilities* (Cm 6041). London: TSO
—— (2004) *Ministry of Defence: The Government's Expenditure Plans 2004/2005 to 2005/2006* (Cm 6212). London: TSO
National Audit Office (2003) *Operation TELIC: United Kingdom Military Operations in Iraq*. London: NAO
Roper, J (ed.) (1985) *The Future of British Defence Policy*. Aldershot: Gower Publishing
Sandler, T and Hartley, K (1995) *The Economics of Defence*. Cambridge: Cambridge University Press
Smith, P (ed.) (1996) *Government and the Armed Forces in Britain 1856–1900*. London: Hambleton Press

Websites

www.cia.gov/cia/publications/factbook/
www.europa.eu.int/
www.mod.uk
www.nato.int/
www.sipri.org/
www.un.org/

Chapter 2

Challenges for defence equipment acquisition

The challenges of defence systems acquisition are many and varied. Some arise from the enduring nature of war which is a uniquely competitive, increasingly complex but sporadic activity to implement national policy. Others arise from the current rapid worldwide advances in many defence-relevant technologies. Yet others arise from the symbiotic relationship between government and industry and from the evolution of their respective policies in response to geopolitical and economic developments. These interwoven challenges must be overcome by the various philosophies and methodologies that are presented in following chapters.

1 Introduction

'It is a truth universally acknowledged' that defence equipment acquisition is one of the most challenging of human activities. Space flight presents greater technical problems, childbirth is more painful and regeneration of an inner city involves more complex socio-political interactions, but defence equipment acquisition is a uniquely demanding bureaucratic morass littered with military, technological, economic and political pitfalls. The difficulties of defence equipment acquisition arise from the environmental factors cited in the previous chapter, from the international security situation, from the nature of modern warfare, from the rapid advance in defence-relevant technologies and from the organisation of democratic government and free-market economics within which acquisition must be accomplished.

In past decades, in the UK and elsewhere, chronic failures to overcome the difficulties involved in acquisition have yielded overruns in the costs and delays in the timescales of many defence equipment projects. Occasionally these difficulties have also produced shortfalls in equipment performance (particularly in reliability), but these shortfalls have generally been shrouded by security classification (and by service willingness to make best use of the equipment delivered) and are less well documented than overruns and delays. Very occasionally, the difficulties in acquisition became so severe that an equipment project was cancelled, writing off the funds already committed and degrading (at least temporarily) the military capability of the armed forces.

This chapter explains how the various difficulties involved in defence equipment acquisition arise from the environmental factors and identifies, where appropriate, the solutions in the next seven chapters which enable defence systems engineers to address and conquer these difficulties.

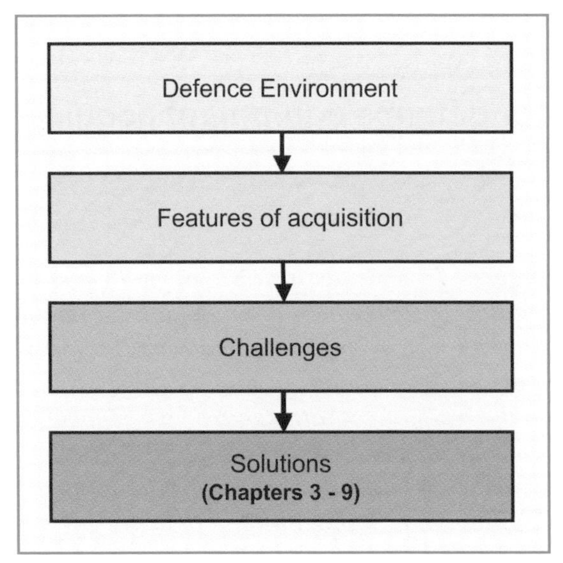

Figure 25. The challenges link the defence environment with the features of acquisition and the solutions.

The environmental factors considered are:

- The uniquely competitive nature of warfare.
- The sporadic and varied nature of wars and other military operations.
- The complexity of modern warfare, reliant on many networked systems.
- The rapid development of defence-related technology.
- The symbiotic relationship between government and industry.
- The limited number of prime contractors able to supply hi-tech systems.

These factors in combination generate the characteristic features which distinguish defence equipment acquisition from other areas of government and commercial business, and hence present an array of difficulties to test the ingenuity and endurance of acquisition personnel.

2 War is competitive

Conventional warfare has always been extremely competitive with uniquely severe penalties for the military personnel defeated in battle (e.g. gruesome death) and for the nation defeated in war (e.g. ravaging, occupation and reparations). There are innumerable historical examples where a disparity in the military capability of opposing forces (which arises largely from their equipment, but also depends on personnel, command, logistics and other factors) has resulted in a crushing defeat for the force with inferior equipment (e.g. Poland 1939, Iraq 1991). It is equally important in modern times to have a marginal advantage in asymmetrical warfare against fanatical terrorists or organised criminals, though in this type of warfare the quality of the national armed forces' surveillance, communication and information

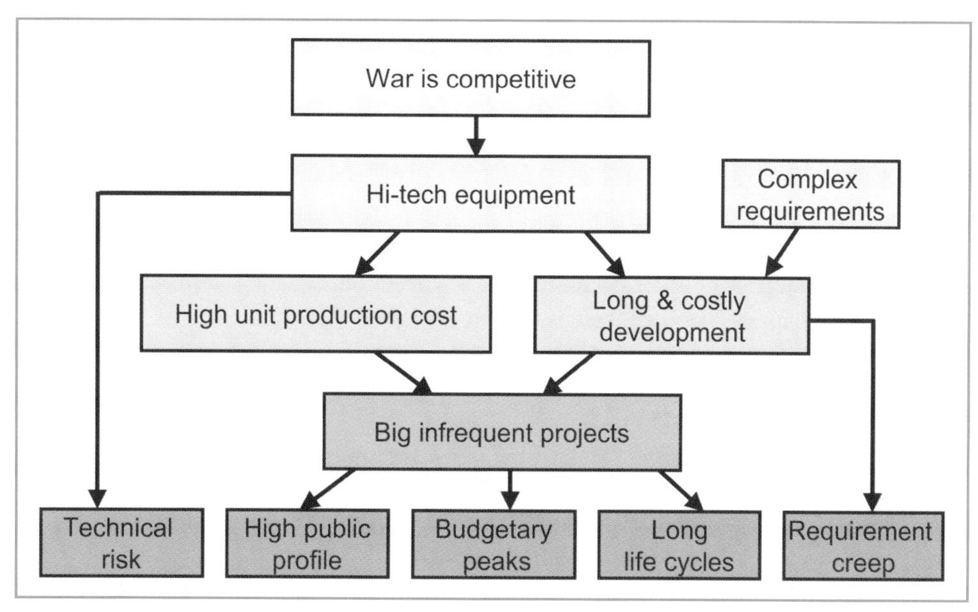

Figure 26. Many factors impact on the need for hi-tech equipment in warfare's competitive arena.

management equipment is at least as important as their firepower, mobility and other traditional parameters of military capability. Nations therefore strive to equip their armed forces with the most effective combat equipment they can afford, since forces with outclassed equipment would be unlikely to accomplish their military tasks and would certainly suffer severe losses in the attempt.

2.1 Risks of untried technology

It follows that the equipment procured for modern combat must incorporate the latest and best defence-relevant technologies. The exploitation of leading-edge (and hence untried) technologies means that defence equipment projects inevitably incorporate some technical risks, which may yield potential shortfalls in performance and/or overruns in cost and timescale. It would be futile to design defence equipment using only proven technologies, since it would be outclassed on the battlefield by equipment designed by more enterprising enemy nations, which have managed the technical risks appropriately. However, the existence of risks in a defence equipment project generates uncertainties in the project's performance, cost and timescale forecasts. In any defence project, risk management (see Chapter 8, Section 3) must be undertaken to identify the most favourable strategies for managing technical and other risks and uncertainties.

To implement the UK government's security policies, its armed forces may have to engage a variety of enemies in different theatres and at different intensities of operation. It would be inordinately expensive to provide different equipment for each and every situation; so most items of defence equipment must be designed to be safe and effective to operate in a variety of climatic and operational situations. Furthermore each item of equipment must have satisfactory interfaces (e.g. mechanical and electrical) with all of the many other legacy and future systems with which it will operate in the battlespace. It follows that the system design requirements for defence equipment are considerably more complex than those for civilian capital and consumer goods.

The untried technologies, the rigorous military requirements and the vital importance of ensuring that new defence equipment is fit for purpose requires the service customer, assisted by the defence systems engineer, to undertake or direct an exhaustive process of test and evaluation (see Chapter 7) before the new equipment enters service.

2.2 Big infrequent projects

Defence systems must incorporate the latest and best technologies to outclass the equipment deployed by hostile nations, and accordingly many types of defence equipment have high unit costs. Since the size of the military market is limited by the peacetime budgets of customer governments (a few per cent of their respective gross national products), it follows that defence equipment is produced in much smaller numbers than most equipment designed for the civilian market and cannot benefit from economies of scale, resulting in high unit costs.

Because defence equipment must incorporate untried technologies, and because service systems requirements are complex and rigorous, defence equipment must undergo a protracted and expensive gestation process of concept, assessment, design, development and demonstration before it can be manufactured for entry into military service. This gestation process can be accelerated in exceptional circumstances when unlimited funds are available to implement an overriding national purpose (such as the Apollo and Polaris programmes in the US), but normally it can last for up to 20 years.

Because of their high launch costs spread across a limited production run, most defence equipment projects exhibit substantial economies of scale (i.e. their unit costs fall as the number procured increases). In this situation it is logical to reduce the number of projects launched by designing equipment to be capable of several military tasks, to be attractive to numerous customer governments, and to remain in service for many years. However this policy tends to make the service requirement even more challenging, further exacerbating the problems of high unit cost and of protracted and costly gestation. Economies of scale not only constrain the customer to procure fewer projects, but also affect the organisation and structure of industrial suppliers as discussed in Section 6 below.

2.3 High public profile

Because defence equipment projects are infrequent and expensive, they assume great importance for service customers, industrial contractors and taxpayers. The Eurofighter Typhoon, for example, will, in the second decade of the twenty-first century, be one of only two (or possibly three) types of combat aircraft in RAF service. Its production will constitute a significant percentage of the output of the UK aerospace industry, and the UK's share of its procurement cost will exceed £20 billion. (Typhoon is a collaborative programme with Germany, Italy and Spain.) Hence, although the UK government's defence budget is much less than its budgets for health and education, individual defence projects have a higher public profile than individual hospitals and schools and thus attract the attention of many stakeholders (with the consequent risks of public hostility and political interference). Defence projects also attract extraordinary attention because their potential contributions to national security are of interest to the whole population (particularly the armchair warriors) in contrast to the purely local interest in most other public projects.

The scale of major defence projects and the consequent incentive to share the up-front investment and risks, mean that they can involve several national governments as customers and a complex and extensive chain of contractors as suppliers. The personnel and organisations involved in such international projects inevitably include a variety of cultures, which complicate project management and attract even more public attention than national projects.

2.4 Budgeting

The scale of defence equipment projects can also create problems in government budgeting. Normally the levels of government revenue and expenditure fluctuate gently through the economic cycle, and it may be difficult to increase the defence budget (and face the unpopularity of cuts in other areas of expenditure or of increases in taxation) during the procurement of a major equipment project such as Trident or Typhoon. It is even more awkward when the peak expenditures on two or more major procurements coincide. The budgeting problem has become more acute as competitive pressure between rival nations has driven the unit cost of defence systems inexorably upwards (for example, the real unit cost of successive generations of combat aircraft has increased since the Second World War at about 10% per year, equivalent to increasing by a factor of ten every 25 years). Only part of this increase has been offset by compensating reductions in the number of systems procured by the services, so the defence equipment acquisition programme now consists of fewer, larger projects than formerly. Some of the resulting problems of affordability can be alleviated by a private finance initiative (PFI) (see Chapter 3, Section 9) whereby a private-sector contractor supplies the funding to procure an asset for the MoD and is recompensed by a regular service charge on the MoD's use of the asset. Long-term contracts must take account of the chance that the MoD requirements may change substantially, or that the contractor may encounter financial difficulties or other changes such as a takeover or merger, before the scheduled end date. To date PFIs have mainly been applied to non-combat facilities and services (such as infrastructure and training equipment) since the risks to combat systems in any operational situation are dependent on political and operational imperatives, and are not amenable to actuarial analysis.

A government may try to reduce its budgetary problems with procurement cost peaks through international collaboration (see Chapter 8, Section 4) with one or more of its allies having similar requirements in the same timescale. In theory, this policy divides the up-front cost of development and production investment between the participating nations, and reduces the unit cost of production via the learning-curve effect on a longer production run. But in practice it can introduce additional complexity to accommodate divergent national requirements and can involve protracted negotiations with the larger number of military, political and industrial stakeholders.

2.5 Long life cycles

In former times, when defence technology was stagnant, defence equipment such as the Brown Bess musket and *HMS Victory* remained in service for many decades. At other times when defence technologies were advancing rapidly, new equipment designs (of rifles and artillery in the nineteenth century, and of armoured fighting vehicles and aircraft in the twentieth) were introduced at intervals of a few years, and even faster in wartime. Today, technology is advancing very rapidly in many areas, particularly in electronic sensors and communications, but the nexus of rising unit costs and falling defence budgets discourages governments from acquiring new projects in periods of peace when they face no clear and present dangers, and encourages them to keep veteran equipment in service for long periods. But this policy yields additional problems of maintaining geriatric equipment for which replacement materials and components may no longer readily be available, and of implementing a succession of incremental upgrades using technology insertion to maintain at a satisfactory level the equipment's military capability against evolving threats.

The long procurement and in-service life of a modern defence equipment project (extending over several decades) requires a through-life approach to project management, with investment appraisal (see Chapter 5, Section 2) of the protracted time profiles of the expenditure associated with alternative systems designs and acquisition strategies to identify the best value for money. That approach involves early planning of integrated logistic support (ILS) (see Chapter 3, Section 7) matched to the levels of reliability and maintainability expected during the system's operation in service, as well as to the relative cost and convenience of service and contractor support.

2.6 Requirement creep

The longevity of modern defence equipment, contrasted with the current rapid development of technology and swift changes in the threats from the geopolitical environment, means that it may become obsolete during its service life, or in extreme cases even before it enters service. Equipment may also become irrelevant to national security following the election of a new government with different policies, or may become unacceptable because of changes in environmental legislation or in public opinion (e.g. on anti-personnel mines and laser-damage weapons). It follows that defence equipment acquisition strategies and systems architectures should be flexible enough to accommodate at least some of the alterations in the service systems requirement (requirement creep) which can arise during protracted development; flexible strategy and architecture can avoid the waste and delay associated with cancelling a project and restarting a new development from scratch (see Chapter 9).

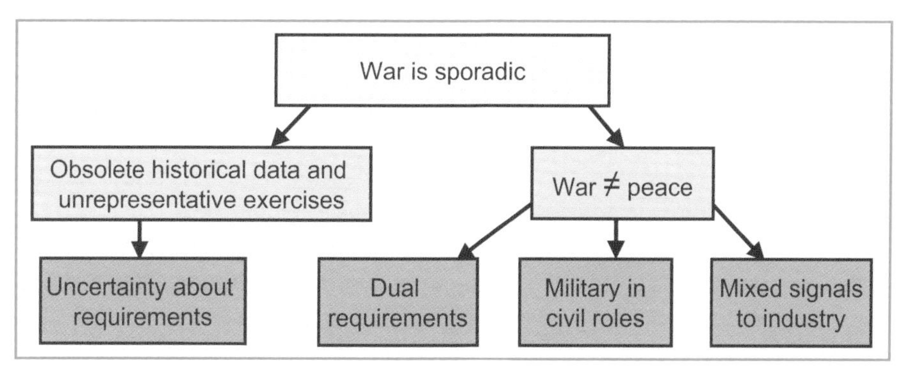

Figure 27. The fact that warfare is not continuous creates a range of difficulties.

3 War is sporadic

In modern times, episodes of high-intensity warfare (for which most major defence systems are designed) occur at fortunately long intervals of one or more decades; during these intervals of peace new military capabilities, derived from emergent technologies, are introduced into service by the armed forces of the UK, its allies and its rivals. It follows that experience and data derived from past wars, which is often incomplete or distorted, or from current exercises which can never be fully representative, are of limited value in forecasting the character of future conflicts and in specifying the additional capabilities which are required to fight them and achieve victorious outcomes. Such experience and data must be supplemented by military judgement and operational analysis modelling in credible future scenarios to identify potential shortfalls in military capability, and thus help to resolve uncertainties about future equipment requirements (see Chapter 5, Section 1).

Because warfare is sporadic, defence equipment must be designed both to be effective in war and economical in peace; it is very important for decisions on defence equipment acquisition to be based on sufficient understanding of these dual imperatives to strike the right balance between these two requirements. The use of inappropriate conventional 'business' models should be avoided. This dual requirement is unique to defence (though variable demand also affects the emergency and health services) and drives decisions on the numbers of units required, on manning levels and on the arrangements for logistics and support. One of the consequences of this duality is that military forces must have sufficient personnel and equipment to undertake operations as and when required. In consequence, the utilisation of defence equipment is high during active operations but much lower in peacetime when it is only used for training. The value to the services of a high level of equipment availability is very different in peace and war, and this difference complicates the requirement for ILS.

Another consequence of sporadic warfare is that military officers trained and motivated for war are available in peacetime for employment in a variety of non-combat roles such as supervising procurement, training or research. Such officers are understandably reluctant to spend long periods in those roles (when experience in command of a battalion, ship or squadron of aircraft is infinitely more congenial and fulfilling, and is also more important to their future careers), but they are equally reluctant to delegate such roles to civilians who may be better trained and experienced but who lack the officers' military knowledge and service ethos. In the UK, military officers are posted to unfamiliar roles for short periods of only a few years, during which time they must remain aware of developments and opportunities in their own branch of their service as well as learning their new duties and (ideally) making a useful contribution to their non-combat task. Sometimes these officers may take a sanguine rather than an analytical approach to risk, and to deciding unhesitatingly, and perhaps rashly, between alternative project management options. These qualities are ideal for active operations, but are ill-suited to project management (see Chapter 8, Section 2). It is only fair to mention that the prevarication of some risk-averse civil servants with a job-for-life culture can be equally damaging.

The MoD's budgetary planning is based on the assumption of continued peace, and is disrupted when occasional conflicts demand that military forces are deployed to a distant theatre of operations to carry out duties in demanding and stressful circumstances for as long as necessary before being repatriated to their peacetime bases. Such conflicts are followed by protracted negotiations with the Treasury to determine the marginal cost of the conflict. The direct marginal costs of victorious conflicts are generally small relative to the MoD's overall budgets, though the impact on particular procurement projects can be very significant. However the indirect costs, including for example any equipment enhancements suggested by combat experience and any adverse effects on recruitment and retention, can be considerably higher. Adversarial bickering on the scale and timing of the uplift to the MoD budgets offers opportunities for some opposing bureaucrats to distinguish themselves by pedantic sophistry and ingenious advocacy, and tends to distract them from more important issues.

Sporadic conflicts also disrupt the MoD's interface with industry. In peacetime, the MoD's priority is value for money in equipment acquisition, but just before and during a conflict its overriding priority is rapid delivery (of urgent operational requirements, for example). Thus the MoD sends mixed messages to its industrial suppliers who realise that rhetoric about taut contracts may be necessary to mollify politicians but what really matters is the contractor's performance *when the drums begin to roll.*

4 War is complex

In a few periods of history, warfare was dominated by a single class of fighting unit, such as the Greek hoplite and later the armoured knight. However, warfare has generally involved several specialist classes of fighting unit, such as Napoleonic infantry, cavalry and artillery, and victory was dependent on the commanders' ability to achieve co-operative synergy between the classes at their disposal. As warfare has developed over the centuries, the number of specialist classes has risen, and the tempo of warfare has tended to increase as new technology has accelerated deployment and communication. Defence operations on a modern battlespace (on land, at sea or in the air) involve the complexities of a fast-paced Scottish eightsome reel, with synchronised interactions between many different types of reconnaissance, command and combat units (national and allied). In this situation, the

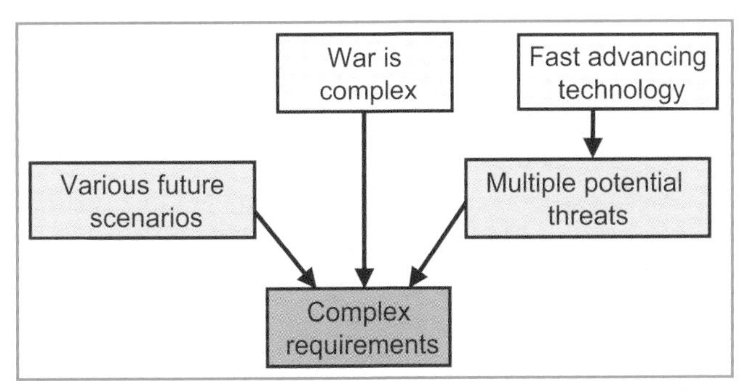

Figure 28. The fact that warfare is complex leads to complicated requirements.

overall military capability of an armed force is generated by the synergistic operation of many diverse networked units with complementary functions, and the effectiveness of individual units is interdependent with others operating in the same battlespace.

It follows that the design of each defence equipment project must take account of its external interfaces with other projects (legacy, current and future), as well as of the internal interfaces between its own constituent sub-systems and components. It also follows that the delay or cancellation of any project can have a disproportionate effect on the overall capability of a national military force. Equipment design must also take into consideration the likelihood of combined operations within a multinational force, and the corresponding need for satisfactory interfaces with allied equipment (e.g. in Identification Friend or Foe). Since it is current UK policy to engage in any future major conflict only when US forces are also involved, the future equipment deployed by UK forces must be suitable for multinational operations. The structured discipline of systems engineering (see Chapter 9) helps to ensure that all the interfaces operate satisfactorily.

Because the modern battlefield is complex, because new technology (see Section 5 below) is creating many opportunities for improving the equipment of UK forces (and that of their enemies), and because it requires many years to bring a new equipment project from concept into military service, it is difficult for the military staff to identify how the UK's armed forces might need to enhance their capabilities on a future battlefield, to prioritise those enhancements, and to illuminate the underlying rationale clearly to front-line commanders, politicians and many other stakeholders. It is even more difficult to formulate a system requirement defining the performance required of an equipment project intended to provide one or more of the capability enhancements needed for various future scenarios, at a time when supporting technological and military evidence is scanty or controversial and when there are divergent views on the merits of the new project and on the relative importance of its various performance parameters. In this uncertain situation it is tempting for military officers to be guided by their own personal experiences and by their affiliation (sometimes called cap-badge loyalty) to a particular specialist branch within a service. The diverse experiences and affiliations of military staff officers can generate an equally diverse range of potential solutions, any of which might provide the required enhancement of the nation's military capability. The comparative assessment of these alternative solutions is difficult because their benefits are expressed in terms of military effectiveness rather than revenue, presenting a three-dimensional problem with effectiveness, cost and timescale axes rather than the two-dimensional problem involving time and money, which is universal and familiar in commercial and financial operations, and has been thoroughly analysed in many books on business management. Assessment is made more difficult by uncertainties about the performance of UK and enemy weapons in future scenarios, and because the consequences of a bad decision in equipment procurement may be disastrous for national security, as well as fatal for the unfortunate service personnel involved. To conquer this problem, the COIEA procedure (see Chapter 5, Section 2) provides a structured and systematic approach to comparing the military and financial characteristics of alternative solutions, but acquisition decisions may also be affected by diplomatic, industrial or other factors.

The system requirement specifying new defence equipment for the armed forces of nations (such as the UK) with global responsibilities must ensure that the new equipment can operate effectively at all times in all climates, against enemies who have every incentive to avoid its strengths and to exploit its weaknesses (if any). The requirement must define a variety of scenarios – ranging from high-intensity conventional warfare through lower-intensity and probably asymmetric peacemaking to humanitarian relief and defence diplomacy – to ensure that the new equipment will be effective in all situations. The system requirement must also ensure that the new equipment project abides by all relevant legal constraints so that it does not endanger its operators or other citizens, and creates only limited disturbance and pollution. Management of the complex system requirement that is characteristic of any defence equipment project can be facilitated by requirements management (see Chapter 3, Section 3).

5 Technology is advancing rapidly

Since the middle of the nineteenth century, the development of defence-related technologies has proceeded at an ever accelerating pace, stimulated initially by international rivalries and

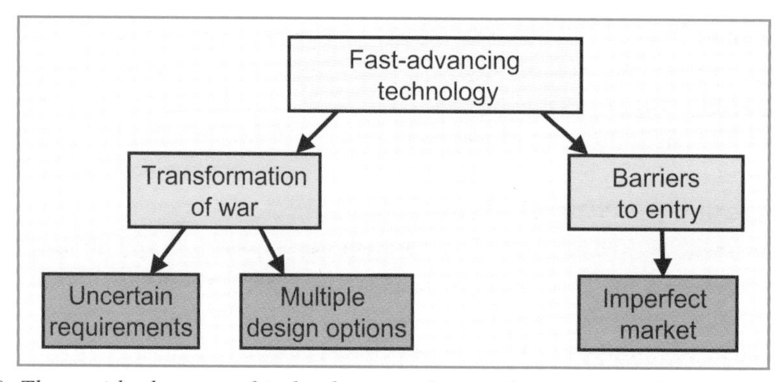

Figure 29. The rapid advances of technology continue to have a major impact on warfare and the provision of new equipment.

the resulting regional and world wars, and more recently by the globalisation of the world market economy. This globalisation has intensified competition between the world's major corporations and has encouraged them to invest heavily in research and development for their new products for the worldwide market. Their civil investment (Microsoft and Intel between them spent over US$9B in 2003), which now far surpasses most government defence research budgets, has provided the impetus for the revolution in military affairs, which is already transforming the capability of US forces by exploiting the potential of the microchip. In electronics, and in many other areas, technological development is offering to military staff a cornucopia of potentially attractive ways of achieving the capabilities they require. Rapid technological development, much of which is available to potential enemies as well as to the UK and its allies, makes it difficult (as noted above) to forecast confidently the nature of future conflicts and the effectiveness of new equipment in such conflicts. Furthermore, the increasing sophistication of defence equipment in many areas acts as a barrier to entry, deterring potential suppliers from entering the market to challenge established contractors, and contributing to an imperfect market.

6 Government and industry

National security, and the maintenance of effective armed forces to provide it, is one of the most important responsibilities of a government. That responsibility cannot be delegated to agencies or contractors, but it can be shared with the governments of allied nations. In a dictatorial regime, decisions on national security can be taken by the head of state or by an official with delegated powers, who is able to overawe or destroy if necessary any dissident factions. However in a democracy, many elected representatives, service officers, industrialists and pressure groups can hold strong and divergent views on defence issues and regard themselves as entitled to contribute to the decision-making process. Defence equipment acquisition therefore involves many stakeholders from a variety of cultures and with different priorities (particularly when the acquisition strategy involves international collaboration).

Several of the major difficulties in defence equipment acquisition arise from the interdependent relationships within the 'military-industrial complex' and from the convergent and divergent interests of government and industry in their roles as customer and supplier of defence equipment and the associated services. This symbiotic relationship is complicated by the interference of other stakeholders.

6.1 Options for acquisition strategy

The UK government or any other can select its acquisition strategy for defence equipment, facilities and services from a range of potential options, including:

- Government owned and operated establishments.
- Client companies operating in close alliance with the government which promotes their prosperity and growth for economic and/or security reasons.

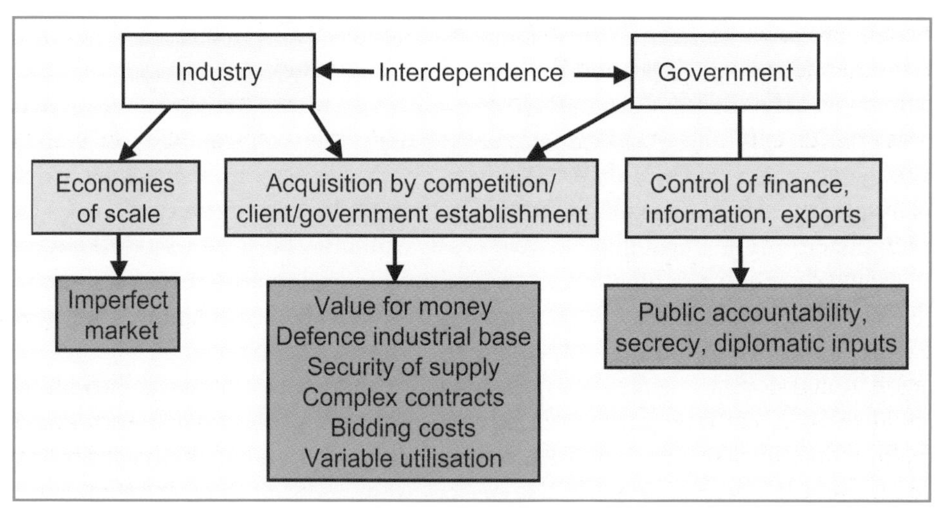

Figure 30. The needs of both industry and government affect the acquisition of new equipment.

- Competition in which the government seeks rival proposals, including from abroad, for each of its projects and selects the tender offering best value for money on that project, or sometimes just the lowest price (see Chapter 3, Section 5).

The government may use different acquisition strategies for different sectors of the defence market, perhaps using its own establishments or client companies to provide strategically vital goods and services (such as nuclear warheads and cryptography) and using competition in areas where the risk associated with a foreign supplier is acceptable. Industry, however, tends to resent apparent discrimination between different sectors if some sectors seem to be treated more sympathetically than others.

If a government chooses to keep the provision of defence goods and services within public-sector organisations (such as the UK's historic royal dockyards, ordnance factories and powder mills), it retains the power to direct investment in research and development and in production facilities to ensure the delivery of military equipment of adequate quality and in sufficient quantity to satisfy the needs of its armed forces. It can ensure that these organisations hold stocks of warlike materials and have sufficient production facilities and raw materials to surge production in a crisis. However, this policy involves the risk that the public-sector organisations, shielded from the stimulus of market forces, may fail to adopt new technologies or to institute more efficient methods of production.

A government moving from supply by its own establishments to competitive acquisition in the global market will probably achieve greater economy in acquisition at the cost of less control and reduced security of supply. But even government establishments cannot provide complete security of supply unless they control the entire supply chain (right back to raw materials) of the equipment they produce, or unless they hold adequate strategic stockpiles of all outsourced materials, components and sub-systems. This policy would certainly be expensive and for the UK it would probably be unaffordable at the present time.

There is a wide variety of potential interdependent linkages between the UK government and a commercial company supplying equipment, facilities and services. Typically, a client company in the defence sector would receive most or all of the MoD contracts in its business area (on carefully negotiated terms to preclude any excess profits), and could seek economies of scale by competing for orders from foreign governments or from the commercial sector. If the client company were successful in these endeavours it would generate higher profits and could offer lower prices to the MoD; conversely if the MoD were to be utterly reliant on deliveries from the client company, it would be virtually obliged to rescue the company from the consequences of bad luck or poor management as happened in the case of Rolls-Royce in 1971.

Negotiations between the client company and the government may be facilitated and the risks reduced by a 'partnering agreement' between a government and a favoured national contractor (sometimes designated as a national champion) by which both parties commit themselves to a long-term association for mutual benefit, accepting limitations on their opportunities to gain short-term advantages. However, since a commercial company may go bankrupt or be subject to a takeover bid within the lifespan of a major defence project, the agreement may have to incorporate protection against these situations, making the favoured contractor almost indistinguishable from a nationalised industry.

If the government chooses to buy defence equipment by open competition in a global market, it may be able to achieve the same military capability at a lower cost but it cannot directly control its suppliers whose decisions will reflect their own financial interests (foreign suppliers may also reflect the policies of their national governments). A government dealing with private-sector suppliers may seek to influence their behaviour by incentives but cannot guarantee that this influence will be sufficient to achieve the intended result. In this situation, the government must recognise that the quality and timing of the goods and services procured are determined by negotiation, and must accept some risk that the planned supply (particularly from foreign suppliers) may be delayed, interrupted or even prohibited, as in the case of the supply of ammunition from a Belgian company for the Falklands conflict.

6.2 Problems of open competition

A policy of open competition in a global market may provide good value for money on each individual project competed, but it could progressively erode a nation's defence industrial base if domestic suppliers go out of business when they fail to win competitions.

An acquisition policy based on international competition must recognise that the market for defence goods and services is unusual. The economies of scale in defence equipment development and production promote a concentration of industrial capacity within a few large prime contractors, and the high cost of major weapon systems limits the number of nations able to acquire them. Thus the market for defence equipment and services is 'imperfect' having few buyers and few sellers, asymmetry of information available to both parties, and substantial barriers to entry. This type of imperfect market can become a monopoly (giving excessive power to the monopolist supplier) unless the customer governments consciously preserve viable competition. Furthermore each government imposes strict regulation on its own national defence industry: limiting foreign shareholding, restricting recruitment to exclude potential spies and saboteurs as well as foreign nationals, stipulating the physical and electronic security of industrial sites, and ensuring that exports of military equipment do not undermine the government's foreign and security policies. The defence market is thus very different from the free markets presented in many textbooks on economics and cannot be managed by simplistic nostrums.

In those cases where the private sector does provide defence equipment, facilities and services, it is important to recognise how and why its interests converge with and diverge from those of the government. When a government and an industrial contractor are together committed for decades on a particular defence project, they have a common interest in its success. However, a government ideally wants defence equipment and services to be available in appropriate quality and quantity just in time to meet sporadic conflicts, at a price which excludes excess profit. Private-sector industry wants a steady guaranteed demand for its products from its national government at prices high enough to satisfy its workforce and shareholders. A government needs the freedom to restructure and re-equip its armed forces to reflect changes in the geopolitical environment and in the available technology, while industry would prefer sustained demand for its traditional products in which it has the comparative advantage of existing physical infrastructure and intellectual property. A government may have moral or diplomatic reasons to prohibit exports of military equipment to some foreign governments, whereas industry wants the scope to sell its products as widely as possible. A government seeks the economic benefits of competition on individual projects, and even on different phases of a particular project where practicable, whereas industry strives for product differentiation in order to establish a monopoly.

The balance of advantage between public- and private-sector provision varies with the nature of the defence equipment and services considered, with the structure of their markets, with the nature and urgency of the threats to national security, and with prevailing international alliances. If the government chooses to allocate at least some provision of defence equipment and services to the private sector, each of the resulting customer/supplier interfaces must be governed by a contract specifying the quality, timing and cost of the deliverables. The difficulties of formulating such contracts increase with the complexity of the customer's requirement, with the time period covered by the contract, with the levels of risk and uncertainty involved, and with the diversity of the financing mechanisms. The difficulties increase further if each representative involved has little understanding of the realities (political, military, industrial and financial) which influence the others. In the UK, many military officers, government officials and industry executives are regrettably engrossed in their own caste and culture, with little empathy for the others.

6.3 Historical evolution of equipment acquisition

In former times, all of the activities in defence equipment acquisition were provided by government organisations, which incorporated specialist skills and infrastructure that were not then available in the private sector. In the nineteenth and early twentieth centuries, the UK and many other countries progressively transferred responsibility for equipment production to the private sector, to exploit the skills which it had developed in mass production for civil markets; these private-sector skills were particularly valuable in meeting the unprecedented demand for quantity production of military equipment during the world wars of the twentieth century. Today, some nations allocate production work directly to favoured national contractors (chosen sometimes for political reasons including their ability to create jobs in depressed regions), some hold competitions open only to national contractors, while the UK and some other nations hold competitions open to international suppliers. Exceptionally, France has, so far, retained its naval dockyards in the public sector.

Recently, some countries (including the UK) have also transferred to the private sector responsibility for the design and development of military equipment, to exploit expertise in the relevant technologies derived from its commercial activities. This policy proceeded more smoothly in areas (such as aero-engines) where the relevant military and civil technologies were very similar, but it proved harder in other areas where the defence technologies were especially distinctive and where the commercial contractors had to accumulate the appropriate expertise and experience. It also proved more difficult to formulate watertight contracts, which appropriately share the financial risks of development and which lucidly transmit the priorities of the service customer through a procurement branch to a prime contractor. This two-stage process provides greater scope for misunderstanding (compounded by divergent financial interests) than when development and design were the responsibility of government establishments.

Following the end of the Cold War and the consequent decline in many national defence budgets, ambitious defence contractors tried to compensate for the decline in production by taking a greater role in equipment maintenance and repair. This policy accords with the through-life approach to defence projects, which is one of the UK's Smart Acquisition policies, and encourages contractors to address in-service issues (e.g. reliability). However, it remains a service imperative to ensure that its equipment is adequately supported in both peace and war (even in a dangerous and unpopular war) and that arrangements designed for economy in peace do not imperil the services' ability to mount effective operations in war. Accordingly, there is in the UK an ongoing tug of war for maintenance and repair work between service branches, civilian agencies responsible to the MoD and commercial contractors.

The governments of most large nations fund defence-related research to enable their armed forces to act as intelligent customers for defence equipment, to encourage innovative solutions to their forces' requirements to enhance their military capabilities, and to ensure the availability of advanced technology in their national industrial bases. Generally such research is done within the public sector, but the UK has recently chosen to put most of its defence research activities within a public/private partnership (QinetiQ) managed, within government restaints, by a foreign bank. At present, QinetiQ receives a guaranteed share of MoD research contracts, but this share will diminish to zero over the next few years after which all such research will be subject to competition. Only a few particularly sensitive areas of defence research have been retained within the MoD's Defence Science and Technology Laboratory (Dstl).

6.4 Current UK acquisition policy

Current UK policy is to select suppliers of almost all defence equipment, facilities and services (research, development, production and support) by open competition between alternative suppliers, including foreign suppliers. Only a few special cases (e.g. research in nuclear, biological and chemical weapons systems and countermeasures, and the construction of warship hulls) are exempt from the requirement to compete globally. Defence contractors, unlike their commercial counterparts selling to a mass market, cannot undertake surveys of customer opinion to assess the future demand for their products; they must accept that their market is governed by a small and ever-changing group of politicians, service officers and acquisition officials whose preferences are essentially unpredictable, despite the best efforts of enterprising contractors to identify rising stars and establish good relations with them.

Another problem for defence contractors is that, because of the long lives of modern projects, development and production work on new projects is intermittent. Any private-sector contractor specialising in one class of defence equipment now faces long gaps between orders from the MoD, sometimes as long as individuals' working lives so that all practical experience is lost before a successor project is launched. These gaps can only partially be filled by export orders and by upgrade work on in-service equipment. In this situation, the contractor's shareholders may not be prepared to tolerate many years of underutilised capacity and low profit margins (particularly since in the UK they cannot be sure of winning any future competition for their products). Such shareholders are free to liquidate the business, or to insist that the contractor withdraws from the defence sector by disposing of its defence-related business.

In a similar situation, another government controlling an ordnance factory or nationalised industry could manage its workload to alleviate peaks and troughs, and could ensure that it remained operational. But because of the perceived inefficiency of public-sector organisations, most NATO governments prefer to buy defence equipment and services from the private sector.

The process of bidding for large complex MoD contracts involves the competing contractors in considerable expenditure, which must be recouped by the winner through the cost of the contract and by the losers through the cost of other contracts they are undertaking for the MoD and for other customers. Thus competition, although it provides an incentive for greater efficiency, also introduces some nugatory expenditure, which increases with the number of companies competing for each contract.

6.5 Equipment and other components of military capability

Military capability is derived from six lines of development, which must all be integrated and synchronised satisfactorily to deliver the military capability required. The lines of development are:

- **Equipment**– Equipment acquisition in the UK involves a variety of activities in the successive phases of the CADMID cycle. In the early project phases, responsibility moves progressively from the government to industry. When combat equipment is in service it is operated by the armed forces but its support is often shared between the armed forces, associated civilian agencies and private industry, with the former doing the work required in the front line and the latter doing all the major repairs and refits.

- **Personnel** – In former times, governments hired mercenaries through domestic or foreign contractors, but today most nations rely on armed forces which are part of the public sector, and which are recruited and controlled directly by the government. Most forces are recruited from the native population but there remain some foreign contingents (like the British Brigade of Ghurkas, the French Foreign Legion and the Vatican's Swiss Guard). Today, multinational companies employ an increasing number of private security personnel (40,000 in Iraq in 2005) who can contribute to peace support operations but who are cheaper and more deniable than the regular forces of nation states.
- **Doctrine** – The doctrine to be used by a nation's armed forces is principally developed by those forces themselves, assisted by expert individuals and organisations, and constrained by political considerations as well as by national and international laws.
- **Infrastructure** – New or improved infrastructure to support military personnel or equipment is generally contracted to private companies with the necessary engineering expertise, perhaps using a PFI to relieve the pressure on government funding.
- **Training** – Programmes may be organised by the armed forces or by private contractors or by a combination of the two; generally contractors lead in areas of training that develop technical skills while the armed forces lead in areas which develop personal qualities and organisational ability.
- **Logistics** – Capabilities to deploy and to sustain military forces have traditionally been provided by a mixture of public- and private-sector organisations. In recent years, the UK government has relied increasingly on commercial contractors to provide logistic services in peacetime (such as accommodation, rations and training) and also to provide such services in far-flung theatres of operations. It has also encouraged civilian employees of defence contractors having specialist knowledge and skills to become sponsored reservists who are liable (like other volunteer reservists) to be summoned to supplement the regular forces in a crisis. The UK government has evolved arrangements whereby transport (such as roll on-roll off ferries) can be used commercially in peace but can be drafted to transport military forces when necessary.

The provision of lines of development may, like the supply of equipment, be allocated to the public or private sectors, or to some partnership between the sectors.

6.6 Value of a national defence industrial base

National industrial policies favouring the defence sector have been encouraged by the nature of warfare for several centuries, up to the mid-twentieth. In this period, the duration of typical wars was much longer than the time taken to train a new recruit or to produce the associated equipment. Accordingly, a nation engaged in war expanded its armed forces as far as its conscriptable population and its defence industrial base would permit, far exceeding the scale of its forces in peacetime. In these circumstances, it was important that the nation had an adequate defence industrial base with a secure supply chain, able to produce military equipment in the quantities required. Nations lacking their own industry were disadvantaged, having to rely on heterogeneous equipment from fickle foreign suppliers, delivered over long and vulnerable supply lines.

In the Second World War, for example, the Allied victory was won because the industries of America, Britain and Russia could far exceed the output of Germany, Italy and Japan, and furthermore they had the research and development capacity to introduce new weapon and electronic systems faster than the Axis powers. Memories of critical shortages of military equipment at times of national peril encourage modern governments to strive for assured sources of supply within their own national borders. Until the Levene (then Chief of Defence Procurement) reforms of the 1980s, the MoD had a specific responsibility to promote the growth of the UK's aerospace and electronics industries.

However, the military and economic situation is now different. The increased speed of deployment and operation of military forces, and the increased accuracy and lethality of their weapons, has reduced the duration of a high-intensity war to a few days or weeks; far less than is needed to manufacture sophisticated modern equipment or to train a recruit to use it effectively. Thus recent wars have been fought by trained personnel using existing equipment, and the scale of armed forces in war is only marginally increased above peacetime levels by the recall of reservists with key skills. Concurrently, economic globalisation has made all industries, including defence industries, increasingly reliant on imported materials, components and software. Today, no nation smaller than the US could supply its armed forces from its own national resources without the continuing goodwill of foreign suppliers.

Policy for defence equipment acquisition must therefore strike a balance between the economies achieved through international competition at the prime contractor or at the sub-contractor level and the security of supply achieved through subsidies (using higher prices, launch aid or other devices) to its own national defence industry. In striking that balance, it should be noted that when wars do occur, the armed forces often identify UORs to meet unforeseen circumstances or to repair the effects of project delays or false economies, and it may only be practicable to obtain these UORs in the required timescale from national contractors with the necessary expertise, capacity and motivation.

6.7 Government controls

Rules are for the guidance of wise men and the obedience of fools.

The acquisition of defence equipment is funded through the Treasury and must therefore follow the rules of public accountability. Governments in the UK and elsewhere closely regulate the market in defence equipment, preventing the production and/or export of equipment in breach of their international obligations or of their national security policies. This close regulation, and the scale and rarity of new equipment projects (discussed above), make the market for defence equipment very 'imperfect' with few (government) customers, few prime-contractor suppliers, and high barriers to entry; this market requires more sophisticated policies to manage it effectively.

The UK government has insisted that all its departments of state use resource accounting and budgeting (RAB) (see Chapter 4, Section 3) to promote a more commercial approach to asset management. This new accounting system has imposed considerable administrative penalties on the MoD, with additional accountants to calculate depreciation and the cost of capital charges on every equipment project. This information is relevant to MoD management of its non-military assets, but many believe that its holdings of combat equipment should be

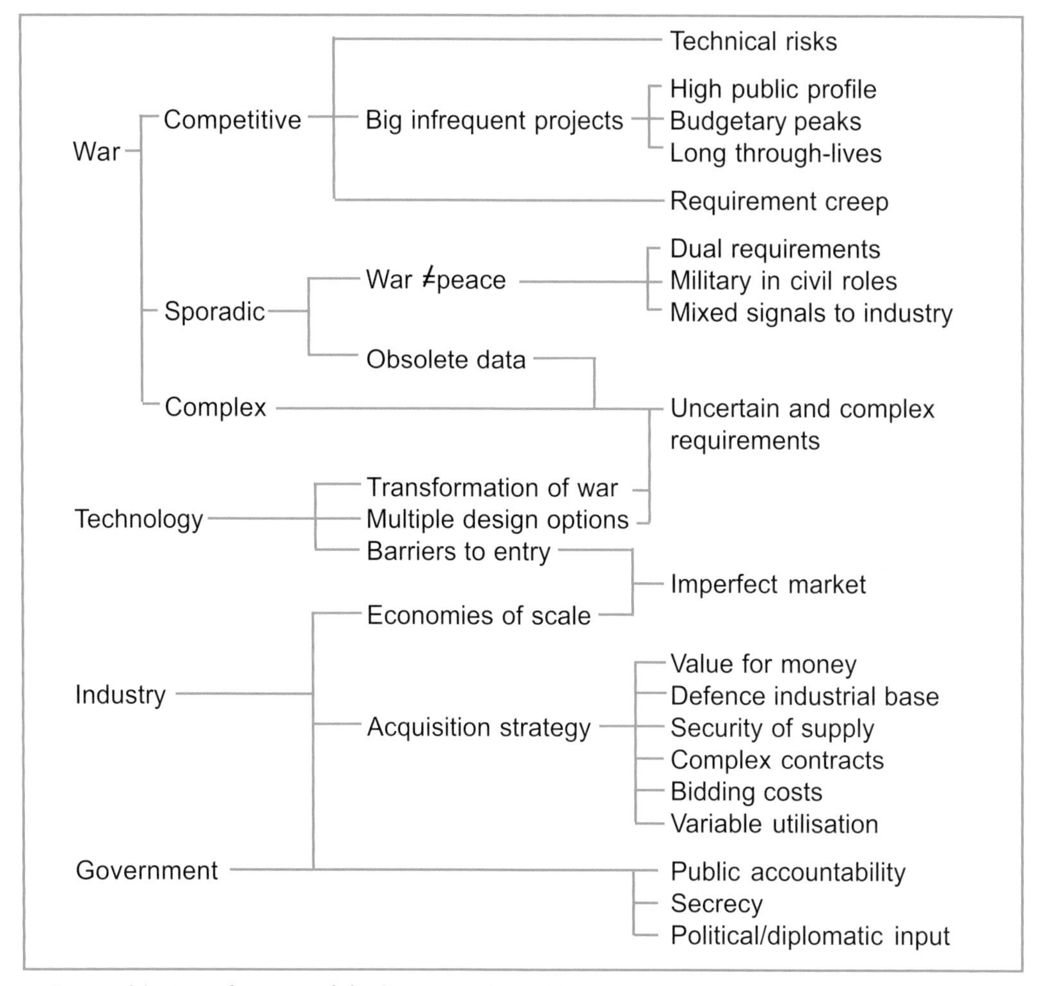

Figure 31. An indication of the large number of linkages that impact on defence equipment acquisition.

determined by the military capability required rather than by any principle of commercial accountancy. It is difficult for some MoD staff to recognise the benefits of the new accounting system, and its introduction is widely perceived as a self-inflicted aggravation.

An unfortunate by-product of government involvement in defence equipment acquisition is its unique ability to suppress debate on issues which might imperil national security, or which might merely be embarrassing. Different national governments have policies of varying severity to screen information on defence equipment performance, cost and timescale and on the reasons why some projects achieve their targets and others do not. Thus the activities of government and industry personnel in defence equipment acquisition are generally shielded from public scrutiny, and these personnel are deprived of the opportunity to learn from each other's experiences. In the UK, the National Audit Office produces an annual report on the progress of the MoD's major projects, but this report concentrates on the cost and timescale of the procurement and provides no definitive information on key aspects of each project's effectiveness.

7 Conclusions

The many challenges of defence equipment acquisition arise inevitably from the nature of the defence equipment itself and from the nature of the environment within which the acquisition process must be managed. Some aspects of the environment are permanent (such as the uniquely competitive nature of warfare) but others have changed over past centuries and will continue to change in the future (as noted in Chapter 1). As the challenges change nations employ new methods and procedures to try to overcome them (e.g. Smart Acquisition adopted in the UK in 1998). The following chapters present some of the approaches which can be used to conquer the challenges of defence acquisition today and tomorrow.

Further reading

Bennett, FN (1990) *The Amateur Managers*. Canberra: Australian National University

Chin, WA (2004) *British Weapons Acquisition Policy and the Futility of Reform*. Aldershot: Ashgate Publishing

Johnson, RV and Birkler, J (1996) *Three Programs and Ten Criteria*. Santa Monica, CA: Rand

Kincaid, W (1997) *A Dinosaur in Whitehall: The True Cost of Defence Procurement Bureaucracy*. London: Brasseys

NAO (2004) *MoD Major Projects Report 2004*. London: TSO

Pick, MJ and Scherer, FM (1962) *The Weapon Acquisition Process: An Economic Analysis*. Boston, MA: Harvard Business School

Chapter 3

Aspects of acquisition

The procedure for acquiring major defence systems is a very complex one, and the MoD's Smart Acquisition process is outlined, followed by an examination of research and technology acquisition. Requirements management is then considered, as well as the importance of human factors. A look at affordability issues and methods of achieving value for money follows. Some thoughts on the use of off-the-shelf equipment are presented. Integrated logistic support is an increasingly important part of any acquisition, as is the operational supportability of fielded equipment, and both are reviewed. The UK public/private partnership and private finance initiative are assessed as important and relatively new parts of the acquisition process.

1 Smart Acquisition

Smart Acquisition, previously Smart Procurement, was introduced in the MoD *Strategic Defence Review* published in 1998 and its current aim is 'to acquire defence capability faster, cheaper, better and more effectively integrated'. The last criterion recognises that a solution which is faster, cheaper and better but which is not effectively integrated may well compromise defence capability, and that integration carries equal weight with performance, cost and time. In the years since 1998 its implementation has been patchy, according to the Chief of Defence Procurement (CDP), and it has not yet achieved the desired impact on the procurement of new equipment. The four objectives of Smart Acquisition stated by the MoD are to:

1. Deliver and sustain defence capabilities within the performance, time and cost parameters approved at the time the major investment decisions are taken.
2. Integrate defence capabilities into their environment, with the flexibility to be adapted as the environment changes.
3. Acquire defence capabilities progressively, at lower risk. Optimisation of trade-offs between military effectiveness, time and through-life cost are maximised.
4. Cut the time for (key) new technologies to be introduced into the front line where needed to secure military advantage and industrial competitiveness.

To achieve these aims, the MoD admits it needs to improve the practice of Smart Acquisition in the equipment area and extend its scope into non-equipment areas. Furthermore National Audit Office (NAO) reports make it clear that deliveries to time and cost are often not achieved on major projects and it is also apparent that optimal trade-offs are frequently not made. Smart Acquisition applies to all types of acquisition and is based on seven enabling principles:

1. A through-life approach, applying through-life costing techniques.
2. Integrated project teams (IPTs) with clearly identified customers.
3. A better, more open relationship with industry.
4. Increased investment in the early phases of projects.
5. Effective trade-offs between system performance, through-life costs and time.
6. New procurement approaches, including incremental acquisition.
7. A streamlined process for project approvals.

It is perhaps surprising that the MoD *Acquisition Handbook* does not include a capability-based approach in this list. The handbook defines acquisition as: *The process of requirement setting, procurement management, support management and termination/disposal implying a through-life approach to defence capability.* It defines defence capability as: *An operational outcome or effect that users of assets or services need to achieve.* Since Smart Acquisition is mainly focused on equipment capability, defence systems engineers must understand the process whereby customers specify the military capability they require but not the type or design of equipment which should provide that capability.

Smart Acquisition requires a more structured approach to requirement setting and better target setting to ensure delivery of fully integrated defence capabilities. Risk needs to be managed more effectively, building on the principles of investment during early project stages and ensuring that risk is owned where it is best managed; risk must be reduced to an acceptable level before the key decision on any major investment is made. Trade-offs between performance, cost, delivery time and effective integration should be balanced to maximise cost effectiveness. Acquiring capability incrementally and the use of synthetic environments also help to reduce risk. Finally, the streamlined process for approvals and the use of peer reviews can provide additional assurance that the proposed delivery is achievable.

Compared to the period prior to the introduction of Smart Acquisition, the key changes are partnering with industry, de-risking new equipment designs and the evaluation of through-life rather than just initial procurement costs. Unfortunately, most of the Smart Acquisition principles have yet to be fully implemented; the only exception according to the CDP being the capability-based approach, which does not appear in the list above. The MoD also wishes to trade-off performance, time and cost, as well as considering wider factors (see Section 5 below) in order to achieve better value for money, sustain the UK defence industrial base and build a constructive relationship with its suppliers. All of these changes will undoubtedly impact on the work of defence systems engineers.

Obtaining best value for money in defence systems acquisition is not a straightforward task. Many different types of consideration have to be weighed against each other by groups of people driven by very varied motivations. Even when the 'fastest, cheapest, best' solution has been selected by the MoD, the resulting choice may still be overridden by political considerations, as in the well-documented saga of the Nimrod AEW (not to be confused with the maritime reconnaissance version), selected to protect British jobs. This decision led to zero deliveries, the loss of £1B and the eventual purchase of the Boeing AWACS.

1.1 Integrated project teams

Every project needs a leader, but is the function of the leader to lead the team or to lead the project?

There are three different types of IPT dealing with large projects, smaller projects and clusters of related small projects. The scope of the work to be undertaken, the complexity, urgency and importance of the work, the competence levels of individuals within the team, and whether positions are created to provide staff development opportunities should determine the size of each IPT. Clearly different projects will allocate different levels of importance to these factors; the IPTs within the Defence Procurement Agency (DPA) range from a minimum of four members to over two hundred. As an IPT increases in size, a greater number of levels of intermediate management is necessary to maintain reasonable spans of control.

To perform effectively, any IPT should possess the skills of leadership, requirements management, project and risk management, project engineering, technical, quality and reliability expertise, integrated logistic support (ILS) management, commercial and finance management, administration and industrial expertise. This list does not imply a minimum team size as some members may have a mix of skills. However, an IPT must include, as core members, a team leader, project manager, commercial manager and finance manager with access to the other skills either through the secondary skills of its core members or through associate members.

IPTs bring together all stakeholders under a team leader able to balance trade-offs between performance, cost, time and effective integration within boundaries set by the service customer. IPTs have clearly defined customer/supplier relationships, allowing them to deliver consistency and continuity throughout a project's life cycle, and ensuring close and effective involvement of all major stakeholders in key decisions. IPTs must have four fundamental characteristics:

1. They are responsible for managing their project from concept to disposal. The change in balance of activities within the IPT from procurement to in-service support will determine the timing of an IPT move from the DPA to the Defence Logistics Organisation (DLO). This through-life perspective, together with a clearly defined customer/supplier relationship, allows an IPT to plan, acquire and support equipment in a consistent manner.
2. They must include all the necessary skills to manage the project. These range from requirements management through project management and engineering and technical skills to equipment support. The IPT will usually include, except during the assessment of competitive bids, representation from industry and, at the appropriate points, inputs from financial and technical scrutineers.
3. Each IPT should be headed by an effective and empowered IPT leader, able to make cost-effective trade-offs between performance, through-life cost, time and effective

integration. The leader will control the core members of the IPT who will be responsible to their leader for their project work. The success of an IPT will depend in part on the calibre of the leader and the team members, their working relationships and the way they deal with industry and their customer.

4. An IPT's members represent the key functional interest in equipment acquisition across the MoD. Functional links remain to senior specialist functional policy owners outside the IPT. Specialist IPT members can obtain guidance from these senior staff to make their contribution to the team more effective.

The IPT leader is answerable to the customer, via customer/supplier agreements, for the acquisition and support of equipment capability, meeting agreed cost, performance and effective integration targets and milestones within the agreed budgeted resources. The leader is accountable to the CDP and/or the Chief of Defence Logistics (CDL) for the propriety and professionalism of the IPT, and the efficient and effective use of resources in meeting the customer's requirements.

Some of the problems that have come from the establishment of platform or system of systems IPTs under the Smart Acquisition initiative arise from their singular dedication to a particular project. IPTs have shown little interest in commonality of sub-systems or harmonisation of logistic support with other IPTs, unless they see a cost saving for their own project. The recent inclusion of the need for effective integration (as a parameter equally important as performance, cost and time) could help to ameliorate this difficulty. The lack of effective cross-links between the various IPTs does not help to solve this problem either from a practical or from a communications point of view.

It will be apparent from Chapter 8, Section 2 (Management of projects) that the role of an IPT leader (IPTL) is very similar to that of a project manager but it is possible to differentiate between leadership in the role of an IPTL and management in the case of a project manager: leadership is about being in charge of a team and inspiring its members; management is the skill or practice of controlling, directing or planning an activity. The similarities are clear; the differences marginal.

1.2 CADMID, initial and main gate

CADMID is the MoD acronym for the current acquisition cycle comprised of six stages – concept, assessment, demonstration, manufacture, in-service and disposal – which has replaced the old Downey cycle. The various phases are described below in more detail. The CADMID cycle includes just two approval stages: initial gate and main gate (described in Section 1.2.7 below). Defence systems engineers must become familiar with the various stages of this cycle and their potential impact on the design of any new system.

1.2.1 Concept phase

This is the first phase during which the embryonic IPT is formed. The capability working group, assisted by the IPT, must produce a basic user requirements document (URD) defining

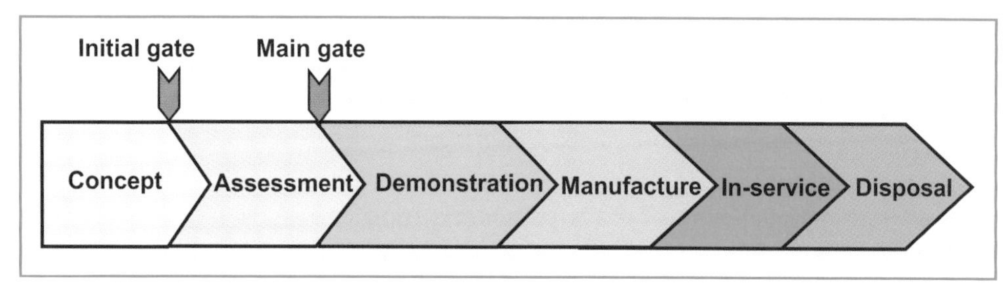

Figure 32. The CADMID cycle showing its relationship to initial and main gates.

the current user need, and identify and cost technological options and procurement strategies for meeting the need that merit further investigation. A business case (BC) must be assembled for initial gate approval.

1.2.2 Assessment phase

The second CADMID phase begins after a project has passed initial gate. The IPT must then produce a system requirements document (SRD) and identify the most cost-effective technical and procurement solution to the requirement. The availability of sufficient funding for this stage should enable multiple, competing designs to be developed. Risk needs to be reduced to a level consistent with delivering an acceptable level of performance to a rigorous timescale and cost target. A more detailed BC needs to be assembled for the main gate approval.

1.2.3 Demonstration phase

The demonstration phase begins directly after main gate approval. The IPT may place competitive preliminary design contracts with industry to implement risk management strategies, further evaluate performance/cost trade-offs, firm up through-life costs, establish the in-service date and assess potential gainshare opportunities. During this phase the prime contractor will often be chosen (in some cases this may happen earlier) and a contract based on the SRD placed. The ability to produce an integrated capability must be demonstrated.

1.2.4 Manufacture phase

In the fourth CADMID phase the IPT delivers the solution to the military requirement. The capability manager conducts systems acceptance. The transfer of the IPT to the DLO and of the customer function from the equipment capability customer to customer 2 (front-line commander) takes place at this time.

1.2.5 In-service phase

The in-service stage starts when the IPT, now under DLO line management, has to provide effective support to the front line. It must maintain the levels of performance agreed with customer 2 and carry out approved upgrades or improvements, refits or acquisition increments.

1.2.6 Disposal phase

The final CADMID phase is when plans are implemented for the efficient, effective and safe disposal of any equipment and its associated support.

1.2.7 Approval stages

A relatively low approval hurdle, between the concept and assessment phases, initial gate is intended to encourage full and early exploration of a broad range of options for meeting a particular capability. A BC at initial gate should confirm that there is a well-constructed plan for the assessment phase that gives reasonable confidence that there are flexible solutions within the performance, cost and time envelope the central customer has proposed that can be effectively integrated. Approval at initial gate, given by the Investment Approvals Board (IAB), conveys no commitment to a project proceeding beyond main gate.

Main gate is 'an exacting hurdle', between the assessment and demonstration phases and the approving authorities must be satisfied that the continuation of the project to demonstration and manufacture represents value for money. A detailed BC at main gate should recommend a single technological and procurement option. Risk should have been sufficiently reduced and the project should have reached a sufficient degree of maturity for the capability manager and IPT leader to set the user and systems requirements with confidence and to deliver the project to narrowly defined performance, through-life cost and time parameters so that it can effectively be integrated. Potential industrial or political issues must be addressed or resolved at this stage. The parameters agreed at main gate will be those used for external reporting and performance measurement with the Treasury and the NAO.

It is at this point that a source selection may be made when procuring major items of operational equipment. Thus main gate approval, given by the IAB, is often the point when the prime contractor is chosen to provide a required capability. If usual main gate confidence levels cannot be demonstrated for the entire programme, subsequent approvals may be needed for those aspects where the risk is deemed too great at the main decision point. The approval criteria for main gate in these circumstances will, however, continue to be determined by the overall cost of the programme, not the value of the first basket of increments.

The BC should provide a full justification for the proposed procurement including the user requirement, and the procurement and support strategies required for meeting it. This will need to take full account of the work undertaken during assessment and, particularly, any trade-offs that have been made between the cost, time, performance and effective integration boundaries. The BC should refer as appropriate to the URD, verification criteria, SRD, acceptance criteria and ITEAP (integrated test evaluation and acceptance plan). Interoperability key requirements (and the interoperability user requirements) should be produced in close consultation with the interoperability joint requirements co-ordinator, core directors EC (equipment capability) and the integration authority, and their views reflected in the case. The customer will need to be satisfied that the highest acceptable cost is affordable. The BC should include robust analysis of how through-life costs will affect value for money and affordability through the equipment's life. Any departures from normal government procurement policy need to be approved (with the rationale being provided in the BC). The BC should also record the outcome of the assessment of defence industrial implications and discussions with the Department of Trade and Industry (DTI). A combined operational effectiveness and investment appraisal (COEIA) is prepared for each procurement decision, including technical specification, support, upgradability and through-life costs.

2 Research and technology acquisition

2.1 Value of research

In modern warfare, a marginal technological advantage (armour that can resist enemy shot, sensors that can detect and track enemy combat units at longer range, or missiles with higher terminal lethality than the enemy's) can make all the difference between success and failure; between winning and losing a battle or a war. Military history is littered with examples where a marginal advantage was decisive. Such minor technological gains arise from well-targeted and well-managed national research programmes, exploited to produce weapon systems significantly superior to those deployed by the enemy. The MoD spends some £450m per year on non-nuclear defence research, equivalent to about 2% of its cash budget, but this is substantially less than the amount spent in 1990.

2.2 Defence research categories

Research activities include:

- Basic research designed to enhance knowledge of particular technologies without reference to any particular equipment project.
- Applied research focused on overcoming a specific problem on a current project, or on reducing the risk associated with a future project.
- Technology demonstration to enhance knowledge of a set of key technologies (and their interfaces) which are required for a future project and are critical to its success.

This spectrum of research can be subdivided into several categories with different labels, as suits the structure of the organisation that is funding and managing it. Some activities could equally well be described either as applied research and funded from a research budget (most research is funded by the equipment capability customer) or as project assessment work controlled and funded by an IPT. All these activities contribute to the body of technological knowledge available to the MoD.

2.3 Purpose of defence research

To implement effectively the UK government's defence policies, the MoD requires access to a comprehensive, up-to-date body of technical knowledge which can be used to evaluate intelligence on emergent threats, to develop appropriate policies and concepts in response to those threats, and to identify cost-effective structures and equipment for the UK armed forces to implement those policies. The Foreign and Commonwealth Office (FCO) also needs access to this body of knowledge to support its participation in international debates on security issues.

This body of knowledge must continually be supplemented by new information generated by the MoD (by funding research in its own laboratories or in commercial organisations), or by information trawled from the global plethora of published books and papers, or by data obtained from allied governments or private companies. Monitoring the global knowledge base requires dedicated MoD personnel with sufficient expertise in the technologies they cover to sort the wheat from the chaff. Unpublished information from other governments or companies must be paid for in cash or in kind (by information exchange), and it is sometimes difficult to assess its reliability if there is no clear understanding of how the information was originally generated and/or of why it is now being provided. There is inevitable risk that it may be biased (subconsciously or otherwise) to promote the objectives of the supplier. If the inflow of new information from all sources were insufficient, the body of knowledge available to the MoD would progressively become obsolete and future decisions would be increasingly prone to error.

The MoD also needs access to technological knowledge in order to be an intelligent customer in defence equipment acquisition. An intelligent customer must be able to make independent assessments of the likely cost effectiveness of alternative equipment projects proposed by rival contractors, and to formulate for each proposal effective strategies for through-life management of procurement, support and logistics. This knowledge must be broad enough to cover all the technologies in all of the alternative projects being considered (and so avoid potentially disastrous pitfalls of ignorance) and deep enough to allow MoD officials to negotiate effectively with industrial contractors.

In some defence technology areas, considered to be particularly vital for national sovereignty and security (such as sonar, cryptography and NBC [nuclear, biological and chemical] weapons and countermeasures), the MoD requires expert knowledge, which is equal or superior to that of any other government or non-state group in order to formulate policies for these critical areas.

The MoD may also wish to have expert knowledge in order to promote the development of first-rate equipment for the UK armed forces. This knowledge must include the application of the relevant technologies to the design and development of new equipment projects so that the MoD can interact with its chosen contractor to optimise the equipment's cost-effectiveness. In former times the MoD acted as design authority and took a leading role in the specification and development of many types of equipment (for which it needed expert knowledge of all the relevant technologies); although today the role of design authority has been largely delegated to commercial contractors, knowledgeable MoD staff can still contribute through the IPT to the effective application of technology to a new equipment project.

2.4 Funding of defence research

The range of scientific technologies includes categories that are wholly civilian, dual-use and defence-specific, though the boundaries between these categories can alter as the nature of warfare changes. Research in wholly civilian technologies such as cosmetics is funded by industry under the supervision of government regulators, and the results are of no interest to the MoD. Basic research in a dual-use technology such as aerodynamics or metallurgy is mostly funded by the MoD or by another government department to promote the national technology base; applied research in a dual-use technology which is directly focused on a particular defence project may be shared between the MoD and the contractor, according to their perceptions of the relative importance of future exploitation for military and civilian purposes.

Research in defence-specific technologies is almost invariably funded by the MoD, seeking to keep the UK's defence technology base abreast or ahead of those in most other nations. Basic research in these technologies offers no prospect of early and profitable exploitation so industry is unwilling to fund it. Even applied research on defence equipment being produced by a contractor for the MoD is generally funded by the MoD, either directly or as part of a contractor's costs.

In exceptional circumstances, when a contractor needs to convince the MoD of the credibility of a proposed future project, the contractor (or a consortium of interested companies) may fund some relevant applied research or a technology demonstrator from its own resources in the hope that its costs will be recouped when the MoD is sufficiently impressed to order the associated equipment project.

Recently, the MoD has established some defence technology centres (DTCs) in which it shares the cost of basic or applied research in a particular technology with a chosen contractor, and accordingly accepts some limitations of its right to exploit the research results. The industry commitment to the three tranche 1 DTCs, established in 2003, amounts to some £13M per year which is a small fraction of the MoD's own research budget; later tranches may expand industry's contribution to a significant level.

The funding of defence research by the MoD must cover not only activities which directly enhance its body of technological knowledge but also the career development of specialist personnel, the construction of test facilities and the development of experimental techniques which are all required to sustain future research at the leading edge of defence technologies.

The MoD seeks to expand its body of knowledge as economically as possible by pooling the results of its own defence research with those funded by the governments of allied nations, where practicable. Ideally such sharing provides all the participants with more information from reduced funding, and can lay the foundation for collaborative projects offering the participating nations better value for money (through economies of scale and sharing the up-front costs) than national projects. However, sharing a technology inevitably increases the risk that it may inadvertently leak to a third party, perhaps to a potentially hostile foreign government or to a foreign contractor in competition with UK industry. It follows that international collaboration in defence research can successfully be implemented only when two or more allies are simultaneously willing to fund complementary work on the same technology, and when that technology is not particularly critical to their national security or industrial competitiveness. Accordingly the scope for collaboration on defence research is limited, and the MoD currently spends only 5% of its research budget on such programmes, despite their obvious economic attractions (the return on investment is typically three to five times greater than would be obtained by an individual nation).

2.5 Management of defence research

Formerly, the content of the MoD research programme was arranged by a dialogue between the technology leaders at its research establishments and the military officers responsible for future force development and the associated requirements for new equipment. In principle, both of these groups could influence the senior official (then the Controller of Establishments and Research) who held and allocated the research budget, but in practice the relatively short tenure and the limited expertise of most military officers put them at a disadvantage in debate. These officers also deplored budgetary arrangements which made it easier to identify the research relevant to a particular technology (because research staff were grouped according to their expertise and to the experimental facilities they used) than to distinguish the work relevant to a particular project; often a research item could contribute to several projects of the same class. It was considered that under this management arrangement the defence research budget was not well aligned to military needs.

Over the last dozen years the MoD has moved through a succession of reorganisations of its research activity towards a programme directed by requirement pull rather than technology push. Today the MoD has adopted an output-based framework for funding and management, with formal customer/supplier relationships between the MoD and the government agency or commercial organisation providing the research. The defence research programme is now guided by the objectives of specific MoD officials to generate advice or technology outputs, as shown below.

Chief Scientific Advisor – Scientific advice on hot topics to key decision-makers.

Policy Director – Scientific advice and analysis to support policy-making.

Deputy Chief of Defence Staff (Equipment Capability) – Specialist advice on equipment capability planning and management. Innovative solutions to enhance UK military capability.

Science and Technology Director – Scientific advice in support of acquisition and technology watch over the global technology base.

Deputy Chief Executive (DPA) – Promotion of appropriate advanced technology in the UK supplier base.

Figure 33. The MoD staff involved in the management of research.

2.6 Conclusions

However it is organised and funded, the MoD's research programme is a vital foundation for the successful acquisition of new equipment. Defence systems engineers must be able to direct the synthesis of all available research information (with caveats as necessary) to define the technology readiness levels (TRLs) of all the technologies involved in a particular project. The TRLs then contribute to the assessment of technical risk and to the derivation of the appropriate risk management strategies. A synthesis of research information is also essential to the process of forecasting the multidimensional performance of the new equipment in a variety of future scenarios, which supports decisions on force planning and selection of the most cost-effective option to provide a required military capability.

3 Requirements management

3.1 Capturing and defining user requirements

The basis of any new military capability, probably but not necessarily including equipment, is the establishment of an identified need that is derived from defence policy and initiated by the identification of a capability gap. Requirements capture is the process of exploring the boundaries of any new project and of defining the capabilities which the project must deliver. The process is influenced by many stakeholders in industry and government, including potential contractors and sub-contractors, various branches of the MoD, other departments of the UK government, allies and pressure groups. The requirements capture process should benefit from inputs from organisations such as the DPA, DLO, Defence Scientific and Technical Laboratory (Dstl), industry or military allies as well as from the various 'Lessons Learned' reports arising from the MoD's post-project evaluations. The capabilities of potential aggressors and the level of world military capabilities are also crucial inputs. Figure 34 demonstrates the many influences that contribute to requirements capture.

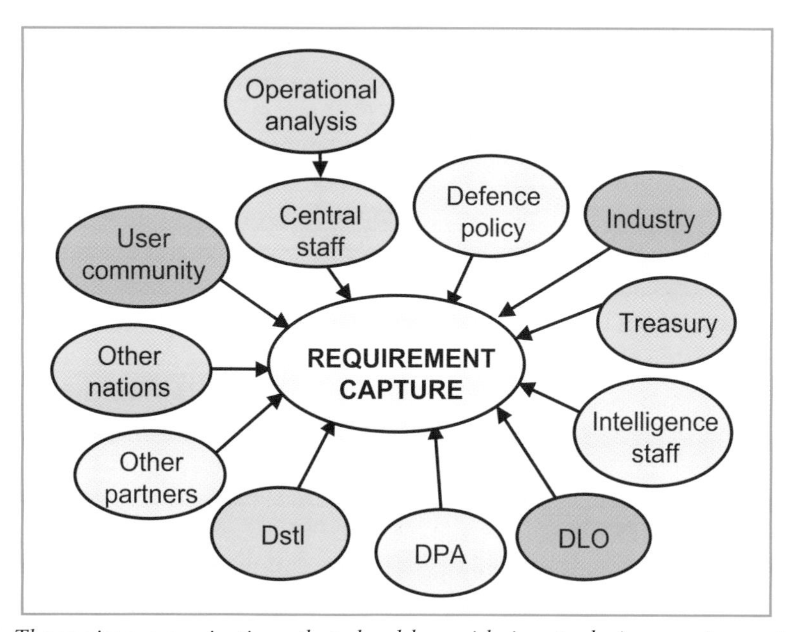

Figure 34. The various organisations that should provide inputs during requirements capture.

The URD is the tool that expresses the need of the customer for a particular capability. It is also the means by which the customer imparts and maintains the requirement throughout the life of a system. The URD should communicate the required system capability without in any way constraining the scope of possible solutions. It should identify the key user requirements but should not refer to contract, project or process requirements.

3.1.1 Purpose of the URD

The role of a completed URD is to:

- Communicate user needs to other stakeholders.
- Provide an initial basis against which trade-offs (between performance, cost, timescale and effective integration), tender assessment and acceptance standards can be made.
- Provide criteria against which the system should be validated once it is accepted into service.
- Link the changing needs and actual capability achieved throughout the system's life.
- Underpin the business case presented during any expenditure approval process.

3.1.2 Stakeholders in the URD

At an early stage it is essential to identify all possible stakeholders of the proposed capability and obtain their URD input. Stakeholders in MoD projects include the equipment capability customer, customer 2, DPA, DLO, Dstl and industry representatives. Other influences may come from other government departments, the general public and intelligence staff assessments. In the MoD, although the central customer has full responsibility for the URD, all stakeholders should be involved in requirements capture. The writing of the document may be contracted out.

3.1.3 URD through the life cycle

The URD is created during the concept phase and maintained as long as the requirement exists. An initial version of the URD is used to support early approval of project expenditure at initial gate, with a refined version used to support later main gate approval along with the SRD. After main gate the URD should regularly be reviewed and amended if necessary, ensuring it represents the current user need. Although URD changes may be required in these later stages, they should not filter down to the SRD unless considered absolutely essential, due to the need to place a contract against a firm requirement and the high cost of contract amendments. Any forecast gap between the URD and SRD will represent an emerging capability gap that may be addressed by a subsequent capability upgrade.

3.2 System requirements

An SRD is a complete description of a system that will meet the user needs stated in the URD. The SRD describes the required system behaviour without prescribing a technical solution. The SRD essentially portrays a high-level model of the system and promotes discussion, some trade-offs and some optimisation prior to the development of a solution. The SRD must be maintained during the whole system life cycle detailing its baseline requirements. An audit trail from the URD to the SRD is also necessary to show the origin of each requirement and how the system will satisfy it.

3.2.1 Purpose of the SRD

The SRD is the method of developing, communicating and maintaining system requirements to:

- Provide a basis for the customer and supplier to negotiate and agree the system performance.
- Explore possible trade-offs between system performance, through-life cost, timescale and effective integration before committing to a design or contract.
- Ensure that requirements are agreed as affordable and achievable, and are reflected in system functions.
- Provide a solid foundation for the whole system, expressing it in the language, terms and detail against which it can be designed, manufactured, delivered and accepted.
- Specify legitimate, but not unnecessary, constraints on system design.
- Focus risk reduction leading to acceptable levels of risk prior to contract.
- Underpin the business case for system development.
- Provide the baseline for through-life system performance to monitor changing user needs and maintenance of system capability.

3.2.2 Stakeholders in the SRD

The SRD provides the focus for system specification leading to contract placement. Its preparation should involve all relevant stakeholders in order to obtain a common understanding between all parties. The SRD is owned by the project manager and is a translation of the customer's requirements into system terms. The requirements manager (who is accountable to the IPT leader), produces it and must ensure that there are suitable processes in place to define the structure of the SRD and manage the interface with the URD. The whole IPT is responsible for the actual capture and specification of the systems requirements. Comparing the URD and SRD stakeholders, the former include a very diverse group from within and outside the MoD; the latter need to be much more technically oriented and to lie largely within the MoD.

3.2.3 SRD through the life cycle

Most work on the SRD should involve the IPT in developing and assessing trade-off options. Early in the life cycle there may be more than one SRD satisfying a single URD. This allows consideration of a variety of disparate system options during assessment. During the exploration of feasible development options, one technology solution is chosen for further development and the IPT then refines the SRD, trading off performance, cost, time and effective integration to optimise the solution. By the end of the assessment phase, the SRD will be firm enough to allow approval for development and production expenditure.

Contractors bid against the SRD that will form the basis of the contract. The SRD will be updated, as required, during the system's life to reflect trade-off decisions, incremental acquisitions and approved system enhancements. During manufacture the SRD is used to track delivery, integration and system acceptance. Similarly, when the equipment is in service, the changing needs and performance of the system will be assessed against the SRD.

3.3 The roles of systems engineers in defining system requirements

Defence systems engineers have two tasks. They must design the right system, keeping options open to compare possibilities; a task that requires brainstorming, an open mind and wide experience. They must also design the system right by closing off options to converge towards a solution, requiring attention to detail, a logical mind, sufficient experience of similar systems, and a full understanding of both the requirement and the system boundary.

There are many possible solutions to any given problem. Defence system engineers have to design the best value for money solution using agreed criteria. The skill lies in knowing which options to consider and when and why to close off unsuitable options. This requires a full understanding of the problem or requirement that is ideally expressed in solution-independent terms. This should be followed by identification of all possible options for consideration; a creative activity involving brainstorming and discussion. The high-risk areas for each option should be identified and agreement reached on how to deal with them. The comparative merits and risks of each of the options can be assessed using objective analysis and sound engineering judgement. A decision is then needed to decide which option or options to pursue, although keeping parallel options open is very resource intensive. Finally a single preferred solution must be agreed.

3.4 Constraints imposed by requirements and suppliers

Requirement statements will inevitably impose constraints on solutions. They should close off solution options not required by the customer – that is their task – but they should not arbitrarily close off acceptable options and so prevent suppliers having the maximum freedom

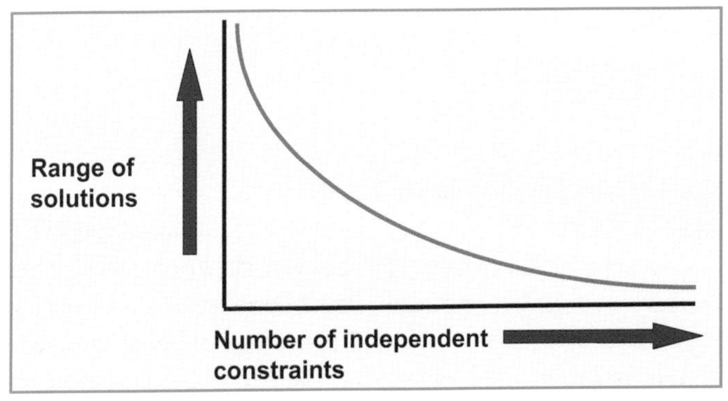

Figure 35. The number of possible solutions is inversely proportional to the number of constraints.

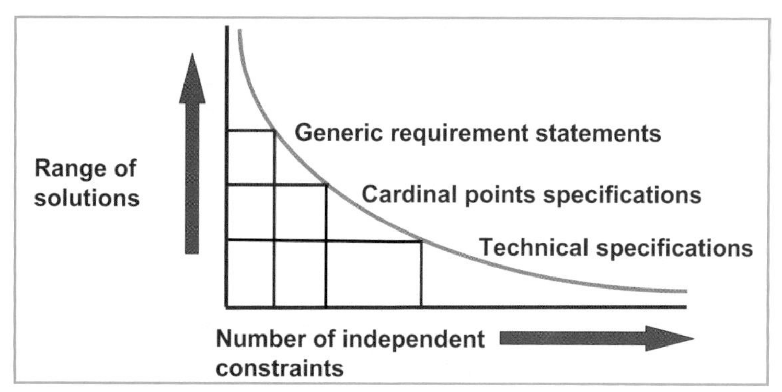

Figure 36. The range of solutions is more limited by cardinal points specifications and technical specifications than by generic requirements.

to find the best solution. Customers can choose the constraints they impose but they do need to understand clearly the impact of these constraints. The more constraints that are specified, inevitably the more the solution is dictated. Conversely, a solution can only be dictated by imposing a multitude of constraints. Alternative specifications include:

- Detailed technical specifications that define a specific solution.
- Cardinal points specifications that allow the supplier some freedom.
- Generic problem statements that allow maximum supplier freedom.

All three approaches are useful, depending on how certain are the user needs. Users can specify a solution but should do this only if they are sure it is what they want and they have done sufficient work to justify their choice. Unfortunately, customers often assume certain solutions without having completed sufficient investigation. Fewer specifications mean less systems engineering work for the customer (and a greater range of acceptable solutions) but more for the supplier.

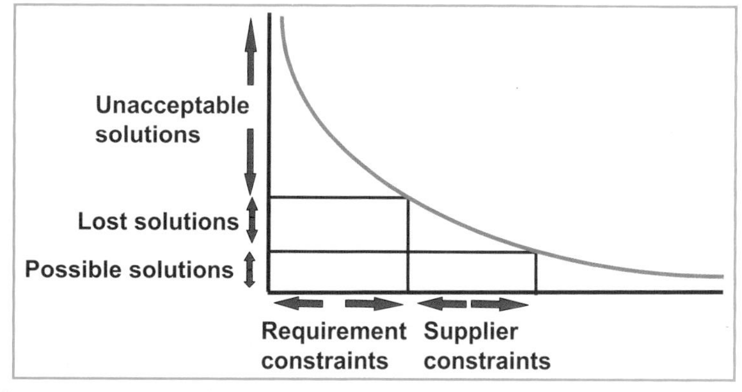

Figure 37. Constraints imposed both by the requirement and those necessitated by the supplier impact on the number of possible solutions.

As well as customers, suppliers will also impose constraints on the range of possible solutions. They will certainly be influenced by their past experience and may have a limited range of creative ideas. They may wish to use existing sub-systems or components and they may be constrained by existing manufacturing capabilities. Inevitably, they will wish to maximise their profit on sales or their return on investment. These supplier constraints will close off many solutions ('We don't make these!') that would have been acceptable and hence the customer may not get the best possible system as a range of solution options will have been lost. This leads to the perennial questions: 'Who is best placed to close off options, the customer or the supplier?' and 'How much or how little should the customer specify?'

Having evaluated a problem and expressed it as a requirement, not as a solution, defence systems engineers usually provide a set of requirement statements to express it fully. It will then be up to potential suppliers to offer physical solutions to meet the requirement.

4 Human factors

4.1 Introduction

Human factors, also called ergonomics, is concerned with analysing and optimising the interface between humans and artificial systems and products. Human factors has many applications in defence systems engineering (DSE) and it is essential to identify the relevant human factors throughout a system life cycle. The study of human factors is interdisciplinary in that it integrates anthropometrics, psychology, physiology and sociology.

Anthropometrics, which includes biomechanics, is concerned with human proportions and ranges of movement and is used, for instance, in seating and doorway design. Physiology deals with the ways humans react to environmental conditions such as light, sound, heat, humidity and odour. Psychology is concerned with cognitive capabilities, limitations and preferences when interacting with systems. Sociology applies when more than one person interacts with a system, and with other people in respect of that system.

The disciplines of human factors have generally been born out of disaster. For example, the multiplicity of accidents resulting from pilots flying into the ground in cloud or at night

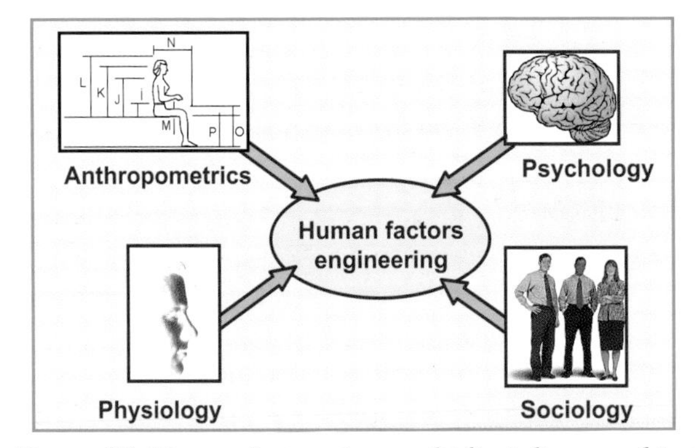

Figure 38. Human factors is a multidisciplinary subject.

as a result of misreading their altimeters led to a redesign that applied human factors principles. Worldwide, aircraft crash investigators have found that around 80% of all aircraft accidents are the result of human factors. Furthermore, lack of consideration of human factors results in a considerable percentage of the enormous number of back and repetitive strain injuries experienced in the UK each year.

4.2 Human factors and ergonomics

The word *ergonomics* is derived from the Greek words *ergon* (work) and *nomos* (laws). The terms 'human factors' and 'ergonomics' are interchangeable and are concerned with the usability of equipment by its potential customers. The Ergonomics Society currently defines ergonomics as ... *the application of scientific information concerning humans to the design of objects, systems and environment for human use.* The techniques of ergonomics originated in the Second World War, when engineers often designed new systems without fully considering the needs and limitations of the people who would be using them. It gradually became clear that all equipment should be designed to take account of human and operating environment factors if it was to be used safely and effectively. Open the manual for any personal computer (PC) and there is a section with a title such as 'Ergonomic computing habits' with warnings like 'Improper or prolonged keyboard use may result in injury', followed by advice on how to set up the PC and use it for comfort and efficiency. There may even be a diagram showing the best way to sit at a PC.

4.3 Usability

Usability is generally attributed to the features of a particular system. It is a judgement about the quality of interaction between the user and the system or its components when both are engaged in a particular task. Usability emerges when the user, the system and the task being undertaken all interact harmoniously. It is therefore essential that defence systems engineers consider both the user and the tasks to be done before starting to design the system.

It important that usability does not just refer to the end user, but covers all those human activities that interact with the system throughout its life cycle. A lack of consideration of the required human factors will have a negative impact on usability, not just in the sense of the operators of the equipment, but also those who build and test the equipment, those who deliver, install and commission it, those who undertake maintenance and system upgrades and finally, those who dispose of the equipment at the end of its life. Thus the conventional view of human factors as only applying to the design of equipment and its interface with users falls far short of the need for human factors thinking in DSE.

4.4 Anthropometrics

Anthropometrics is the study of human variability and preference. It includes biomechanics, the study of the mechanics of human movements. Information is available on the size

Figure 39. A naval workstation with multiple displays that must be viewed and read in comfort, as well as several different types of input device. (Photo courtesy BAe Systems.)

variability of human beings and concentrates on percentiles. Thus, a sample of 100 individuals would show that their heights vary and that there is no such thing as an average person; the 50th percentile is the nearest thing to an average. Everyone is different and one size does not fit all.

How do the bones and muscles operate? How strong are they and what are the key measurements of the likely population of users of a system? In systems design, consideration must be given to user ability to be located comfortably and able to reach any required controls. Workstation design is of critical importance if the operator is to provide the best performance, while cockpit seating must be able to accommodate all aircrew in safety, including during ejection.

In *Human Factors for Designers of Equipment* (Def Stan 00-25) there is a significant amount of information on the results of body measurements and other biomechanical data to help designers of defence equipment consider human factors at an early stage in the design process. Left-handed people represent some 10% of the population and are rarely considered by designers; ambidextrous controls are required to avoid compromising this section of the user community. So-called portable equipment must take into consideration the strength and stamina of the proposed carriers.

It is important to remember that anthropometric factors do not remain constant. The average height of the UK population is still growing by around 1mm per year and the number of people who are overweight or obese is rising even faster. There are changes of the gender mix in the armed forces as a whole and in particular functions within the services. The same is true for the ethnic mix. Furthermore, the standards of usability that are expected are increasing dramatically, supported to an extent by health and safety legislation. Finally, it is no use designing a system just for today's users. With equipment service life now sometimes exceeding 50 years, it is essential to try to predict requirements for the design life of the system.

4.5 Psychology in human factors engineering

The way human brains work affects people's cognitive functions. In systems design, the key factors are the way displays are 'seen' and the way controls are managed. It is also known that aesthetically pleasing human/machine interfaces can improve performance. In everyday life, people are looking at displays and operating controls for significant periods day after day; driving a car and sitting at a PC are both good examples. As a result, everyone has developed certain expectations, known as stereotypes, about the way information is presented on displays and the way controls function. The hands on an analogue watch are expected to move clockwise as time passes and the needles on speedometers and air-speed indicators similarly to move clockwise as speed increases. People are also programmed that red is danger and green is safe. It must be remembered, however, that around 10% of men and 1% of women suffer from colour blindness (colour-vision deficiency) and that difficulty distinguishing red and green is the most common problem.

On the control side, similar stereotypes are found such as the way of turning the steering wheel of a car. It is, however, important to recognise that there may be no such thing as a 'natural' sense of movement. Most student pilots have difficulty using the rudder pedals when learning to taxi an aircraft, as they move in the opposite sense to a bicycle's handlebars!

For many controls, some form of feedback is important. A switch that gives an audible click when it is turned on or off is helpful, as is a 1 and 0 to show its position. The tactile feedback provided by a computer keyboard is essential to the ease of operation of this device.

The most common forms of controller are the keyboard and the mouse, with the roller ball, joystick, wheel, pedals and sidestick controller also popular in military systems. Care is needed in the choice of controller and its control laws that may, with advantage, be operator adjustable. In addition, consideration is required in deciding whether to use a displacement or force control. The former, in theory, takes longer to provide the operator's required control deflection, but is less susceptible to operator-hand vibrations.

The problem with security, and particularly information security, is that it can be difficult and boring. Consider the straightforward case of a password. The rules are simple. The password must not be associated with the operator – date of birth, partner's name – should comprise a mixture of letters, numbers and punctuation marks, must be changed regularly and often, and yet must not be written down. This is a virtually impossible set of criteria to give to any human being. Even the carrying of a pass results in a small percentage of people forgetting their pass on occasions. In designing secure systems, the memory failings of human beings must be taken into account. Finally, people do not always act as expected. It is important to question whether a design is 'foolproof'. In addition, it is not uncommon to find humans abusing systems; computer abuse can vary from the user swearing at the computer to using physical violence, in the extreme case breaking part or the entire computer.

4.6 Physiology in human factors engineering

The human body has five senses. Vision, hearing and touch are obviously the key ones from a DSE point of view, though smell may be a consideration in adverse environments with high levels of chemical pollutants. Taste is the least likely sense to need consideration but is often closely associated with problems affecting smell. It is worth noting that the mechanism of the inner ear can produce nausea and even balance difficulties when the body is subjected to rapid rotational movement or prolonged exposure to vibration. Perhaps some of the earliest examples of human factors engineering were in the use of hammocks for sleeping (to reduce the effects of ship's roll) and in the provision of lemons to avoid scurvy.

4.6.1 Vision

For manned platforms, vision is crucial and may require first-class all-round vision, as in an air-defence fighter, or the best that is compatible with safety, as in a main battle tank. Artificial lighting is usually needed in enclosed spaces and red light is essential for those who need to use their 'night-vision' outside. Users may have to wear correcting glasses or even gas masks when operating equipment and these factors must be taken into account.

4.6.2 Hearing

Noise can be high enough to cause physical pain and prolonged exposure to high levels of noise causes a gradual loss of hearing. Ear protection must be provided for those working in noisy environments. The frequency of the noise as well as its level are factors that impact on human operation of military systems. Hearing needs to be protected, for example from the noise of a gun firing in close proximity, and background noise should be minimised. At the same time, good intercommunications between team/crew members is essential and the ability to communicate over long distances is equally important. Working with coalition forces highlights language and comprehension difficulties that must be taken into consideration.

4.6.3 Touch

Touch impacts in two areas: the first is in physical comfort, particularly when seated for long periods; the second is in tactile feedback when using the fingers. Typical examples of this type of feedback are found in switches and keyboards. Remember too that users may have to wear gloves for hand protection in case of fire or when NBC warnings are in force.

4.6.4 Smell

Difficulties affecting smell are not uncommon. They occur in such diverse environments as, for example, inside a tank turret when the main armament has just been fired and in the manufacture of composite materials, when nose and mouth protection become important. Aircrew can experience nausea when they first use an oxygen mask, and the insides of aircraft have a particular smell. The same is true of warships and main battle tanks.

4.6.5 Other factors

It is the five senses, amongst other factors, that lead to the need for all designers to consider the human physiology of the users when engineering equipment. The physical environment that exists, particularly in times of war, is a demanding one. The physiology of the human body requires it to operate in a carefully controlled environment.

Excess temperature can lead to heat stroke or even death, as well as burns to the body. Excess cold may result in uncontrollable shivering and frostbite. Deaths due to the cold were highlighted during both Napoleon's and Hitler's retreats from Moscow. Thus the provision of heating, air conditioning and suitable clothing should be given high priority. Humidity is also a factor in human reaction to temperature, particularly when high or low. Dehydration can be debilitating and in severe cases can result in death.

Many air pollutants can cause problems and carbon monoxide, the result of inefficient burning in internal combustion engines, is poisonous in relatively low concentrations; death occurs within one hour at concentrations as low as 0.16%. It should be noted that many systems contain poisons, from high performance oils to depleted uranium, all of which may require special handling or the use of protective clothing.

Reduced air pressure as altitude increases affects human performance. Above 3,000m, oxygen is required to maintain performance and, above 10,000m a pressure breathing system is needed in case of aircraft pressurisation failure. Above 16,500m, blood boils and a full pressure suit is necessary. Furthermore, going rapidly to an unpressurised altitude of 10,000m can cause the bends, though symptoms disappear when altitude is reduced. The same effects impact on divers, where returning to the surface too quickly can result in severe bends. For diving to significant depths, nitrogen narcosis is a danger and a helium/oxygen mixture is used, which has a side effect of causing the frequency of the voice to rise dramatically. Even at sea level, it is essential to maintain around 20% oxygen in any air that is breathed and keep the carbon dioxide content (which all humans breathe out) low, as a rise to just 0.06% causes a feeling of stuffiness. Prolonged exposure can be lethal with the adverse effects becoming more rapid as concentrations reach 3% and above.

Trained aircrew can cope with as much as +9G and –3G, though withstanding the high positive levels needs the use of a G suit and a carefully thought-out seating position. The problem is that high levels of positive G can lead to greyout, blackout and then unconsciousness, while high levels of negative G can lead to redout and damage to blood vessels in the eyes and brain. The use of tilted back seating and effective G suits can mitigate the impact of G loading in combat aircraft. The effects of negative G are more difficult to overcome. Flying a parabolic manoeuvre allows aircrew to experience zero G for around 30 seconds only, but continuous exposure (e.g. an astronaut) introduces a number of problems associated with normal activities and bodily functions.

The level of illumination impacts on the ability to see and read. Furthermore, any light source that is not red has a deleterious effect on night vision. Good contrast between text and background helps legibility, with black on yellow particularly effective. Where light levels are poor, self-illuminating screens are invaluable. Clarity and readability, both of documents and signs, are indications of the effective implementation of human factors guidelines.

Vibration causes fatigue and, in extreme cases, can result in vision impairment. The use of suitable damping systems, including in the seating, is a key factor. Shock has short-term effects and in severe cases can cause serious injuries, particularly to the back.

Two main sources of radiation are likely to impact on system design. The first is nuclear radiation, low levels of which occur in nuclear-powered submarines and near depleted uranium shells. The detonation of nuclear weapons produces extreme levels. The second are those produced by radar and radio transmitters. These sources of radiation can harm human health so methods of minimising radiation levels and avoiding exposure require careful consideration during system design.

The operating environment provided for military personnel must be a major consideration during the design phase. Either the environment in which the human operates must be controlled, or the individuals must be provided with protective clothing. It is also worth noting the increasing use of lightweight armour; the helmet and body armour provide individual protection, and the use of camouflage hinders an enemy's visual detection of the individual soldier.

4.7 Sociology in human factors engineering

Systems usually require people to work in groups and co-operate together to get the best out of any system. Once groups are formed, the individuals concerned share common interests and develop a loyalty to each other. Furthermore, they tend to reject outsiders. It is important to consider these factors and try to benefit from a set of team characteristics that give synergistic benefits. An IPT is an example of a group that will be involved in any new system's design for military use.

For any group to work effectively, the first requirement is good communication. Humans achieve this primarily by the use of their voices, backed up by facial expressions and hand gestures. The written word is a reasonable alternative but can be much more prone to misinterpretation. Touch, smell and taste have minimal impact on communications, though touch can be a powerful tool if someone has had a traumatic experience and it is said that humans can 'smell' fear.

If it is not possible to communicate face-to-face, then major thought must be given to the best alternatives. It is well known that remote voice communication can result in misunderstandings: the world's worst aircraft accident, involving two jumbojets, was caused primarily by poor communications over radio links. The quality of sound over such links is often unacceptably poor and may be exacerbated by platform or battlefield noise. Video links often provide a better interface between separated people, but are not always possible. They certainly provide the ability to view 'body language'.

The way in which humans co-operate on tasks means that consideration is needed when breaking down complex tasks to be undertaken by several people. There are plenty of examples of one person doing a task and the next person checking the work to see that it has been done correctly. But checking procedures cannot be used for parallel working. Furthermore, the morale of a team can impact on the efficiency of the way it works. This means that defence systems engineers must consider both how tasks are split and any need for team training during system design.

Inside a large aircraft there may be opportunities for face-to-face discussion, but most communication will be over the intercom with significant background noise from the engines and airframe. Long flight times affect the physical comfort of the crew and their ability to

Figure 40. Protective clothing and breathing apparatus worn when fire-fighting on a warship can make interteam communication difficult. (Photo courtesy BAe Systems.)

concentrate for lengthy periods. Similar problems occur in ships and fighting vehicles where teamwork is crucial. Fire-fighting on board ship is an example where the need to wear specialist equipment can hamper communication in a dangerous and smoke-filled environment.

4.8 Safety

The Defence Ordnance Safety Group is the MoD's focal point for ordnance, munitions and explosives and is responsible for ensuring that they are 'safe' to use. The Health and Safety Executive (HSE) is the UK body tasked with proposing human safety legislation and ensuring its implementation. It publishes a number of useful leaflets available as Internet downloads. Relevant topics include: confined spaces, display screen equipment, diving, engineering, lifting operations, personal-protective equipment, regulations, repetitive strain injury (RSI) and visual display units. Laws protect the health and safety of all individuals at work, including military personnel in peacetime. It is thus essential that all systems are designed to enable operators to use them within this legislation's requirements. Crown immunity is generally not applicable, but the MoD is not always under the usual employer's duty to maintain a safe system of work where service personnel are engaged with an enemy in the course of combat. Nor do members of the armed forces in combat owe each other a formal duty of legal care.

4.9 Standards

If consideration of human factors is to influence design appropriately it must be considered early in the design phase. UK defence standard Def Stan 00-25 provides a single guidance document on human factors issues. It is a sourcebook of data and guidance for defence equipment designers and covers the various different aspects of human factors. ISO 9241 is the international standard dealing with the human/computer interface and usability. MIL-STD-1472D/E/F covering human engineering design criteria for military systems, equipment and facilities is probably the most important of the many US military standards dealing with human factors. The US Army's MANPRINT program is targeted at human factors on the battlefield. It is an umbrella concept dealing with the integration of human factors, engineering, personnel, training, health hazards assessment and system safety. MANPRINT focuses on total system planning. It investigates system design and associated support so that systems can be operated and maintained in a cost effective and safe manner consistent with human resources, structure, personal aptitude and skill, and training-resource constraints. The methodology emphasises the need for front-end planning. There are also several NATO standards applying only to human factors in aircraft.

4.10 Task analysis

Task analysis is any step-by-step assessment of what a user does and why. It employs this information to help design a new system or analyse an existing one. The term 'task analysis' refers to a methodology that can be carried out by many specific techniques to describe or evaluate the interactions between humans and a system or a particular piece of equipment. It can be used to make step-by-step comparison of the capabilities and limitations of an operator with the requirements of a system. The resulting information is useful for designing not only equipment, but also operational procedures and training.

Ideally, task analysis should be employed when designing a system. By including it early on in the process, the user's capabilities and limitations can be incorporated into the design of the equipment, procedures and training. However, like the overall design process, task analysis is an iterative process. After the results of the analysis are incorporated into the system design, the task analysis must be performed again to ensure that the changes do not produce unforeseen consequences. In addition to providing useful information to incorporate into the design of the system, task analysis data can be used to develop and improve personnel and training requirements. A good ergonomics approach will improve comfort, productivity and quality, as well as health and safety.

Evaluation and design of a system using task analysis more effectively integrates the human element into the system design and operations. System design must consider the human as a component of the system to ensure efficient and safe operation. The entire system must be regarded as comprising the following components: the human operator, the equipment, both hardware and software, and the operating environment. The defence environment inherently places many restrictions on the system design, which makes it even more important to consider these three components as a whole at the design stage to devise an effective system. This systematic analysis of the user tasks can result in equipment that is safer to use, easier to maintain and simpler to operate using effective procedures.

4.11 Conclusions

Human factors impact on every aspect of design and need consideration throughout a system's complete life cycle. Training can help users to improve their performance and, at the same time, save customers significant sums of money involved in operating complex systems. The operator's or supporter's varying workload must be considered while trying to make the environment in which they have to work as pleasant and safe as possible. Finally, it is important to use published human-factors data and guidelines, and to ensure that whatever has to be designed is user friendly and meets current and predicted safety legislation.

5 Affordability and achieving best value for money

How is it possible for the MoD to optimise the achievement of best value for money during the selection of affordable capability solutions? As well as considering the issues surrounding affordability and what it means, this requires examination of the various sources of value for the MoD. These include who gets value and the significance of the various different military roles, the impact of political acquisition decisions, how value changes with time, any value in getting more than has been requested, capability requirements and the impact of budget setting on value, the effects of short-termism and finally dealing with individual bias.

5.1 Affordability

Affordability is defined as either having enough money, time etc. to spend on something or being able to do something, or allowing it to happen, without risk. The classic meaning of affordability is having or having access to enough money to spend on something. As budgets derived from the equipment plans and short-term plans are now set in resource terms (as well as cash), it follows that project affordability must also be established in cash and resource terms. There are two clear elements to affordability: procurement affordability and through-life affordability. Procurement affordability demonstrates whether the resources needed to obtain an asset or service can be contained within existing control totals. Through-life affordability is an assessment of the longer-term consequences of owning, operating, supporting and disposing of an asset. This will involve the generation and comparison of cost of ownership statements showing the resources consumed or planned for each year of a project's life; it may prove extremely difficult to cover the whole project life, which may exceed half a century and may incur unquantifiably high disposal costs. Furthermore, since the cost of any major project is subject to uncertainty, cost overruns (and underspends) can alter affordability of a project during its life cycle, as can changes to the MoD's equipment budget for other reasons.

Then there is the other definition of affordability: enough time? This may be related to delivery time, but it is more apposite to relate it to management personnel time. So, it might be argued: 'Can we afford the time to go collaborative on this programme, knowing that it will require a major investment of time by senior managers (and ministers) as well as delaying the in-service date?'

There is another issue surrounding time: affordability is time related. The statement 'We can't afford it now, but we can next year' is not uncommon. Acquisition budgets (and

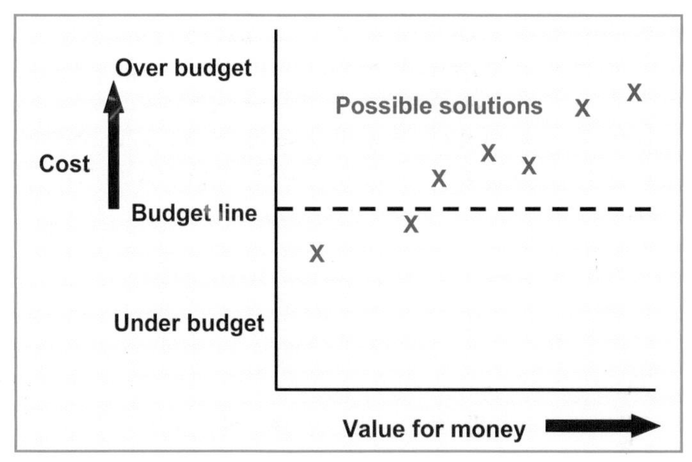

Figure 41. Many possible solutions are likely at different prices offering different value for money.

capability statements) are regularly juggled to ensure that all the required equipment can be afforded. The result of this is likely to set ceiling prices on individual projects, which may or may not represent best value for money. Perhaps worse, they may result in 'quick fix' solutions that certainly do not represent best value for money through life! In addition, trade-offs between project budgets at annual budget reviews may reduce the resources available for some projects.

Providing a satisfactory case can be made based on value for money, the MoD could justify acquiring anything it needs; its problem is that it cannot afford everything. Rather than seeking best value for money, normally the most appropriate value for money should be sought. Affordability issues need to be rigorously distinguished from value for money issues. Indeed where different options for investment are being compared, the scheme which shows better value for money can be less affordable than the alternative. Figure 41 shows that the best value for money solution is well above the budget line.

With the alignment of the IAB scrutiny and approvals processes with resource accounting and budgeting (RAB), affordability is presented in business cases, separately identifying cash and resource implications. The two distinct elements to an affordability assessment are:

1. Demonstration that the resources needed to acquire the asset/service can be contained within existing (and anticipated) resource control totals.
2. Assessment of the longer-term financial consequences of owning, operating and supporting the new equipment once it enters service.

As budgets are set in resource terms, project affordability is established in resource terms, and business cases include the expected cost against the likely annual budgetary provision for the project's life. An assessment of through-life affordability involves comparing cost of ownership statements, including savings from equipment or infrastructure being replaced.

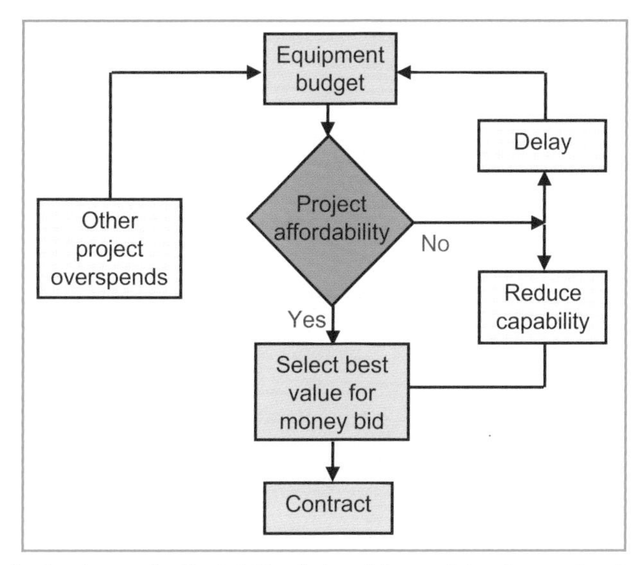

Figure 42. How budgeting and affordability fit in with acquiring best value for money solutions.

Business cases submitted to the IAB must show, amongst other things:

1. How, given the alternative ways of meeting the requirement and the scope for trade-offs, the optimised military capability or business benefits can be delivered in a way that offers best value for money through-life.
2. How the investment will be afforded within existing and foreseeable future budget provision, taking account of the cost of ownership.

5.2 Value for money

Obtaining best value for money is the aim of all MoD acquisitions and many issues need consideration during bid evaluation. The IPT's mission in selecting the contractor is also important. Furthermore, industry has to make a major effort to ensure its offerings represent best value for money. A wide range of political, cultural and legal factors come into play and overall any negative bias must be avoided.

Value can be defined as 'the degree of usefulness or desirability'. However, value as worth in monetary terms is in such common usage that care has been taken to avoid this definition. Thus what the MoD appears to be seeking is the 'degree of usefulness for a given amount of money'. It is also important to recognise that the value of equipment and services lies in the eye of the beholder, in this case the IPT evaluating a bid.

Defence Acquisition (MoD 2001) defines value for money as: *In all areas of acquisition the MoD seeks to achieve best value for money. This does not mean that it simply acquires the cheapest available item or accepts the lowest bid in a competition. Best value for money denotes the solution that meets the requirement at the lowest through-life cost.* However, it is not possible to estimate with any real degree of accuracy the through-life

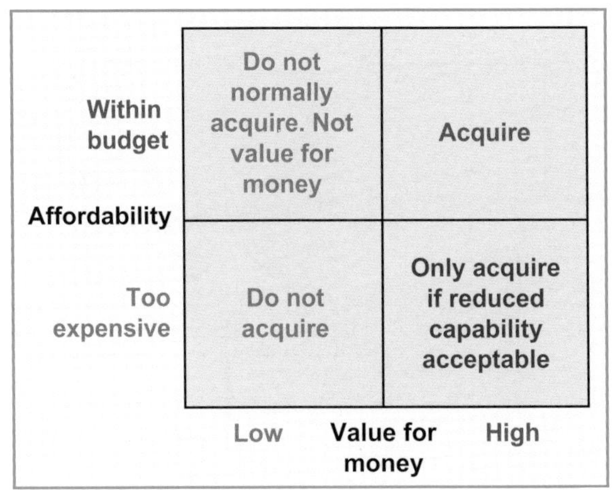

Figure 43. A diagram that shows the interrelationship between affordability, value for money and making an acquisition decision.

costs for a major item of equipment with a life of several decades at the time an acquisition decision is made. Furthermore, the definition is unsatisfactory because it excludes any solution that is marginally non-compliant with the requirement, even though it may be significantly cheaper.

The Minister for Defence Procurement has said *Best value is more than just the lowest price, best value includes what will bring the best service at the price we can afford for the British armed services.* The Chief of Defence Procurement has stated that in many cases the whole concept of value for money is itself a value judgment, so it is possible to draw different conclusions from the same set of data depending upon people's position and aims.

Awarding contracts on the basis of open competitive tendering remains the MoD's preferred approach and obtaining the greatest advantage from competitive leverage, at prime and sub-contract level, remains a major tool in defence acquisition. The aim, therefore, is to continue to select contractors by competition wherever it provides best value for money.

The NAO suggests that while traditionally the MoD has purchased *the cheapest solution consistent with quality requirements,* in future value for money could embrace *all aspects of capability; worth – balancing affordability, effectiveness and the risk of not taking action across all desired capabilities; and longer term health of the supplier base.*

The Office of Government Commerce provides the following definition of value for money: *the optimum combination of through-life cost and quality (or fitness for purpose) to meet the user's requirement* and continues that this is rarely synonymous with lowest price.

An interesting note from an MoD report states under the heading 'Measuring value for money': *Each main management area has its own system for monitoring and measuring performance. Although from a central MoD perspective these systems meet individual budget holder requirements, they are generally not mutually compatible or presented in a format that allows value for money to be assessed across the Department. The study is therefore unable to conclude that the current provision gives best value; indeed, there is every indication that it does not.*

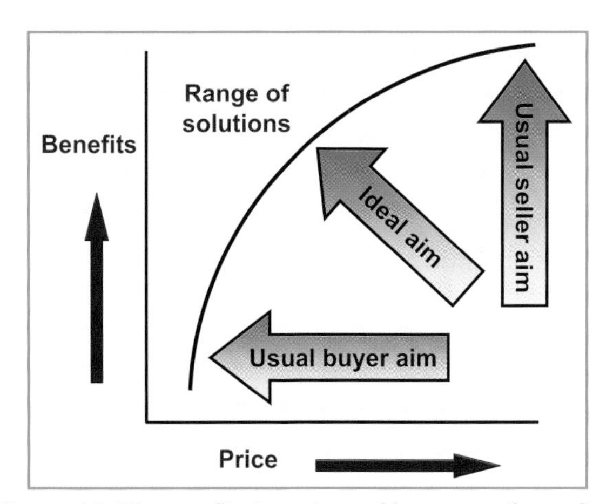

Figure 44. The conflicting aims of buyers and suppliers.

Despite the DPA and the DLO aiming to obtain best value for money, and suppliers trying to offer best value for money, it is apparent that buyers have the habit of trying to negotiate the price of any offering down, while suppliers attempt to offer better value without reducing their price. These different aims are shown in Figure 44 that demonstrates the classic non-linear connection between value and money. In an ideal world, both parties should be trying to increase value for money.

5.3 Sources of value for the MoD

It should be apparent to any defence systems engineer that money has to be considered as an engineering constraint. The MoD's Smart Acquisition policies endorse the importance of achieving best value for money in all acquisitions. The MoD has stated the factors that its staff consider in bid evaluation. The factors divide into six main groups that are listed in Figure 45 overleaf. It is noteworthy that at the time the MoD paper cited in the figure was written, the term 'more effectively integrated' had not been added to 'performance, cost and time!' Clearly the inclusion of integration factors when measuring value is necessary.

The various sources of value can be divided into those for which there is objective evidence and those for which subjective evidence must be used. Furthermore, the factors any MoD evaluation team chooses to employ when measuring value during tender assessment will be unique to that particular evaluation; the same factors cannot be applied to all bids, not least because the capability required will differ. In addition, the values of the equipment capability customer (ECC), the DPA and the DLO naturally vary. The ECC is primarily interested in obtaining the required capability for the minimum expenditure. The DPA is concerned with minimising the risks involved in contracting to obtain the ECC's required capability. The DLO worries about ease of support and through-life costs. Commercial staff will look after the contract terms and conditions and, with major systems' acquisition, soft issues should also be considered. Nominated 'scrutineers' are responsible for reviewing business cases and advising any changes that would be needed to take account of their views. If the advice

1. Estimates of operational effectiveness.
2. Estimated delivery timescale: in-service date; initial military capability followed by full operational capability.
3. Estimates of through-life costs.
4. The evaluation of risk including soft issues; economic and financial standing, technical capability and management ability of suppliers.
5. Commercial terms and conditions.
6. Wider factors taken into account include:
   - The ability to compete future requirements and security of supply.
   - The risk of losing any of the very small number of capabilities that for national security reasons should be retained within the UK industrial base or any implications for foreign and security policy interests.
   - Certain key technologies for future defence capabilities.
   - Future export potential.
   - Industrial capabilities needed in the UK industrial base for defence reasons or the high value they bring to the economy or for the impact on regional activity (including UK jobs created/sustained).
   - Factors that raise legal issues with UK or international law or are affected by the MoD's environmental, security, personnel or estates policies.
   - Transferability into wider commercial applications outside defence.

Figure 45. The factors to be considered by IPTs during bid evaluation.

cannot be incorporated, they may prepare an independent review for submission with the case. Clearly the solution should provide optimum value for money for the MoD not just the IPT.

Wider industrial issues tend to get resolved at the MoD political level. Within the Defence Council, the politicians are likely to have significantly different views of value for money from civil servants and armed forces members. The Cabinet and the Treasury may appear to

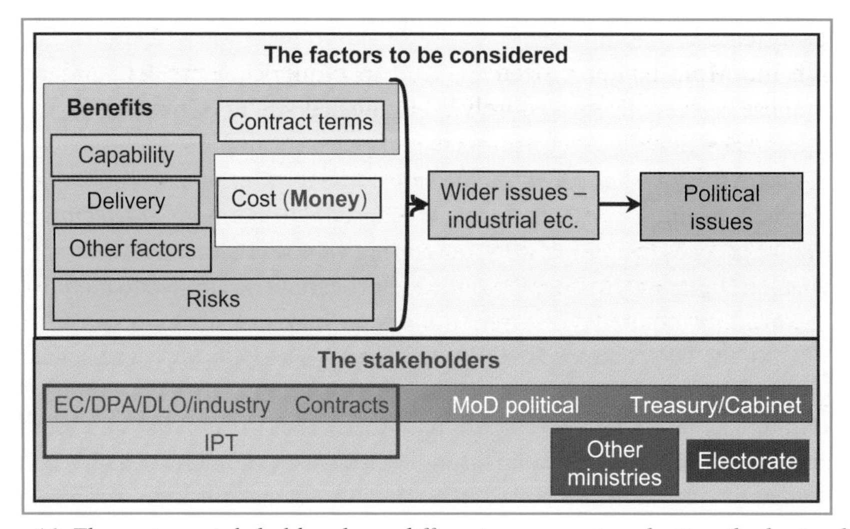

Figure 46. The various stakeholders have different concerns in selecting the best value for money solution.

'interfere', either to improve value for money from their perspective, or on occasions, to reduce the MoD's value for money in order to meet political imperatives such as unemployment. By way of contrast, an IPT inevitably is solely motivated to provide the best value for money capability for the MoD.

There are sometimes short-term financial issues, where a better solution with lower through-life costs is rejected in favour of an alternative that has a lower initial cost despite higher running costs. This is generally budget driven; if there is not enough money in the budget to cover the more expensive initial cost, despite a lower through-life cost, the solution may well be ruled unaffordable.

5.3.1 Group considerations

The budgeting process in the MoD largely defines which EC branch bears the cost of any new acquisition, though the cost may be divided somewhat arbitrarily in the case of tri-service procurements. The value, however, may or may not accrue to the department that carries the cost. A classic example from the Second World War was the procurement of petrol cans for the British army. These were cheap and prone to leak badly, but it was not the supply branch of the army that suffered. It was the teeth arms that often faced chronic fuel shortages. The capture and use by the teeth arms of the vastly superior German jerrycan led to a specification change and a better-value can for the users.

Seamen, soldiers and aircrew all consider that the views of their particular service are paramount and that the views of other service personnel are of lower importance. Thus, individual service priorities impact on each service's view of the value of the other two services' and tri-service procurements. IPTs have a wide range of members divided into core and associate members but also, on occasion, with some attached members. The influence of members depends on which of the armed forces or civilian branches they belong to and also their primary role; attached members normally being functionally oriented.

Although the MoD tender procedures aim to minimise subjective judgements by individuals, these biases can never entirely be eliminated. Members of the IPTs, assessment teams and the IAB will all have personal views, based on their role, personal background and experience, as well as their personality and individual mood at the time decisions are made. However, the the provision of appropriate training, for staff working in IPTs, on the acquisition management system (AMS) processes should help to reduce individual characteristics.

Getting best value for money sometimes involves procuring equipment from overseas. Such action with, for example a US supplier, will erode the UK or European defence industrial bases. It is important to maintain UK industry's ability to support military operations and regenerate critical equipment stocks in crisis and war. The impact should also be assessed on the UK's ability to continue to influence future collaborative programmes and provide significant medium/long-term industrial contributions.

Exports of equipment, developed for the MoD, provide benefit by lengthening production runs and subsequent equipment support timescales. They also provide value to the nation in the form of royalty payments, improvement to the balance of trade and increased employment.

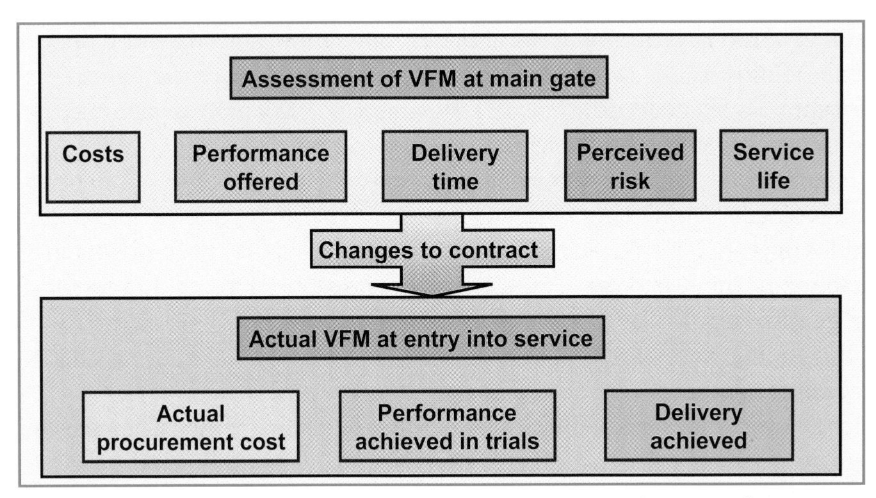

Figure 47. Factors affecting value for money (VFM) change with time.

The MoD *Contracts Manual* states: *The primary object in assessing competitive tenders is to get best value for money and normally the lowest satisfactory tender should be accepted. However, in deciding which tender will give the best value for money not only price but also delivery, performance, quality, life of the equipment, spares requirements, after-sales servicing and perhaps other relevant matters will need to be taken into account in consultation, where appropriate.*

It is important to realise that value for money will change throughout the life of an equipment. Figure 47 shows that the value perceived at the time a contract is placed with a supplier is likely to have altered significantly by the time the equipment enters service. Value is then likely to reduce throughout the service life of the equipment up to the point of disposal, when a final assessment could be made of the value for money achieved, in the unlikely event that all the data were available.

It is well understood that it is the last few percentage points in any capability that can make a compliant solution inordinately expensive (see Figure 48). Paradoxically, however,

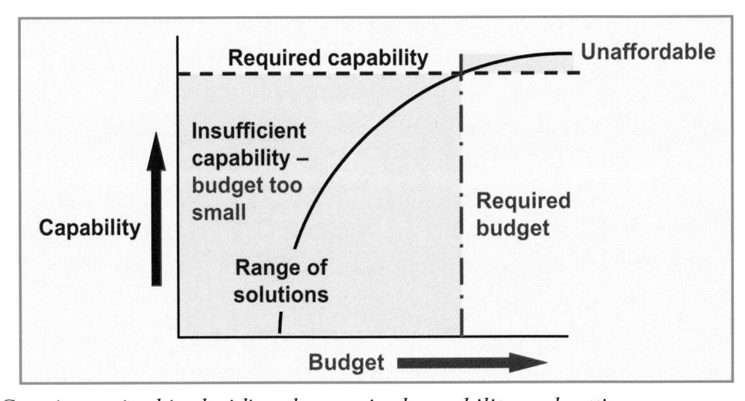

Figure 48. Care is required in deciding the required capability and setting an appropriate budget.

those last few points may also give a decisive military advantage, albeit at a price that may be viewed as unaffordable. It is therefore important for those working in EC to discuss with potential suppliers how far the various aspects of a capability statement may be pushed before the resulting technical solution becomes too expensive.

It is equally clear that too small a budget may result in a very inferior solution or an inadequately sized force. Thus budgets must be established with care to ensure that they are sufficient for the capability required. This again requires discourse with potential suppliers while, at the same time, generating independent cost estimates to make sure that suppliers are not suggesting too low a price just to get themselves into a favourable position on the bidder's list. Neither the demands for too great a performance nor the allocation of too small a project budget appears to result in equipment that offers best value for money.

The rapid change in technology affects the MoD's perception of the value of many defence equipment acquisitions. What was the latest technology yesterday is already obsolescent today and obsolete tomorrow! Nowhere is this more apparent than in information technology (IT). In contractor source selection, there should be an initial assessment of value for money. When delivered, the new equipment, assuming it meets the required capability, has a certain value. As the equipment ages, its value reduces as new and better equipment, and countermeasures, become available. Some aspects of performance may also reduce until disposal, and worsening reliability allied to increased problems with maintenance are also likely throughout any equipment's life.

The MoD acquisition stakeholder good practice model (Figure 49) shows only six groups of stakeholders. However, the AMS provides the following list of the stakeholders during the CADMID cycle in its set of stakeholder function diagrams.

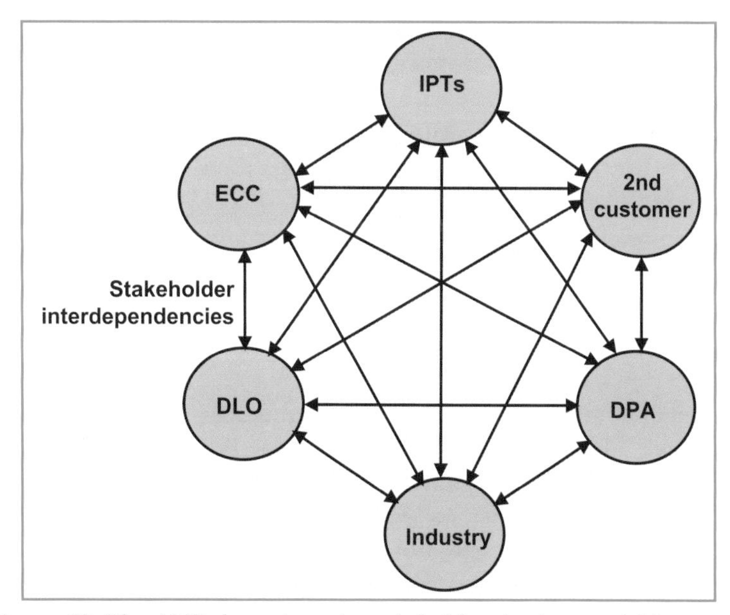

Figure 49. The AMS shows just six stakeholders in the acquisition process!

- Equipment capability customer (ECC)
- Customer 2: Front-line commands (FLC)
- Scientific intelligence
- Director Force Development
- Chief Scientific Adviser Technical Scrutiny
- Head of Defence Export Services

- DPA
- DLO
- Dstl
- IPT
- Industry

Surprisingly, the IAB and the MoD management, other ministries (Treasury, DTI, FCO) the Cabinet and Parliament have not been included in either list. Major procurements by the MoD often involve political debate and scrutiny. Undoubtedly, the Secretary of State for Defence will vigorously defend the MoD's choice of supplier, but may on occasions be overridden for one of a number of political reasons, such as:

1. Not placing the contract with an overseas supplier to protect UK jobs.
2. Not placing the contract with an overseas supplier because its government's policy is running counter to that of the UK government.
3. Awarding the contract overseas as part of a larger supply deal requiring offset in a technical area.

Overriding the MoD recommendation may offer benefit to the government of the day, but not necessarily to the MoD and its various stakeholders, nor to the MoD recommended supplier or the British taxpayer. Such action cannot be considered unreasonable, as the following two quotations from Cranfield and London universities indicate.

1. *However, no state makes defence acquisition decisions without regard to the wider economic and political consequences.*
2. *Defence projects are procured with public funds and, as such, are constrained by the necessity of public accountability and by political considerations. Defence projects have many interested stakeholder organisations (armed forces, contractors, allies, taxpayers etc.) all of which have an interest in the project. Stakeholders may have divergent views on what constitutes success and how it should be achieved i.e. the armed forces seek capable equipment, contractors look for profits, allies expect complementary capabilities and taxpayers require responsible spending of public money.* It could be added that governments seek re-election.

It is thus clear that obtaining best value for money in defence systems acquisition is not a straightforward task. Numerous diverse sources of value and many different types of consideration have to be weighed against each other by groups of people driven by very different motivations. Even when the 'fastest, cheapest, best and most effectively integrated' solution has been selected by the MoD, the resulting choice may still be overridden by political considerations, usually to protect British jobs, and end up giving worse value for money than the originally chosen bidder.

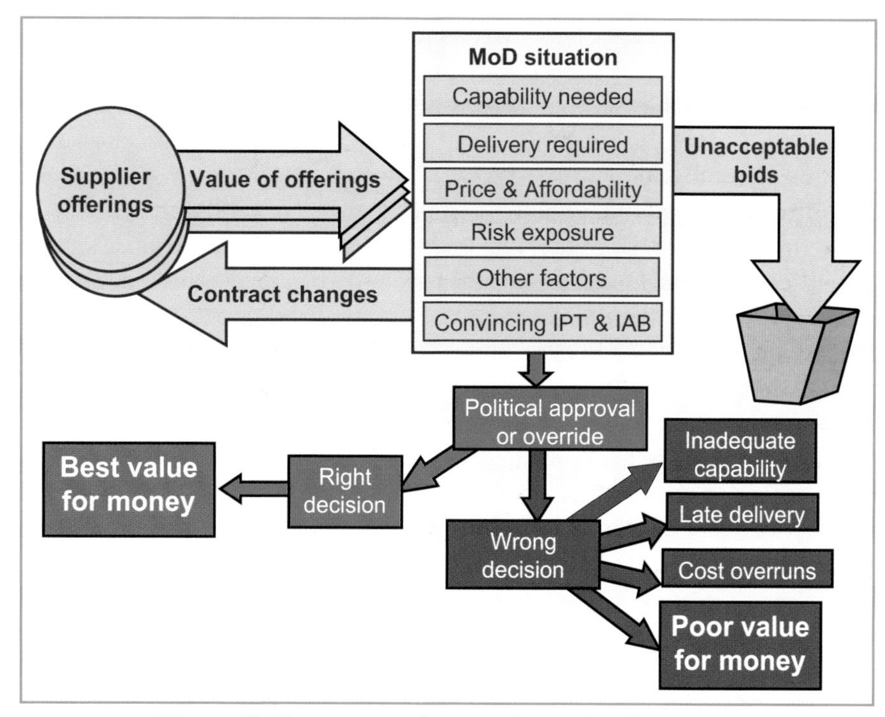

Figure 50 The process of getting best value for money.

6 Off-the-shelf equipment

Off-the-shelf is the term applied to anything that has already been developed, is readily available and is purchased without any modification. Commercial off-the-shelf (COTS) is the term given to systems or equipment available from commercial sources. The MoD considers it inconceivable that it will acquire any major systems without some COTS parts. It is important here to distinguish equipment that has been developed for an overseas government's military (or other government) forces and is now available commercially. This is categorised as military (or government) off-the-shelf (MOTS or GOTS). From this point, MOTS is used to refer to both GOTS and MOTS.

6.1 COTS and MOTS

COTS solutions can range from staff cars to items of furniture, from computers to hospital equipment; all have the advantage of low prices due to volume production. In most cases, the fact that they have been designed for commercial purposes is not a disadvantage, as their use in a military environment will not differ significantly from their original civilian application. However, they are unlikely to be suitable for deployment in the field, as their capability in environmental terms is likely to be limited; boots are a good example where the temperature found in desert operations is likely to exceed OTS specifications.

A distinction needs to be made between complete COTS solutions and systems with embedded COTS equipment. The former offers significant cost and risk reductions, but the latter may need considerable development work that will require ongoing effort to deal with obsolescence and to provide technology upgrades. Furthermore, modification of complete COTS systems or embedded COTS to meet a military requirement is often inordinately expensive and makes support and future upgrades particularly difficult.

There are many attractions of MOTS. Technical risks are reduced as development has already been completed and funded, and new purchases can readily be added on to existing production runs. The customer nation pays only a small and retrospective contribution to the fixed costs already incurred by the supplier nation. Inevitably, however, the equipment is not perfectly matched to the requirements of the customer, so MOTS equipment often has to be modified to suit the particular scenarios that are important to the customer nation, and to be compatible with its existing range of legacy equipment. MOTS equipment sometimes requires additional test and evaluation to satisfy the customer's safety clearance regulations. It follows that the expenditure incurred by the customer in a MOTS procurement is in general rather greater than the price quoted by a foreign supplier.

After the MOTS equipment has entered service its logistic support is generally more expensive than for a national project. In some cases, all major repairs and maintenance are done at the supplier's overseas factory, in which case the customer nation incurs higher costs of transport and liaison. In other cases, a sub-contractor within the customer nation is equipped with the necessary tooling, test equipment, stocks of spares and intellectual property required to undertake logistic support. Furthermore the customer nation may incur involuntarily the cost of upgrades agreed between the supplier and its principal customer, and may have to withdraw the equipment from service prematurely when the supplier decides that it can no longer economically be supported. Additionally, in time of war, the supplier nation may embargo support for the equipment. These added costs and risks must all be considered when assessing MOTS procurements against other alternatives.

In some cases the customer nation successfully negotiates 'offsets' whereby its national industry undertakes sub-contract work for the equipment supplier, either on the equipment procured (though this may increase its cost) or on related products. These offset arrangements help to improve the customer nation's balance of trade and to sustain its industrial base, though not always in the same sector. Negotiations on offsets as part of a MOTS procurement usually involve government departments concerned with industrial and/or regional policy.

Any decision to go the OTS route is needed early in the acquisition process as much of the CADMID cycle is foreshortened. At the concept stage, key issues include the management of obsolescence, long-term support and interoperability. Safety, security, reliability and environmental requirements should also be considered at this stage. Moving to the assessment stage, potential suppliers may propose very different OTS solutions with different features and capabilities that will need careful trade-offs by the IPT. The acceptance authorities' involvement in this should be early and continuous. Consideration must be given to open, expandable OTS-based systems that will keep pace with technology and offer an economic and low-risk path to essential capability upgrades. Through-life cost estimating for some COTS solutions, such as vehicles, benefits from existing experience. For other items such as IT, experience is often unreliable, resulting in uncertain predictions.

6.2 Problems to be addressed

Being tied to a monopolistic supplier may be a consequence of choosing a COTS solution (or a bespoke one) and steps must be taken to mitigate its impact. In addition, liaison with other IPTs is important where the same COTS sub-system is a part of more than one project. Finally, further consideration is needed of critical through-life support issues. The essential topics involved in employing most COTS and MOTS solutions are as follows:

6.2.1 Obsolescence

Advances in COTS technology are market driven and are rapidly incorporated into products. As a result, COTS products tend to become obsolete rapidly, being superseded by an improved version or disappearing from the market. In addition, MOTS equipment is already in service with the supplier nation and is likely to be nearer obsolescence than a bespoke solution.

6.2.2 Requirement trade-offs

COTS solutions are designed for the commercial market and are unlikely to match perfectly a particular military need. The same is often true for MOTS equipment that has been produced to meet the supplier nation's military specification; it may require changes to meet the UK's needs. Requirement relaxation will be needed throughout the acquisition process if the benefits of using OTS solutions are to be achieved without risky and expensive modifications.

6.2.3 Open standards

COTS solutions generally employ open or de facto standards. These may cause problems with interoperability and continued support of both the equipment and the standards.

6.2.4 Lack of product control

Commercial factors drive the support and life cycle of COTS equipment. The military market usually represents a very low proportion of the total sales of any COTS equipment (less than 1% for COTS IT). Thus the MoD has little influence if it requires any changes to be made, or in the case of COTS IT, to get bugs fixed. Where MOTS equipment is already in service with the supplier nation, the MoD may experience problems influencing future improvements.

6.2.5 Changing contractor relationships

Where COTS-based sub-systems are integrated into defence equipment, there is a demand for a long-term contractor relationship. The MoD contractor may have difficulty obtaining such support from a commercially oriented supplier.

6.2.6 System flexibility

COTS-based systems often offer the opportunity to incorporate state-of-the-art upgrades and thus respond to changing threats and operational scenarios. Such flexibility requires great care in managing such upgrades.

6.2.7 Interfaces

Even when procuring a complete OTS solution, there will normally be a need to interface to legacy equipment and existing support systems. The development of suitable interfaces is usually expensive and delays the in-service date.

6.3 COTS IT

Of particular interest and relevance is COTS IT, the area in which much of the MoD COTS expenditure lies. The motivation for a move away from increasingly expensive bespoke IT came in the 1990s from the industrialised nations' policies to reduce their defence budgets following the end of the Cold War. US Defense Secretary William Perry's 1994 policy statement 'Specifications and Standards – A New Way of Doing Business' paved the way for acquisition reform by requiring COTS IT to be used whenever possible and the MoD has applied a similar policy. COTS IT is widely employed by the MoD for 'business applications', and a common operating environment has been specified for operational use. However, COTS IT use in safety critical systems still leaves many unanswered questions.

The initial motivation for the move to COTS IT was to save money and there is little doubt that the initial purchase price should be lower. However, the eventual outcome is still unknown on the question of through-life costs. It is arguable that using COTS IT is the only way to obtain the best performance and that in any case the military has no choice.

COTS IT is all-pervasive in military equipment and can be used in a number of main areas; these include business applications and logistics management, C^3I (command, control, communications and intelligence) systems and sub-systems, embedded in platforms and weapons, and for training and simulation. However, it is a mistake to think of all COTS IT as similar. Many applications impose demands on both the hardware and software in ways that are not dissimilar to those found in a military environment. This is illustrated in Figure 51.

A number of key factors affect the use of COTS IT in operational military equipment. The first is the very rapid rate of change within the IT industry; an industry mostly located outside UK. Others include:

- Industry is investing heavily in existing and new areas.
- Hardware and software are already developed.
- There are regular improvements and updates to both.
- Low costs are the result of the high-volume commercial market.
- Delivery times are short.
- Hardware and software are familiar to users reducing training needs.
- Equivalents made to defence or military specifications are not available.

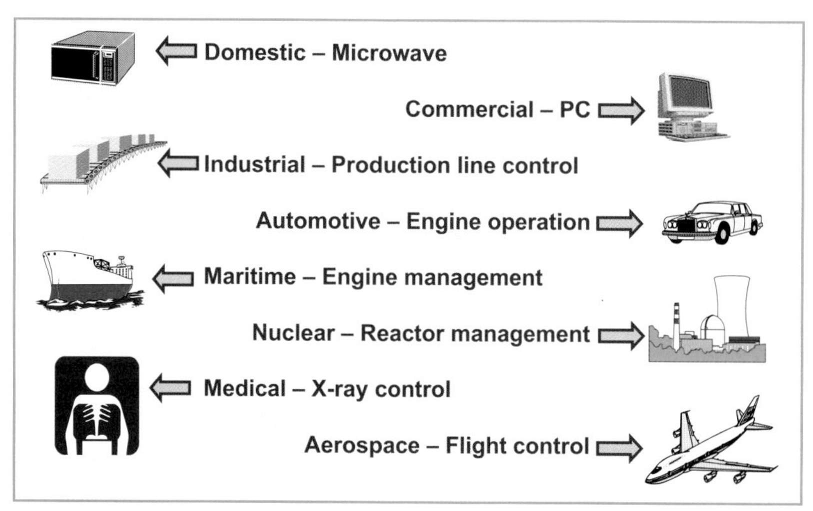

Figure 51. The suitability of COTS IT for a specific military application often depends on the original application for which the COTS IT was designed.

Despite these advantages, the employment of COTS IT in operational defence equipment has some serious snags. Of course it is not customised to meet MoD requirements, and any modifications are likely to prove expensive and negate many of the initial benefits of using a COTS solution. Interfacing COTS IT to legacy equipment can cause significant difficulties and hardware and software upgrades are often far from straightforward. COTS IT solutions become rapidly obsolescent, in as little as 12 to 18 months, followed by the rapid withdrawal of any original equipment manufacturer's support. Any COTS IT used will also be available to potential enemies, which will give them an insight while developing countermeasures. COTS IT also has the significant disadvantage that it is insecure and care must be taken with networking and the use of firewalls.

However, there is no alternative to COTS IT. Military and defence specification equivalents are no longer available and no government could afford to match the investment currently made by the commercial IT industry, either in hardware or software. The present way forward is to wrap both hardware and software. Hardware wrapping involves fitting standard circuit boards in protective housings that shield the hardware from the external environment, both physical and electrical. Software can also be wrapped, for example by placing a bespoke security system around an application. The major problem is that each time the application is upgraded, the wrapper will also have to be modified.

Because of the rapid obsolescence of COTS IT, military systems must be designed to allow the insertion of new technology. This starts during the design and manufacture stage, when the final choice of hardware and software must be left as late as possible in the cycle to avoid premature obsolescence. With a fast-moving field driven by commercial developments, COTS IT offers a potential cutting edge in conflict, but its life cycle is completely out of step with military platforms, in which it is extensively employed, requiring the latter's design to be adaptable.

6.4 Conclusions

While using OTS solutions offers many benefits, not the least in the initial purchase price, great care must be taken by system designers to ensure that any shortcomings are overcome by careful planning during the early stages of any project and feedback during in-service stages.

7 Integrated logistic support

It is a challenging task to provide support requirements for the wide range of complex defence systems but careful thought during the design process can simplify their support requirements. Both replenishment and technical support are needed for the very different systems deployed at sea, on the ground and in the air to ensure that they achieve satisfactory availability over their entire life cycle, both during peacetime and wartime.

To achieve satisfactory cost effectiveness, a new defence system must be designed both to be effective in envisaged combat operations and to be economical to operate and support. It is therefore necessary to consider during the design process a proposed system's likely use of consumables such as fuel and ammunition in training (which will depend on the type of system, how it is used and where it is deployed) and its likely demand for skilled labour, tools, test equipment and spare parts to undertake planned maintenance or unexpected repairs. Economy in support is achieved by designing any new defence system to include appropriate levels of reliability and maintainability and by planning for suitable levels of logistic support.

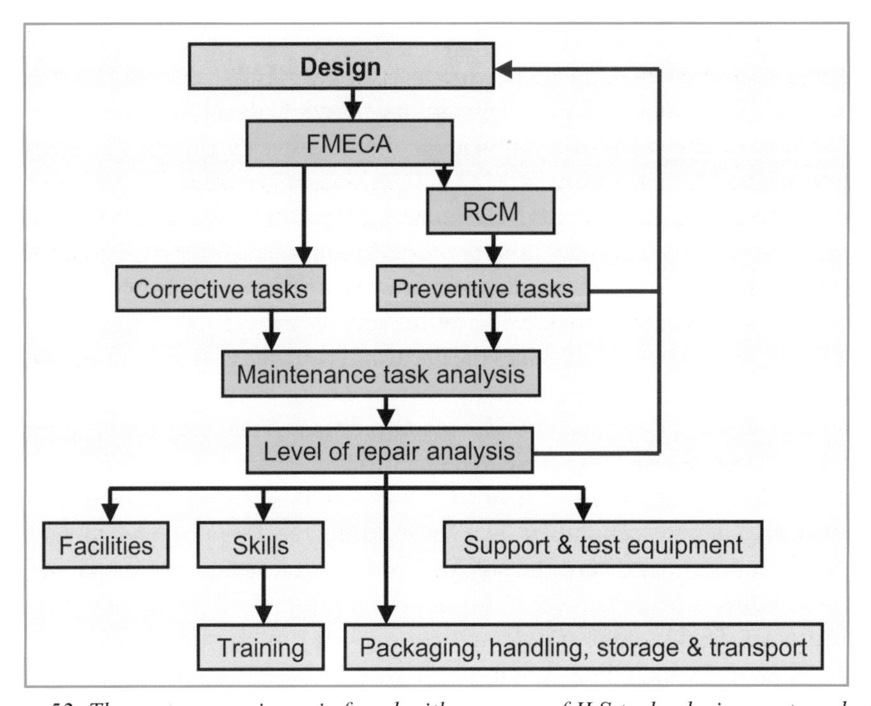

Figure 52. The systems engineer is faced with a range of ILS tasks during system design.

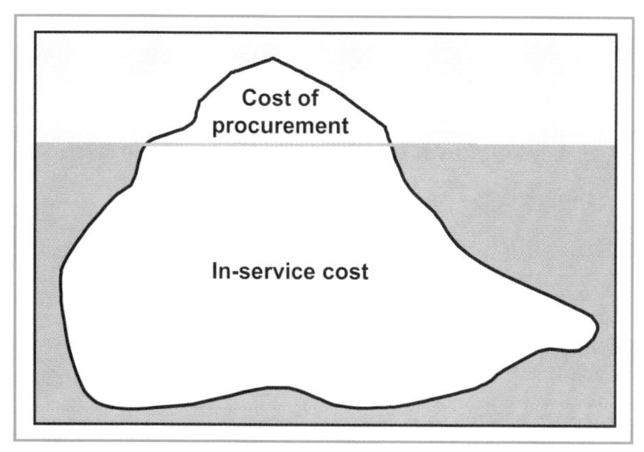

Figure 53. For many projects, the initial procurement cost is a fraction of the through-life costs.

ILS is a structured and interactive process of selecting and providing the optimal combination of reliability, maintainability, personnel, logistics and other support elements to ensure that a new system satisfies its operational requirements at the minimum through-life cost. ILS involves both the MoD and industry, and its principal aims are to:

- Analyse the through-life requirements for support.
- Formulate plans to supply sufficient resources.
- Influence the system design.
- Deliver support resources economically when required.

ILS is a challenging task because many of a new system's in-service costs are not accurately known early in its life cycle and because these costs may overshadow the system's initial procurement cost. It is vital that the support requirements of every project are addressed right from the beginning. It is essential to make early decisions rather than having to change course once equipment manufacture has commenced. Additional finance may be needed during the early stages of the project in order to make savings downstream.

The ILS defence standard (Def Stan 00-60) defines eight elements covering a wide range of topics:

1. Maintenance planning.
2. Supply support.
3. Support and test equipment (S&TE).
4. Reliability and maintainability (R&M).
5. Facilities.
6. Manpower and human factors.
7. Training and training equipment.
8. Technical documentation.

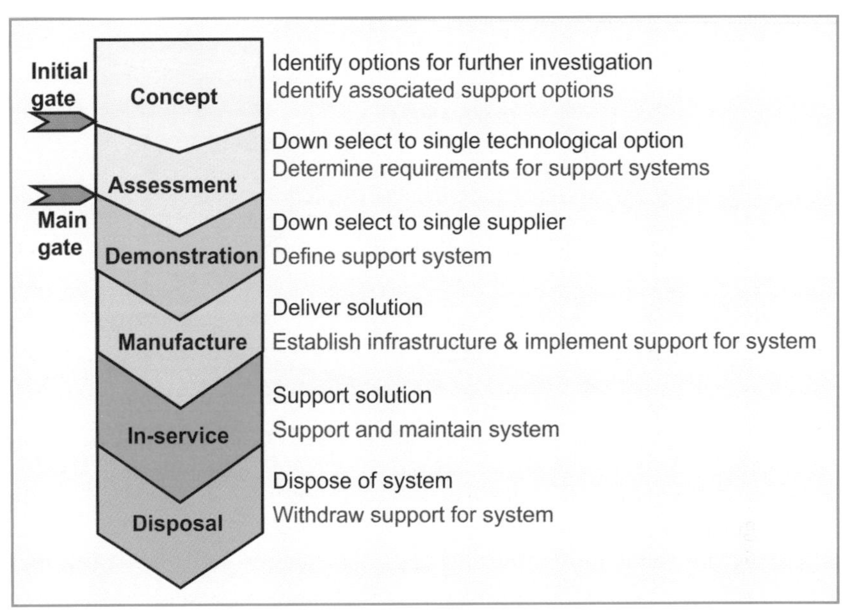

Figure 54. The life cycle phase diagram highlights the importance of making early decisions rather than having to change direction once production has begun.

The applicability of each of these elements will vary from project to project and can be expanded to include: design influences, packaging, handling, storage and transportation, non-operational computer resources, through-life costing and in-service monitoring of logistic performance.

The main ILS tool is logistic support analysis (LSA), which employs a set of standard tasks with defined objectives and outputs. These are intended to influence the design to enhance its supportability, and to identify both the equipment support cost drivers and the resources needed once the design has been completed. Since every project is different, the tasks and requirements are flexible and can be tailored to the project. This helps to prevent inadequate provision on large, complex systems. LSA can result in the generation of information that needs to be readily accessible to both design and support areas, allowing it to be used for many projects, reducing duplication of effort and improving consistency. Information is normally stored in a logistic support analysis record (LSAR) as a spreadsheet or database.

Def Stan 00-60 is an anglicised and expanded version of a former US MIL-STD. It includes emphasis on total ILS, not just LSA, and includes electronic technical documentation using AECMA 1000D, integrated supply support procedures using AECMA 2000M and LSA for software.

7.1 Supply and support

Arrangements for peacetime supply and support of a new defence system must consider both the planned supply of consumables including fuel, ordnance for training and spares and supplies for scheduled maintenance, as well as the unpredicted provision of spares and replacement items following equipment failure or accidents. Supply arrangements must also consider how they could be enhanced in wartime to support the demands of intensive combat operations, particularly for fuel and ordnance. In parallel, the supply arrangements must provide food, water, mail and medical care (with the last need enhanced in wartime by battle casualties) to the personnel associated with the new system. Repair and maintenance work can, in principle, be done by the crew of the system during its mission, in a service mobile workshop or fixed depot, or at the manufacturer's factory. The right policy depends on factors such as the sophistication of the facilities required, the nature of the mission, the duration of the repair/maintenance work and the associated supply chain. The different UK services adopt various policies for diverse types of equipment in their different environments.

Ships are very complex systems, with missions measured in weeks, sometimes months. Their support involves the crew in undertaking nearly all maintenance using carried on-board spares, together with general-purpose and special-to-type test equipment, diagnostic aids and customised repair facilities. Supply of consumable items such as fuel, spares and ammunition is generally by rendezvous with specialist supply ships.

The support of land vehicles is different, since their missions are gauged in days. Vehicles are also complex and their crews can only undertake limited maintenance. Specialist technicians have to be called in to recover and repair vehicles, with problems sometimes fixed on the spot, but often requiring return to a suitable maintenance workshop. The support of ground-based systems depends on their role; if they are required to operate continuously, redundancy will be built in allowing off-line maintenance. Supplies for vehicles and other ground-based systems are provided by the Royal Logistics Corps and include fuel, oil and lubricants, food and ammunition. The Royal Electrical and Mechanical Engineers (REME) provide the workshops and qualified staff to undertake the technical support.

Supporting aircraft, with mission times of only a few hours, is an extremely complicated task involving a wide range of skills. Most work is undertaken at an airfield, although

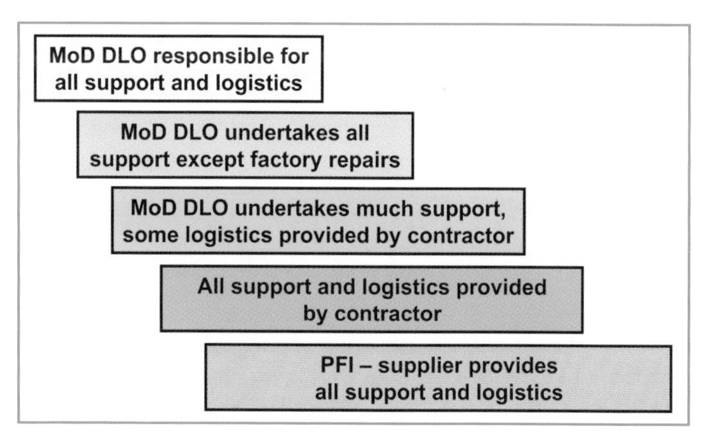

Figure 55. There are several different approaches that can be taken for the provision of support.

limited maintenance may be undertaken at remote dispersed landing grounds used by tactical fixed-wing vertical take-off and landing (VTOL) aircraft and helicopters. Aircrew themselves can do very little beyond help to turn their aircraft around between missions; a task normally left to specialist ground crew. For more serious problems, squadron engineers will carry out repairs mainly by replacement.

Many one-shot devices, such as the TOW anti-tank missile, are sealed in containers and need no support prior to use, although a check after a number of years may be scheduled. Other items, such as bombs, may need little support apart from fuzing by an armourer and fitting to an aircraft. However, all explosives require careful long-term storage.

It should be clear that design of the support arrangements must be related to the design of the system, but often the design of a new system can be compromised by existing support for legacy sub-systems. System design and support-system design must evolve together; changing one without regard for the other will inevitably lead to a sub-optimal solution.

7.2 Through-life costing

Through-life costing (TLC) involves identifying and forecasting the costs not only of development and procurement but also of operations, support and disposal during the life of the equipment. TLC must be considered during supplier selection and the subsequent design phase. Suppliers to the MoD are asked to provide TLC data as part of tender submissions.

7.3 Logistic support analysis

Logistic support analysis (LSA) allows the analysis of items of equipment as they are being developed and the identification of any design features that could result in unnecessary in-service expense. These areas can then be traded-off in design improvements that reduce these cost drivers. The development phase analysis identifies all the logistic resources necessary for equipment support and the impact on the present infrastructure. The purpose of LSA is to identify the repair and maintenance tasks that are likely to be required for the support of a new defence equipment project, and to plan how these tasks might most efficiently be accomplished. The results of the analysis can identify cost drivers in a proposed design and thus stimulate trade-offs, which reduce support costs without unacceptable penalties on the project's performance, timescale or procurement costs. LSA includes several related activities:

- Failure modes effects and criticality analysis (FMECA) to identify potential failures and their consequences.
- Reliability centred maintenance (RCM) to consider alternative policies for inspection and scheduled maintenance.
- Maintenance task analysis (MTA) to identify the resources (personnel, tools, test equipment) required for each task, and its likely duration.

- Level of repair analysis (LORA) to determine if repairs should be undertaken by an operational unit, the supplier or an intermediate depot. This analysis balances the delay and resources required to move equipment rearwards against the cost of underutilised repair resources assigned to operational units, within the constraints of existing policy.

During equipment design, failure analysis should be carried out. The procedure for doing this is defined in Def Stan 00-41 and provides a means of determining:

- The functions the equipment is required to perform.
- How these functions could fail.
- What could cause these failures.
- The impact of these failures on the equipment's performance.
- The criticality of these failures.
- Data for the safety programme.

LSAR is a common database that is used to store and sort LSA data and should be accessible to all areas so that everyone uses the same data to reduce duplication. Def Stan 00-60 specifies a relational database with more than 100 data tables and approaching 600 data elements. Analysis allows the most cost-effective maintenance methods to be assessed where analysis suggests that potential failures may occur. These failures are then analysed to decide whether to employ corrective or preventive maintenance. It is used to determine the most appropriate maintenance level for equipment repair.

There are two types of LORA: economic and non-economic. The former is only used if the cost of repair is the only variable. The latter is applied if there are overriding factors affecting the repair location such as existing policy, accessibility, available skills or equipment size.

7.4 Technical documentation

The technical documentation associated with equipment projects contains all of the information and data needed for operations, servicing, repair, support and disposal. It covers not only the equipment itself but also special tools and test equipment. The documentation may be held as text or drawings on paper, microfiche, in electronic format, video or a combination of these. For modern projects, electronic documentation is prescribed by Def Stan 00-60 Part 10 and is generally the most cost-effective solution.

7.5 Contractor logistic support

Contractor logistic support (CLS) involves an agreement between the MoD operator and a contractor whereby the contractor undertakes repair, maintenance and logistics and is paid a fee related to equipment availability. Such an agreement with the original equipment contractor gives a strong incentive to achieve high availability by judicious design and careful planning, and it relieves the MoD of the need to invest in spares and test equipment. However, CLS requires a seamless interface between the contractor and the service personnel who will provide support in and close to the front line. The transfer of responsibility between these two parties is complex. It often involves questions of where intellectual property rights lie and legal issues where contractor staff are involved in operational situations. There is a need for visibility of equipment maintenance history, and it is important to note that some contractors may lack the experience necessary to provide a satisfactory level of CLS.

7.6 Difficulties in implementation

There are many problems facing defence systems engineers looking at logistic support for new equipment. There is still a dearth of data on current systems, difficulties in providing an accurate forecast of the characteristics of future systems, particularly when they incorporate new technology, and the sheer complexity of planning and providing cost-effective ILS for large systems. These difficulties are often hindered by the resolution of short-term problems by solutions that do not offer long-term value for money.

The amount of equipment usage (and abuse), the environment in which it is operated and the duration of its service life are all uncertain for military systems, making forecasting logistic support needs and their costs particularly difficult. Furthermore, the number of organisations likely to become involved, and their interactions, in the support of complex defence systems requires careful planning. The individuals involved in these organisations will alter every few years due to career changes, promotions, postings, sickness and retirements. Their personal goals may well not correspond exactly with the optimal policy for the project on which they are working, and short-term decisions may not match long-term ILS goals.

8 Operational supportability

8.1 Introduction

To maximise the capability provided by a complex defence system it should be ready for sustained use at any time. A period of time when the system cannot be used reduces the capability to deploy the system, and will increase the through-life costs as a system that cannot be used will need repairs or maintenance to restore its usefulness. Its durability should be such that it will achieve its designed service life using only normal planned in-service support.

Reliability provides an assessment of the number of times that a system fails to provide the operational capability it was acquired to deliver and will therefore require maintenance or repair to restore its operational capability. Maintenance is a measure of the resources (people, spares, time and facilities) required to restore a system to full operational capability. Availability is a function of both reliability and maintenance, and provides a measure of the percentage of total systems that can be used, or percentage of time that a system can be utilised.

Reliability, maintainability and availability (RMA) are emergent properties of a system's design. They can be improved by redesign and modification in the same way that performance can be improved, but the aim of all system designs should be to maximise the reliability and availability, and reduce the maintenance required within the performance, cost and timescale constraints of the system design phase. The customer may specify the RMA requirements, but it is the system design authority that is responsible for achieving the requirements. The customer has little direct influence on the achievement of satisfactory levels of RMA other than providing adequate requirements. Any action to try to influence these parameters during the design and development phase of a system's life cycle may be seen as customer interference.

The system design authority must ensure that the RMA of a system meets the customer requirements. It is also the responsibility of the system design authority to assess and to demonstrate to the customer that these three requirements have been met. Def Stan 00-42 indicates what the system design authority should do to convince the customer that the RMA requirements have been met. There are many good textbooks on RMA, but the MoD defence standards (00-40 to 00-49 series) should not be ignored as they provide an excellent starting point for advice and guidance.

8.2 Reliability, maintainability and availability of defence systems

Reliability, maintainability and availability are important aspects of a complex defence system's life. They provide a means of measuring the frequency and the effects of failures, the level of maintenance required, and the number of systems that are ready for use. The provision of methods to measure RMA means that stakeholders involved in the design, acquisition, operation and support of complex systems can assess the progress of programmes undertaken to improve reliability, decrease support and increase availability. The assessment of RMA does not automatically lead to progress, but other actions such as redesign and improved production processes may lead to improvements.

8.3 Reliability

Reliability is an important characteristic of all complex systems; a system that fails to work in accordance with its specification cannot deliver the required performance characteristics needed by the user. The unreliability of a system is characterised by failures. A failure is any event that prevents the system from fulfilling its performance requirements, and/or requires some unscheduled maintenance.

From an operational command perspective, a system that has failed is similar to a system that has been destroyed by enemy action. It cannot be used and requires additional resources to replace it. It represents a loss of capability. Failures also lower morale, require repairs to be undertaken, consume resources, require dedicated support personnel, and take time to restore the operational capability.

If there were no need for assumptions in the design and manufacturing process, systems could be produced that did not fail. The complexity of most modern defence systems means that there will be many unknowns in a system and the way it operates. These unknowns lead to failures. The designer can calculate the probability distribution of operational loads on a system during its anticipated mission profiles and hence the probabilities that particular loads will be exceeded. If in practice higher loads occur more frequently, the system may fail more often.

Failures are often characterised as systematic and non-systematic. Systematic failures have a cause that can be identified and resolved by redesign or a change in manufacturing, support or operational procedures. Non-systematic failures are thought to be random events for which no cause can be found, or more commonly for which no cause can be found from the investigation. All failures have causes, but some are difficult to establish and the cost of finding the cause of the failure may be exorbitant compared with the cost of the repair which may occur infrequently.

A failure prevents a system from delivering its full performance. Some failures prevent the mission from being completed; these are called mission failures and are used in the assessment of mission reliability. At the other extreme, basic failures are events that require some maintenance, they may or may not affect the completion of the mission, and are used to assess basic reliability. As an example, the failure of an aircraft engine would be a mission failure; the failure of a vehicle sidelight would be a basic failure.

Counting the number of failures that occur provides a simple way of assessing reliability; the combination of numbers of failures and a period of operational use (such as time, distance, rounds fired) provides a simple measure of reliability – mean time between failure.

Mean time between failure (MTBF) = Time period of use/Number of failures.
Failure rate (λ)= Number of failures/Time period of use.

A common assessment process is to calculate cumulative MTBF as each successive failure occurs. This calculation provides a simple assessment of whether the reliability is changing (improving or degrading). The change of reliability can then be used to make decisions about the system, for example, to use more effort during a trials programme to improve the reliability, or to replace a system that is becoming less reliable as it reaches the end of its life. Note that failure rate is the reciprocal of MTBF.

Reliability only becomes visible in the phases of development when prototypes undergo realistic trials. During trials, the reliability of a system is often improved and reliability growth models can be used to monitor the changes in reliability and to predict reliability at the conclusion of the development activity. Reliability development trials use a number of systems and each time a failure occurs it is investigated and a redesign undertaken. Thus the build standard of the system constantly changes during the development activity; this is often called the test-analyse-fix cycle. A simple reliability growth model is the Duane model, which is defined by a simple equation:

$$\text{Cumulative MTBF} = K(\text{Time})^{\alpha}.$$

K is a constant for the data being assessed, and α is known as the growth factor and provides a measure of the rate of growth of reliability. The growth factor is also a measure of the development activity and is typically between 0.3 and 0.6.

There is sometimes a need to demonstrate formally the reliability of a system, and a reliability demonstration trial is undertaken. This is a fixed-build-standard trial, using one or more systems. A demonstration trial measures the reliability of a sample and makes assumptions (based on a statistical distribution) about the reliability of the whole population. The cumulative MTBF of the sample is measured and compared with the reliability requirement. If the reliability of the sample is higher than the requirement there is a likelihood that the population will have a reliability that meets the requirement; if the reliability is less then the population is unlikely to meet the requirement.

8.4 Maintainability

Maintainability is the activity of servicing and repairing systems to restore them to a fully operational state, and provide a measure of the resources required. The measurement of maintainability is concerned with the resources required to undertake the maintenance activity and includes people, diagnostic tools, special test equipment, spares and workshop facilities.

Preventive maintenance (also called scheduled servicing) is undertaken at planned intervals (measured in time, distance or other operational parameters), or when certain conditions occur (specific level of oil contamination or wear to a certain pre-planned level). Preventive maintenance is undertaken to try to stop failure from occurring during the operational period of use. Preventive maintenance is the primary way of ensuring that systems, which exhibit many catastrophic failure modes (such as aircraft, guns and nuclear-propulsion systems) are as reliable as possible. The burden of high levels of preventive maintenance is demonstrated by the high number of person-hours of maintenance performed on aircraft for every flight hour. For example, it is reported that the C17 Globemaster aircraft requires 19 person-hours of maintenance for every flight hour.

Corrective maintenance is a policy of fixing failures as and when they occur. There may also be some preventive maintenance, but because in these systems failures typically do not lead to catastrophic failures (e.g. a single bulb failure in a vehicle) it is simpler and often more cost effective to only maintain the system when it fails.

The time taken to complete a repair is defined as the mean active repair time (MART), which is based on using skilled personnel with all spares and tools to hand, in ideal conditions, with all diagnoses completed before the repair is started. It is an unrealistic measure and does not relate to repairs in operational conditions, but it provides a consistent comparison.

The need to undertake maintenance on a complex system has a number of effects. The need for preventive or corrective maintenance means that the system will be taken out of service for a period to enable the work to be undertaken. If it is necessary to provide a continual capability then additional systems will have to be acquired to provide this capability. These additional systems will add to the cost of the capability. The facilities to provide the maintenance will have to be acquired with the system, or adapted from existing facilities, and personnel will have to be trained to undertake the maintenance. Defence systems engineers should remember a particular problem frequently found with software maintenance and upgrades is that after the work has been undertaken, the systems will fail to function despite extensive pre-installation testing. This will then usually require a rapid remedial response from the supplier.

All maintenance activities (both preventive and corrective) should take as short a time as possible and the design of the system should ensure that access is provided to enable maintenance to be undertaken. The provision of access means that the design cannot be optimised in terms of space or volume, and additional space must be provided for people to work on the sub-systems and to enable them to be removed and replaced as quickly as possible. The provision of hatches and access panels can affect the structural integrity of aircraft and the protection levels of armoured fighting vehicles.

8.5 Availability

It is important to recognise that it is all but impossible to create a complex defence system that will be available to work whenever it is required. Most defence systems need maintenance at regular intervals and repairs at irregular intervals to restore their full capability. The number and duration of the maintenance activities reduces the time and number of systems available for operations. A system with low availability reduces its operational capability and becomes a liability rather than an asset as morale is reduced, combat effectiveness falls, and support costs increase.

Availability is a measure of the percentage of time that systems are available, or the percentage of systems available and ready for use. The assessment of availability has two main uses: to enable field commanders to estimate how many, or much, of the force will be useable, and enable them to consider augmenting the force if the availability is low. The assessment of availability also provides a measure against which availability improvements can be monitored.

Availability may be assessed in a number of ways and some simple measures are shown below. Note that availability is a probability and is often expressed as a percentage.

Availability = useable time period/total time (for a single system).
Availability = number useable/fleet size.
Intrinsic availability = MTBF/MTBF + MART.
Operational availability = MTBF/(MTBF + MART + logistic delay).

As examples of these, the availability of a system that can be used 25 days in a 50-day period is 50%; similarly if 75 systems can be used from a fleet of 100 the availability is 75%. Intrinsic availability is assessed using the reliability and maintainability measures of MTBF and MART: if the MTBF is 200 hours and the MART is 10 hours, the availability is 95%. Intrinsic availability is the best level of availability that a system will achieve, and operational availability includes a logistic delay (the total time between a failure occurring and the repair commencing); if this is 20 hours then the availability of the system is 87%.

8.6 Availability and the system life cycle

Availability must be considered from the earliest stages of the system life cycle; if the availability of a system is low then more systems may need to be purchased to ensure that an adequate number are available for operations. High intrinsic availability is achieved by high reliability and short preventive and corrective maintenance times. It is important to remember that simply specifying a high intrinsic availability may not be sufficient to achieve an acceptable operational system. For example, consider an intrinsic availability requirement of 95%. MTBF = 1000 hours and MART = 50 hours or MTBF = 10 hours and MART 0.5 hours. Both satisfy the requirement, but a system that fails every 10 hours is unlikely to be acceptable in an operational situation.

Availability is not a performance parameter that can be directly measured by a single trial, or even a series of short trials. It requires the collection and assessment of data over a lengthy period to provide a robust measure. Availability is improved by reducing the need for maintenance activities. Lengthening the period of time between service intervals, using long-life components, and reducing or removing the need for adjustments can reduce the need for preventive maintenance. Making the system more robust so there are fewer failures can reduce corrective maintenance. This requires a better understanding of the conditions and environment of use; many failures can be attributed to components that are insufficiently robust for the extremes of the performance envelope once the equipment enters service.

8.7 Failure-free operations

8.7.1 Introduction

The concept of a failure-free operating period is attractive to the users of complex systems, whether they are defence or commercial systems. A period of time when the operator, or owner, can be confident that the equipment will not fail, or need any unscheduled maintenance, offers the opportunity for the system to provide maximum capability. Any form of maintenance, whether planned or unplanned, reduces the capability provided by the system. In an ideal world equipment would not fail, or need any maintenance, during its entire service life.

The specification of a failure-free operating period by the customer can mean that the customer wants/needs a failure-free operating period for operational reasons, or is trying to encourage the system design authority to achieve the highest level of reliability possible. It is important to recognise why the failure-free operating period is being specified. If it is vital for operational reasons then this should be made clear. If it is being used as an incentive to achieve high availability, other routes to achieving this should be considered, such as

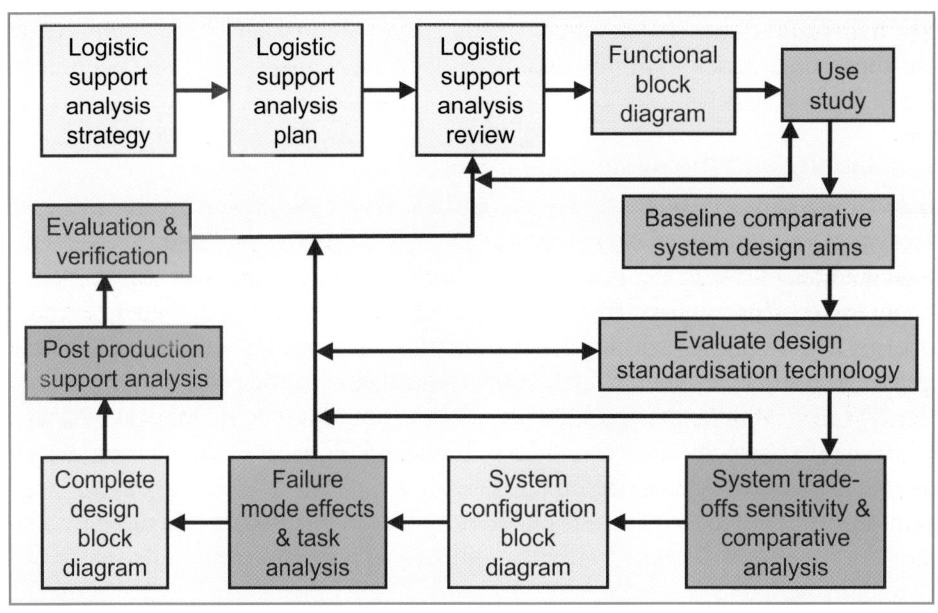

Figure 56. An approach to logistic support indicating a number of feedback loops.

reliability-growth programmes or contractual incentives. It is important to be honest when specifying system requirements; half-truths or misinformation will lead to problems in the future.

8.7.2 Causes of failures

Typical examples of failure causes include lack of strength, poor interfaces, poor assembly, material defects and operator errors. The designers of complex defence systems intend their solutions to be as reliable as possible, but they have to make assumptions and these assumptions lead to failures. Assumptions are made because there are unknowns in the specification that cannot be answered by the customer, or because there are unknowns in the analysis, materials, testing or manufacturing processes used.

Failures are predominantly caused by ignorance, a lack of understanding, or assumptions in the design and manufacturing process. Failures may show that the way the equipment is used, and the environment in which it operates, are not fully understood by the supplier. They may be caused by user or maintainer abuse. Failure modes may also have their origins in poor requirements and specifications that do not describe the operational use of the system sufficiently. Parts that break may not be strong enough, parts that wear out may not be robust enough, parts that corrode are often made of the wrong material, and parts that do not work with other parts often have poorly defined and controlled interfaces.

Other sources of failures are the compromises that a system designer needs to make. For a system to be successful the system design should be optimised, not the sub-system design. In some cases the sub-system design may be compromised, or sub-optimal, to achieve a satisfactory system design. This sub-optimisation of sub-systems, necessary for the successful system, may lead to reliability problems. For example, in a system where weight is a severe design constraint, it may be designed to a weight limit that prevents the sub-system from having sufficient strength to meet all of the expected in-service loads. This may lead to failures.

8.7.3 Failure-free operating periods

A failure-free operating period means that no failure will occur in the defined period, although planned maintenance may be allowable. To ensure that the system does not fail, the way it operates, the environment in which it operates and the way it is used must be known or controlled. It is common practice with aerospace systems to design for the performance envelope in which the loads and stresses can be determined and used in the design. In practice, the aerospace system cannot be used outside this operating envelope and constraining the performance is used to create a failure-free operating period. Vehicle engines can be de-rated to increase both reliability and the probability of completing a failure-free operating period.

9 Public/private partnership and private finance initiative

9.1 Introduction

The government's public/private partnership (PPP) and private finance initiative (PFI) are relatively new both in terms of the projects likely to use them and in terms of the lifetimes of contracts already placed. They are certain to have a significant impact on the approach taken by any defence systems engineer to the provision of a capability for the MoD contracted under the terms of these schemes. The move towards an increase in the percentage of procurements acquired through PPP and PFI represents recognition of the need to move towards long-term partnerships with industry.

The benefit of PPP/PFI is that these projects are off the balance sheet but this is living now to pay later. The unanswered questions include the on-going increase in MoD revenue expenditure, as well as it losing some control. What will happen in time of war, and whether industry will continue to invest in defence depends on the revenue justifying the investment. Finally there is the political issue of whether it is privatisation by the back door.

The number of defence-based PPP/PFI contracts continues to grow and includes several building projects, the provision of training, the supply and operation of strategic tankers and sealift, managing satellites, leasing transport aircraft and partnering industry on ship building. What exactly are PPP and PFI?

9.2 Public/private partnership

PPP is the government's generic term for relationships between private-sector companies and public bodies such as the MoD. The aim is to utilise private-sector resources and expertise to provide public-sector assets and services. PPP working arrangements may involve loose and informal strategic partnerships, formal joint-venture companies, or contracts to design, build, finance and operate facilities and services. The use of PPP is intended to improve both performance and efficiency.

Partnering is the term given to co-operation between a supplier and the MoD for the long-term mutual benefit of both parties. The objective is to establish long-term co-operative contractual relationships to meet the MoD's performance, quality and delivery needs at the lowest through-life cost and at a price yielding fair profit for the contractor. In partnering, both parties need to address all aspects of the cost of doing business together; not just focusing on unit price. Partnering should avoid duplicating quality checks and planning processes, misunderstandings between the MoD and its partners, abortive work, claims and legal disputes, and delays in payment to contractors. It is claimed that it should also enable partners to minimise total costs, reduce lead times, deliver better value for money and obtain a competitive advantage.

The listed attractions for the MoD and contractors are based on the fact that many requirements are surrounded by uncertainty, involve complex, high-value and high-risk work, and require a constant search for innovation and continuing cost improvement. Normal practice is for the MoD to use competition to choose a partner and then get the partner to provide regular reassurance that the MoD continues to achieve value for money.

9.3 Private finance initiative

Contracts that come under the PFI involve long-term service contracts between a government department (such as the MoD) and the private sector, and are typified by the provision of both capital assets and associated services, with combined payments for investment and services. There is an integration of design, build, finance and operations, while risk is allocated

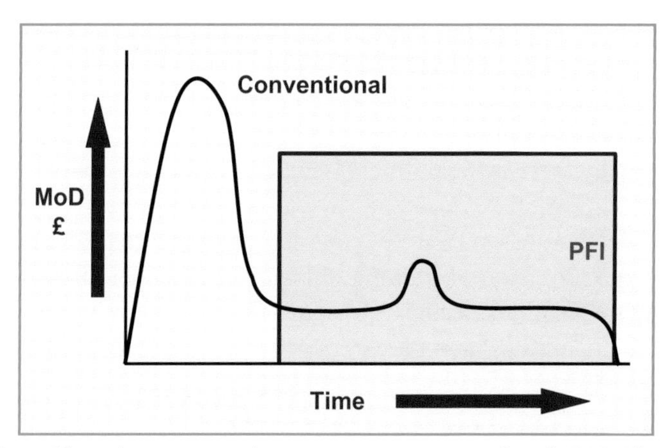

Figure 57. Cash profiles of conventional procurement compared with PFI. The areas under the curve and the rectangle should be roughly equal, depending on whether PFI provides similar, improved or less value for money.

to the party best able to manage and price it. Any services must be delivered to performance standards and there will be a performance-related payment mechanism.

The benefits of PFI should be improved quality of service (as the level is 'guaranteed' by contract), the integration of services with supporting assets and contract incentives, and finally a flat MoD budget. This last item allows more concurrent capital-intensive projects to be implemented whilst at the same time avoiding large peaks in expenditure profiles. Only after a considerable period of time, bearing in mind the lengthy timescales of PPP and PFI contracts, will the true benefits of the approach, or their disbenefits, become apparent.

Risk is always a key issue in major MoD procurements and PFI projects aim to provide better allocation of risk to those able to manage, control and cost it most effectively. Clearly the degree of risk transfer from the MoD to industry will vary from project to project, but the aim is to achieve optimal and sensible allocation of risk between the MoD and its suppliers; risk and reward going hand-in-hand. The hope for the MoD is that risk transfer will spur suppliers to deliver cost effective and higher quality services on time. The PFI project risks that government has identified as suitable for transfer to suppliers include:

- Project financing.
- Design, construction and commissioning.
- Operating and support.
- Demand/volume/usage.
- Technology or obsolescence.
- Residual-value risk.
- Legislative risk

It is unclear precisely how industry is supposed to deal with legislative risk that is imposed by government. It is also suggested that the MoD should consider transferring risk of variations

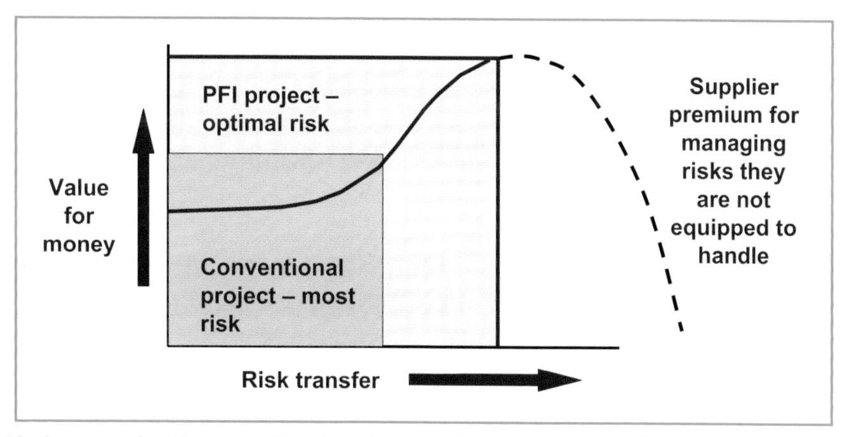

Figure 58. Compared with conventional projects, value for money in PFI projects increases if risks that the supplier is equipped to manage are transferred from the MoD.

in the MoD demand, though clearly the MoD should be better at judging its own variations in demand than industry!

One of the benefits of PFI is that it gives incentives to contractors. Risk transfer gives suppliers incentives to improve management and performance; payments depend on a satisfactory flow of services and meeting performance; the linkage creates continuing incentive for efficiency improvements throughout the project and finally assets are often more valuable to the private than to the public sector.

The basis of any PFI project structure is that the contractor is responsible for design, asset build, service delivery, ongoing operation, maintenance and any required update or renewal, though there may be variations on this theme. Because construction and usage are combined, this approach should ensure that assets are fit for purpose but no more, lowering the cost of post design services and modifications. Assembly and operation efficiency are optimised by applying existing expertise, maximum benefit is gained from introducing new technology and business processes, asset design can improve resale value or the capacity for transfer to new users and, of course, the best use is made of available skills.

PFI offers clearer focus on the responsibilities of the MoD and the supplier, more appropriately reflecting the strengths and skills of each; the MoD concentrates on what its armed forces require while the private-sector contractor focuses on how to deliver the required capability. Selling temporarily surplus capacity, developing assets surplus to MoD needs and the sale or licence of designs developed for the MoD, can all generate third-party revenues.

It is essential to be able to recognise the types of projects best suited to a PFI approach. The most obvious case is, where services are acquired, by the MoD paying an agreed remuneration for a defined service or output. This leads to greater private-sector ownership and its involvement in the operation of assets. Most MoD PFI opportunities will be of this type. Other forms of PFI – joint ventures and financially freestanding projects – suggested by government for other departments are considered unlikely for the MoD.

Innovation is important in PFI and the MoD tries to encourage and develop innovative approaches in order to provide fullest potential for improving value for money by moving from established or preconceived methods and ideas. There are two forms of innovative approach. The first is acceptance of unsolicited ideas for new or better ways of doing business through innovative proposals not submitted in response to a formal invitation to tender. The other is the acceptance of innovative bids in response to invitations to tender, which contain imaginative or novel solutions to meet the MoD's needs which also meet the specified essential requirement, though not necessarily in a way that the MoD envisaged.

Examples of PFI projects at the end of 2004 include the Skynet 5 satellite contract with Paradigm, the MoD's incremental acquisition and partnering with BAE Systems on the Type 45 destroyer, and the leasing of C17 aircraft from Boeing.

Further reading

Bird, R and Gummett, P (1999) *Cold War, Hot Science: Applied Research in Britain's Defence Laboratories 1945–90*. Amsterdam: Harwood Academic Publishers

Downey, WG (1969) *Report of a Steering Group on Development Cost Estimating*. London: HMSO

Health Services and Health Policy Research Unit (2001) *Public Services Private Finance: Accountability, Affordability and the Two-Tier Workforce* (report for UNISON). London: Health Services and Health Policy Research Unit

Kirkpatrick, DLI (1998) Partnering, not partnership: the implementation of Smart Acquisition, *RUSI Journal* June: 77–82

—— (2002) Smart Implementation of a Capability-Focused Approach. *World Defence Systems* (7): 55–7

—— (2004) Defence acquisition in crisis, *RUSI Newsbrief* December: 133–5

—— (2004) Problematic partnering: UK government and industry entering the 21st century, *RUSI Defence Systems* Autumn: 32–3

—— (2004) *Smart Acquisition: Unfinished Business*. Memorandum to the House of Commons Defence Committee (HC 572). London: TSO

—— (2004) The cost effectiveness of Smart Acquisition, *RUSI Defence Systems* January: 93–6

MoD (1998) *Learning from Experience*. London: HMSO

—— (2001) *Defence Acquisition* (Policy Paper No. 4). London: MoD

—— (2001) *British Defence Doctrine* (Joint Warfare Publication 0-01). Swindon: MoD (JDCC)

—— (2002) *Defence Industrial Policy* (Policy Paper No. 5). London: MoD

—— (2002) *Soft Issues Bid Evaluation Tool (SIBET) User Manual* (www.ams.mod.uk/ams/content/docs/toolkit/gateway/guidance/linkdocs/sibet.rtf)

National Audit Office (1986) *MoD: Control and Management of the Development of Major Equipment* (HC 568). London: HMSO

—— (1989) *MoD: Reliability and Maintainability of Defence Equipment*. London: HMSO

—— (1994) *MoD: Developments in the Reliability and Maintainability of Defence Equipment* (HC 690). London: HMSO

—— (2002) *Implementation of Integrated Project Teams* (HC 671). London: TSO

—— (2003) *Through Life Management* (HC 698). London: TSO

—— (2004) *The Management of Defence Research and Technology* (HC 360). London: TSO

—— (2004) *MoD: Driving Successful Delivery of Major Defence Projects*. London: TSO

National Statistics (2004) *UK Defence Statistics 2004*. London: TSO

Rowan, DD (1968) *Research and Development Management*. New York: Meredith Corporation

RUSI (2004) *The Innovative Use of Private Finance in Defence Acquisition* (Whitehall Paper 63). London: RUSI

Shillito, M and de Marle, D (1992) *Value: Its Measurement, Design and Management*. New York: Wiley

Suh, NP (1990) *The Principles of Design*. New York: Oxford University Press Inc
Taylor, T (2003) *Defence Acquisition, Management and the Industrial Dimension*. Cranfield: Royal Military College of Science, Cranfield University
US Department of Defense (1995) *Handbook for Human Engineering Design Guidelines* (MIL-HDBK 759). Washington, DC: US Department of Defense
—— (2004) *DoD Acquisition Handbook* (MIL-HDBK 502). Washington, DC: US Department of Defense
Weiss, A (2004) Why isn't Smart Acquisition working as it should? *RUSI Defence Systems* Autumn: 38–9
Wickens, G and Liu, Y (1998) *An Introduction to Human Factors Engineering*. New York: Longman

Websites
www.manprint.army.mil/manprint/
Available from the MoD On-line Acquisition Management System www.ams.mod.uk:
The Acquisition Handbook
Contracts Manual
MoD Guide to Integrated Logistic Support
Resource-based Approvals: Principles
Smart Approvals: General Instructions and Guidance on IAB and Delegated Approvals for All Investment Projects
Smart Requirements Model

Chapter 4

Financial matters

Before substantial funds are committed to a defence project, its likely cost and timescale must be forecast as accurately as possible to support budgetary planning and resource allocation. These forecasts must be made when many details of a project's design characteristics and in-service operations have yet to be determined, and when traditional bottom-up costing methods are inapplicable. Assessment of alternative defence projects to deliver a given capability, or assessment of alternative ways of managing a particular project, generally involves the comparison of different time profiles of expenditure; investment appraisal provides a structured method of making such comparisons. The MoD has adopted a commercial-style accounting system to encourage better management of its assets. Defence system engineers need to be aware of the implications of that change.

1 Cost and timescale forecasting

During the concept phase of a defence equipment project, the integrated project team (IPT) must generate credible forecasts of the project's likely cost and timescale. These forecasts are necessary inputs to the IPT's case for approval at initial gate and later at main gate, and to many aspects of its through-life management plan (TLMP). Because the project is not well defined in the concept phase, the forecasts of its cost and timescale made during this phase cannot be very accurate, and they must be progressively refined later in the project cycle as more information becomes available. However, since the early forecasts form the bases of many key decisions on project management and budgeting, it is vitally important that these forecasts of cost and timescale should be formulated as rigorously as practicable, without serious bias or omissions.

Poor forecasting in the early stages of a project can have many adverse consequences in addition to distorting project management decisions. It is notorious that in recent decades many defence projects have overrun their original definitive, approved forecasts of cost and timescale. It should be recognised that similar overruns of cost and timescale affect many large and complex projects in the commercial sector (notably in the areas of construction and information technology). These projects encounter many of the difficulties characteristic of defence equipment acquisition, so it is similarly difficult to forecast their costs and timescales accurately.

1.1 Scope of forecasting

In accordance with the through-life approach advocated by Smart Acquisition, cost and timescale forecasts for defence equipment projects are now expected to cover the complete

CADMID acquisition cycle. The forecast of a project's through-life cost (also called whole-life cost or life cycle cost) must include many different components such as:

- Concept and feasibility studies, and technology evaluation.
- Initial design and assessment, project planning and risk reduction.
- Full development, trials and demonstration.
- Production facilities investment and series manufacture.
- Operational investment in infrastructure, initial spares, logistics and support equipment.
- Operations – personnel, consumables and munitions.
- Repair and maintenance – personnel, spares, replacement equipment and test equipment.
- Post and continuing design services, as required.
- Disposal.

Each of these cost components involves different activities by different organisations in different (but overlapping) time periods, so they are normally forecast separately and then added to produce a total through-life cost (TLC). Although cost and timescale forecasts of different components are made separately, they are all to some degree interdependent, and key management decisions (on, for example, integrated logistic support) can affect several components in the acquisition cycle.

Some of the cost components (such as the costs of operation and support) depend closely on the number of items of equipment to be procured and operated by the MoD. Further components (such as design and development) are virtually independent of the number of items procured. Yet other components (such as manufacturing cost) increase with the number

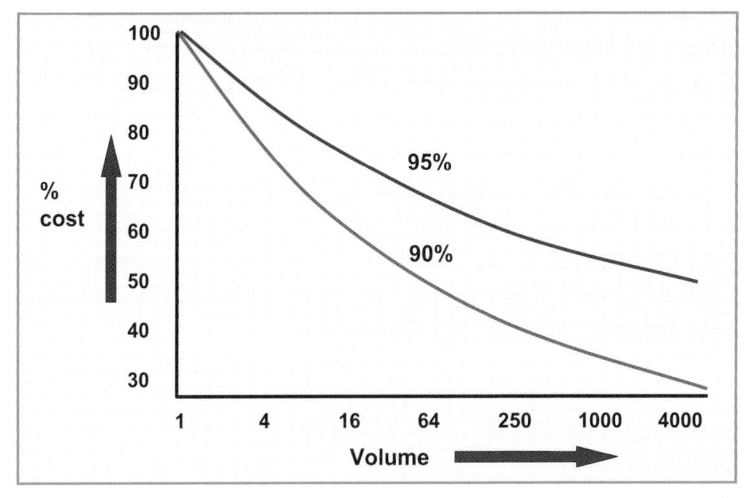

Figure 59. Typical learning curves show the way unit cost reduces each time the production volume is doubled.

of items procured, but in less than direct proportion. It follows that a project's through-life costs exhibit some 'economies of scale' by which the unit cost falls as the number procured is increased; it also follows that the average unit cost of the project is greater than the marginal cost of adding another unit to the number procured.

In association with forecasting the cost of each project activity, its timescale is forecast and used to formulate a time profile of annual future expenditure on that component. Later these time profiles are combined to obtain a time profile of annual expenditure on the whole project. This information is required as inputs to an investment appraisal (see Section 2 below) and to ensure that no forecast annual expenditure significantly exceeds the funds budgeted to the project for that year.

In any project cost forecast it is important to define the scope of the costs to be considered, and hence to determine whether the forecast needs to include only the direct costs of personnel, equipment and supplies exclusively dedicated to the project or whether it also needs also to include some indirect costs, attributable overheads and (unmarketed) social costs or benefits. For defence projects, the last category might include any emission of greenhouse gases and other pollutants, any potential damage to the health and safety of service personnel or civilians, and any annoyance caused by noise or other environmental impacts. In most defence projects these social costs are negligible relative to the overall cost of the project and can be ignored in cost forecasting, though their potential political impact should be recognised.

The indirect costs and attributable overheads might, for example, include the administration, support services and security of the bases where the project is deployed, and a share of MoD headquarters branches and basic training establishments. Many of these costs are virtually independent of the design and performance characteristics of the particular project considered, and are unaffected by the decisions of MoD staff responsible for its procurement, operations and support. Hence in cost forecasts to support day-to-day project management decisions it is often convenient to include only the direct costs of the project. However, in cost forecasts to support an investment appraisal of the acquisition of a major project, it is necessary to take account of the acquisition's effects on future levels of service personnel, MoD real estate and administrative organisation. These effects will depend on concurrent developments in other parts of the equipment acquisition programme, and on the current demand for labour, land and other resources in the commercial market. A project cost forecast derived for one purpose in one set of circumstances may not be appropriate in other cases.

Each project cost forecast must consider carefully, and specify clearly, the boundary round those cost elements relevant to that forecast, and the significance of the cost elements excluded and included by that boundary. Any analysis based on the cost forecast must appreciate the existence and relevance of the chosen boundary.

1.2 Master data and assumptions list

To ensure that all of the separate cost and timescale forecasts for the different activities within a project are consistent, it is absolutely necessary that the IPT compiles a master data and assumptions list (MDAL) which includes all of the project design and management information affecting the cost and timescale forecasts, and which is endorsed by the MoD and other stakeholders involved. The MDAL incorporates:

- A complete technical description of the project.
- The adopted acquisition strategy, and target dates for entry to and withdrawal from service.
- The planned schedule and distribution for the deployment of equipment.
- Arrangements for repair, maintenance and logistics.
- The economic conditions assumed for the forecast.

Formulating and agreeing an MDAL for a defence equipment project is a rigorous and demanding process. However, it ensures that all the personnel involved in forecasting share a common perception, and it provides a traceable record of any technical, organisational and economic changes which affect the project during the acquisition process. The first MDAL (formulated early in the acquisition cycle) must be revised and updated, as additional information becomes available, to support cost and timescale forecasts made later in the cycle; successive versions of the MDAL will progressively include more data and fewer assumptions.

1.3 Methodology

Cost and timescale forecasts for defence equipment projects are generally based on previous experience of similar projects on the same class of equipment. This empirical approach helps to avoid the 'optimism bias' which sometimes afflicts forecasts derived theoretically, without reference to the actual historical values of cost and timescale achieved on past projects. Parametric cost and timescale forecasts (i.e. forecasts derived from design or operational parameters of the project considered) can be made at different levels – system, sub-system and work package – depending on the progress of the project and on the level of detailed data about the project's design and management characteristics which are then available to support the forecast.

- A system forecast is based on some of the project's overall design and performance features, such as the payload and speed of a vehicle. It can be derived almost as soon as the initial design of the project is conceived.
- A sub-system-based forecast can be made later, when the project's principal sub-systems have been defined in sufficient detail to generate individual forecasts of their costs. The sub-system-based cost forecast is compiled from forecasts of costs for the individual sub-systems as well as costs of the associated assembly and integration activities. The timescale forecast is derived from forecasts of development, manufacture, integration and test and evaluation for each of the sub-systems and for the system itself. Individual timescale forecasts are then combined, in series or in parallel as appropriate, to forecast the project timescale.

- Forecasts at the work package level can be made when the project has defined each of the work packages to be undertaken through the CADMID cycle. The manpower, materials, energy and overheads for each work package can then be forecast (by comparison with similar packages on previous projects), evaluated at the chosen economic conditions and combined via a spreadsheet to produce the overall system cost forecast. Similarly, the timescale of each package can be forecast and combined via a PERT (programme evaluation research technique) chart. Forecasting at the work package level is the most accurate method, but it cannot be implemented in the early phases of a project.

The process of forecasting any cost component (at any level) in a new project should follow a series of discrete steps. Timescale forecasts follow a similar process.

1. Assemble a database of the costs of that component on earlier, similar projects and adjust these data to the economic and programme characteristics of the new project. This adjustment should take account of monetary inflation in the intervening years, of different lengths of production runs, and of different acquisition strategies. The accuracy of the forecasting process depends critically on the number and consistency of the earlier projects on which relevant data can be discovered and interpreted intelligently.
2. Identify those project characteristics (called 'cost drivers') which have the most important effect on the cost component considered (e.g. mass for aircraft production cost, number of firings for missile acceptance trials, etc.) and derive a cost-estimating relationship (CER) linking the cost drivers to the value in earlier projects of the cost component considered. This process is illustrated below by a graph plotting the cost

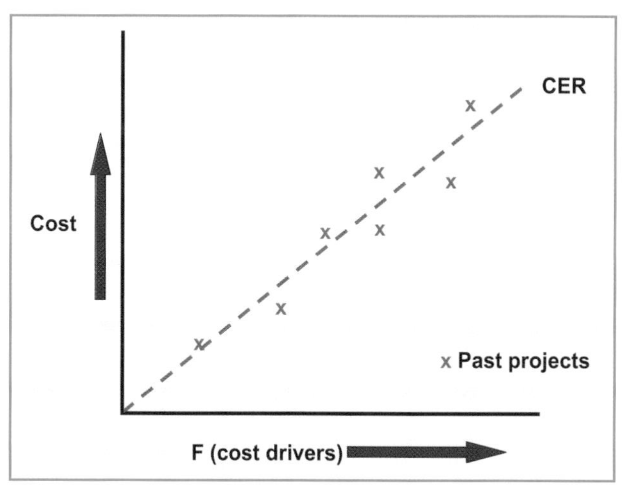

Figure 60. Historical data plotted against cost drivers enables the derivation of a cost-estimating relationship.

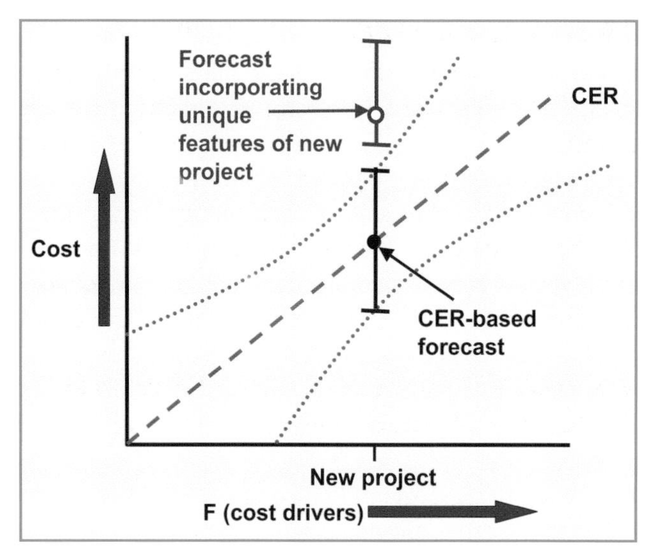

Figure 61. A CER-based forecast of cost and a forecast incorporating unique features of a new project can be derived.

component against a mathematical function of the cost drivers, the function being chosen to obtain the best possible correlation.

3. Use the CER and the characteristics of the new project to forecast the expected value of that cost component for the new project. That calculation also yields a CER-based estimate of the upper and lower confidence limits around the expected cost. The range between these limits defines where the actual cost is likely to fall (e.g. the MoD use of 10% and 90% confidence limits implies an 80% probability that the actual cost will fall within that range). The distance between the confidence limits depends on the number of historical data points and on their scatter, which arises from the simplification inherent in the CER and also from the risks typically associated with similar projects.
4. Adjust the cost forecast and the confidence limits to take account of any unique technological or managerial features of the new project which may affect the level and the variability of the cost forecast.

Cost and timescale forecasts for a new class of equipment (such as the first satellite, guided missile or stealth aircraft) must be derived partly by reference to previous experience of those sub-systems (e.g. propulsion) developed from earlier military or civilian designs, partly by reference to the costs and timescales associated with experimental trials of the new sub-systems (e.g. stealth materials), and partly by engineering judgement. The technology demonstration programmes, which are necessary to reduce the risks of new classes of equipment, can also yield useful data on the costs and timescales of unfamiliar activities.

1.4 Commercial forecasting packages

Cost and timescale forecasts made by the MoD or its contractors may be based on the organisation's own intramural database and analysis (as described above) or they may be obtained using a commercial software package designed to transform project data into credible cost and timescale forecasts. Commercial packages are convenient because they relieve the organisation of the need to commit its own resources to timely data collection and analysis. Some (but not all) of the commercial packages available have established creditable reputations by providing forecasts which have later proved to be reasonably accurate, but because the data and methods used are confidential their forecasts are not traceable or open to debate. It is generally preferable for an organisation, with expertise in its own specialist field, to apply that expertise and experience to take responsibility for its own forecasting, using specialist consultants for advice and assistance as required.

1.5 Errors in forecasts

In past decades, cost and timescale forecasts for defence equipment projects have been prone to various errors. Some have been affected by unexpected technical or management difficulties, particularly in those projects exploiting advanced technology or innovative management arrangements; the impact of such difficulties can be reduced by effective risk management (see Chapter 8, Section 3). Other forecasts have incorrectly omitted some important cost element (such as VAT), have used obsolete/inappropriate data or methodologies or unjustified assumptions, or have incorporated an unrealistic degree of optimism. In addition, forecasts can become inaccurate during the early phases of a project due to changes to the equipment specification or to the project plan arising from technical developments, geopolitical changes or budgetary crises.

Even when forecasts are made to the highest professional standards and when a project is not subject to unanticipated difficulties, there are bound to be some discrepancies between project forecasts and outturns due to random exogenous variations (such as weather, illness and accidents) which affect some projects more than others, and due to the simplifications inherent in any cost-forecasting methodology. Ideally such discrepancies are unbiased and acceptably small, so their overall effect on an organisation running scores of projects in parallel should be minimal, though some reallocation of resources between projects may be necessary.

1.6 Conclusions

To improve the quality of cost and timescale forecasting (which is one of the stated objectives of Smart Acquisition), it is important that forecasters have a good understanding (or access to good advice) of all the technical, industrial, operational and logistic aspects of their project. The forecasting team should also have an encyclopaedic knowledge of the history of earlier relevant projects, so that their CER is well founded and able to account for all the important cost drivers.

The forecasters should resist the temptation to rely on long-established rules of thumb without judicious assessment of their relevance to a modern project. They should also strive to include the best practicable forecast for even the most unpredictable cost components, since the alternative option of setting the cost of those components equal to zero is undoubtedly wrong.

It is vitally important that the chosen forecasting methodology should avoid unwarranted sophistication and spurious precision, and should be traceable and transparent for all stakeholders.

2 Investment appraisal

It is common knowledge that it is advantageous to accelerate receipts and to delay payments, whenever practicable. It is advantageous because funds can generally be safely invested to yield a positive real rate of return, equal to the interest rate payable on the investment minus the concurrent rate of monetary inflation. This real rate of return, also known as the 'time value of money', and most frequently as the discount rate, is a manifestation of the social time preference rate defining the relative value which society attaches to present and to future consumption. It can be used to compare the benefits of cash receipts and the penalties of cash payments of different amounts of money in different years. For example, it is better to receive £(0) now, at $t = 0$, rather than £(t) in the future t years ahead only if:

$$\pounds(0) > \pounds(t)/(1 + i)^t (1 + r)^t$$

where i is the average inflation rate expected in the intervening period and r is the corresponding real rate of return on a low-risk investment.

2.1 Application of investment appraisal in private and public sectors

The above principle has been used to develop the methodology of investment appraisal (IA) which has been widely used in private- and public-sector organisations over many years, and which is mandatory for all UK government projects involving expenditure of substantial public funds. IA is a structured process of assembling and analysing all the costs, benefits and risks associated with a planned project, and it may be used to assess:

- Trading activities where the expected future costs and benefits are financial.
- Projects involving non-marketed costs or benefits (such as pollution or safety) to which monetary values can be assigned. Analysis of such projects is called cost-benefit analysis.
- Projects that provide alternative means of achieving a particular government policy goal. Analysis of such projects is called cost-effectiveness analysis, and is used in the MoD to assess alternative defence equipment options intended to provide the military capability required by a service customer on or before a specified date.

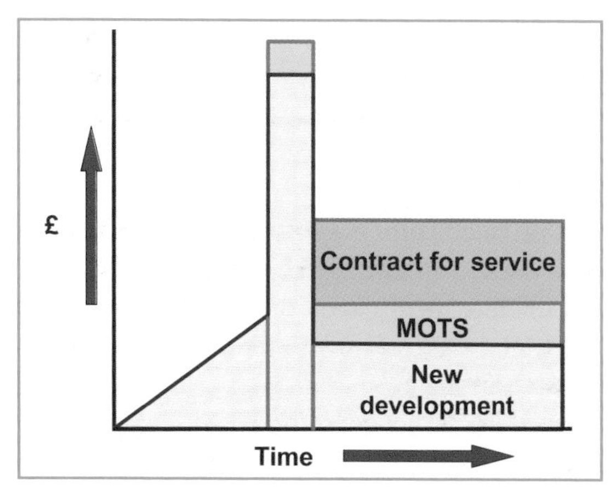

Figure 62. Alternative time profiles of expenditure superimposed on each other. New development has the largest up-front cost, MOTS often has the highest peak and higher in-service costs. Contracting for the service has no up-front cost, but usually the highest in-service expenditure.

For example, the MoD could choose to provide some required increment in defence equipment capability either by funding the development of new equipment, by procuring some existing equipment off-the-shelf, or by contracting for the service provided by equipment owned and supported by a private company. These three options generate different time profiles of expenditure (stylised examples are shown in Figure 62) which can be compared using an IA.

2.2 Investment appraisal procedure

Any IA for the MoD involves eight discrete activities, as shown below:

1. Define the timescale of the appraisal with reference to the project to be considered. The time period should normally cover the service life of any asset procured, and the IA should cover all costs and revenues relevant to the project (see Section 1 above on cost forecasting).
2. Identify and specify a list of alternative options; this process should involve wide consultation among the stakeholders and the list should not exclude any promising option (however unpopular) which merits detailed assessment. The list of options must include a 'do-minimum' option to act as a baseline for assessing the impacts of the others.
3. Forecast for each option the likely time profiles of the future cash flows of revenues and payments over the time period chosen, and hence forecast the net revenue £(t) in year t in real terms excluding inflation. It is important in any IA to identify all the consequences of selecting a particular option and hence to include all the associated revenues and costs, including those associated with disposal of the assets at the end of the period. Forecasts should be made in terms of real resources, excluding any

transfer payments not associated with the delivery of actual equipment or services and excluding the effects of monetary inflation. (It is necessary to assess project affordability by calculating both a cash-flow forecast including predicted inflation and a resource cost forecast, but these are NOT used for investment appraisal.)

4. For each option use the discount rate r to calculate the discounted net revenue in year t as $£(t)/(1 + r)^t$. A private-sector organisation may choose the value of the discount rate to suit its own current financial circumstances, but public-sector organisations must use the discount rate specified by the Treasury, representing its best judgement on the average real rate of return over future years on low-risk private-sector investments. The Treasury discount rate is re-evaluated at intervals of about a decade in response to change in market conditions; at present (2004) it is set at 3.5%.
5. For each option, add the discounted values of net revenue across the project life cycle to obtain the net present value (NPV) of that option in year zero as:

$$NPV = \Sigma\ £(t)/(1 + r)^t$$

6. A commercial project is judged favourable if NPV > 0. For a defence equipment project the value of NPV (invariably negative) represents the scale of the fund which, if it were allocated to the project in year zero, could meet all the expenditure required by the project in future years; the NPV is thus a quantitative measure of the economic burden imposed by the project.
7. Explore how the NPV for each option might be affected by the risks and uncertainties (see Chapter 8, Section 3) associated with it. The effects of risks may be represented by confidence limits above and below the forecast NPV within which the actual value of the NPV is very likely to fall; for MoD studies the confidence limits represent the 10% and 90% points in the forecast distribution of NPV. The effects of uncertainties may be represented by alternative values of the forecast NPV which would result from different outcomes of some future event.
8. Consider how far the NPV for each option would be affected by credible variations in the inputs to the IA; this process is sometimes called ‘sensitivity analysis’. The calculated effects of variations indicate whether a decision based on the relative values of two NPVs is robust, i.e. on whether the decision would be reversed by relatively modest variations in the data and assumptions used for the appraisal. The resulting values of NPV and other characteristics of the alternative options considered may then be compared to identify the option offering best value for money.

All of the eight above activities are important but the third is probably the most challenging. Any IA in the private or public sector presents problems, but it is particularly difficult to forecast the scale and timing of the cash flows associated with defence projects. Such projects often involve innovative technology (which may require expensive and protracted development to overcome unexpected difficulties) and unfamiliar management arrangements (which may generate unusual interface costs and delays) and long through-lives (during which the operation and support of the project may be drastically changed in response to geopolitical and other developments). It is especially difficult to forecast the costs and revenues arising many years in the future, such as those resulting from the disposal of defence equipment after it is withdrawn from service. The cost of safe destruction will depend on the environmental legislation current at that future date, and the revenue will depend both on market demand for the equipment considered and on current government policy on weapon proliferation; neither is easily predictable, but fortunately the effect of discounting reduces the significance of these issues in the overall result. While the results of an IA cannot be definitive, intelligent application of cost forecasting methods and of the other IA procedures yields useful results that assist decision-making.

In any IA comparing similar options, it is often convenient to exclude those items with revenues and costs which are common to all the options considered. This exclusion does not affect the ranking of options to identify the most advantageous, and it can significantly reduce the time and resources needed for the IA. But before making this simplification it is necessary to establish beyond doubt that the excluded items are truly identical for all options, and that they are identically affected by the relevant risks and uncertainties. It is also important to avoid any bias in the treatment of alternative options by ensuring that all assumptions are consistent and incorporate equitable levels of realism.

2.3 Key Treasury guidelines

The Treasury's guidelines describe its approved procedure for IA and should be consulted as necessary. Some key points are presented below:

- Since the IA is concerned with the future effect of a current decision, all 'sunk' costs which have already been paid, or which are irretrievably committed, must be excluded.
- Forecasts of future costs and benefits for alternative options should be adjusted as appropriate for any anticipated relative price effects which are expected to affect particular inputs (e.g. price of commodities becoming more scarce) and for any differences in taxation.
- The IA methodology is based on discounted cash flow, so all notional costs (such as depreciation and return on capital) are excluded.
- The IA itself should take no account of potential macro-economic effects on, for example, national levels of employment or the balance of payments, since such issues are assumed to be perfectly reflected in the market prices for resources used in cost forecasting.

2.4 Investment appraisal in defence equipment acquisition

An IA provides a logical and evident (i.e. traceable) chain of reasoning from the inputs (known and assumed) to a quantitative result. The IA methodology therefore forms an integral part of good defence systems engineering, and of good management in other areas of government and business. Within the CADMID cycle, IA may be used in:

- Balance of investment studies, contributing to force development.
- Selection of the project proposal offering best value for money.
- Assessment within a chosen project of alternative financing or organisational options.
- Integrated logistic support (ILS) studies to minimise through-life costs.

In such studies the IA illuminates the financial aspects of the alternative options and thus its result provides a sound basis for decision-making, along with other factors, e.g. ideological, industrial or diplomatic.

The table below provides an illustrative example of an IA calculation, assuming for simplicity that the discount rate is 10%. The calculation compares the financial results of introducing through year 0 a modification to a fleet of vehicles to reduce its annual running cost from £10M to £6M. The modification would cost £16M but would have no effect on the other characteristics (effectiveness, safety etc.) of the vehicles. In both cases the vehicles cease operations and have no net value at the end of year 4.

Year	0	1	2	3	4	Total
Discount factor = $1/(1 + r)^t$	1	0.909	0.826	0.751	0.683	
Real running cost now	10	10	10	10	10	50
Discounted cost	10	9.09	8.26	7.51	6.83	41.69
Modification cost	16					
Real running cost modified	8	6	6	6	6	32
Total cost of option	24	6	6	6	6	48
Discounted cost	24	5.45	4.96	4.51	4.10	43.02

Figure 63. An illustrative investment appraisal calculation.

This table shows that the modification would reduce cash expenditure from £50M to £48M, but it would increase the NPV (because of the large expenditure in year 0) and therefore should not be implemented. It might be attractive if it was introduced via a crash programme at the start of year 0 reducing the running cost from £10M to £6M in that year, or if the payment for the modification work could be spread over the later years. The results of such spend-to-save calculations depend not only on the amounts of cash involved but also on the current discount rate and on the number of years between the expenditure and the saving.

3 Resource accounting and budgeting

3.1 Introduction

Traditionally, UK government departments and private companies have used different management accounting systems. Government departments have focused on their annual budgets for cash expenditure, as voted by Parliament. Private companies by contrast have striven to manage effectively the assets funded by their shareholders. Over the last several years the MoD and other government departments have adopted resource accounting and budgeting (RAB). This section outlines the rationale for RAB and its likely effect on defence equipment acquisition.

3.2 Commercial accounting

A commercial company needs a variety of financial information on its current operations in order to guide management decision-making. This financial information is normally arranged in three accounts:

- Cash flow (revenue and expenditure).
- Profit and loss.
- Balance sheet (assets, creditors, liabilities).

The cash flow account is necessary to monitor the fluctuations of the company's cash in hand, to ensure that enough cash is available for the timely payment of wages and salaries and of bills for the supply of goods and services. Failure to make such payments as expected would gravely damage the company's reputation. Cash flow accounts are compiled daily, weekly or monthly (as required by the company's activities); the profit and loss account and the balance sheet are normally compiled annually.

The profit and loss account considers not only the inward and outward cash flow associated with the company's trading activities but also the loss in value (called depreciation) of the company's fixed assets such as land, buildings, vehicles and other equipment. The annual depreciation on a particular asset may be calculated by dividing its original market price by its expected service life (or by using more complex formulae); the standard service life varies according to the nature of the asset, e.g. 50 years for buildings and 4 years for computer equipment. Hence:

Depreciation = original cost/service life.
Profit = revenue – expenditure – depreciation.

The company is considered to be operating successfully only if its trading activities are generating a positive cash flow sufficient to fund the replacement of its fixed assets, as and when that becomes necessary.

This conventional approach to depreciation assumes implicitly that the market price of a replacement asset will be similar to the price of its predecessor. In practice, the price of different classes of assets may remain at about the same level, or they may rise or fall significantly; however, the depreciation calculation provides a useful indication (albeit approximate) as to whether the company's operations can be sustained into future years. If it is known that at the end of its service life the equipment will have a significant sale value or disposal cost, the depreciation charge can be reduced or increased accordingly.

In any particular year the total depreciated value of the company's fixed assets plus any liquid assets (such as cash deposits or easily marketed securities) defines the 'capital employed' in the company's trading activities. The annual balance sheet details the company's capital employed as well as money owed to the company by its debtors and the money owed by the company to its creditors. If:

$$\text{Capital employed} + \text{debtors} - \text{creditors} < 0$$

the company is technically bankrupt and should cease trading, unless the creditors collectively believe that its financial position will soon improve substantially. This calculation presumes that the depreciated value of the fixed assets being used by the company is broadly representative of their current market price. In practice, the current prices of different classes of fixed assets vary considerably due to variations of supply and demand in their markets. The balance sheet value of capital employed provides only a broad indication of the company's situation, and a decision to cease trading requires a more rigorous valuation. It should be noted that current level of capital employed may be more or less than the capital originally subscribed by shareholders when the company was formed, depending on its success in the intervening period.

The profit generated by the company is divided into tax payable to the government, an increment in the fixed or liquid assets of the company, and a dividend paid to the company's shareholders. If the ratio of the dividend paid to the capital employed by the company is unacceptably small, and shows no credible likelihood of early improvement, the shareholders may terminate trading, liquidate the assets of the company and invest the funds more profitably somewhere else. That ratio, called the return on capital employed (ROCE), must therefore exceed the return that shareholders could obtain by other comparable investments.

Some private organisations produce only a cash flow account. They can manage their affairs satisfactorily on that basis when they have no significant long-term creditors and when their assets are relatively small or are assumed to be fully depreciated when purchased (because they are replaced frequently or because they have no significant market value for alternative use). In such cases (e.g. consultancies) cash flow alone is a good measure of prosperity.

3.3 Government accounts

Until recently, UK and other government accounts were also presented in terms of cash flow alone. The cash flow of government revenue and expenditure was (and remains) important because any imbalance requires unexpected borrowing of funds from the money market, which can raise interest rates and thereby affect the development of the national economy. But government accounts based only on current cash flow take no account of the future benefits generated by current investment, or of the value embodied in current fixed assets, or of the need to replace assets when they are no longer useable. Such cash flow accounts promote a hand-to-mouth approach, with sub-optimal investment in the infrastructure for which the government is responsible. That approach was (barely) acceptable when government assets were small (quill pens and red tape) or were regarded as inalienable (the British Museum) or were acquired to meet a particular crisis (e.g. rearmament). But cash flow accounts became increasingly unsatisfactory through the twentieth century as governments took responsibility for managing activities involving substantial fixed assets.

3.4 Reasons for RAB

In order to promote a better approach to investment and asset management within its departments, the government in 1995 directed that they should prepare resource-based accounts, and that they should be allocated from the Treasury resource-based budgets including allowances for current depreciation and ROCE. The actual depreciation and ROCE would be repaid annually to the Treasury to provide (notionally) a fund to replace departmental assets as required and a return to the taxpayer on the capital employed by the departments.

Under this system, the burden of a capital investment is not incurred by an operating organisation in the year(s) in which the investment is made, but is spread over the subsequent years of the asset's service life as depreciation and ROCE payments. This facilitates new investment for which these payments are exceeded by the consequent reduction in running cost. Similarly, this system encourages departments to manage their existing assets to reduce depreciation and ROCE (by reducing the value of the assets employed and/or extending their service lives) and thereby to free more funds for current expenditure.

RAB has been introduced not because any government department might have to terminate its essential operations but because it sends more accurate signals to budget managers, encouraging decisions that minimise the burden which their department imposes on the national economy.

3.5 RAB in the MoD

In implementing RAB, the MoD has faced particular problems because of the scale and value of its assets. In 2004, these included:

100,000 acres
70,000 sites and building (incl. 650 historic buildings)
120 ships
670 aircraft
66,500 vehicles

The asset value of MoD combat equipment and associated capital stores is nearly £70B, about two and a half times the size of its annual cash budget. The MoD also faces problems because many of its major defence projects are bespoke and bought over many years via stage payments, rather than standard designs (e.g. a new school or hospital).

In the MoD, the procurement of equipment is managed by the Defence Procurement Agency (DPA), and its operation in service is managed by the front-line commanders (FLC) supported by the Defence Logistics Organisations (DLO). Under RAB, the resource budgets of the DPA and the FLC are both very different from their cash budgets.

The illustrative example below presents a simplified representation of expenditure in the first years of a defence equipment project, in cash and in RAB terms. The project costs £100M to develop over two years and consists of two items that cost £200M each and are delivered at the end of the third and fourth years. The value of each item is depreciated at 20% per year over its expected service life of five years with the FLC. The development cost is capitalised and transferred to the FLC with the capital value of the first item delivered, at the end of the third year, and is depreciated (by convention) at the same rate as the equipment. The equipment is assumed to have no residual value or disposal cost at the end of its service life.

Year	1	2	3	4	5	6	7	8	9	Σ
Development	50	50								100
Production		100	200	100						400
Capital employed by DPA	50	200	400	200						
ROCE @ 5%	3	10	20	10						43
DPA operating cost (of IPT etc.)	5	10	10	5						30
DPA cash cost	55	160	210	105						530
DPA resource cost	8	20	30	15						73
Transferred development				100						
Transferred production				200	200					
Capital employed by FLC				300	440	340	240	140	40	
Depreciation @ 20%				60	100	100	100	100	40	500
ROCE @ 5%				15	22	17	12	7	2	75
FLC operating and support cost				40	80	80	80	80	40	400
FLC resource cost				115	202	197	192	187	82	975

Figure 64. A simplified representation of the expenditure (and total spend) over the first nine years of a defence project. Green indicates cash, red indicates RAB.

Under traditional cash accounting the through-life cost of the project would be:

	£M
Expenditure within the DPA	30
Expenditure by the DPA on procurement contract	500
Expenditure by the FLC on operations and support	400
Total	930

Under RAB, the resource cost to the DPA would be the sum of intramural expenditure and ROCE, £73M, and the resource cost to the FLC would be £400M + £500M + £75M = £975M, though only £400M is in the cash cost of operating and supporting the equipment.

It should be noted that in reality most equipment would stay longer in service and its depreciation would accordingly be lower. The current ROCE is 3.5%.

The above example shows that under RAB, the DPA resource budget depends not only on the amount of work to be done but also on its duration; any delay will increase the ROCE payable by the DPA and hence yield an overrun in its resource budget. The introduction of RAB should make DPA project managers even more determined to avoid delays. Under RAB, the FLC is liable to pay not only the in-service costs (as formerly) but also depreciation and ROCE charges on the transferred costs of development and production; cost overruns in either of these areas could strain the FLC resource budget and/or constrain operation of the equipment. The FLC now has a distinct incentive to keep the equipment procurement cost as low as possible.

Although the above example omits for simplicity any detailed consideration of ILS, it is equally true that the FLC now also has a similar incentive to minimise up-front investment in specialist tools and test equipment, stockholding of spares, training infrastructure and other similar items.

RAB is unlikely to affect decision-making and defence policy at the highest level. FLCs are not empowered to sell nuclear submarines or aircraft carriers on the open market in order to lower their level of capital employed and hence reduce their expenditure in resource terms. They may, if they have to reduce their fleets, choose to release for sale a newish ship rather than an older one which is fully depreciated and so no longer attracts depreciation or ROCE charges. RAB is more likely to affect decisions at lower levels, encouraging budget holders to reduce their holdings of real estate and to dispose of any items (such as the notorious stock of mule shoes and thermionic valves) for which there is no credible future requirement.

The introduction of RAB makes equipment apparently more expensive relative to personnel (the investment in a trained pilot is not regarded as capital employed), and therefore discourages the persistent trend towards more capital-intensive forces. It also discourages the services from holding large stocks of fuel, consumables and capital spares (for which under RAB they are charged depreciation and ROCE) and encourages them to adopt just-in-time arrangements like commercial industry, *provided* supply can be accelerated during conflicts to match increased consumption and avoid potentially disastrous shortfalls.

3.6 Conclusions

The introduction of RAB has been widely received within the MoD with considerable annoyance, requiring extra staff and resources to identify and value assets and thus allow preparation of resource as well as cash accounts. MoD personnel, particularly those in the armed forces, consider their situation to be totally different from the commercial world in which RAB is appropriate. Yet RAB (when used intelligently) can give MoD budget holders relevant information to help them manage their assets as cost effectively as possible.

Further reading

Glautier, M and Underdown, B (1991) *Accounting Theory and Practice* (4th edn). London: Pitman Publishing

HM Treasury (1991) *Economic Appraisal in Central Government: A Technical Guide for Government Departments*. London: HMSO

—— (2003) *Appraisal and Evaluation in Central Government* (Green Book). London: TSO

Kirkpatrick, DLI (1996) *Choose your Weapon: Combined Operational Effectiveness and Investment Appraisal (COEIA) and its Role in UK Defence Procurement*. London: RUSI

—— (2000) Life cycle costs for decision support, *Defence and Peace Economics* April: 333–68

—— (2000) Whole life cost forecasting, *RUSI Journal* August: 25–9

MoD (1996) *CAPITAL: Resource Accounting and Budgeting – An Introduction for Managers in Defence*. London: MoD Central Services CS(M)G

—— (1998) *DFMS Resource Accounting Policy Manual*. London: MoD

National Audit Office (1992) *MoD: Planning for Life Cycle Costs* (HC 174). London: HMSO

Pilcher, R (1973) *Appraisal and Control of Project Costs*. London: McGraw Hill

Seldon, MR (1979) *Life Cycle Costing: A Better Method of Government Procurement*. Boulder, Colorado: Westview Press

Stewart, RD, Wyskida, RM and Johannes, JD (1995) *Cost Estimators' Reference Manual*, New York: Wiley

Website

www.hm-treasury.gov.uk/about/resourceaccounts/

Chapter 5

Assistance from analysis

In the commercial world, the benefits of a new project can be assessed entirely in financial terms. However, in defence systems engineering, it is necessary to assess the benefits of a new defence equipment project in terms of the additional military capability which it will provide in future conflicts. Operational analysis can be used, alongside military judgement, to obtain such assessments and thereby to conquer this complexity. The assessment of commercial projects may be based on a single criterion (i.e. net financial returns) but the selection of defence equipment involves the two independent criteria of finance and military effectiveness. The challenge of two-dimensional decision-making in the MoD has been conquered by the COEIA procedure. In defence systems engineering most decisions are subject to uncertainty about, for example, the outcomes of future risks or the consequences of an unprecedented development. Individuals and groups may adopt several approaches to help them identify the best decision in the circumstances.

1 Operational analysis

1.1 Introduction

Operational analysis (OA) is the application of scientific methodology to the study of military operations. It is used to measure the military capability of the armed forces of the UK (and of other nations) in current or future operations, and hence to determine how it might most economically be improved. OA thus measures, albeit imperfectly, the output of UK defence expenditure. Accordingly the Treasury now insists that OA studies must be provided and combined with military judgement to support proposals for equipment acquisition.

OA of military problems is closely related to the operational research (OR) methods used in commerce and industry to address problems in manufacturing, distribution and service provision. There are many features common to OA and OR but the former must always allow for the enemy's capacity to inflict damage and disruption and must address hypothetical conflicts on which there is (fortunately) little relevant evidence. Most OA studies for the MoD are done by the Defence Science and Technology Laboratory (Dstl), assisted by specialist sub-contractors.

1.2 Modelling military operations

Models are physical, graphical or mathematical representations of reality and are widely used in government and industry to assist in analysis and planning. Typical models include a sketch of a new product, the floor plan of a building, the flow diagram of a manufacturing process, a working prototype delivering (most of) the capabilities of a new system, a wargame, a hardware-in-the-loop simulation and a computer-based simulation of the national economy. Such models can be used to optimise design, to predict performance, to plan activities and to assess alternative policies. The ideal model should be:

- **Faithful but simple** – the model must incorporate all the important features of the subject being modelled, but omit features which are trivial or irrelevant. Simple models tend to be easier to create, more economical to use and easier to comprehend.
- **Verifiable** – the operation and outcome of the model should be compared with reality to ensure that the model's representation is satisfactory. A predictive model cannot be fully verified, but can be compared against past or current reality.
- **Unbiased** – the model should not be influenced by the prejudices or interests of any of its creators or other stakeholders.

Models of existing systems or operations provide a cheaper and safer method of determining the effect of changes to the status quo. Models of future systems or operations can predict the results of alternative decisions and thus guide planners towards the most favourable option.

When modelling military operations, a fighting unit (either a single weapon system or a military formation incorporating a number of systems of different types) may be represented

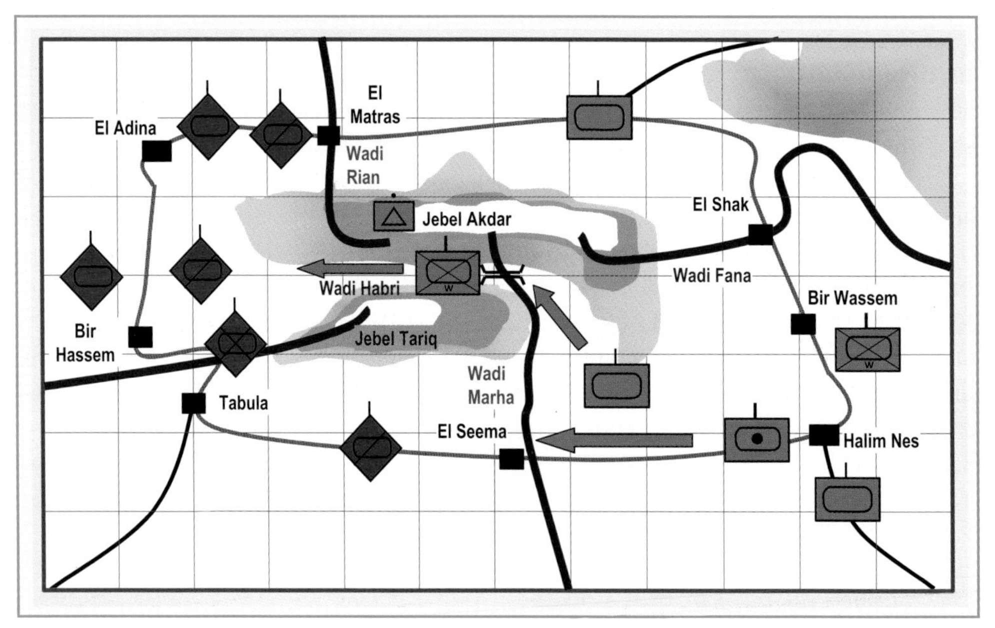

Figure 65. Wargames can help commanders to think through their responses to a range of enemy moves.

by a few of its key characteristics which normally include mobility, firepower and protection. A conflict between opposing Blue and Red task forces (with UK units constituting some or all of the Blue force) may then be modelled in accordance with predetermined rules governing the operations of the units involved, and using tactics chosen by the opposing (human or computer) commanders. The results of the wargame conflict indicate which task force would be victorious if the conflict had been fought in reality; a series of such conflicts allows analysts to estimate the advantages to be gained by improvements to a system's performance, by alteration of the UK force's structure and by changes in the tactics it employed.

Commanders have always recognised that there are symbiotic relationships between different elements in their forces, and have striven to exploit the resulting synergies to best advantage. Because of the interactions between different elements, the overall effectiveness of a task force is not simply the sum of the effectiveness of individual units but is a non-linear function of the numbers and types of units involved. It is therefore important to model the interactions between units as realistically as possible, and this factor is becoming ever more important as an increasing number and variety of units are linked in interdependent networks.

The key characteristics of the weapon systems or military formations modelled, and the rules governing the operations within the model, may be derived from analysis of recent or ongoing operations, or from performance predictions for new equipment designs. The tactics employed in the virtual conflict are likewise based on current tactical doctrines (known for Blue and assumed for Red) and are validated by military officers attached to the OA teams. The result of a virtual conflict may either be definitive, in which case the Red force might lose a particular number, for example 23 armoured vehicles, or stochastic (resolving the encounters within the model using probabilities and random numbers) in which case the Red force might have different probabilities of losing any discrete number of armoured vehicles from zero upward. Stochastic models must be run many times to reveal the probability distribution for the different possible outcomes of a virtual conflict.

In recent years the scope of OA has been extended to cover peace support operations in which military forces and other national and international organisations are seeking to create or restore a stable and prosperous society. Modelling peace support must integrate the provision of security with the establishment of adequate utilities and public services, development of markets and employment, and creation of satisfactory legal and constitutional arrangements. This modelling relies on 'softer' disciplines such as psychology and economics, rather than the traditional disciplines (e.g. ballistics and electromagnetic propagation) characteristic of military OA.

1.3 The hierarchy of mathematical models

Current models of military operations form a hierarchy, ranging from the functioning of a particular sub-system (such as a warhead) up to campaign models of the operations of many Blue and Red units over an extended period of time. The warhead of a surface-to-air missile (SAM), for example, can be modelled mathematically to calculate how many fragments are likely to hit an aircraft at a given distance from the warhead's detonation. Similarly, the performance of the missile itself (speed, manoeuvrability, guidance, etc.) can be modelled to determine how closely the missile would pass an over-flying aircraft. These calculations can be combined to estimate the probability that an engagement would result in the destruction of the targeted aircraft as a function of the aircraft's speed, signatures and track relative to the missile launcher.

At a higher level the operation of the missile battery can be modelled to take account of the warning it might receive of an approaching aircraft and of the time needed to acquire and track the target before the missile can be launched. This model could incorporate the effect of poor visibility and terrain screening to determine the geometrical combinations of aircraft altitude and crossing range at which a missile launch would be practicable, and the probability of destroying the aircraft on those occasions. This one-on-one engagement model could then be expanded to model the action of several SAM batteries defending a target from a force of attacking aircraft, including some assigned to suppress the SAM batteries directly.

At an even higher level, a campaign model could represent a protracted series of interdependent operations extending over several days or weeks, such as a bombing campaign to facilitate later ground operations or to destroy the infrastructure of the enemy nation attacked. Campaign models must take account not only of the performance of the combat units engaged but also of their ability to relocate and reload, of the sensors and communications available to direct their operations, of the logistics and support organisations which provide provisioning and repair, of the reinforcements which either side might receive, and of the development of the strategies of the opposing commanders as the campaign evolves.

These mathematical models form a hierarchy in which the results of lower-level models are aggregated and used as input data to the higher-level models. The former can be validated by experiments and trials (e.g. by detonating a warhead near a geometrical outline of an aircraft and counting the resulting number of fragment hits) but the higher-level models can be assessed only by comparison with the outcomes of actual conflicts (and partially from the results of major exercises or wargames).

Analysts addressing a particular question from military staff must select the appropriate level of detail in system modelling and the appropriate level of model in the hierarchy to obtain an answer of satisfactory accuracy while minimising the timescale and resources involved. Although computers have made it possible to develop and run larger and more detailed models than formerly, it is still preferable to answer any question at the lowest practicable level and incorporate only the relevant detail, since the answers are then more likely to be comprehensible and traceable.

1.4 Scenarios

The effectiveness of weapon systems depends on the circumstances in which they might be used, so that effectiveness must be assessed within a 'scenario' representing some potential operation by UK forces in fulfilling one of their military tasks. The scenario must specify the information needed for operations modelling, including the:

- Topography of the terrain insofar as it affects cross-country movement, lines of sight, and the potential for field fortifications; similarly maritime scenarios must specify the depth, temperature and salinity of the underwater battlespace.
- Features of the local climate and weather, which may affect the performance of sensors, weapons and personnel.
- Number and type of Blue units (including UK units) and of Red units which are expected to participate.

In each scenario there are likely to be some 'vignettes' describing particular operations that must be studied in greater detail because they are particularly numerous or critical. The vignettes may be identified in advance of the study, based on the judgement of the analysts and officers involved, or they may emerge from the results of the initial phases. Typical vignettes include an:

- Attack on a fortified village.
- Air attack of a column of armoured vehicles.
- Air-to-surface missile attack on a naval task force.

The results from detailed study of the vignettes are then used as inputs to the campaign modelling of operations in the scenario.

Some of the information required for any scenario, such as the area's geography and climate, may already be available within international databases. Other information (e.g. on the depth and marshiness of local rivers, and the architecture of local villages) can be gleaned by diligent, and perhaps clandestine, investigations in the area considered. The third category of information (e.g. on the tactics to be employed by the Red commander, or the weather during a conflict) cannot be determined and the scenario must rely on judicious assumptions.

OA for the assessment of alternative equipment options is generally based on a range of scenarios, though in special cases equipment may be assessed only in the scenario for which it is specifically procured. The scenarios for any assessment must be chosen from an MoD-approved set (of perhaps two dozen) which are not predictions of future conflict but are representative of the areas and circumstances in which UK forces might have to fight. When an equipment option is chosen for MoD procurement because it has done well in a range of chosen scenarios, it is presumed implicitly that it will also be effective in a future conflict which might actually occur. Where scenarios involve allied forces, the effectiveness of UK forces must be assessed in terms of their contribution to allied capability, which is a more complex calculation dependent on the number and characteristics of the allied forces deployed.

1.5 Sensitivity

The results of an OA study depend (like all studies) on the validity of its input data and assumptions. There may be considerable doubt about forecasts of the performance of future weapon systems, particularly if they rely on untried technology or if they are being developed by foreign nations and hence are screened by security. It is therefore necessary to test the robustness of the study's conclusions by exploring the effect of credible variations of the input data and assumptions. The importance of consistent sets of assumptions cannot be overemphasised especially when radically different weapons are being considered. Whether it is better to acquire a slow-moving, cheaper, high-fire rate, land capability or a fast, highly manoeuvrable, expensive, lower delivery rate, airborne capability will be radically affected by the assumption made about data on the target's location and the timeliness of that data; thus the output of a comparative assessment could depend on the quality of the intelligence which may not be part of the particular acquisition process.

The results of such scrutiny of input data and assumptions may reveal, for example, that warship A remains more cost effective than warship B by between 15% and 30% for any credible variations of the study inputs, in which case warship A can confidently be selected for procurement. Alternatively it might be found that warship A's usual 15–30% advantage could become a 10% disadvantage if its new radar system encounters insuperable problems in development and falls significantly short of its performance target; in this case it may be prudent to delay approval until further technology demonstration has resolved (or at least reduced) the doubt about the radar's likely performance.

1.6 Operational analysis through the life cycle

OA can be applied to support all phases in the life cycle of a defence equipment project. Even before the project is conceived, OA of current or future operations by UK forces can identify shortfalls in their capability, and can guide research to explore those areas of technology which are likely to yield the required enhancements. When a user requirement document (URD) has specified a capability enhancement, OA studies of alternative classes of equipment can indicate which might most cost-effectively provide that enhancement, and can support the formulation of a system requirement document (SRD). Later, a more detailed OA study can compare alternative proposed equipment options (following the COEIA procedure) and help to identify the option offering best value for money. During the procurement phase of the chosen option, OA can be used to evaluate the operational benefits or penalties associated with trade-offs in equipment design and performance. In parallel, OA by other MoD branches can explore the best tactics to exploit the new equipment, and identify the most economical arrangements for its maintenance and logistic support. Such studies should be repeated during the service life of the equipment in response to changes in the threat, or to the introduction into service of another related UK or allied project, or to the restructuring of the service and/or industrial organisations responsible for support.

1.7 Operational analysis in war and peace

During a war, OA of ongoing operations can develop improved tactics for existing equipment, and can identify priority requirements for new or improved equipment to offset any current or anticipated area of enemy superiority. Such OA work is done under the urgent pressure of continuing UK casualties, and the outcome of its recommendations becomes evident through prompt feedback (favourable and unfavourable) from the battlefield. The analysts involved must therefore bear a heavy responsibility for the success and/or survival of their service counterparts, as well as having to undertake rigorous and rapid analysis under pressure.

Successful OA in wartime requires a high level of mutual trust and respect between the military and the analysts. The military must report their experiences accurately and completely and the analysts must base their recommendations on a good understanding of actual operations. It helps if analysts have some experience of field exercises or operations, sharing the discomfort (and some of the danger) faced by the troops which they are trying to assess.

OA in peacetime is less urgent (with bureaucratic deadlines rather than operational ones) but it is more challenging in other ways. A period of peace yields no data on the effectiveness of current weapon systems and analyses of operations cannot be validated. Analysts must be alert to avoid a progressive divergence between the accepted ideas about future warfare and the reality of that warfare when it occurs, and to resist any pressures from stakeholders (in government, the services or industry) which tend to widen that divergence to benefit their own political, of four alternativeinstitutional or commercial interests. Analysts must (as in wartime) seek rapport with other stakeholders, while remaining aware of where their interests coincide or diverge. In peacetime, without supporting evidence from current operations, analysts must be particularly persuasive in presenting unwelcome recommendations in order to have any hope of having them adopted.

1.8 Operational degradation

OA studies must recognise that service personnel operating equipment in combat may be subject to considerable physical or psychological stress. They may be tired, hungry, uncomfortable or frightened, and their ability or willingness to perform assigned tasks may accordingly be degraded (despite earlier training to prepare them for combat). This degradation in personnel performance is sometimes represented by a 'jitter factor', indicating how military personnel under fire use their weapons much less accurately. Furthermore, during combat operations they may be faced by an ingenious enemy who has a very strong incentive to avoid the strengths of UK weapons and to exploit their weaknesses. It follows that the effectiveness of equipment on the battlefield can be significantly less than inferred from peacetime trials, even when these trials have replicated important factors such as the terrain and weather of combat conditions as faithfully as possible. Battlefield effectiveness can be very much less than predicted by simplistic theoretical studies in the concept phase. Studies of historical combats suggest that operational degradation, from all causes, can reduce a weapon's effectiveness by up to 90% of the theoretical level. The level of operational degradation depends on the culture, motivation and experience of the personnel considered, and on the circumstances in which they engage the enemy; the personnel of crewed weapon systems (e.g. armoured fighting vehicles) mutually reinforce each other's courage so such systems suffer less degradation. It is important to remember that these same considerations must be applied to both sides in a conflict. This would reveal the benefits of superior training

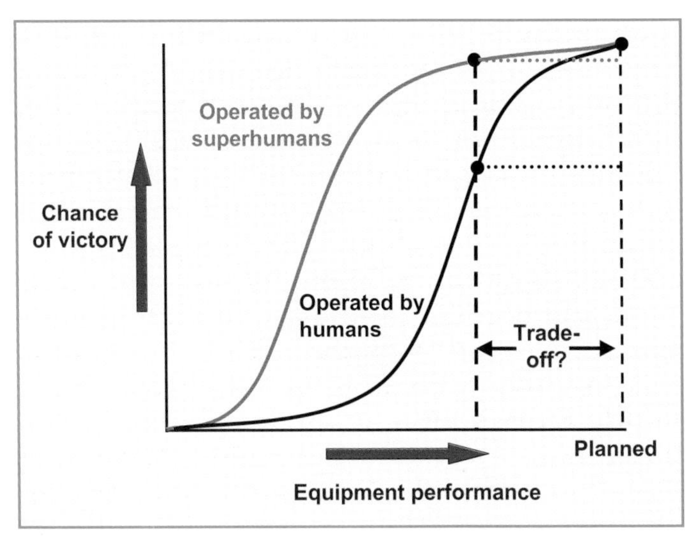

Figure 66. When considering the impact of equipment performance on the chance of victory, it is essential to make a realistic assessment of the trade-offs bearing in mind the capabilities of the end users.

and battle readiness of regular, as opposed to conscript, forces. Whilst it has often been said that 'an army marches on its stomach', there is no doubt that a reasonable night's sleep is better preparation for a conflict than suffering a 'shock and awe' night.

If operational degradation is ignored (as too difficult or too embarrassing to evaluate), OA studies can yield over-optimistic predictions of the complete defeat of the enemy with little cost to UK forces. Such results can encourage project managers to accept trade-offs leading to lower levels of equipment performance, which might appear to be satisfactory but would be entirely inadequate on a real battlefield. OA studies should therefore incorporate estimates of operational degradation derived from battle reports and extrapolated from realistic exercises.

It is also important that defence systems engineers do not place excessive demands on the strength, robustness and courage of military personnel. Although selection, training and discipline mean that military personnel do possess these qualities to an unusual degree, they are not all superhuman. They are inevitably inclined not to operate equipment in the prescribed way if this involves a high risk of injury or significant discomfort, and equipment design must therefore include consideration of human factors (see Chapter 3, Section 4).

1.9 Strengths and weaknesses

OA provides quantitative assessments to support decisions on force structure, equipment selection, trade-off options or operational tactics. The results are traceable from agreed input data, scenarios and modelling assumptions, and they provide the basis for a constructive debate between factions which may accept or reject their conclusions.

On the other hand, an OA study can take much longer to reach a conclusion than an experienced officer takes to reach a considered judgement, particularly if the OA study requires development of a new model to represent conflict against unforeseen opponents on unfamiliar terrain. OA analysts may themselves have little if any experience of military operations, and may not fully incorporate in their models the friction and fog of war which affect actual operations. To counter this problem, the MoD sends young analysts on field trials and exercises, and embeds experienced officers within OA teams.

A stochastic OA study can provide a probability distribution for the outcome of a military operation, ranging from victory to disaster, and hence predict the most likely outcome. If the study had perfectly represented all key features of the operation, the results of an infinite number of such operations would reproduce the same probability distribution of possible outcomes if the analysis were also done perfectly. However OA cannot predict the success or failure of a single operation. Before the allied landings in Normandy on 6 June 1944, General Eisenhower knew that the landings were likely to be successful but he could not be sure of the outcome of the actual operation. Accordingly he drafted two communiqués announcing respectively victory and defeat. Nevertheless the OA prediction of the most likely outcome is valuable to system designers trying to optimise their equipment and to officers trying to optimise their tactics. Both can be guided by OA to select those options which make it more likely that the actual outcome of an operation will be favourable.

1.10 Conclusions

The contributions of OA to MoD decision-making are more likely to be successful if the OA studies involve an interactive relationship between the analysts and their military customers, to obtain results which combine the professionalism of both groups. Such results can significantly assist MoD decisions on future policy, acquisition and operations.

2 Combined operational effectiveness and investment appraisal

The combined operational effectiveness and investment appraisal (COEIA) procedure was adopted by the MoD in 1991 to assist decision-making on the selection of defence equipment. The procedure was not entirely new, since a comparable analysis had been done as part of the Tornado aircraft project and a very similar procedure called cost and operational effectiveness evaluation (COEA) was already in use in the US.

After a balance of investment (BOI) study (see Chapter 1, Section 3.2) within an area of equipment capability has identified the class of equipment which might most economically provide the enhancement of that capability required by a service customer, the COEIA procedure helps to identify, from a range of proposed projects in that class, the option offering the MoD best value for money. A COEIA includes only assessment of military and financial issues, so its results must be considered alongside other factors (such as industrial and diplomatic) that might influence the MoD's decision on procurement.

2.1 Difficulties in defence equipment selection

In defence equipment acquisition, the selection of the optimal proposal from a range of alternatives is often more difficult than in other sectors of the economy for the reasons cited below:

- Major defence projects are large, complex, expensive and have very long lifetimes.
- Most defence projects must be close to the leading edge of technology, to avoid being outclassed when they enter service, and hence incorporate some risks of failure to attain the project's targets of performance, cost, timescale and effective integration.
- The enhancement to national security provided by a defence project is delivered many years after the procurement decision, is difficult to predict precisely in a changing geopolitical situation, and is poorly understood outside the MoD branch responsible.
- The funds for defence projects are drawn from the Treasury and have been reluctantly contributed by millions of taxpayers.
- Many stakeholders – such as those in the MoD branches responsible for procurement, operation and support, in the Treasury and in other government departments, in UK and foreign industry, in allied governments and international organisations – are all vitally interested in the selection and claim their rights to influence it.
- A blunder in equipment selection could cost the lives of UK service personnel and could endanger the success of future UK military operations.

Projects in the commercial sector and in other parts of the public sector share some of these problems, but only defence projects suffer from the whole list.

2.2 Evolution of selection procedures

Decades ago, the MoD's acquisition of defence equipment was a two-stage process. In the first stage, the defence staff justified their need for some new equipment, and specified within a staff requirement its target performance and desired design features in considerable detail. In the second stage, the Procurement Executive assessed the proposals received from contractors to determine which were 'compliant' (i.e. satisfied all of the design and performance requirements), and then identified which of the compliant proposals was the most economical. This should have meant selecting the compliant proposal which had the smallest net present value (NPV) over the project's life cycle, in accordance with Treasury guidelines on investment appraisal (IA) (see Chapter 4, Section 2). In practice it often meant deciding on the compliant project which had the lowest procurement cost and which fitted most comfortably, alongside other current projects, within the limits of the MoD equipment budget.

Even when it took proper account of the through-life cost, this procedure had the disadvantages of ruling out any equipment proposal which did not satisfy the staff requirement in (virtually) every detail, and of giving no credit to any equipment which significantly exceeded some of the requirements.

Subsequently, the Procurement Executive adopted a 'scoring and weighting' procedure for the assessment of rival proposals. In this procedure, each of the design and performance features of any potential proposal was compared to the corresponding part of the staff requirement and then allocated a score related to the excess or shortfall of that feature of the proposal relative to the requirement. That relationship might be linear or non-linear, with or without break points, according to the expert judgement of the MoD officials responsible.

The scores for a particular project (derived from dozens or hundreds of targets depending on the scale and complexity of the project) were then combined to produce a technical figure of merit for the proposal. This was often done by multiplying each score by an agreed weighting factor and then adding the products, or by some other multi-attribute decision process. There was inevitably scope for debate on which scoring scheme should be adopted for each aspect of design and performance, and on the relative size of the weighting factors. The proposal's likely cost and timescale could be compared with the appropriate budgetary and delivery targets, scored and weighted like the other features of the proposal and incorporated within an overall figure of merit; alternatively, and more frequently, the proposal's cost and timescale would be considered separately alongside the technical figure of merit to discover which proposal would yield best value for money.

Both of these former tender assessment procedures offered a traceable path between the characteristic features of a proposal and its selection (or rejection) for procurement. But decisions on whether or not a project was compliant, and on the appropriate methodology for scoring and weighting, inevitably involved subjective judgement and could generate ferocious debate. Both procedures relied heavily on the particular targets specified in the staff requirement and on the expertise of the procurement staff.

The selection process was simplified in some cases by specifying in the staff requirement only the most important criteria, called cardinal points. This approach reduced the volume of work in tender assessment and gave more degrees of freedom to the contractors' design teams, but it required early in the acquisition cycle an extensive debate on which requirements should be included in the list of cardinal points and which could safely be excluded.

Following the adoption of COEIA, the assessment of an equipment proposal now (2005) includes parallel analyses to determine its operational effectiveness (OE) in war and an IA of its through-life cost in peace. The proposal's OE is obtained by operational

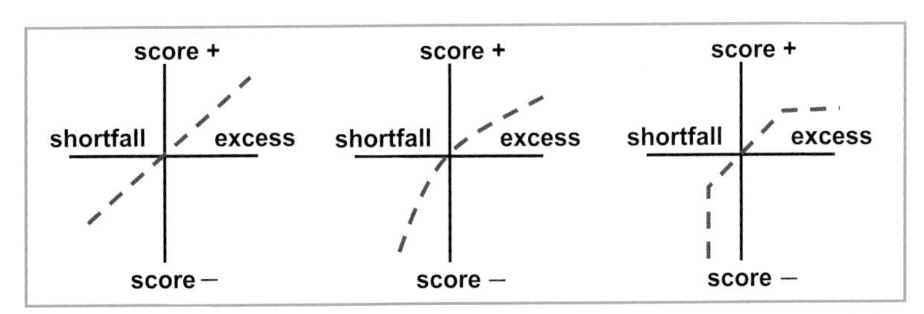

Figure 67. Some alternative ways of relating score to the shortfall or excess of the proposal's features compared to the requirement.

analysis, modelling its performance in several scenarios against specified hostile forces. Operational analysis has the advantage that it yields a relatively small number of measures of effectiveness (MoE) for the proposed equipment (such as the resulting Red/Blue exchange ratio), it allows explicitly for the performance of hostile and friendly units likely to be deployed in some future conflict, and it enables quality/quantity trade-offs by comparing the effectiveness of the proposed equipment with that of larger numbers of a cheaper variant. Operational analysis has the disadvantage that it requires sophisticated models of military operations which must be developed and validated at considerable expense for (or ideally in advance of) the assessment of a particular project, and which must be clearly illuminated to win the confidence of all the stakeholders.

When the COEIA procedures were introduced, the modelling of individual weapon systems and their effects on enemy personnel and materiel was well understood but it was more difficult to model the operational effects of improvements in command, control and communication systems, which might convey more or better or faster information to and from military commanders. Such systems continued to be assessed by traditional methods, using judgement to relate their performance to the quality of a commander's decisions, but recent studies now provide a rationale for more rigorous quantitative assessments of the value of information.

2.3 COEIA concept of analysis

The structure of a COIEA divides into four parts – concept of analysis, operational effectiveness, investment appraisal and the presentation of the results. This is shown in Figure 68. The concept of analysis provides the foundation on which the COEIA can soundly be constructed, and it must be completed and agreed with all stakeholders before starting the later phases. It defines all the key aspects of the COEIA, as given opposite, and a plan for its accomplishment.

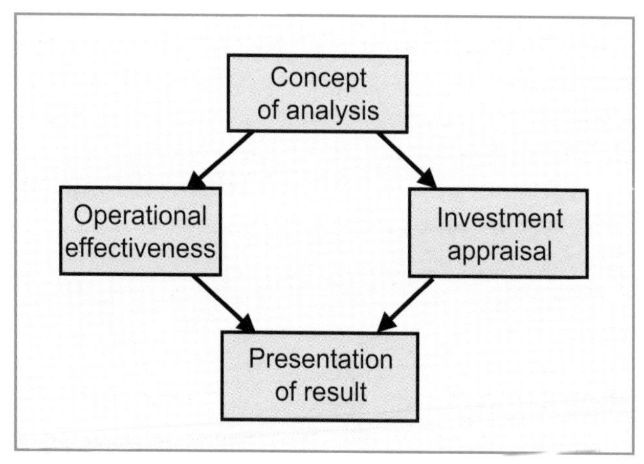

Figure 68. The COEIA procedure consists of four phases.

1. The range of equipment options to be considered and associated plans for their procurement and support:
   - A do-minimum option of continuing to operate the current equipment with normal repair and maintenance until it is withdrawn from service having become unsafe to operate, or impotent on the battlefield, or inordinately expensive to support. The Treasury insists that this option, which provides no improvement in capability, is always included to provide a benchmark from which the additional capability and cost of other options can be measured.
   - Refurbishment of the current equipment to extend its service life, or its replacement by bought or leased equipment with the same capability and a longer service life.
   - Upgrading some or all of the existing fleet to enhance its unit effectiveness, coupled (generally) with refurbishment to extend its service life.
   - Procurement or lease of off-the-shelf equipment which will provide at least some or all of the enhancement of capability required by the service customer.
   - Funding the development and production of new equipment (as a national or as a collaborative project) which will provide the enhancement of capability required by a service customer.

   Each of these options might include several sub-options with variations in the design, management or financing arrangements. Some of the options may be homogenous fleets, while others may be heterogeneous fleets comprising two or more complementary designs which together provide the capability enhancement required. It is important that the range of options does not omit potentially attractive proposals which do not incorporate advanced technology and hence may appear unglamorous to both a service customer and to the industrial suppliers. NASA developed (expensive) pressurised ballpoint pens for American astronauts to use in space but their Russian counterparts used pencils!
2. The chosen measures of military effectiveness to be used in the assessment of alternative proposals and a series of scenarios (drawn from the MoD-approved list) in which the assessment will be made.
3. The time period to be covered by the COEIA, yielding a robust and fair comparison between alternative proposals; this is particularly crucial when some proposals have different dates of entry to service and withdrawal from service. The preferred time period is normally 20–40 years after main gate approval.
4. Any significant military or financial interactions between the proposals in the COEIA and other concurrent projects, whose cost or operational effectiveness might be affected by the COEIA's recommendation.
5. A framework for the clear and equitable presentation of results.

2.4 COIEA operational analysis and investment appraisal

When the concept of analysis has been agreed, the OE and the IA studies are done in parallel by different teams, with only sufficient liaison between them to preclude any emergent inconsistency. This separation helps to restrict unnecessary dissemination of the intelligence information used in the operational scenarios and of the commercial information embodied in rival contractors' proposals. The conduct of IA is described in Chapter 4, Section 2.

2.5 COIEA presentation of results

The presentation of COEIA results must synthesise and illuminate the military and the financial aspects of the alternative proposals. The results are presented, along with industrial, political and diplomatic factors, in the business case (BC) submitted to the MoD's Investment Approvals Board, seeking authority to invest in the next phase of a project. A preliminary BC is submitted at initial gate and a more definitive BC is submitted later at main gate; both versions incorporate the results of COEIA based on the best information then available. The BC should be as succinct as practicable (currently a maximum of 40 pages including appendices) but can refer to supporting papers containing more detailed data and analyses.

It is often helpful to present the results of COEIA studies on alternative proposals as points on a cost-effectiveness graph whose axes are the proposals' effectiveness in war and the NPV of their associated expenditure in peace. Where practicable, the number of units associated with each of the options is scaled (e.g. option 2 in Figure 69 below) to provide the same enhancement of military capability, allowing the comparison of cost at constant capability. In some cases where the number of operational units or organisational units is small (and it is impractical to procure 3.5 ships or to equip 2.8 regiments), the option must be scaled in discrete jumps to get as close as possible to the target capability.

Each plotted point may be replaced by a splodge whose scale represents the assessed risks to the cost and effectiveness of that proposal and the robustness of its results to variations in the scenario assumptions. Each plotted point (or splodge) actually summarises time profiles of effectiveness and of expenditure through the chosen time period of the COEIA, and each proposal should be examined to ensure that these profiles do not contain unacceptable troughs in effectiveness or unacceptable peaks in expenditure. If such peaks or troughs do exist,

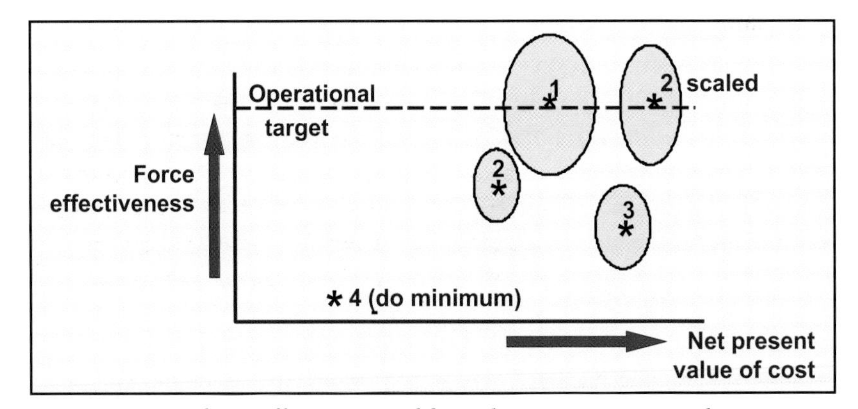

Figure 69. How force effectiveness of four alternative options relates to cost.

they probably need to be eliminated by adopting different plans for scheduling and/or financing and the proposal should then be reassessed on the amended basis.

2.6 Lessons learned

Since the COEIA procedure was adopted, it has been found that the resources required to accomplish it vary widely, from £10K to over £1M. When there are many credible options for a major project, with intense political/industrial antagonism so that rival contractors amend their proposals frequently in search of competitive advantage, the cost and time required for a COEIA study can be significant. In other cases, when the issues are well understood and concern only a small group of officers and officials with well-established mutual respect, the COEIA can be done relatively cheaply and quickly. Expenditure on COEIA of some 0.1% of the project's forecast procurement cost is regarded as an appropriate level.

The COEIA procedure demands the assessment of a wider range of proposals than was considered in former years (because the options considered do not all have to be fully compliant with a service requirement), and the new geopolitical situation demands consideration of a wider range of scenarios than formerly. This imposes a severe strain on the MoD's analytical manpower. But the time and cost of a COEIA is well spent if it identifies a proposal offering significantly better value for money than an inferior proposal which might have been favoured at the start of the study.

3 Decisions under uncertainty

3.1 Introduction

In the early stages of any defence equipment project, risk analysis makes it evident that the project may be affected by a variety of internal problems and external events and that its outcome is therefore uncertain. However, the project manager must still make decisions and adopt policies which lead to the best outcome possible. The first step is to derive, from the perceived probabilities and impacts of the risks associated with the project, an array of values of, for example, the final cost of the project, depending on the outcomes of the risks.

3.2 Expected values

Decision-making can be guided by the expected values of alternative options. For each option, the expected value of cost E(£) is the sum of the products of the probabilities p and the costs £ of the possible outcomes.

$$E(\pounds) = \Sigma\, p_i \pounds_i$$

Thus, for example, the expected value of buying a £1 lottery ticket with a one in a million chance of winning £100,000 is:

$$
\begin{aligned}
E(£) &= (1 - 10^{-6})\,(-£1) + (10^{-6})(£100{,}000) \\
&= -\,£1 + 10^{-6}\,(£99{,}999) \\
&= -\,£1 + £0.099 \\
&= -\,90p
\end{aligned}
$$

which implies those buying such tickets value the euphoria of a period of hope at more than 90p.

Consider, as another example, a project having a chance (judged to be 10%) of encountering a difficulty in development which would cost £100K to overcome. The project manager could implement a contingency plan which would cost £20K and which would enable the difficulty (if it occurred) to be overcome for £50K.

Using expected value methodology:

$$
\begin{aligned}
&E\text{ (no contingency plan)} = 0.10\ (£100K) + 0.90(0) = £10K \\
&E\text{ (contingency plan)} = 0.10\ (£70K) + 0.90(£20K) = £25K
\end{aligned}
$$

This calculation could be repeated to illustrate the effect of credible variations of the probabilities and costs, but as it stands it would be reasonable for the project manager to forgo the contingency plan. If faced with many comparable difficulties with similar expected values on the project, the no-contingency policy would (probably) be more economical than implementing contingencies in every case.

However, if the manager was responsible for only that one project and chose to forgo the contingency plan, he would have to be able to fund the £100K to overcome the difficulty if it arose; the manager's chosen option (to insure or not to insure against that difficulty) would then depend on the relationship between the potential cost and the available finance, just as householders may adopt different policies with regard to insuring their house and its contents.

3.3 Decision trees

More complex projects, involving a sequence of future risks and decision points, may be represented by a decision tree. In this representation, the current decision is the point at which the trunk divides into two or more branches (options) and the upward branches continue to divide in response to successive risks and decisions; the tips of the uppermost twigs are marked by the outcome costs associated with each different potential sequence of risks and decisions. If the probabilities of each risk outcome are known, the decision tree can indicate the sequence of decisions which would yield the lowest expected cost.

The construction of a decision tree helps to illuminate assumptions about the project and provides a framework in which stakeholders can debate their different views. By presenting an overview of the project, it can help defence systems engineers to understand how different risks may be related and to adopt a holistic approach. However, for very large projects the decision tree must be simplified or subdivided to remain comprehensible (and within a systems engineer's 'headful').

3.4 Payoff table

An alternative aid to decision-making, particularly when the probabilities of different outcomes are unknown, is the 'payoff table', presenting an array of possible outcomes of the project. The payoff table for the example described in Section 3.2 above (writing costs as negative) is:

OPTION	OUTCOME		WORST
	No problem	Problem	
No contingency	£0	–£100	–£100K
Contingency	–£20	–£70	–£70K

Figure 70. An example of a payoff table showing a variety of possible outcomes.

The payoff table can be used to identify the worst option associated with each option; the 'maximin' approach then recommends choosing the option providing the most favourable result irrespective of the outcome of the problem. In this case, the project manager would choose to implement the contingency plan and limit the additional cost to £70K whatever happens. This is a very cautious, risk-averse approach which takes no account of the probability that the difficulty will arise and would still opt for a contingency plan even if it cost £49K.

Another example was published in the *Economist* (30 March 1996). Following the first death in 1985 of a British cow from bovine spongiform encephalopathy (BSE), known as mad-cow disease, the number of cows dying each year rose exponentially (doubling every year up to 1992 when 3,500 died). The government did not know whether cattle with BSE might infect humans and/or pass the disease to their own calves, but it had to decide between strong action (of mass slaughter, draconian food regulation, etc.), masterly inactivity or a modest compromise. For this illustrative example, it is assumed that if no action were taken and infectivity proved high, the cost of the disease would be 100 but that mild or strong action (costing 10 or 40 respectively) could reduce the cost of the disease by 50% or 90%.

The payoff table for these assumptions is:

OPTIONS	INFECTION RATE			WORST
	Zero	Medium	High	
Do nothing	0	–50	–100	–100
Mild action	–10	–35	–60	–60
Strong action	–40	–45	–50	–50

Figure 71. An illustration of the possible outcome of BSE infection in cattle.

In this situation, an optimistic government might choose to do nothing and hope that the infection rate proves to be at or close to zero, but a cautious government following the maximin approach would take strong action.

3.5 Regret table

An alternative approach to the above problem uses a 'regret table' which is constructed by identifying the best outcome for each assumed infection rate and subtracting from it the outcomes resulting from other policy options. The result measures the government's regret associated with its choice of an inferior policy. The regret table, derived from the illustrative assumptions in the mad-cow example above, is:

OPTIONS	INFECTION RATE			WORST
	Zero	Medium	High	
Do nothing	0	15	50	50
Mild action	10	0	10	10
Strong action	40	10	0	40

Figure 72. A regret table illustrating the impact of choosing a particular course of action.

This table shows, for example, that if infectivity proved to be zero and the government had chosen to take strong action its level of regret would be 40. The table also suggests that the government could limit its regret to 10 (irrespective of the actual infection rate) by taking mild action. In reality, of course, the situation was more complex, with a large number of potential policies which could be applied to agriculture and food processing. Although this example is veterinarian rather than military, similar uncertainties must be faced by military officers planning operations against hostile forces whose capabilities and/or intentions cannot be defined with confidence, or by defence systems engineers implementing an unproven technology or when collaborating with a lukewarm ally.

Payoff and regret tables can clarify the options available to a government, or to a defence systems engineer, in situations where the probabilities of alternative outcomes are unknown. The estimated costs used in the tables can be varied within credible ranges to discover if such variations affect the selection of the best (or least unattractive) option. It is important to bear in mind that costs fall unevenly on the various individuals and organisations involved in a crisis (so that each stakeholder group has its own individual payoff or regret table pointing to the policy it would prefer), and to remember to anticipate diverse hostile responses to a chosen policy (however judicious it may appear at the level where the decision is made).

3.6 Multi-criteria decisions

Hitherto this section has assumed implicitly that the outcome of a decision can be measured in terms of a single variable, such as cost. That assumption is reasonably valid for commercial companies seeking to maximise returns to their shareholders, but in defence systems engineering it is necessary to measure the outcome of a decision in terms of performance, cost, timescale and effectiveness of integration of the resulting equipment project. In the BSE example described above, the government would have had to consider alternative policies in terms of the impact of human deaths from vCJD (variant Creutzfeldt-Jakob disease), and in terms of diplomatic loss of face and potential electoral defeat, as well as the costs to the agriculture and food industries.

When a decision must be evaluated against several independent criteria, a variety of scoring and weighting procedures can be used. Sometimes the outcome of the decision in terms of each criterion is scored, each score is multiplied by a weighting factor representing the relative importance of that criterion, and the results are added to provide a measure of success for the decision thus assessed. Alternatively, the outcome of a decision could be plotted in multidimensional space, which is divided into unacceptable, acceptable and desirable zones. Multi-criteria decision procedures may be followed by individuals or by groups; the latter approach demands greater resources but it tends to eliminate individual bias and to generate wider acceptance of the decision finally selected.

3.7 Conclusions

Each situation is different and it is often impossible to be sure (until years later) whether the best option has been chosen. However, even simple decision-making techniques help to illuminate the issues, provide a framework for debate and build a consensus of acceptance to the decision adopted.

Further reading

Air Ministry (1963) *The Origins and Development of Operational Research in the RAF*. London: HMSO.

Blackett, PMS (1962) *Studies of War*. New York: Hill and Wang

Coyle, RG (1972) *Decision Analysis*. London: Thomas Nelson

Forder, R (2004) Operational analysis in the Ministry of Defence, *Journal of Defence Science* 2(4): 319–32

Goodwin, P and Wright, G (1991) *Decision Analysis for Management Judgement*. Chichester: Wiley

HM Treasury (1988) *Policy Evaluation: A Guide for Managers*. London: HMSO

Kimball, GE and Morse, PM (1970) *Methods of Operational Research*. Los Altos, CA: Peninsula Publishing

MoD (1996) *Guide for the Conduct of COEIAs and Requirement Definition Studies* (note by DCS(S&A). London: MoD

—— (1997) *Principles of Cost Effectiveness Analysis* (note by DCS(S&A). London: MoD

Moffatt, J (2002) *Command and Control in the Information Age*. London: TSO

Chapter 6

Supplier issues

The UK defence industry is crucially affected by the health of the world economy and expenditure on defence equipment; a factor that affects its ability to grow its export markets. It also has to deal with the impact of UK and EU legislation, as well as MoD security policy, and ensure that the politicians in the MoD are managed to best advantage. The financial drivers for industry differ considerably from those of the MoD and it is important that defence systems engineers understand these differences. Industry must take careful account of the effort and resources necessary to bid for and win major defence contracts. The choice in industry of whether to grow a systems business by acquisition, joint venture or the use of sub-contracting will depend on the needs of the company and the particular circumstances, but is an essential aspect of producing major defence systems. Classic supply-chain management can be used to reduce costs and improve quality, delivery and reliability. Better understanding of the supply chain can be achieved by taking a systems approach that reflects on the complexity associated with products, transactions and capabilities. Finally consideration is also given to the features of defence equipment contracts.

1 World and national economics

1.1 Introduction

Why should anyone interested in defence systems engineering be concerned with UK or international economics? Defence systems are, by definition, expensive and long-term projects. Thus, their initial and through-life financing, as well as their possible export markets, are subject to the vagaries of the economic situation of the world, and to the impact of any financial stringency on defence spending. The through-lives of some major platforms are worth considering. The Nimrod maritime reconnaissance aircraft, currently undergoing a mid-life update, is expected to have a service life of 60 years. The American B52 bomber first flew in 1952 and the H variant, still in service 53 years later, is currently undergoing an engine upgrade programme with a planned life of a further 40 years.

1.2 Key economic factors

The armed forces of the world are as dependent on the international economic situation as any other sector, and the impact on them of the severe economic downturn that occurred in

1929 is well documented. The consequences of any recession are likely to impact on defence spending and affect the financial health of the vast majority of large companies. The dramatic rises in the price of oil by OPEC in 1973 and on subsequent occasions also caused significant economic problems worldwide. Other fundamental issues include:

- National inflation rates and perhaps more important, comparative inflation rates, particularly with major trading partners.
- National interest rates which impact on the cost of money itself, and comparative interest rates, again particularly with major trading partners.
- Exchange rate variations where the UK is presently in the unenviable position of having to deal with three much larger trading partners. Their currencies, the dollar, the euro and the yen, fluctuate dramatically and unpredictably against sterling.

Economists continue to struggle to forecast correctly the future trends in all these crucial areas.

1.3 Defence spending

After the fragmentation both of the Soviet Union and the Warsaw Pact, world defence spending fell markedly over the 8-year period starting in 1989, driven by 'peace dividend' cuts in Europe and North America. It has been growing ever since. Despite these cuts, military spending by the US, the world's only superpower, still dwarfs the expenditure of other nations and, together with Canada, accounts for nearly half of the world's total on manpower and equipment.

While Europe has perceived a reduction in the level of threat of regional conflict, the rest of the world has not and, in many cases, has tended to augment defence budgets. This has produced a steady increase in spending in the developing world. The new millennium has seen a dramatic increase in the perceived level of terrorist threats and this has produced some increase in defence spending by the industrialised nations in their attempts to win 'the war against terrorism'. Add to this the US tendency to get involved in conflicts across the globe (Iraq, Afghanistan and Somalia are recent examples), which has led to a consequent increase in military budgets to cover these substantial operations. Chapter 1 gives details of defence expenditure worldwide.

1.3.1 Global defence markets

The main worldwide defence suppliers are the US, Russia, France, Germany and the UK. While the US has dominated, over the last two decades the share of the market held by countries of the former Soviet Union has reduced. Today Russia has the lion's share with the Ukraine some way behind. The shares of the UK, France and Germany still dominate those of the other industrialised nations with Italy and Holland some way behind the top three European suppliers. The biggest threat to the established order is China, but there are likely to be growing sales by other arms-producing nations such as Brazil, India, Israel,

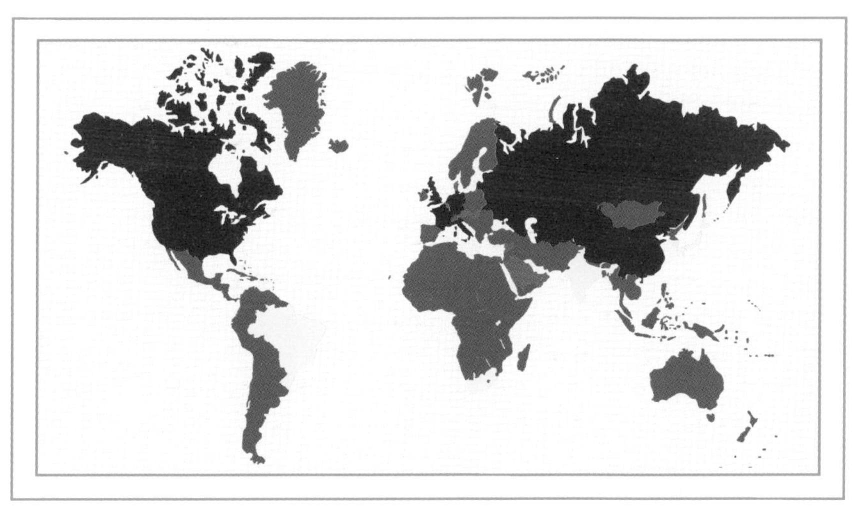

Figure 73. The dominant defence equipment supplying nations (red) and those likely to threaten that dominance (yellow).

Japan (the last was prohibited from exporting arms following the end of the Second World War but is now rebuilding market share) and South Africa. All these nations have established burgeoning aerospace industries with considerable defence manufacturing capabilities. Furthermore, labour costs in Brazil, China, India and the Ukraine are still significantly lower than in the industrialised nations.

Defence exports are important to the economic well-being of many nations and especially to industrialised nations' trade balances. Exports also prolong the length of time equipment remains in production as well as the period over which support of the equipment is available economically to the armed forces which operate it both in the exporting nation and its customers. Overseas sales are used selectively to support 'friendly' nations but are also denied to some nations, particularly those identified as currently belonging to the 'axis of evil'.

2 UK export markets

The UK is currently the second largest supplier of defence equipment behind the US. It is followed by France, Russia and Germany, but there are rapidly expanding defence exports from countries such as the Ukraine and China that could challenge the UK's position. Exports support the UK defence industrial base, help with the balance of trade and provide income for the government by means of royalty payments. They also ease the support of equipment sold to the MoD by lengthening the period that it continues in production and spreading one-time costs and manufacturing efficiencies (learning curve) over a larger production base.

From an industry point of view, exports are essential to obtain an adequate return on the development of defence systems. Significant sums of money and the work of key staff must be invested in the design of new defence equipment and the size of the UK market is too small to give an adequate return. Thus exports are essential if any UK defence contractor is to remain competitive in world markets. Over the last five years, defence-sector exports have slightly reduced and tend to be dominated by the air sector.

Values in £M	1999	2000	2001	2002	2003
Identified defence export orders	5,044	4,737	4,160	5,041	4,882
Split by equipment type:					
Air sector	3,385	3,501	3,245	3,553	3,526
Land sector	360	616	341	509	303
Sea sector	148	475	50	464	252
Not specified	1,151	145	524	515	801

Figure 74. UK defence export orders for equipment and services over the last five years.

The importance of exporting is recognised in the mission of the Defence Export Services Organisation (DESO), part of the MoD. Its role is to help UK defence exporters succeed.

- Giving assistance to company-led marketing campaigns.
- Nurturing relations with key decision-makers in overseas governments.
- Harnessing other parts of the MoD, armed forces and Whitehall to support industry.
- Negotiating and supporting government-to-government agreements.
- Advising the DTI on export-licence applications.
- Ensuring UK defence export policy is reflected in other MoD policies/activities.
- Supporting the MoD's defence diplomacy efforts.

Figure 75. The main tasks of DESO in support of UK industry.

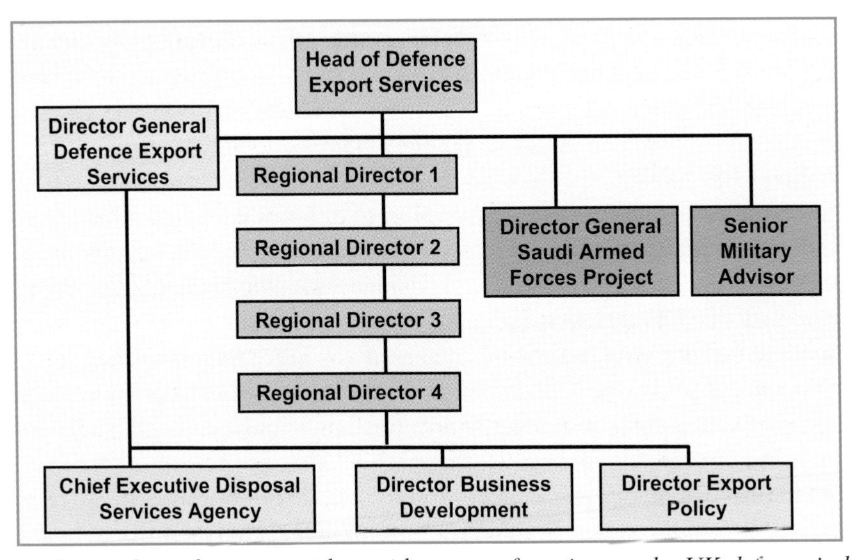

Figure 76. DESO employees provide a wide range of services to the UK defence industry.

DESO carries out a wide range of tasks in support of UK industry's efforts to win orders across the globe. Its structure is shown in Figure 76.

3 Industry and politics

In the UK, the defence industry includes a very broad range of capabilities including research and development, manufacturing, major civil works, estate management, software production, financial services, training, logistics, equipment operation and support. Industry is classified as British by the MoD if the technology is created, skills and intellectual property rights reside, jobs are created or sustained and investment has been made within the borders of the UK. The defence industry worldwide has been consolidating over the last decade and UK industry has to abide by the rulings of the Monopolies and Mergers Commission (MMC) and, where mergers with overseas companies are concerned, those of the MMC and the EU competition commissioner, as well as the equivalent US authorities. Trade associations are important to the defence industry, and organisations such as SBAC (Society of British Aerospace Companies), FEI (Federation of Electrical Industries) and DMA (the Defence Manufacturers Association) will lobby government on behalf of industry. They also publish useful data on their industry sector's performance.

Security clearance is critical for staff working on most MoD contracts and, for some work, individuals must have been born in the UK. In addition, computer networks need to be secure, providing significant problems for interconnectivity with the outside world. There are special issues for joint military/civil site working, though the increasing need for commercial security is reducing differences between the two. Export policy on defence equipment involves both the Department of Trade and Industry (DTI) and the MoD, with overall policy on 'friendly nations' being set by the Foreign and Commonwealth Office (FCO). One result is that the policy is in a continuous state of flux.

Political factors arise from three sources; local, national and European. Local government affects industrial companies in many ways, such as basic infrastructure (transport and communications links, electricity, gas and water), the availability of suitable homes for employees and, in times of expansion, planning permission. UK legislation has even more impact, setting employment laws, corporate taxation levels and, until its relatively recent move to the Bank of England, interest rates. Recent changes have been made to health and safety regulations as well as to human rights laws (where the EU also has an effect) and the government has recently set a minimum wage. Industry must implement these new regulations and provide evidence this has been done; the resulting bureaucracy is imposing a growing cost burden. One of the outstanding political issues is whether the UK will join the euro currency bloc and if so, when.

MoD ministers providing both defence and acquisition policies are required to report to Parliament. They are quizzed regularly by the parliamentary select committees that can call for evidence from senior civil servants and uniformed members of the MoD as well as defence industry leaders. The National Audit Office (NAO) examines the MoD's performance on a regular basis, publishing annual major projects reports as well as one-off publications

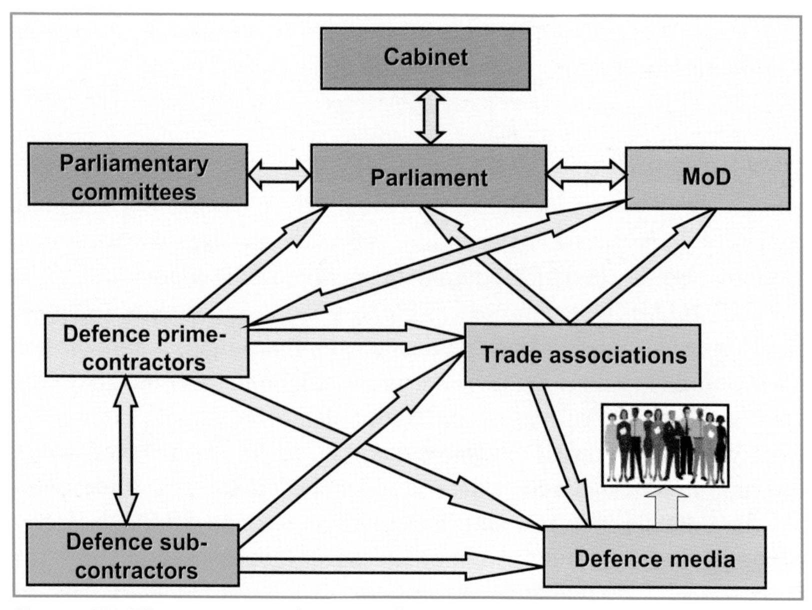

Figure 77. The interaction between the various players in the defence field.

such as: *Operation TELIC – United Kingdom Military Operations in Iraq*, *The Management of Defence Research and Technology*, and *Battlefield Helicopters*.

For any defence contractor, regular contact with its local MPs is crucial so that the company can provide them with briefings on the importance of forthcoming defence contracts and the likely impact on its finances and workforce. The local council needs to be briefed regularly to cover their interest in local industry and the employment it creates. Defence ministers should be briefed on a company's approach to providing a major new capability, as should members of the Commons Defence Select Committee. Some companies pay to get help lobbying, though this can, at times, prove counter-productive!

4 Economic issues for industry

The MoD is an organisation that has to live within its allocated annual budget and fight politically each year for its share of government expenditure, with requests for special allocations to cover the cost of any significant wars it has to fight.

Unlike the MoD, which is non-revenue earning, industry is motivated by making a profit for its shareholders. It is also driven to try to increase its share price and to remain in business. Payment of corporation tax is the main industry contribution to the government coffers; some of which goes to fund the MoD.

Industry has to deal with three main groups of stakeholders: its shareholders, its customers and its employees. Of course, the employees may be members of one or more recognised trade unions. It has to satisfy all three financially, which is a difficult balancing act for the board of any company. Investment funding comes either from shareholders, cash reserves or

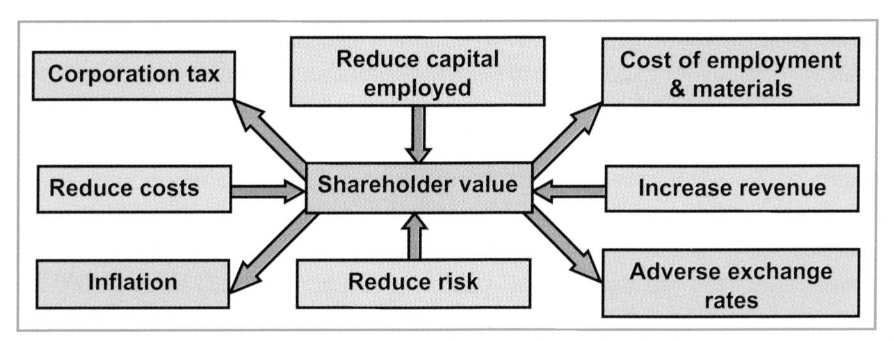

Figure 78. Defining the factors that influence shareholder value (either increasing or reducing it) is an important first step to understanding what motivates industry.

by borrowing; occasionally from customer contracts. The return on investment (ROI) is of key importance both to the City and to the shareholders. It is one of the key drivers of the share value and of the dividend paid to the shareholders twice each year.

Industry worries about exchange-rate variations with its main competitors; a weak pound benefits UK industry competitiveness in both domestic and overseas markets, but a strong pound has exactly the opposite effect. Differential inflation between the UK and the other industrialised nations is also a major concern; higher than average inflation saps competitiveness as it increases industry's UK costs.

In addition, both offset and barter are not uncommon when dealing with major defence contracts. In the former case, the supplier has to commit to its country giving an amount of work to contractors from the nation making the purchase. This amount may be less, equal to or greater in value than the contract. The MoD has historically placed offset requirements on suppliers when it acquires major systems from abroad, particularly the US. In the case of barter, the supplier is paid with goods to an equivalent value to the contract. In the Middle East, oil has often been used in barter deals, and the supplier will usually try to find a dealer to pay cash directly for the oil so that it does not have to become involved in an unfamiliar market.

It is common to find companies placing manufacture overseas, as well as other types of work. The reasons for this are based on a number of factors. First, labour costs are significantly lower in the developing world than in the industrialised nations. Second, dispersal of production can simplify the support of equipment supplied to a worldwide market. Finally, some nations will only place large contracts with foreign contractors if a percentage of the work is carried out in their own country.

The cost of employment and the cost of materials are the two key financial drivers for any company and in the UK, employment is often considered to be a fixed cost for the first year, since redundancy costs are generally of the same order of magnitude as one year's employment.

Company pricing policies for their products depend on the changing needs of the organisation. It is common in the defence industry to attempt to maximise the return on sales, but shareholders are really interested in the return on capital employed. More companies go out of business because they have run out of cash than fail due to lack of new orders.

Thus pricing to maximise net cash inflow is not uncommon nor is pricing to utilise available resources, which might otherwise have to be made redundant. Finally, companies also employ pricing policies to increase market share, to establish a new market position or to develop new technologies.

Companies also try to minimise their exposure to risk that may come from project performance shortfalls, cost or timescale overruns, or integration difficulties; all of these are not uncommon problems with major defence contracts. The other major sources of risk are obtaining and retaining the desired quality of employees and, for systems with long timescales, adverse inflationary and exchange-rate variations.

Export markets increase the volume of sales achieved by a company and introduce diversification into its markets. However, success in winning contracts overseas is affected by exchange-rate variations between the pound sterling, the US dollar and the euro. Furthermore, almost all military equipment is likely to require an export licence and sale of some items to some countries is prohibited.

Market research is essential if a company is to have a successful share of world defence markets, but such research is difficult to carry out in this field. It needs to look at opportunities, customers and competitors, but with a small community of customers and suppliers, allied to complex capability requirements for small numbers of systems, normal techniques such as questionnaires are inappropriate. Direct contact with the relevant defence staff of likely customers is the normal way of data gathering.

Since companies need to keep growing their profits to survive, Figure 79 shows the various tactics that can be employed. Market penetration involves winning business from the competition, something that is never easy. New products and systems may be developed and sold into existing markets such as defence. New markets can be developed for existing

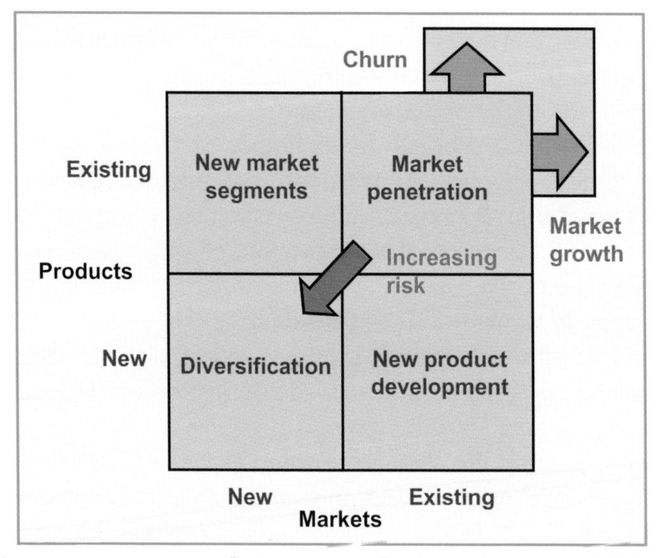

Figure 79. There are many ways of winning new business (an expanded Ansoff diagram).

products; a key driver behind exporting. Diversification, new products into new markets, is not recommended due to the high risk of failure. Finally, some markets grow – not defence at the moment – and many companies employ churn, making existing products obsolescent by developing new replacements. Nowhere is this more apparent than in the information technology (IT) field where products rapidly become obsolescent and their suppliers cease to support them.

The way in which international and national economics interact to affect defence spending is complex, but many of the issues are straightforward and need to be firmly entrenched in the mind of every defence systems engineer. The era when Sir Henry Royce demanded engineering excellence for its own sake is long past. Many practitioners today consider that money is an engineering parameter. To manage this view, it is essential for defence systems engineers to understand the economic issues and pressures that may impact on the solution they are producing or planning to develop. In times of boom, defence systems engineers should anticipate that large companies will give priority to their civil marketplace customers and vice versa in periods of recession. In times of economic downturn, they should review the risk of a budget reduction. When inflation is high, they should expect rising interest rates to try to control it, and prices in the home market to rise. When exchange rates are adverse for sterling, they should plan for the higher cost of any imported equipment. When unemployment rates are low, they should anticipate the problems of recruiting and retaining qualified staff. An understanding of these economic issues will help defence systems engineers to:

1. Recognise the risk that the UK government or one of its collaborating nations may have financial problems and may be forced to cut project funding.
2. Recognise the risks of exchange-rate variations, rises in inflation and industrial disputes.
3. Take a realistic view of export prospects.
4. Anticipate more or less delayed deliveries as suppliers switch resources.

5 Bidding for programmes

Any company bidding for new programmes requires a number of factors to be taken into account. The first is the timescale of the bid and any subsequent work if a contract is won, together with any likely slippage in the bidding timescale and any changes to the requirement. In addition, thought must be given to any investment needed to win the contract (the cost of bidding, any pre-contract work and any required capital expenditure), the MoD's view of the company compared to that of its competitors, as well as the company's current and projected workload and other opportunities for similar business. The cost of bidding for the contract and the resources needed are also major factors.

Support for a programme can be crucial when bidding into the MoD (or any other customer). Who is supporting the programme in equipment capability (EC), who in the Defence Procurement Agency (DPA) and who in the Defence Logistics Organisation (DLO)? Furthermore, who is giving support at the top level in the MoD and is there political support for the programme? It is also critical to arrange for a company employee to be seconded to the IPT as the industry member to improve the company's understanding of the customer's requirement, even though this person will be excluded during the bidding and bid evaluation.

Company planning for winning new work is driven by time to market for new systems, products and services. It is also constrained by a number of factors: the life cycles of existing contracts, the opportunities for winning new business (the ones the company forecasts it will win, plus a number of back-ups to these forecasts), and finally the expected phasing of the company's deliveries.

Contracting with the MoD is often arduous for industry. It is an expensive process (a successful bidder could well spend up to 10% of the value of the contract as could its losing competitors, adding up to a great deal of nugatory effort), the terms and conditions often cannot be flowed down the supply chain, and contracting frequently produces an antagonistic customer/supplier relationship. This is neither good for the MoD, nor for its suppliers, but one of the aims of the Smart Acquisition initiative, 'a better, more open relationship with industry' should improve this situation.

6 Acquisitions and joint ventures

In business, a company needs to grow if it is to keep up with the competition and satisfy the needs of its shareholders. The acquisition of another company is often used to gain access to complementary capabilities or specialised manufacturing facilities. Acquisitions are also useful for providing access to new markets, where the cost of entry can require a significant investment, as well as for increasing market share. This has been a major feature of the acquisition policy of large UK defence contractors (such as BAE Systems) needing access to the US Department of Defense market. Similarly, the French company Thales has made important acquisitions in the UK that have significantly simplified access to the MoD. Sometimes acquisitions are made by smaller companies to reach an effective business size or by larger ones because they feel they can run the combined business more efficiently.

Joint ventures are less aggressive than acquisitions and involve two or more companies setting up a joint-venture company incorporating resources from the parent companies. Joint ventures are often employed to pool complementary capabilities, to access new markets, to reach effective business size, to share investments and risks or to compete with a market leader. A good example of this comes from the missile field and is shown in Figure 81.

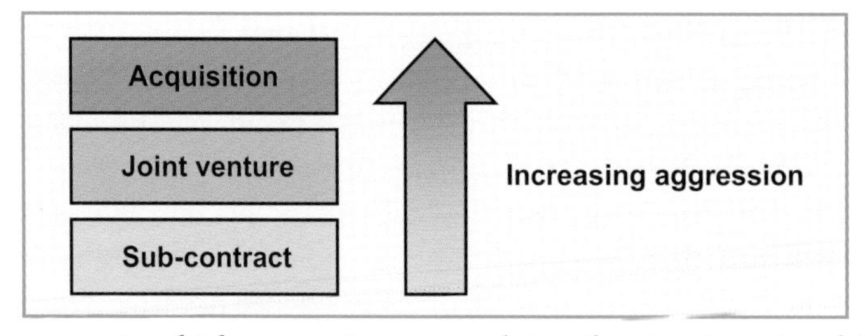

Figure 80. Three ways in which companies can work together to win major defence contracts.

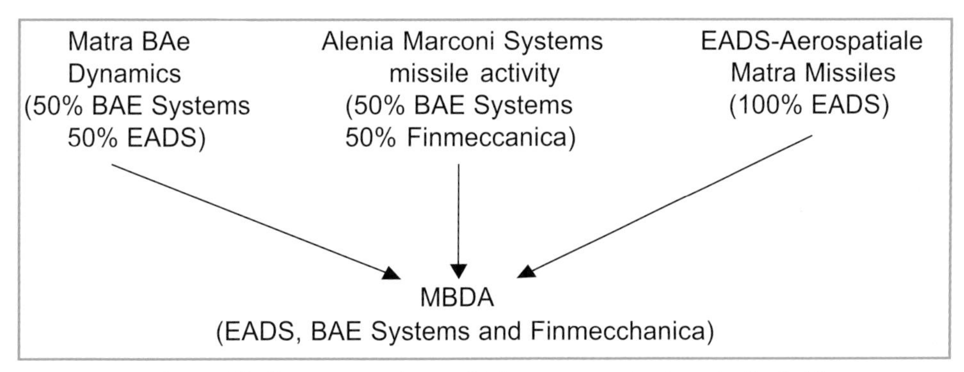

Figure 81. Two generations of joint ventures in the missile field.

A company can undertake a contract that is uncomfortably large for its own resources by the use of major sub-contractors, which produce systems, products and services that are integrated into the prime contractor's offering without the prime needing to invest in every single area of what is being offered. Dealing with sub-contractors involves forming supply chains, which tend to improve communications, reduce the prime's costs and investment, reduce risk both for customer and supplier and enable joint problem-solving. In a good supply chain, the prime contractor will share likely future sales information with sub-contractors to encourage supplier investment in research and development, production facilities and building for stock. Once trust is established, the repetition of final inspection prior to despatch by the sub-contractor, followed by inwards inspection by the prime can usually be avoided by merging these two consecutive stages into a single operation. All these benefits help both the prime and the sub-contractor, providing a classic win-win situation.

In gaining major defence systems contracts in today's world market, companies can rarely stand alone and expect to win the largest programmes. Experience has shown that they have to team with other potential competitors if they are to win the business and remain competitive.

7 Supply chains

7.1 Introduction

Just as defence acquisition procedures have developed and become more refined, so companies have improved their operations management. The driver for this development is, as always, the need to pare costs to the minimum commensurate with retaining business, but has been brought more sharply into focus in the UK since the 1970s by the extreme reluctance or even refusal of government to assist companies in difficulty. Other factors include the increasing competition from abroad, from companies with very low labour costs, and evidence that foreign companies are also leading in the development of new systems and procedures to enhance operational efficiency. Important among these are Kaizen, Kanban, lean manufacturing, Six-Sigma (see Further reading) and supply-chain management. The boundaries between these doctrines, and there are others, are not clearly drawn but they have the common aim of improving efficiency.

7.2 Supply-chain management

Effective supply-chain management (SCM) can contribute to cost reductions and improvements in quality, delivery and reliability. At its most simple, SCM can be thought of as a means of matching internal processes to external suppliers in unique supply chains to optimise manufacturing strategy. Classically, SCM concerns supplier selection (possibly rationalisation from existing lists) and management (operating with an improving supplier performance).

A defence systems engineering approach to SCM has to start from the premise that the supply chain is not merely a useful set of small- or medium-sized enterprises that produce make-to-print parts or low value sub-assemblies for the prime contractor. Effective SCM is an integral part of systems engineering; it must consider all the users and producers, their roles in research and development, in production, in service and in disposal, and possible effects on subsequent generations of equipment. Much of operations management has for over a decade recognised that SCM is not a narrow subject but concerns the whole value chain of end users, customers and suppliers. Founded in operations management literature, SCM is concerned with logistics, process re-engineering (e.g. just-in-time, product postponement, mass customisation and the exploitation of third-party logistics), organisational and manufacturing strategy.

Looking at SCM in this inclusive way highlights its complexities. If this view encapsulates all the relevant issues and solutions, how can the concept be simplified to understand better the inherent complexity? Three possible related solutions are described below that focus on product nature, transactions and capabilities.

7.3 Simplifying supply-chain complexity through product design

Complexity in production chains is strongly determined by the nature of the equipment. Complex systems such as military aircraft have integral architectures where major sub-systems (airframe, avionics, hydraulics and engines) cannot be made up from off-the-shelf components. Such systems also have high part counts that may require large numbers of suppliers with diverse capabilities.

Where product complexity can be reduced this may contribute to decreasing complications in supply chains. Potentially, this may be achieved through:

- Reducing the number of parts within systems. For example, it is noteworthy that the parts count between Tornado, Hawk and Typhoon aircraft on average has halved between each generation.
- Replacing integrated architectures with modular ones. For example, reducing the number of option configurations in a system by adopting commonality in design not

only reduces the number of parts, but also takes out design hours and manufacturing cost. Some components and raw materials can even be purchased off-the-shelf because they are commodities, i.e. when they are un-differentiated products. Already, procurement for such commodities and raw material inputs for defence systems can be purchased through EC B2B (electronic commerce business-to-business) web-based trading systems. Further commoditisation of parts may assist transparency and visibility in supply chains.

Reducing the number of parts per system and developing modular architectures both simplify supply-chain complexity as the total number of suppliers can be reduced. This may make it simpler to specify 'family trees' of suppliers to form a demand chain. Demand-chain management is the supervision of supply production systems designed to promote higher customer-satisfaction levels through electronic commerce. Electronic commerce can facilitate physical flow and information transfer, both forwards and backwards between suppliers, manufacturers and customers.

With fewer stages of production and reduced physical volumes of parts it may be simpler to convert push (infinite capacity planning systems) into pull systems (finite capacity). With fewer activity stages it may also be easier to plan production stages. Potentially, unplanned work-in-progress (WIP) is less likely to build up between stages. Other advantages from a simpler production system may result when design changes are introduced mid- or post-planning. When there are fewer stages in a production system it may be simpler to reconfigure operations within firms and across the chain.

7.4 Simplifying complexity through transactional efficiencies

Significant cost savings can be achieved when organisations reduce the number of suppliers they have for homogenous products. Indeed, unless capacity is an important issue, then maintaining more than one supplier for a certain piece of equipment can only be justified on strategic grounds. Theoretically, alternative sources of supply may be useful for two reasons. First, strategic supply can reduce the impact of a 'hold-up' when a supplier opportunistically exploits a monopolistic situation. Secondly, strategic supply potentially covers the risk of a supply source that fails to deliver. Arguably, a long-run strategic partnership between buyer/supplier, where there is a high degree of transparency between the parties, should negate the need for strategic supply. Achieving this goal is no simple matter.

In addition to specifying simpler, efficient supply-chain architectures, reducing the complexity of transactions between organisations may assist supply-chain development. A transaction represents an exchange of information or goods between stages of a production process. Potentially, transactions include those that take place between value-adding stages within a company or, alternatively, purchases made by buyers from supplier firms. Many transactions within a value chain may be iterative and where multiple stakeholders are involved may have long durations and be highly complex. Different transaction options have different costs and risks that will determine supply-chain efficiency.

The most expensive way of managing a transaction is usually by vertical integration; retaining all the necessary capabilities in-house. This is costly as it is necessary to pay for the specialist capabilities themselves rather than for their outputs. One benefit of in-house transactions may be that employees within the organisation can communicate more frequently and easily with each other than employees communicating between companies. Thus, when operational problems arise it may be simpler and cheaper to rectify them internally. A second benefit of in-house transactions is that where they concern core capabilities, appropriate strategic premiums can be charged for their productive outputs. It may be less easy to make a profit on a bought-in capability.

Efficiencies in supply-chain management are likely to result when transaction costs can be reduced. Some transaction-costs savings can be achieved by supply-chain restructuring that eliminates duplicated or unnecessary supply-chain operations. For example, in a supply chain it may not be necessary to retain traditional sales and procurement functions between every tier of the supply chain if organisations are strategically and operationally linked.

Less costly transactions may also result when capabilities are outsourced. The cheapest form of transaction is to buy on the open market using little trading information other than delivery date, price and quantity of a standard product. Where little transactional data is required electronic commerce can greatly reduce costs. Thus, the notion of an electronic commerce-enabled market approach may be an important first stage in better supply-chain management where it is associated with forward and spot auctioning of commodity stocks.

At a higher value-adding level in the supply chain, an electronic commerce-enabled market approach may not be so efficient. Contracts associated with sophisticated transactions are always incomplete and more complex buyer-supplier interaction is necessary. An intermediate or hybrid approach may therefore be more appropriate where contracts require additional unspecified activities for completion. In such circumstances, electronic commerce may be less helpful in reducing transaction costs but this is not to say that it does not facilitate any aspects of an intermediate approach. Technologies such as common databases, system translators, data-transfer protocols and intra- and inter-factory networks economise on transactions and improve their quality.

When company activities are strategic rather than operational, then the issue of undefined capabilities in supply chains becomes a major issue. Perfect supply-chain efficiency is likely to exist in theory only because of competition between supply-chain organisations. When transactions are affected by transaction-specific investments there may be a strong incentive

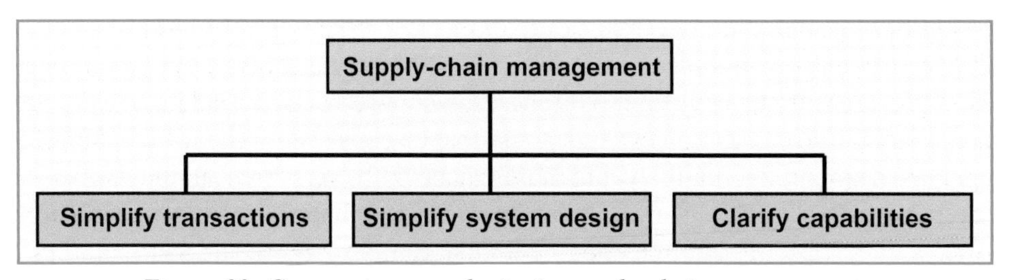

Figure 82. Conquering complexity in supply-chain management.

for companies to behave opportunistically. Opportunism can occur when one party in a transaction tries to exploit the other. For example, a supplier may develop a company-specific capability demanded by its customer. Subsequently, the customer could demand that additional activities associated with the capability should be the responsibility of the supplier. Equally, suppliers could behave opportunistically if they demanded higher prices when a customer had no alternative sources of supply. Effectively, a supply chain for complex equipment represents a series of transaction-specific investments between organisations. Thus, strategic opportunism risks are often high in SCM. These issues are likely to remain uncertain, complex and hard for defence systems engineers to forecast.

7.5 Simplifying complexity by clarifying capability roles

What organisations actually do in a unique supply chain is a crucial issue. The total stock of capabilities and their quality within a supply chain will be important relative to competitor supply chains. However, much of the preceding discussion suggests that capabilities may not be well defined. Consequently, in dynamic supply-chain environments it may not be clear precisely what is required of organisations. Examining the resources of a company can provide some insight into capability identification.

In the 1990s, the resource-based view became a dominant approach. Company-specific assets were seen as a significant feature of competitive advantage through which companies could leverage positions in the business environment. Core products are seen to be the result of the core competencies of a company and they provide bases from which to respond to the dynamics of the environment. Less crucial 'threshold' competences may also be important as generic capabilities that all companies in an industry must have in order to win business.

In theory, competencies drive company strategy. However, the lack of empirical evidence underpinning this view has called it into question. The major problem with the resource-based view of strategy may be how to translate broad concepts into meaningful and practical managerial capabilities.

Two approaches could be useful for describing capabilities that may be relevant to defence systems engineering. First, the range of capabilities for a supply chain could be defined crudely in defence through broad supply-chain tier activities. This may be useful in specifying modest architectures for supply chains. These are frequently conceived as having a pyramid form with the chain broadening as it descends, encompassing more companies and more skills and technologies. Pyramids may not accurately represent supply-chain structures and nets, webs or other complex systems may be more appropriate in some cases. However, for capability identification purposes a hierarchy between tiers may be a useful simplification. For example, aircraft manufacture can broadly be considered as dependent on tiers of base assembly, large- and small-scale integration, valued-added parts and assemblies, make-to-print parts and assemblies, and raw materials. This may be a helpful categorisation process for providing defence systems engineers with routes for adding value to industry-specific activities. Other classification schemes for non-aerospace defence supply-chain tiers may have similar structures.

Secondly, a more detailed approach to defining activities may be provided by defence systems engineering. Operationally, complex products can be decomposed into work-based and product-based activities using a work-breakdown structure (WBS). A WBS is a hierarchical breakdown of the work needed to complete a project including all deliverable items and associated services. WBS methods assume that work and product needs can be satisfied rationally by a series of sub-contractors. However, supply chains are not static and many strategic games could be played both before and after the contract-award stage. Potentially, SCM will gain the greatest benefits from new electronic commerce tools that enhance the transparency and visibility of capabilities linked to WBS. These will enable a better insight into which organisations are required to undertake which product and process stages of a manufacturing system.

Attempts to generate more generalised frameworks for supply-chain capabilities have also been developed that are relevant to defence systems. In the strategy area, an approach to capability identification was developed at the end of the last century using strategic benchmarking. It identified a set of critical technological and managerial capabilities for small- and medium-sized aerospace sub-contractors. The capabilities were tested using a questionnaire to establish the ideal global sub-contractor profile. At the start of this century, several complete aerospace supply chains were studied, including details of some military aircraft. They identified a strategic aerospace driver and response framework (see Figure 83) to assist with the selection of capabilities and resources for the whole supply chain. The interactions between the drivers and responses were found to be highly complex and only the category headings are presented here. Within the categories, a large set of lower-level drivers and responses were identified and these competency lists have been used in strategic-planning tools to assist with competency audits within aerospace suppliers.

7.6 Conclusions

SCM, in its broadest sense, can be seen as part of an holistic approach to company management. A defence systems engineering approach to conquering complexity in SCM can usefully focus on three types of systems. These systems include the systems of transactions and capabilities within and between organisations, and on product design. Optimising systems of transactions and capabilities with equipment or system design potentially provides greater transparency within a production system. With greater transparency, it may be possible to improve system quality, delivery and reliability at a lower cost. These are crucial factors highlighted as a key part of the improvements required by the DPA.

Defence systems engineers need to be aware of the procedures and disciplines now being applied in industry. To drive down costs, companies are monitoring inventory performance and, as far as is possible, removing stock from shelves. They are espousing standardisation and are ever more reluctant to undertake special work. In the MoD, similar efforts to reduce stockholdings have given rise to a policy of dovetailing stockholdings of spares and equipment to the declared readiness of the military units. Under these restrictions, contracts may be negotiated but orders are not placed with industry until the decision to deploy or bring forward the readiness state is declared. However, while a supplier may have given a general undertaking on delivery time when a contract was negotiated, the circumstances of the day

Drivers	Responses
Manufacturing, scheduling and performance	Manage manufacturing, scheduling and performance
Competition, price and cost	Through-life management
Supply-chain performance	Manage supply-chain performance
Offset, economic, social and political	Workforce and organisation
Civil product requirements	Understanding customers' sales and marketing
Military product requirements Offset Finance Diversification, acquisitions and mergers Managing politics	Contracts and intellectual property rights (IPR)

Figure 83. List of strategic drivers and responses for aerospace sector supply chains.

The related supply-chain system concepts for considering complexity	Problems	Solutions
Transactions	Are transactions duplicated?	Remove unnecessary duplicated transactions (rationalise supplier lists)
What is the cost of the transaction?	Can the transaction be simplified?	Consider ways to simplify transactions by organisational structures (intra- and inter-organisational links, make or buy decisions, on- or off-shore)
Design		
What is the cost of the design?	Is the design modular or integral? Can the design be simplified?	Introduce modular design where appropriate Introduce commonality in design where appropriate
Capabilities		
Who does what in the system?	What capabilities are needed in the system? Can the capabilities be clarified?	Identify system capabilities Identify work-breakdown system

Figure 84. Questions and solutions relating to the supply-chain system.

may make such assurances of little value. Certainly companies no longer hold stocks on their shelves in advance of receiving orders and it is unwise for defence systems engineers involved in equipment acquisition in the MoD to believe that 'It will be alright on the day'. However, defence systems engineers, in embracing the above disciplines within their own acquisition activity, must appreciate that defence suppliers are also applying the same degree of rigour to their own operations. In all probability, there will be no slack, no spare, no reserve and no contingency unless it is planned, specified, ordered and paid for.

8 Contractual issues

8.1 The role of contracts departments

In the MoD, the Director General Commercial Organisation develops commercial policies, provides central guidance on commercial policy to staff in the MoD and gives advice on intellectual property rights (IPR) and legal issues. Contractual powers are delegated to contracts staff who will work with the IPTs in procuring defence systems.

In most companies, the purpose of the contracts department is to protect the company from unacceptable business risks. The role of a contracts department is to deal with all contracts and legal issues, mainly working on agreements, IPR and government documentation as well as preparing and signing contracts. It is also normally responsible for submitting the price and for leading contractual negotiations with the customer. In addition, it often deals with the shipping of systems to their destination and obtaining payment from the customer.

8.2 Contracts

With the complexity of most defence systems, formal contracts are essential to define who is to do what work, when and for what price. The contract should protect both parties if something goes wrong and should cover every eventuality, ranging from a fire at the supplier's factory or strike action to contract cancellation by the customer.

A contract is a legally enforceable promise. The key criteria used to judge the existence of such a promise are the 'consideration' and the 'agreement'. The key definitions are:

The consideration – is the price of the promise.
The agreement – requires both an offer and an unqualified acceptance.
An offer – is normally written and is either refused, subject to counter-offer, accepted or expires (if the potential customer takes no action). Counter-offers negate the original offer that can no longer be accepted unless reoffered.
An acceptance – agrees to the offer under the conditions made in it. It must be unconditional otherwise it is a counter-offer. Once accepted, the contract binds both parties.

Figure 85. Legal definitions of four key terms used in all contracts.

8.3 Contract pricing

'The price is the price is the price' really does not apply to defence systems. First, the time from the start of the contract to completion is years if not decades and the cost will be affected by inflation. Secondly, if parts of the system are purchased from foreign suppliers, variations of exchange rates will impact on the supplier's costs. Thirdly, payments are likely to be phased across the duration of the project. There are many adjectives used to define the various types of prices used in contracts. The following terms are widely used:

8.3.1 Fixed or firm price

Firm price and fixed price are two contentious terms, which are variously used to imply prices inclusive or exclusive of inflation.

> **Either** – A price fixed in money terms, including an allowance for inflation made by the supplier.
> **Or** – A price that is exclusive of inflation, usually containing a contract-price adjustment clause.

Fixed and firm price is another possible description of a price that includes inflation.

8.3.2 Budgetary price

A budgetary price enables potential customers to put realistic figures into procurement budgets. Any budgetary figure must be tied to an order timescale to remind the customer to include any necessary escalation. A 'not to exceed' price is a form of budgetary price that carries the same escalation caveats; it is an attempt by customers to prevent suppliers quoting unrealistically low budgetary figures in order to get themselves into a front-running position.

8.3.3 Cost plus

A largely obsolete form of price, where the purchaser pays all the actual costs of doing the work plus an agreed fixed percentage. While clearly encouraging suppliers to do as much work as possible to maximise profit, it is still sometimes used in research contracts, where the amount of work to be undertaken is all but impossible to estimate.

8.4 Contract documentation

A contract for a defence system is normally a collection of detailed documents. There is the contract itself, including the total price, payment terms and other terms and conditions, the delivery timescale and a description of the equipment and/or services to be supplied. Normally, there is a more detailed technical description that may include the original technical proposal from the supplier, though amendments made during negotiations usually make a reissue more satisfactory.

The aim of the technical document is to enable compliance with the requirement to be proved at delivery; this is more difficult when the purchaser issues only a capability requirement. Inevitably, there may be other even more detailed documents, such as spares lists, contents of training courses and building-interior specifications. The amount of paper in technical documents can easily fill a filing cabinet and on the largest and most complex defence systems takes significantly more space. There is an apocryphal story of a US admiral saying that the paperwork specifying an aircraft carrier would completely fill the ship! Care should be taken in agreeing which documents are part of the contract, which are not, and their order of precedence.

8.5 Contract terms and conditions

Purchasers in requests for tenders usually propose contract terms and conditions; normally prepared by their contracts departments. Some clauses are almost certain to be standard ones. In the case of the MoD, these are defence contracts conditions (DEFCON). Since such a set of terms and conditions unilaterally represents the desires of the purchaser, a supplier's response will normally take exception to certain terms, offering replacements that reflect their concerns and reduce the risks they face. For the selected supplier, such clauses may be negotiated in an attempt to obtain a contract that addresses both parties' respective concerns and interests.

8.5.1 Intellectual property rights

All intangible rights including patents, registered designs, copyrights, trademarks, confidential know-how and trade secrets are defined as IPR. An increasing problem with defence systems, particularly but not exclusively those with large amounts of software, is the retention of IPR by the vendor. Public procurement policies have attempted to escape from proprietary solutions, in order to avoid being locked in to a particular contractor, by gaining access both to intrinsic IPR (that associated with the offering) and also to background IPR (that relevant to a broad range of the supplier's work).

This is a slippery slope for suppliers, who may subsequently find they are parting with manufacturing drawings to be bid on subsequently by competitors. The supplier's typical response to such overtures by purchasers is the use of undetailed manufacturing drawings, which are of no practical use without additional design work. A company that has invested significant amounts of its own money in parts or all of a new defence system will always wish to protect its IPR. This single issue can take disproportionately large amounts of effort in negotiating to a satisfactory contract, particularly where the MoD has also paid for part of the development.

8.5.2 Liquidated damages

After price, probably the most important factor in a defence system contract is the delivery date. Liquidated damages is the term used to define and limit the amount of money payable for a breach of contract of this type. These damages are intended to be a fair and reasonable constraint to the liability of the supplier. However, for the MoD it is difficult to prove actual financial loss, often making it challenging to impose liquidated damages on the contractor.

8.5.3 Force majeure

Force majeure is an unforeseen event causing excusable delay to or default of a contract. Such occurrences would otherwise involve both customer and supplier in expensive and extended litigation. Since the law does not define the term, contracts should always include a definitive statement, detailing problems such as strikes, fires, outbreak of war and theft.

8.5.4 Passage of title

The point of transfer of ownership is often a key element of a contract. With most defence systems, the point of transfer is far from clear unless carefully defined, and for software elements particularly so. Occasionally, customers may be happy to accept their defence systems at the factory gates, but the vast majority will want the equipment transported to the customer's selected site; often installed and commissioned there. In many cases, the defence systems will actually be built on site. The International Chamber of Commerce INCOTERMS defines the relevant terms and periodically updates them. The most commonly used are:

Ex-works – Title (ownership), along with risk and the cost of transporting the goods from the seller's works to the desired destination pass to the buyer when the purchaser accepts the goods that the seller has made available at the factory.
FOB – Free on board is a widely used term signifying that the goods will be loaded onto a ship (or aircraft) at a named port, the seller's obligations being fulfilled when the goods pass over the ship's rail. From that point onwards, the buyer has to bear all the costs and risks of loss or damage to the goods.
CIF – Cost, insurance and freight to a location is an alternative arrangement in which the seller purchases and pays for the insurance and freight costs on behalf of the customer. Delivery is still effected when the goods are loaded, as with FOB, so that problems after this point will result in the buyer benefiting from any insurance claim settlement.

Figure 86. The common INCOTERMS likely to apply to MoD procurements of defence systems.

The MoD's acceptance of a system, or parts thereof, is covered in DEFCON 5, and the key document is MoD Form 640 (Advise and inspection notes), which is used to obtain payment to the contractor. Clearly the form of inspection and test of part or all of the system will have an impact on acceptance. More information about these criteria is given in the next chapter.

8.6 Conclusions

Defence systems contracts are of necessity complex and use legal language and contractual terminology. Specialist knowledge is essential when drafting and agreeing contracts, but it is vital that defence systems engineers involved in procuring or producing defence systems have a basic appreciation of what is involved in contracting. Finally, any contract that leaves both parties with the feeling that they could have done better is probably a reasonably fair one. Certainly, neither side should feel they have 'pulled a fast one' on the other party since, as the project progresses, the other party may feel aggrieved and seek retribution.

Further reading

Chalmers, M et al (2001) *The Economic Costs and Benefits of UK Defence Exports*, University of York monograph. York: University of York

Choi, T, Dooley, K and Rungtusanatham, M (2001) Supply networks and complex adaptive systems: control versus emergence, *Journal of Operations Management* 19: 351–66

Collier, B (1980) *Arms and the Men: The Arms Trade and Governments*. London: Hamish Hamilton

Fine, C and Whitney, D (1996) *Is the Make-Buy Decision Process a Core Competence?* Boston, MA: MIT Center for Technology, Policy and Industrial Development

Frohlich, M and Westbrook, R (2001) Arcs of integration: an international study of supply chain management, *Journal of Operations Management* 19: 185–200

Gansler, JS (1989) *The Defence Industry*. Boston, MA: MIT Press

Gross, JM and McInnis, KR (2003) *Kanban Made Simple: Demystifying and Applying Toyota's Legendary Manufacturing Process*. New York: Amacom

Hamel, G and Prahalad, C (1993) Strategy as stretch and leverage, *Harvard Business Review* 17(2): 75–84

Hax, A and Majluf, N (1996) *The Strategic Concept and Process*. Upper Saddle River, NJ: Prentice-Hall

Latham, N (2003) *Defence Industry in a Global Context: Policy Implications for the UK* (Whitehall Paper 57). London: RUSI

Maurer, R (2004) *One Small Step can Change your Life: The Kaizen Way*. New York: Workman Publishing

MoD/CBI (1998) *Partnering Arrangements between MoD and its Suppliers*. London: Partnership Sourcing Ltd

National Audit Office (1989) *Support for Defence Exports* (HC 303). London: HMSO

Pande, PS, Neuman, RP and Cavanagh, RR (2000) *The Six Sigma Way: How GE, Motorola and other Top Companies are Honing their Performance*. New York: McGraw-Hill

Sampson, A (1978) *The Arms Bazaar*. London: Coronet Books

Taylor, T and Hayward, K (1989) *The UK Defence Industrial Base: Development and Future Policy*. London: Brasseys

Weiss, A and Willson, S (1994) *Winning Major Business*. Kenilworth: Greenfield Publishing

Womack, JP, Jones, DT, Womack, J and Jones, D (1996) *Lean Thinking: Banish Waste and Create Wealth in your Corporation*. New York: Simon and Schuster

Websites

www.cdi.org/

www.dasa.mod.uk/

www.mod.uk/

www.nao.org.uk/home.htm

Available from the MoD On-line Acquisition Management System www.arms.mod.uk: *Contracts Manual*

Chapter 7

Test and evaluation

Test and evaluation of any defence system is a crucial stage towards its acceptance into service. It is important for defence systems engineers to understand the various processes involved and the facilities needed. There are special requirements when testing software, and for all systems care is needed in documenting the results. There is no substitute for practical experience if real benefits are to be obtained from the test and evaluation process.

1 Introduction

Prior to entry into service, all systems, simple or complex, are subjected to some form of test and evaluation. This can range from a visual inspection to a complete test-to-destruction depending upon the nature of the system and the customer's requirements. It may occur at the point of sale or continuously throughout the systems design and development stages. The testing objectives may encompass suitability for purpose, attainment of required performance, system safety assessments, usability, durability, and even assessing the risk of not successfully achieving a viable system in the time or at the cost allotted. Testing to meet any of these objectives, and many others, and the evaluation of the acquired data is collectively known as 'test and evaluation' or 'T&E'.

1.1 Requirements

A requirement is not a requirement unless it is testable.

Crucial to the development of any system is the requirement for feedback on what has been achieved. This allows progress to be measured against some plan, indicates potential outstanding issues and allows the future activity to be planned. This is as true for the management and procurement of any system and the resulting product acceptance as it is for any active vehicle control system.

Historically, many have considered this test and evaluation to be the acceptance process by which a product is evaluated prior to release into service. This view has been reinforced by the US procurement cycle that, unlike most other nations, has as a requirement the legal obligation to use independent test and evaluation to demonstrate safety and performance at the end of the procurement process. The outcome of leaving system evaluation to some final demonstration is that any identified deficiencies are discovered at a time when rectification is both more costly and more time consuming. Accordingly, some testing has always been performed by all nations throughout the acquisition cycle, much of it being hidden under terms such as - development tests, contractor tests and live-fire tests. This is recognised within the systems engineering process by making test and evaluation a throughout-life process involving all programme participants.

This thinking has repercussions throughout the life cycle and has particular significance at the requirements' drafting stage. By viewing test and evaluation as a feedback process, it is clear that a requirement is not a requirement unless it defines what is required, how achieving it is to be measured, and what resources are needed to perform this evaluation. Furthermore, programmatically, it is also vital to define who needs the information, when it is needed and whether the defined resources are budgeted within, and available to, the programme. These needs will lead to tension between those desperate to create and deliver 'something' to the customer and those who have to estimate the resources needed for the whole programme. Even today, getting this message across is extremely difficult since the option of leaving test and evaluation to be viewed as the finale of the programme process reduces potential conflict and allows many issues to be overlooked. It encourages sloppy requirements to be written, e.g. 'it shall be better than the previous system'. It often allows a low cost of testing to be presented, 'testing to destruction may be the only way a badly written requirement can be demonstrated', and it can give erroneous timescales and risks; 'test pieces such as realistic targets may take longer to develop than the weapon system itself'.

To mitigate these risks it is essential that, early in any project, a test plan be created which is continuously developed and improved as the project requirements are better defined and their costs are rigorously forecast. No requirement should be accepted unless the accompanying test and evaluation needs are also defined and costed. Currently in the UK this plan is known as the integrated test evaluation and acceptance plan (ITEAP). (In the US it is the TEMP or test and evaluation master plan.)

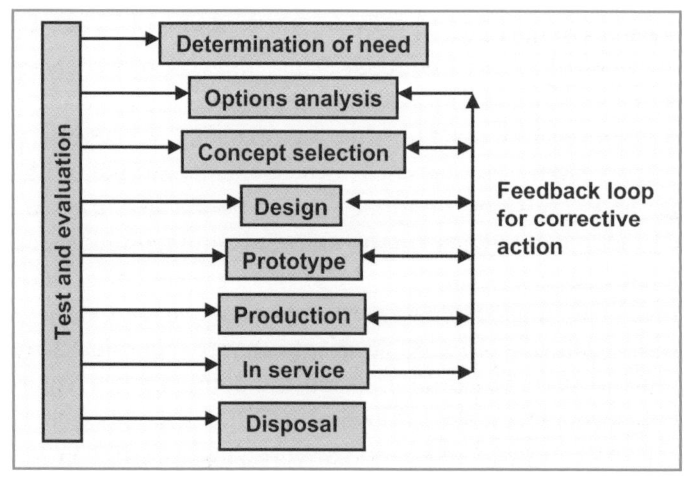

Figure 87. Test and evaluation is carried out at every stage of an equipment's life cycle to enable corrective action to be implemented as early, and economically, as possible.

1.2 Testing

Build a little test a little.

There are many reasons why testing is performed; these vary according to the type of acquisition and the desired objective. The procurement of commercial off-the-shelf systems will have different testing needs from the acquisition of a revolutionary air defence system. Repeat buys may need different tests from the purchase of research and development items. Examples of reasons to test are:

- Do not trust the supplier.
- No knowledge of testing previously performed.
- System too complex to understand.
- Want to use system for other than designed purpose.
- Legal protection.
- Undesirable 'emergent properties'.
- Prove engineering concepts.
- Demonstrate component functions.
- Verify performance meets contractual specifications.
- Validate component integration.
- Evaluate system operation.
- Ensure producibility.
- Verify system effectiveness.
- Evaluate combat effectiveness.
- Estimate system operations cost.

Figure 88. There are numerous reasons why testing is seen as essential.

What to test is a judgement that requires total system awareness. Clearly in a large complex system it will not be practical, or cost effective, to test everything. Previous experience with systems of the relevant type as well as extrapolation from current systems is beneficial but the general rule is to consider testing everything and to reduce the level of testing only based on a positive decision that not testing represents an acceptable decision. These decisions are test assumptions that should be recorded in a risk register since subsequent system changes may render the risk unacceptably high. The temptation is to test only doubtful areas, or items that are thought to be risky, or worse still only those for which knowledge of how to test exists. Emergent properties from complex systems are still not totally predictable – the relationship between contract cleaning and the MRSA bug in hospitals is an example. There must therefore be a compromise between testing everything, random tests, and testing a single item (as in acceptance tests). Decisions need to be taken on the level of testing for all hardware and software, by manufacturers, suppliers and operators. As with all defence systems engineering this is a team decision involving all stakeholders.

When to test is another judgement call that will clearly depend upon the nature and complexity of the system or sub-system. Generally, testing must take place throughout the procurement to enable the build-up of an acceptance case based on the 'build a little test a little' approach. This may establish sufficient confidence to render full product testing unnecessary or impractical; the US lunar landing programme was one such example. Alternatively, random batch testing may be the only way forward – test firing every round of ammunition to confirm consistency is clearly idiotic!

To assist in resolving these issues it is essential to have an awareness of the model that is being used for the procurement considered. This will exist in all acquisition processes. It may in some cases be an individual's understanding of how a relatively simple system works but for complex procurements it will be paper-based ('the process') and/or exist as a software or hardware representation of the acquisition process and the desired system. This may only be a notional model at the outset but as a project develops it too must be developed and refined to increase the model's relevance. The testing that is performed should be that which resolves conflicts within the model or which confirms, or denies, the relevance of assumptions made within the model, thus enhancing the value of the model for this procurement and allowing judgements to be made on further test activity.

1.3 Test engineers

Don't shoot the messenger.

Although test and evaluation is a recognised skill in the US where there are dedicated test and evaluation branches in the armed services, in the UK it is generally perceived as an add-on skill with very few qualified practitioners. This led to the introduction of an MSc test and evaluation option within the DEG suite of courses but there are virtually no other T&E specific courses in the UK. Often, testers do not call themselves by this title preferring to refer to themselves as Research and Development Engineers or Trials Engineers or even Experimenters. Test and evaluation appears in many guises such as:

- **Development T&E (DT&E)** – testing used during product development.
- **Contractor T&E (CT&E)** – testing performed by a project contractor.
- **Live fire T&E (LFT&E)** – testing involving explosive material.
- **Operational T&E (OT&E)** – testing primarily to ascertain operation roles and performance.
- **Marketing T&E (MT&E)** – testing to establish extent of market place and product acceptability.
- **Production T&E (PT&E)** – testing to ensure repeatable, safe and cost effective manufacture.
- **Research and development T&E (RDT&E)** – testing usually to establish viability of options.

Figure 89. Some of the titles testers use and the tasks they carry out.

In all cases the skills required are the same: a good understanding of the environment and operational role of the final product, an awareness of the impact on the system of these, and experience of similar system testing to identify what is practical and likely to be relevant.

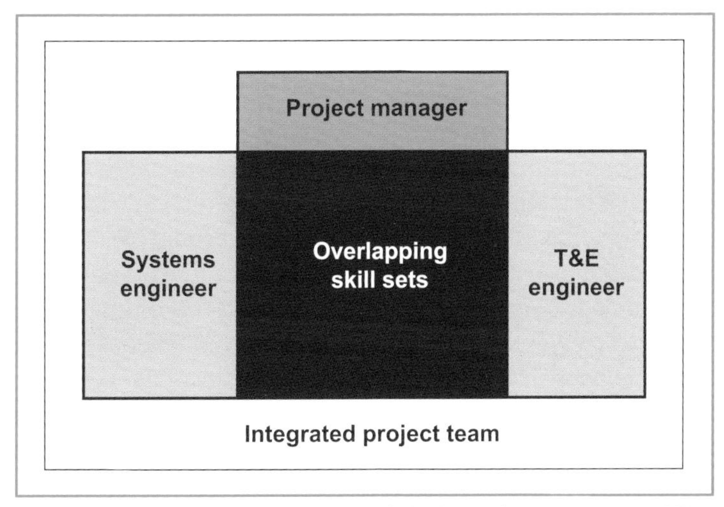

Figure 90. The overlapping relationship of skill sets between some IPT members.

Complex system testers need to have knowledge of a wide technology base, the ability to understand new technologies, a clear awareness of likely programme risks, good communication skills and the ability to analyse, interpret and explain results. Management skills are also vital, creating a similar skills set to those needed by both systems engineers and project managers.

2 Test process

Bertrand Russell published in 1931 a description of a scientific method or law (based on earlier work by Bacon in the seventeenth century), which suggested three basic steps:

1. Observe the significant facts.
2. Develop a hypothesis that, if true, would fit with these facts.
3. Deduce from this hypothesis consequences that can be tested by observation.

Today these can be translated for test and evaluation, a basic scientific process, as:

1. Identify the system under study, its environment, boundaries and requirements.
2. Create or obtain an appropriate model/models based on item 1.
3. Identify parameters that require measurement to confirm that the model is a reasonably representative. In particular seek out expected 'emergent properties', forecast their occurrence and levels, create tests to verify these predictions and feed results back to improve the model's accuracy and relevance.

By adopting this approach the test and evaluation process can be readily seen as an application of scientific method to establish a system's worth.

2.1 The system under study

The system under study and its environment is that which it is agreed to be.

Identify first the system under study, its environment, boundaries and requirements. In Chapter 9 the importance of understanding the boundaries of the system under study is discussed as are the limitations that it is intended to impose over its interaction with the environment in which it is destined to operate. If designing a multi-purpose radio receiver, it is unlikely that it will be possible to afford to test its installation in every candidate vehicle. Some aspects of the environment must be taken as 'given', usually in the form of interface/environmental standards. In the radio receiver example these would limit extraneous emissions and define the maximum field strengths that are assumed to exist in any of the vehicles. (Note that the example only refers to electromagnetic compatibility (EMC) issues and has ignored the man/machine interface discussed in Chapter 3, Section 4.) This bounding is essential in the creation of a meaningful understanding of what needs to be tested, what is being tested, and how and when to test.

It is also necessary to evaluate the requirements relevant to the system under study; remember that a requirement is not a requirement unless it is testable. Ideally all of the system's requirements will have had the associated parameters and tests defined as each requirement was created. This utopia is virtually unknown so interaction between the stakeholders and the testers is inevitable, continuously throughout the project, and is essential to establish the trade-offs between testing costs/timescales and 'nice-to-have' requirements. Different stakeholders will have different requirements and differing priorities. Production managers will focus on producability issues such as cost, rework, timescale and risk, whereas system operators will primarily be concerned with factors such as man/machine interfaces, operability, availability and performance. Both may have equally valid priorities and judgements will have to be made on which tests, if any, are to be performed to meet their needs.

2.2 The 'model'

A model is never the same as the real thing, only a partial representation of its full behaviour.

Create or obtain an appropriate model(s). The definition of an appropriate model relies very heavily upon the use to which it is to be put. Establishing potential military effectiveness is likely to involve a software representation of the relevant battle environment and the system under test, whereas evaluating the range of environments likely to be encountered across a variety of vehicles will often require field measurements using hardware elements from the system under test and, perhaps, the creation of a suitable test facility. It is also necessary to consider what already exists that is relevant, rather than reinvent the wheel, but care must be taken that the inherent assumptions contained in any model do not limit or even negate its relevance to the task in hand.

The expected level of confidence to be demonstrated also has a very important impact on the type of model to be used. The safety of a totally new military weapon will require very high confidence levels to be achieved by the testing, and is likely to involve analyses using a software model, a paper evaluation and physical testing of some or all of the hardware, whereas minor changes to the delivery packaging for repaired system elements may be agreed after just a paper assessment.

2.3 Testing emergent properties

Emergent properties are not always those that you want.

Identify parameters that require measurement in order to confirm that the model is reasonably representative. In particular, seek out expected/unexpected 'emergent properties', forecast their occurrence and levels, create tests to verify these predictions and feed results back to improve the model's accuracy and relevance.

Having established a model of the system under study, it is essential to confirm that it correctly represents the system, that it has been built to meet this understanding, that it has been properly created and is accepted as a valid model for the intended purpose. This activity is often referred to as validation, verification and accreditation or VV&A. Once this has been achieved, the model can be used to extrapolate and to predict likely outcomes in a range of scenarios. Scenarios are used to improve awareness of the ranges of condition likely to be encountered and also to assist stakeholders to ensure that their concerns are being covered. In a large complex system there will inevitably be a hierarchy of models, which range from limited but widely applicable software representations to detailed hardware-in-the-loop rig testing of sub-systems.

Using this range of models it is essential to identify which items require to be tested. This should be based on the concerns of the stakeholders and agreed by the project manager. Using the results of the modelling, tests should be devised to reduce the risk in the forecast outcomes. The results from this testing are then fed back to confirm the correctness of the representation or otherwise.

Expected results will allow additional extrapolation whilst unexpected results will require the model's applicability to be reviewed and may require the model to be changed. Alternatively, after consulting the stakeholders, the requirement may be changed to accommodate the new results within the existing model. Continuously cycling through this process should reduce the risk that the system, when produced, will fail to meet all the final set of stakeholder requirements or will display unacceptable additional characteristics.

3 Test facilities

Military personnel may form part of the required test facilities.

Test facilities take many forms. Full-scale testing of complex military systems, if practical, will require expensive and extensive facilities (or a war!) such as underwater acoustic ranges, air-to-air combat ranges and firing ranges. All will involve significant safety issues and are generally government owned. Complex, but physically more contained facilities such as environmental chambers, wind tunnels and test aircraft may be found in both the private and public sectors. Test rigs, vibration tables and the like are more usually found in the commercial sector. This is particularly true for those test facilities established for production purposes.

However, when planning trials it is essential to consider not only the real-estate facilities but also the manpower and test pieces that will be necessary. Does the planned test require combat troops, the use of a real submarine or destruction of a real target? If so, these will require significant forward planning and advanced warning, and may dictate the project's timescale.

4 Software testing

Human perverseness should not be overlooked.

It is not possible to go into all the details of the special requirements of software testing but it is vital to mention some of the particular issues that software can raise. Of major importance are the failure modes that can occur. Whereas with hardware systems these are generally finite, and hence can be evaluated, with the software elements of a system it may be impossible or impractical to test every conceivable path. They should be evaluated to the greatest extent practical, but then significant system/sub-system testing must be undertaken. This should include 'experts' trying thereafter to 'break' the systems as well as potential in-service operators being allowed to do their worst. As is regularly demonstrated whenever a new virus or worm hits the streets, many computer users who should know better often act

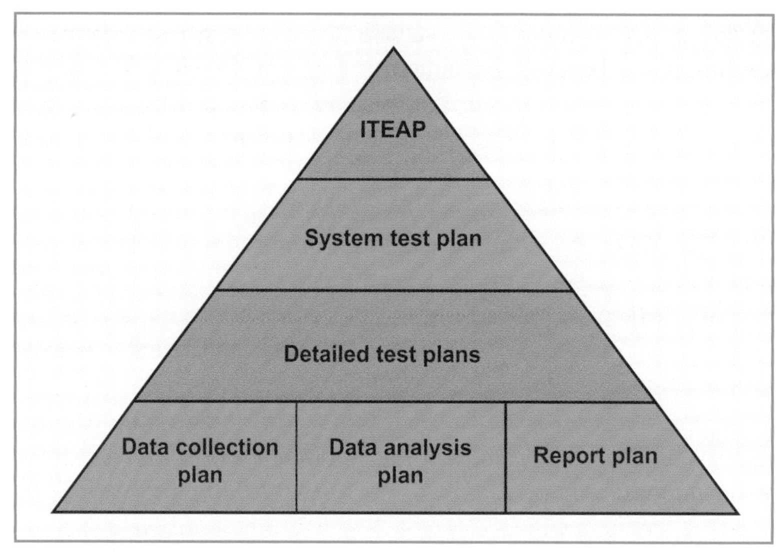

Figure 91. A number of individual plans build up into an integrated test evaluation and acceptance plan.

against sensible practice with costly outcomes. This human perverseness should not be overlooked when designing test schedules.

4.1 Synthetic environments

Often, the 'model' described above will exist only, or largely, in a software form. Using this model to test a hardware system is referred to as testing using a 'synthetic environment'. In some systems it may be impossible to use any other type of testing – following the agreed ban on nuclear testing, any assessment of likely outcomes of nuclear explosions can only be tested theoretically using a synthetic environment. Clearly this leads to two types of testing: the first is that in which the model or synthetic environment is tested to ensure that it represents the environment of interest, and the second is when testing of a system takes place within the synthetic environment to assess effectiveness of the new system. The importance of validation, verification and accreditation for both types of testing cannot be overstressed.

5 Documentation

A man's word may be his bond but a definitive test report is invaluable.

The end result of the test process should be a traceable set of documents describing the tests, models, results and limitations, that have reduced the project risk to an acceptable level. This documentation should be such that at a later date tests could be repeated to verify the results.

An outline of the various levels of documentation is given in Figure 91. At the highest level, the integrated test and evaluation and acceptance plan forms an essential part of the project approval documentation set. Within it there will be a number of system test plans, broken down into detail test plans, with full descriptions of the data collection activities, how the information is to be analysed and what it is trying to verify, how it is reported and to whom. This hierarchy of plans must also include details of facilities, test pieces and personnel required, as well as intended timescales, costs and recipients of the outputs.

6 Practical experience

No matter how frequently project managers are reminded to include test personnel, test requirements and test facilities early in their planning process, it is still quite common for the testing to be seen as part of the product acceptance process. Consequently, requirements are accepted into the project without identifying how they are to be evaluated, who is to be responsible for their evaluation and what is to be done with the results. Worse still, requirements are often seen which break the golden rule – if it is not verifiable/testable it is not a requirement. Typical examples are 'it shall be acceptable to an average combat-ready soldier', 'it shall be the best available', 'it shall interface with all (NB not defined) systems in service at the time', 'there shall be room for expansion', or 'it shall be cost effective'. The outcome of an imprecise requirement of this type is, inevitably, argument as to whether it has been met. This leads to cost and timescale overruns, a series of expensive modifications or the product being accepted but not meeting the full set of intended requirements. The time to resolve these issues is when the relevant stakeholder is in the process of approving the requirement – in the rush to get the project launched do not allow stakeholders to waffle vaguely about their requirements.

Another very common experience is testing scheduled to take place late in the programme (it may require a significant piece of the system to be built); any unexpected results may cause the project programme to slip. It is very easy to reduce the time available for testing in order to recover the slippage with no apparent cost. Naturally, there will be a cost; when the system enters service it will be carrying a higher risk than it should. A similar argument applies to funding. It is then quite common to suggest that the testers are 'gold-plating' the test programme and that savings can easily be made by reducing/cancelling parts of the test programme. Allocating insufficient funds for testing, or utilising the funds to cover up cost overruns, will only lead to a more expensive project in the long run when deficiencies occur after it has entered service.

It is also common practice to treat unwelcome test results as rogue answers. Clearly, if the testing reveals emergent properties that have not been foreseen and which are unwelcome this will embarrass the project. Sweeping them under the carpet to be rediscovered later does not serve the customer in the long term but may allow delivery to be scheduled thus meeting political expediencies, and may well allow the project leader to move on before the real results are discovered!

It cannot be too firmly stated that the systems engineering process represents a distilled and effective method for delivering successful projects, but only if the testing is integrated into the process as a continuous feedback activity throughout the whole acquisition programme.

Further reading

Equid, R and Dvorak, M (1998) *Principles of Test and Evaluation*. Adelaide: Systems Engineering and Evaluation Centre, University of South Australia

Reynolds, M (1996) *Test and Evaluation of Complex Systems*. New York: Wiley

Sydenham, PH (1997) Philosophy of master-planned test and evaluation, *Defence Science Journal* 47(4): 445–54

Websites

www.unisa.edu.au/seec/

Available from www.disa.mil/index.html: *Defense Acquisition Management Policies and Procedures*

Available from http://www.dtic.mil/whs/directives/corres/html/89101m.htm:*Procedures for Management of Information Requirements*

Available from www.defenselink.mil/: *US Test and Evaluation Manuals*

Chapter 8

Key aspects of management

The management of people has always been a difficult task, especially with the many and varied cultures found in the defence community, as well as when dealing with the customs of foreign defence organisations and suppliers. Defence systems engineers need to understand the difficulties of project management and also appreciate the impact of a decision to collaborate internationally on any major project. Such collaborative projects bring a host of problems not found with national programmes and it is essential that their advantages and shortcomings are understood. The performance, timescale and cost of a typical defence project are significantly affected by the outcomes of a multitude of events through the project's life cycle and these risks must be managed proactively and effectively to avoid as far as possible unacceptable shortfalls in performance, delays or increases in cost. The lack of successful management of risk has affected many high-profile defence projects.

1 Organisational structures and cultures

Three different groups with very varying cultures are involved in the life cycle of defence equipment; members of the armed forces, civil servants working for the MoD and people in a wide range of industrial companies. In terms of formality, the armed forces are pre-eminent with their uniforms, badges of rank and saluting. A quote by Admiral Cunningham emphasises their special quality. At the height of British naval losses in the Mediterranean in 1941, when it was suggested that withdrawal would be the best solution, he said: *It takes three years to build a new ship but 300 years to build a tradition.* Civil servants are less formal but still more so than industrial employees. The defence industry in the UK tends to mirror the culture of the MoD, whilst its degree of informality depends on its role, the type of work it carries out, the size of the organisation and the attitudes of its directors.

However, the biggest variation arises from the fact that the primary task of industry is to make money for its shareholders. Thus financial issues are of primary importance to all those who work for any defence contractor. Decision-making is more easily delegated in industry and, of course, the decision-makers do not face the Public Accounts Committee – only the annual shareholders' meeting that is usually much less hostile. It is also noticeable how, in the 1990s and in the new millennium, traditional defence contractors have become increasingly less reliant on defence business and on the MoD as a customer.

Individuals in each of these three groups have common interests and a loyalty to each other, resulting in team characteristics providing synergistic benefits. As a result, they may well initially tend to reject outsiders. It is important to recognise these differences in integrated

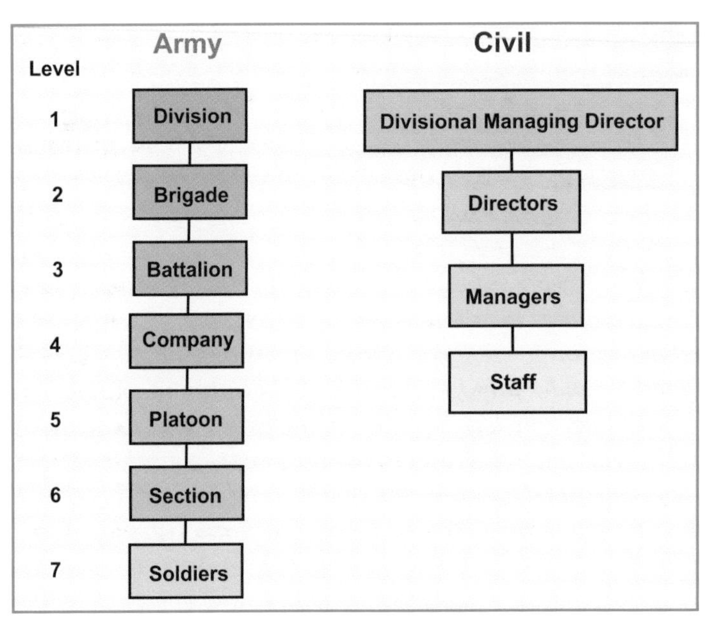

Figure 92. A military division tends to involve many more layers than its industrial counterpart, which usually has a flat organisation.

project teams (IPTs) where synergistic benefits are essential. It is also essential to avoid the trap of 'group think'; a mode of thought that people engage in when they are deeply involved in a cohesive group, and when the way members strive for unanimity overrides their realistic motivation to appraise alternative courses of action.

The structural differences between military and civilian organisations are illustrated in Figure 92. Industry has significantly slimmed down the number of layers of management, when compared with a classic military organisation. However, both tend to split top responsibilities. In the armed forces, the commander takes the executive decisions whilst the chief-of-staff deals with the day-to-day issues of running the force. In industry, the chairman is responsible for the long-term strategy of the company while the chief executive manages running a smooth business routine.

Both military and civilian organisations vary considerably in size, often involving multiple locations. There is a penalty involved with multiple sites affecting formal and informal communications, the development of different local cultures as well as the cost of staff travel and equipment shipping. Industrial companies can be larger than the UK armed forces and are generally broken down into autonomous units. The term 'division' is widely used and generally refers to units with between a few hundred and a few thousand employees. Individual sites may be product or function (manufacturing, engineering, finance, marketing) oriented. Matrix management is still common, where resources from the different functions are put into teams to deal with individual projects.

Some defence contractors, particularly the large ones, tend to be vertically integrated. As an example, a single company might build interceptor aircraft, manufacture its airborne intercept radar and make the key electronic components in the radar. It is very difficult for management to supervise all these very different sectors and to provide the necessary future investment in each area. Other organisations making products such as strike aircraft choose to act as systems integrators. They sub-contract the engine and its associated equipment, the flight controls, some flying surfaces, the flight instruments and ejection seat, the landing gear and all the avionics. The system integrator then builds the airframe and assembles the sub-systems into the airframe before carrying out system tests and finally flight tests.

To be a successful system integrator requires judicious purchasing, well-organised and competitive sub-contracting, and good supply-chain management. System engineering skills are essential and the risks to the company from a sub-contractor default are comparatively high. Most large industrial concerns have recognised the many benefits that follow from well-planned supplier partnership deals. These win-win situations improve communications, reduce customer costs, minimise risk for both parties, ease supplier investment decisions and enable joint problem-solving by both parties.

A product supplier, on the other hand, operates at a single level:

- Materials – e.g. steel, carbon fibres.
- Components – e.g. tyres, integrated circuits.
- Sub-assemblies – e.g. hard disks, fuzes.
- Sub-systems – e.g. undercarriages, workstations.

The risks of such operations are lower than for the system integrator, due to the relative simplicity of the products and the greater number of potential customers, but generally the competition is fiercer and the profit margins slimmer. It is essential for defence systems engineers to recognise the types of companies they deal with so that they can check out their organisational suitability for the award of any particular contract.

Involvement with foreign nationals occurs for a number of reasons. International collaboration in acquisition involves working with people from the participating countries. Membership of a military alliance such as NATO involves dealing with a significant number of representatives of other nations whilst individual members of the armed forces may work on overseas exchange tours. While it is important not to stereotype people from other countries, Figure 93 does illustrate some of the significant differences between six nations:

Understanding foreign cultures

In the UK, you can do it providing it's not forbidden.
In Germany, you can do it – if it's allowed.
In France and Italy, you can do it even if it isn't allowed.
In Switzerland, if it isn't forbidden, it's compulsory.
In Saudi, only men are allowed to do it.
In the US, you need a lawyer to tell you if it's forbidden, allowed or compulsory.

Figure 93. A light-hearted illustration of the wide variation of cultures.

When dealing with individuals from other nations, remember that spoken and written languages are different; speak clearly and not too fast, avoiding synonyms and slang. Get feedback to ensure what has been said has been understood and remember that the quality of communication is language-familiarity based, not intellect based.

National values vary depending on a number of factors such as geography, actual and perceived nationality, politics, history and religion. Thus in the UK the Royal Navy has always been regarded as the senior service, due to the threats of invasion from the sea over the last five hundred years. It is important to be aware of national sensitivities and also the fact that values differ, particularly between the UK and both the countries of Southern Europe and many developing nations.

2 Management of projects

Project management and systems engineering are closely related. The systems engineering on a complex defence project cannot be carried out effectively unless it is managed properly, and a complex project cannot be managed effectively without a sound understanding of the systems engineering involved. The MoD project teams responsible for acquiring new defence equipment carry out both functions but industry often distinguishes more clearly between them, and may have different career structures for systems engineers and project managers.

In his provocative book *The Amateur Managers: A Study of the Management of Weapon System Projects*, Fred Bennett gives a good definition of project management as, *The art of leadership of a multi-disciplinary team in a one-shot, time and resource-limited undertaking for the definition, approval, procurement, bringing into service and provision of future support of a new weapons system with specific scope, performance and quality.* Bennett's definition emphasises that project management is a dynamic and creative activity involving people, rather than a procedure-driven process with foolproof recipes, and the same applies to systems engineering. In the final analysis, systems only go wrong because people make errors.

Both project management and systems engineering try to minimise the risk of cost and time overruns and of inadequate performance. Since there is inevitably a degree of risk associated with new, high-technology military projects that must perform better than existing equipment, it is necessary to understand fully the trade-off between performance and risk in order to make realistic estimates of the time and cost required for a new programme. The balancing of time, cost, performance and risk is a four-dimensional challenge. Emphasis on the first three parameters, as in the above definition and in the Smart Acquisition initiative, is the province of project management, but the true impact of risk on performance can only be established by paying proper attention to systems engineering.

2.1 The MoD perspective

In the MoD, a project manager must effectively manage the interface between the government and the prime contractor, with the contract acting as the interface specification However, before the contract is established, there is an important period of discussion, clarification and negotiation between the two parties. Any weakness in the resulting contract will be reflected in the final system and therefore it is essential that all communications are as open and frank as possible so that each side understands the aspirations, constraints and risks of the other.

MoD project managers have many constraints beyond their control. These include pressures from a multiplicity of stakeholders with their own hidden agendas, levels of resources that do not fully match the needs of the job and a lack of flexibility in cash flow, which is a result of government financial procedures.

A project needs a flow of funds that matches the progress made. Contractors should be paid for milestones achieved, not simply for time expended. However, the MoD, as a government organisation, needs to match its annual cash flow to its predicted expenditure. These two factors are often incompatible and the inability to carry over unspent funding to subsequent years imposes pressure on project managers to apply spending rate adjustments that run counter to the interests of the project.

Project managers are responsible for estimating the cost, time and resources required for their project but are rarely given those that they seek. Costs may be limited by pre-set budgets, timescales may be constrained by required in-service dates and cuts in staff resources are often made, either to rescue other projects or to save money. There is institutional pressure to produce low initial cost estimates in order to produce a good cost-benefit analysis that helps to ensure project approval when competition for limited funds is fierce. It is interesting to note that Smart Acquisition emphasises the need for more realistic cost estimation without indicating how this might be achieved.

In summary, despite all these external constraints and pressures, the MoD project manager is responsible for the project and may be held accountable for anything that goes wrong. That approach confers responsibility without the appropriate authority over finance and personnel and this is probably the most significant challenge faced by the MoD project manager. It has to be overcome by reasoned argument, perseverance and persuasion, in addition to the necessary project management and systems engineering skills and competencies.

2.2 The industrial perspective

From an industrial point of view, project management is all about completing to time, below cost and to specification – a perfect match for Smart Acquisition's demand of faster, cheaper and better. To achieve this, companies require a pool of people with the requisite project management skills, supported by suitable project management tools. In addition, any project manager will be hamstrung without some contingency funding to cope with the risk of unforeseen events.

The stance adopted by companies towards project management and their strategy for such a function can be a critical success factor in a competitive market. Defence customers are trained to look at an organisation's management expertise in this area. For the MoD, this assessment will be carried out by the IPT. Keeping cadres of suitable people available within a company is an organisational challenge. The choice of project manager designate and the company's attitude to project management are certain to be examined during tender evaluation. Most customers know from bitter experience that difficulties in their relationship with the project manager will make the whole implementation process more cumbersome and risky.

There are likely to be three classes of project manager in companies: the first is the person who manages the development of a new system; the second is the individual responsible for a production line; the third is whoever is answerable to the customer for the implementation of the whole contract.

One of the major management challenges of the twentieth century was the problem of running major international industrial teams. This problem is likely to continue in the new millennium. The problems facing the project manager of an international programme are particularly awkward, despite the fact that the partners are working towards the same objectives. They demand political skill, tact, management of people and often the understanding of a foreign language and culture.

2.3 Customer-furnished equipment

The provision of customer-furnished equipment or facilities can lead to more squabbles with the purchaser than almost any other topic. The problem is to ensure that the customer delivers what has been promised to time and quality. When, as happens from time to time, this fails to occur, then the supplier faces a timescale overrun and consequential cost escalation. This is where the difficulties with the customer begin, with claim and counter-claim quickly souring what was previously a good working relationship. Tight definitions of interfaces and responsibilities are vital to avoid nugatory recrimination should problems arise.

2.4 After-sales support

Project support often lies within the project management function and used to be a real Cinderella. Increasingly, companies are taking a far more positive view of support activities and it is not uncommon to find 25% of turnover and 50% of profit being generated by this single area. The key need for defence contractors is to find enthusiasts to run the support business and keen sales executives to sell that support. However, customers are becoming much more aware of their needs in terms of logistics, spares and upgrades. They are including these costs in their through-life cost analyses and often insisting on, for example, fixed prices for spare parts over a 10-year operating life.

This professionalism amongst customers is threatening the previous mechanism (adopted by some devious contractors) of winning the original contract at low margin and then bolstering it through captive spares sales mark-ups, as high as 300% to 400%. Technology is also now available which enables manufacture of spares in very short timescales based on reverse engineering of the original worn component. This is usually a much cheaper proposition than the spares quoted by the original equipment supplier. The user's support staff must take care, however, as some high-tech solutions still have components hand-picked during manufacture to ensure that they meet tight tolerance requirements, which may not be clear to the purchaser. As the design authority, defence systems engineers may get involved in solving such problems.

2.5 Conclusions

For the acquisition of any new defence system to be successful, it is clear that experienced and capable project managers are an absolutely fundamental requirement both in the MoD and in the prime contractor. The two must be able to work closely together and be prepared to be open with each other about potential problems or risks that might adversely affect the delivery timescale, price or performance of the system.

3 Risk

3.1 Introduction

The planning of all human activities involves some uncertainty, since future actions by the people involved and future developments in the physical environment cannot be definitively predicted. The sources of uncertainty are called 'risks' and are defined as future events, which have two or more potential outcomes. For example, the planned schedule of a trip by car is subject to a variety of risks such as breakdown, weather, other vehicles, traffic signals, road works, etc. Defence projects are prone to many risks because they involve a number of stakeholders engaged in complex activities involving new technology over a long period in a changing environment.

Each of the various potential outcomes of a risk is characterised by a probability and by a set of these impacts (on performance, cost and time). In the commercial world almost all impacts can be assessed in financial terms, but in defence projects each outcome can affect performance, timescale or cost or all three (the effects on these three dimensions are not independent, and the project manager may be able to trade-off one against another). When the alternative outcomes are discrete (e.g. the success or failure of a trial) the probability of each outcome and the associated impacts on the project can be estimated and tabulated. When the estimated outcomes are continuous, they can be represented by probability distributions.

The simplest type of risk has only two potential outcomes, the favourable outcome having no effect on the project management plan and an adverse outcome having a low probability p of an incremental penalty q on one of the project's characteristics (such as cost). Such risks are often represented and ranked by the product pq of probability and impact (though this can blur the distinction between low-probability high-impact risks and high-probability low-impact risks and the different strategies appropriate for them). In the special case when a project has a large number n of such risks with the same probability and penalty, the likely penalty can be represented by a Poisson distribution with a mean value equal to npq. Accordingly the value of $\Sigma p_i q_i$ is often used more generally as an approximate indicator of the likely overall penalty arising from the project's risks, even though the individual risks may actually have various different levels of probability and impact. In most defence projects this simplification is invalid, since many risk outcomes have separate impacts on performance, timescale and cost (i.e. three-dimensional rather than one-dimensional impacts), since many risks have more than two potential outcomes, and since project risks are often interdependent (such that an adverse outcome in one risk may make adverse outcomes in the others more likely or more severe).

In reality, risk outcomes can be more or less favourable than the most likely value, and hence can present either opportunities or dangers. When pessimistic project managers focus exclusively on dangers, they forgo the benefits from exploitation of any opportunities that arise.

3.2 Classes of risk

It is often useful to divide risks into different classes which typically require different risk reduction strategies. Some risks are 'internal' arising from the technical and management activities within the project itself, and some risks are 'external' arising from the environment (commercial, military, financial and political) within which the project exists. Although the project manager cannot influence the latter class, their potential impacts can damage the project's chances of success and plans should therefore be developed to mitigate their effects.

Risks may also be divided into those where the probabilities and impacts may be estimated from statistical evidence (the insurance industry has generated a vast literature on this class), those where the estimates of probability and/or impacts rely on judgement (these are sometimes called uncertainties to distinguish them from statistical risks), and the high-impact risks which are beyond the normal scope of project management and which might have impacts requiring response at national level. The adverse effects of high-impact risks generally have no relevant precedent, so analysis of such risks must be based on theory and judgement; such analysis should be done outside and in parallel to normal risk reduction activities and the conclusions should be presented separately. The table below provides some examples of risks in each class, and possible risk management strategies, which the project manager might consider to be appropriate in each case.

There is an understandable but regrettable tendency for project managers to concentrate their attention on the top left cell of this table. These are the risks which they understand

	Evidence-based	**Judgement-based**	**High-impact**
Internal	Shortage of resources *Outsource*	New technology *Experiment*	Nuclear meltdown
External	Foreign exchange rates *Buy forward*	Government policies *Contingency plan*	9/11 in Whitehall

Figure 94. Examples of risks and possible risk management strategies.

best, those which they can address most effectively and those which are susceptible to quantitative analysis. However, the other classes of risk can also be very damaging and deserve a due proportion of the managers' attention. There is a similar tendency for engineers to focus on technical risks and to neglect those arising from human fallibility.

3.3 Risk management

Risk management is a systematic approach to deciding what (if any) action should be taken now to reduce the variability of the future performance, timescale and cost of a project. The extent of the risk management activities should be proportional to the scale of the potential risk impacts, the size of the project's budget and the importance of the project's planned contribution to UK military capabilities. The MoD recommends for defence projects a risk reduction process that employs four sequential tasks: Identify – Analyse – Plan – Manage.

3.4 Identification

For each project, a comprehensive register of the associated risks must be assembled using any, and preferably all, of the following activities:

- A checklist (from the acquisition management system or elsewhere) of risk areas common to defence projects.
- Systematic analysis of the project itself to identify its vulnerable points.
- Review of MoD/NAO reports on the risks encountered in earlier projects of the same class.
- Consultation with relevant experts in the MoD and beyond, including the safety authorities.
- Brainstorming by stakeholders familiar with the project considered and with other relevant projects using the same technology or management arrangements. It is often useful to include 'outsiders', representing different professions or social groups, who are more likely to think 'outside the box' and to challenge accepted assumptions.

The risks identified by these activities might include:

- Immaturity of the relevant technologies and difficulties of systems integration.
- Inexperience of the planned engineering processes.
- Threats to the financial, commercial or management stability of the chosen contractors.
- Dependence on the successful development of a concurrent project.
- Unsynchronised lines of development for equipment, training and infrastructure.
- Inadequate annual funding to cover expected project cost through its life cycle.
- Health and safety hazards.
- Lack of political commitment by the UK government and any foreign collaborators.
- Fluctuations in the prices of scarce goods and services, or of foreign currencies.

The identified risks should be listed in a 'risk register'. Each entry should include a serial number, a description of the risk and its potential outcomes, estimates of the probabilities and impacts of each outcome, the name and post of the official assigned to manage that risk, and a description of the risk reduction strategy which has been adopted. After a risk reduction strategy has been adopted, the resulting 'residual' values of probability and impacts should also be included.

If the project's acquisition strategy uses international collaboration, the project is subject to additional risks. The introduction of more stakeholders with varying cultures, and with diverse constitutional and financial arrangements, inevitably yields more risks whose assessment relies largely on diplomatic judgement. Furthermore, the philosophy of collaboration requires that risks should be shared, so the risk reduction must be planned at an international level. This process may itself introduce additional risks of misunderstanding and dispute.

3.5 Analysis

Having identified the risks in a project, it is then necessary to assess the probabilities and outcomes for each of the risks. The assessment should be documented and traceable, and it should be endorsed by all the relevant stakeholders. Such assessments must include the effects of a particular outcome on all aspects of the project (in all phases of the project's life cycle) as well as the consequential effects on other projects in the MoD acquisition programme.

Preliminary assessment of a risk often uses qualitative criteria, grading the probability and impacts of the outcomes as high, medium or low. Such assessments of the project's risks may be plotted on a probability/impact grid, with the nine cells scored or colour-coded to illustrate the relative seriousness of the risks plotted in different cells. However, the use of this grid implies that all the impacts of the risks may be combined in terms of a single criterion, such as cost; this is not always possible in defence projects for which separate grids for performance, timescale and cost may be necessary.

The results of qualitative assessment focus attention on the most serious threats to the project's success and attract risk reduction activity to those areas. Fair and balanced qualitative assessments of two or more competing projects can indicate which is less risky.

However, only a quantitative assessment of a project's risks can contribute to the three-point forecasting of the project's cost and timescale (most likely values with confidence limits) required for approval at initial gate and at main gate, and only quantitative assessment of a particular risk can justify the allocation of substantial funding for risk reduction activities. It follows that a quantitative analysis (however approximate) is required early in the life cycle of every project. Risk reduction studies at the early stages are more difficult and uncertain, but they can identify risks early enough to allow a wide range of possible pre-emptive strategies which are invariably cheaper than remedial actions later in the project.

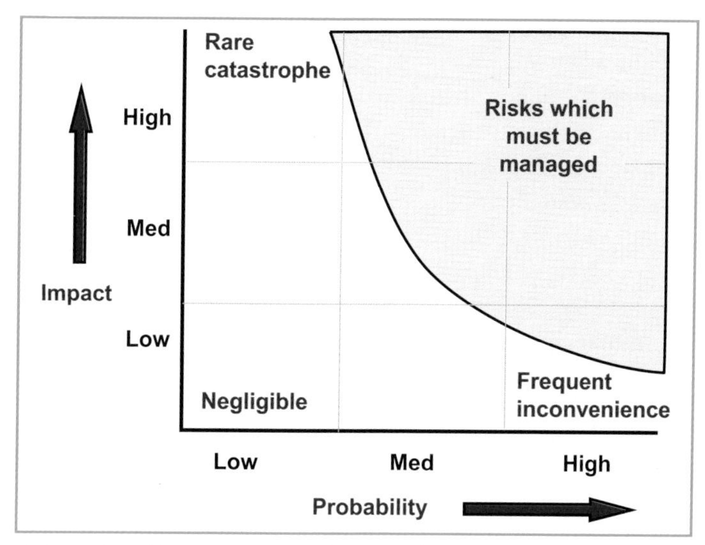

Figure 95. Probability/impact grid showing the risks that need to be managed.

3.6 Planning

The process of identification and analysis provides useful information, but it is even more important to act constructively on that information to reduce where appropriate the probability and/or the impacts of the risks associated with a project to an acceptable level. There are four potential strategies that may be adopted and each has its characteristic disadvantages:

- Accept the risk, recognising that it may in the future have an adverse impact on the project and retaining appropriate contingency funding to deal with that impact. This option preserves the uncertainty associated with the risk's potential impacts on the project.
- Avoid the risk by adopting an alternative technological or managerial approach. This option negates the risk considered but it may introduce other (smaller?) risks and it forgoes the advantages in the approach originally chosen.
- Transfer the risk to another organisation, perhaps to an insurance company that has the resources to absorb financial risks or to a contractor who has the expertise and experience to address it effectively. This option invariably involves payment of a premium to compensate the organisation accepting the risk, and thus increases the most likely cost of the project to the MoD. It must be remembered that even if part of the financial risk is transferred to another organisation, all of the operational risk remains with the MoD.
- Reduce the probability and/or the impacts of the risk through additional experimental work to enhance understanding of the risk and hence find ways to mitigate it. This option is often unpopular with budget managers because it incurs extra costs early in the project's life cycle.

The last three of these strategies accept some deterioration in the project's most likely outturns (in terms of performance or timescale or cost) in order to reduce the variability of those outturns. This is a difficult trade-off for each individual risk, both because the probabilities and impacts of the risk's potential outcomes may not be defined accurately and because the penalty associated with a combination of impacts on a project's performance, timescale and cost may appear different to different stakeholders at different times. Some stakeholders devote much more attention to variations of performance, timescale and cost in their target levels than to the absolute values of those levels; such stakeholders are very risk averse and may devote excessive resources to risk reduction. the right risk-reduction strategy would be characterised by seven 'As':

1. **Appropriate** – at the right level between panic and doing nothing.
2. **Affordable** – economical and within the available budget.
3. **Actionable** – able to deliver results in time to help the project.
4. **Achievable** – feasible with the resources available.
5. **Assessed** – monitored to learn lessons to help this and other projects.
6. **Agreed** – attracting stakeholder consensus and commitment.
7. **Allocated** – assigned to the responsibility of an individual manager.

Figure 96. Each risk reduction plan must satisfy seven criteria.

3.7 Management

Risk identification and analysis, and the resultant planning of risk reduction, must be undertaken not only at the start of a project but also at successive stages through the life cycle. The risk register must be regularly updated, deleting those risks whose outcomes are now known and adding any others which have lately become apparent. The analysis of current risks should be revised in view of the latest technological and managerial information. Current risk reduction plans should be monitored to ensure that they are progressing satisfactorily, and new plans must be formulated to deal with any additional risks which have emerged. The risk management plan is therefore a living document, which evolves throughout the project. It is an integral part of the through-life management plan and should be linked to many other project management activities (on safety, budgeting, cost/effectiveness, etc.)

Reports on the progress of risk reduction should be communicated to budget managers, to project managers facing similar risks and to managers of any dependent projects which would be affected by the risk outcomes. The post-project evaluation (PPE) written towards the end of a project should record the risk reduction strategies adopted and their effects.

3.8 Challenges in risk management

Because people in the UK and other developed countries live in a relatively secure environment, they are generally poor at estimating risks. Some have a limited grasp of statistics, and some place undue trust in speculative reports biased by ignorance or vested interests. Accordingly risk analysis is afflicted by misrepresentation (ranging from unconscious bias to downright dishonesty) by the stakeholders involved in the analysis. Furthermore many project managers are prone to:

- Defer to the majority view or to some 'expert'.
- Keep faith in an initial assessment long after its sell-by date.
- Reject the possibility of extreme outcomes.
- Trust glossy software without understanding its limitations.

Another challenge in risk management is to ensure the allocation of sufficient funding early in the project to support the various risk reduction activities required to reduce risk to an acceptable level. At this stage the probabilities and impacts of the original risks, and the benefits from activities to reduce them, are often doubtful and some project managers are reluctant to strain their budgets in the assessment phase to mitigate a potential problem which might arise more than a decade later.

A crucial challenge is how to illuminate the risks associated with a particular project to a variety of decision-makers with diverse types of expertise. With a single criterion (such as cost) the overall effect of multiple risks can be represented by a probability distribution. The distribution may be summarised by some or all of representative values such as:

- Lower confidence limit.
- Target.
- Most likely.
- Expected.
- Approved.
- Upper confidence limit.

The upper and lower confidence limits are set by the chosen percentage probability (the MoD currently uses 80%) that the actual cost will fall between the limits if the risk analysis is accurate. The target and approved levels are set subjectively to provide, respectively, a challenging but attainable goal for the project management team, and to constrain the cost overrun allowable before the project must be reviewed and re-approved. While risks to one parameter (performance, cost or timescale) lead to a one-dimensional range of possible outturns, risks in defence projects lead to a volume of possible outcomes in three-dimensional space with axes for performance, timescale and cost. This volume is not spherical since some dimensions are more prone to risk than others, and it is not symmetrical because the management team can respond to risk outcomes by trading performance, timescale and cost to optimise value for money.

3.9 The MoD and its suppliers

In an ideal project, the MoD and its suppliers would have similar views on the severity of various risks to the success of a project, achieved perhaps through a joint risk management process. If however some political or corporate risks were withheld from this process, the perspectives of customer and supplier would be significantly different.

Similarly, the contractual arrangement in an ideal project would encourage a common view of the relative importance of project performance, timescale and cost, and hence a common view on how risks should be managed to achieve project success in these terms. But zero-sum arrangements, whereby a financial gain by customer or supplier is matched by an equivalent loss to the other, are invariably divisive and detrimental to good risk management.

In the cost-plus contracting era all the risks in a defence project were borne by the MoD so the suppliers understandably showed little interest in risk management. In the following era of fixed and firm price contracts, the suppliers accepted some of the financial risks and the MoD's interest waned. Today, under Smart Acquisition, the MoD and its suppliers are seeking win-win contracting arrangements in which their mutual interests coincide and so that they can tackle risk management co-operatively.

3.10 Risk maturity model

The competence of any organisation in risk management is indicated by the extent to which its risk management is forward-looking, proactive, continuous, inclusive and integrated across the organisation. Qualified assessors can grade an organisation at one of four levels, 1 to 4, and at the top level it would have:

- Good risk-based processes in place and regularly updated to guide corporate decision-making.
- Risk-aware staff, well trained in the latest risk management techniques and sharing relevant information throughout the organisation.
- Leaders who set a good example, reward proactive risk management and encourage constructive dissent.
- Comprehensive and honest records, and the ability to learn from its own and others' mistakes.

3.11 Benefits of risk management

The primary purpose of risk management is to minimise the chances of unacceptable shortfalls in performance, delays in delivery or increases in cost, but it also yields many other secondary benefits.

First it demands a close scrutiny of every project with scrupulous attention to detail. This should ensure that the project chosen from alternative options, and the strategy chosen for its acquisition, have no unidentified dangers and that the identified risks are well understood by all stakeholders. This scrutiny also encourages greater realism in budgeting and scheduling, and helps to avoid later disappointment and embarrassment. Secondly, a systematic and well-documented risk management provides valuable data, which can later provide a good baseline for future projects. Finally, the involvement of all stakeholders in addressing risks promotes better communications and team spirit within the organisation.

4 International collaboration

In the middle of the twentieth century many nations were able to fund the design, development and manufacture, by private- or public-sector contractors within their own frontiers, of defence equipment for service with their armed forces and for export to other friendly nations. This acquisition policy had the advantages of providing equipment which was well matched to a nation's particular requirements for military capability, and of sustaining the nation's defence industrial base. However, as the unit cost of defence equipment increased more rapidly than national defence budgets and hence fewer units of each type of equipment could be procured, this national acquisition policy became increasingly uneconomic. There was less opportunity for learning on shorter production runs and the fixed costs of the project's development, production investment and operational investment had to be allocated to a smaller number of units procured. These 'diseconomies of small scale' affect particularly those classes of equipment, such as aircraft and guided weapons, where the ratio of fixed/variable costs of a project is comparatively high because of the scale and complexity of the development work required.

In this situation, some nations chose to abandon their technological and industrial capabilities in some classes of defence equipment and adopted a policy of buying purpose-built military equipment in these classes 'off-the-shelf' from a larger friendly nation, which had already deployed such equipment with its own armed forces. This acquisition policy is called military off-the-shelf (MOTS) to distinguish it from COTS equipment bought directly from commercial companies. Off-the-shelf procurement is discussed in Chapter 3, Section 6.

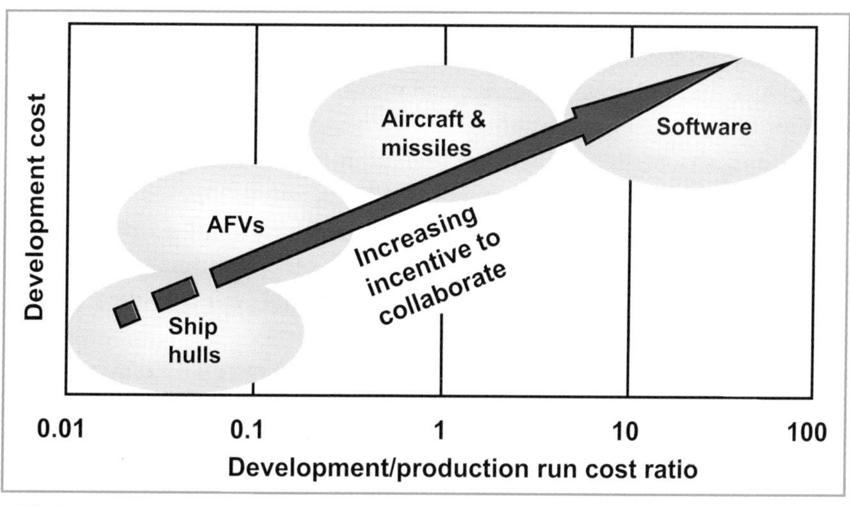

Figure 97. International collaboration becomes more attractive as the development cost and the ratio of development to production cost increase.

As an alternative to MOTS procurement, a group of allied nations with similar requirements sometimes choose to collaborate in the design, development and production of defence equipment, provided that the members of the group together have the full range of technical expertise required. This acquisition policy enables the collaborating nations to share the up-front costs (of development etc.) and to benefit from economies of scale in production and in in-service support. For example, a three-nation consortium in an ideal arrangement to produce a modern combat aircraft might theoretically reduce its procurement cost by about 33% relative to a national project, but this will depend on the fixed/variable cost ratio, the learning curve in production and all the nations taking identical aircraft and support facilities. The cost-effectiveness of the collaborative project's design may benefit from complementary areas of technical expertise within the partner nations, and the military strength of their alliance may be increased by the operational flexibility conferred by interoperability of the common equipment deployed by allied forces.

4.1 Benefits and penalties of collaboration

In practice, the economic benefits of international collaboration are often eroded by divergent opinions and selfish chauvinism among the partner nations. There may be differences in the judgement of their military forces on the capabilities required from the equipment, and reconciling these judgements tends to demand protracted debate. Such debates can yield improvements in the equipment concept by challenging national prejudices, but they always impose a substantial delay between the emergence of the services' requirements and the launch of a well-defined and funded project. If the divergent views on the project's capability are not fully reconciled, the resulting design may be larger (and hence more expensive) than a national design. Even if the overall capabilities are agreed, each of the partner nations may insist on a national variant incorporating its preferred sub-systems and design features, and thereby forgo some of the benefits of collaboration. Furthermore, each nation may insist that its own traditional test and evaluation procedures must be undertaken by its own officers/officials, and that it should have the national prestige conferred by a final assembly line within its frontiers.

Some nations distribute work packages to the most efficient of competing contractors, but others may prefer to allocate work to politically favoured contractors in economically depressed regions (thus using the project to promote industrial or regional policies at the cost of project efficiency). This problem can be exacerbated by national aspirations to develop technological expertise, and by overlapping capabilities or distorted views of the capabilities of various contractors within the partner nations, so work-sharing arrangements on collaborative projects are rarely optimal. Even the best-organised international collaborative projects incur some additional costs from transporting people and goods over greater distances, from translating documents into several languages and from satisfying a greater variety of standards (safety, environmental, security, etc.) and laws governing employment and contracts. As a result of all these factors, the savings on procurement cost for the project cited above is likely to be substantially less than in the ideal arrangement; the likely saving might be about 20% but if the project were poorly organised it could be insignificant.

4.2 Project management

It is invariably challenging to create for the collaborative project a management structure which not only yields prompt and judicious decisions but also safeguards the vital interests of various stakeholders in national parliaments, armed forces and industries. There may be a dedicated international project office to supervise a special industrial grouping, both having links to the national governments and to sub-contractors within the partner nations and beyond (and both generating the costs and complexities arising from expatriate organisations). Alternatively, separate national project offices may liaise collectively with each other and with pre-existing contractors. Whatever structure is created, its personnel must overcome language and cultural barriers and a variety of legal and constitutional constraints, avoid large nugatory meetings, resolve industrial rivalry for work share in the most attractive areas of technology, and accept the occasional paralysis of the project by political or budgetary crises in one or other of the partner nations. The financing of a collaborative project may also be disrupted by fluctuations in the foreign exchange rates between partner nations (which were particularly severe during the monetary turbulence of the 1970s and 1980s).

The project management plan for a particular international collaborative project, and the associated forecasts of project cost and timescale, must take account of all the features discussed above and make allowances for the circumstances of the project considered. The plan must be sufficiently flexible to accommodate the customary variations of policy within the partner nations, and the cost and timescale forecasts will inevitably be subject to greater risks and uncertainties, reflected in extended confidence limits, than for a national project.

4.3 US and European issues

A collaborative project involving the United States presents a special problem because its national financial contribution to the project is generally much larger than that of any potential collaborator, to reflect the larger number of units which the US will need for its more numerous forces. Hence the views of the US representatives on the supervisory board tend to prevail on issues related to the equipment capability required, to the technical features of the equipment designed to provide that capability, and to the project management plan to deliver that equipment. Only if the US has no strong preference can foreign representatives influence the project to favour their own national objectives.

Similarly, a project involving several European nations has its own characteristic problems arising from diverse national constitutional, legal and industrial arrangements, as well as diverse social customs and practices. The institutional problems are now being systematically addressed by the Organisation Conjointe de Coopération en Matière d'Armement (OCCAR) created in 1996 to facilitate future projects, and social problems are being progressively eroded by tourism and industrial globalisation. Language barriers are diminishing through the increasing use of (American) English as a lingua franca, and residual difficulties over terminology and concepts can generally be resolved by the enthusiasm of zealots with a common purpose.

4.4 Successful collaboration

Despite the many disadvantages and difficulties of international collaboration, discussed above, its potential financial benefits appear so enormous that since the 1960s the UK has followed a policy of collaboration on the development and production of defence equipment whenever it appears practicable and advantageous. Some international collaborative projects have foundered because the military requirements and/or the financial circumstances of the nations involved proved to be irreconcilable, or diverged after the project was launched. However, other collaborative projects have overcome all difficulties and have produced equipment which has served with distinction (in conflicts and exercises) in the armed forces of the partner nations and has been exported to their allies. By January 1999 equipment from 31 collaborative projects involving the UK was already in service, 20 more projects are in the development or production phases of established and funded programmes, and another 13 projects are engaged in concept and feasibility studies. These 64 projects involve a total of 19 other nations, with France, Germany and the US being represented in more projects than the others. At the end of the 1990s these collaborative projects together accounted for 13% of the MoD's annual expenditure on the procurement and support of equipment, and that figure will rise to nearly 50% if all the current projects mature as planned.

The ideal circumstances for a collaborative project arise when a group of nations have common political aims, a common military requirement for similar numbers of units to be delivered in the same timescale, and comparable levels of complementary technological and

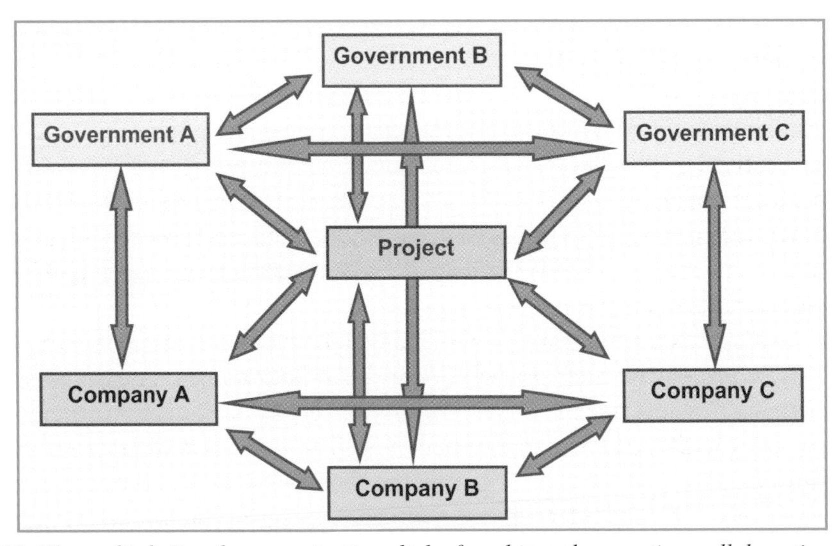

Figure 98. The multiplicity of communications links found in a three-nation collaborative project.

industrial capabilities. The project should be larger than any of the individual nations could conveniently afford, and its procurement timescale should be sufficiently long that the delay introduced by negotiations on collaboration is not significant. It is also advantageous if the project has a high ratio of fixed to variable cost, so that the large potential savings from collaboration provide the collective incentive to overcome the obstacles that inevitably arise.

The ideal number of national partners involved in an international project must always be a compromise between the financial benefit from adding an additional partner (the extra benefit diminishes as the number of partners increases), the problems of accommodating the additional partner's military, political and industrial requirements, and the complexity of managing a larger consortium. Figure 98 shows one possible arrangement of the interfaces between governments, companies and the project; the number of interfaces escalates faster than the number of nations involved. Experience suggests that a consortium of between two and four equal partners is manageable but that a larger number must be organised in layers with different degrees of responsibility.

4.5 Industrial issues

In ideal industrial circumstances, the participating companies in a collaborative project would all be committed to its success, compatible in terms of expertise and capabilities, and have an effective working arrangement. The legal structure and working arrangement of any consortium or joint venture are also important. The location of the project office will impact on staffing, language needs, communications and travel.

The partners must deal with a range of financial issues, such as differential inflation rates and fluctuating exchange rates, which are likely to alter throughout the project. These factors may also impact on work-share agreements and choice of sub-contractors. The way contracts are let can vary. One nation may contract on behalf of all, or for European projects OCCAR may let the contract. Alternatively, each national government may contract with its national company, in which case common terms will be needed to avoid conflicting incentives; delays by one nation will postpone the start of work.

When looking for a partner on a collaborative programme, it is important to be able to make an objective assessment of potential companies. A competitor analysis will ask appropriate questions as to whether some companies will be suitable partners. In fact, it is quite common for companies to collaborate on one contract and compete on another. The setting up of 'Chinese walls' is a normal practice in such situations to avoid one team learning what a competing one is doing.

Further evaluation will follow from a shortlist of potential partners, which will be contacted and visited by a team from the company. At the outset, it is important to consider how to resolve differences quickly and agreeably between the parties. To avoid bias, if at all possible the same individuals with the right mix of skills, should make up the team visiting every company.

The sales executive can look at the attraction of the partner to the customer and assess the level of contact that already exists. The project manager designate can consider the way the potential partner manages projects and examine possible incompatibilities or other difficulties in working together. Depending on the type of project, someone from operations or engineering will need to assess capability and finally, though possibly at a later stage, a member of the commercial department will have to prepare a collaborative agreement.

Since such organisations are commonly competitors, either directly or remotely, discussions may need to be somewhat circumspect despite the existence of a confidentiality agreement. Those involved will need briefing on the appropriate degree of openness.

4.6 Conclusions

International collaborative projects can be organised and managed more successfully if the military, technical and industrial personnel in the partner nations have previously established mutual respect and good personal relationships, and if each nation contains a military or political leader who is fanatically committed to its success. Good relationships are promoted by frequent international military exercises and officer exchanges, by collaboration and information exchange agreements in research, and by the globalisation of multinational enterprises. Transatlantic projects should in future be facilitated by the UK/US Declaration of Principles agreed in February 2000, and European projects by the Six Nation Framework Agreement signed in July 2000. These agreements both resolve previous difficulties on, for example, the security of supply of defence goods between partner nations, intellectual property rights and the security of information transferred, export control procedures and the harmonisation of military requirements. Even so, there are ever-present dangers arising from the lack of any unambiguous individual ownership of the whole project, and from the temptation to blame others (especially foreigners) for poor project performance.

As well as cost savings and enhanced military effectiveness, collaborative projects can provide a valuable stimulus to the development and restructuring of the defence industries in the partner nations, and can promote closer political collaboration between those nations in achieving their shared security objectives. However, the move by the MoD towards an increase in the percentage of procurements acquired through international collaboration inherently lengthens the time taken to get equipment from initial concept into service.

Further reading

Anon (2004) Living dangerously: a survey of risk, *The Economist* 24 January: 10–14

Augustine, NR (1983) *Augustine's Laws*. New York: AIAA

Bennett, FN (1990) *The Amateur Managers: A Study of Management of Weapon System Projects*. Canberra: Strategic and Defence Studies Centre, Australian National University

Brooks Jr, FP (1995) *The Mythical Man-Month: Essays on Software Engineering*. Boston, MA: Addison Wesley Longman

Buchanan, D and Huczynski, A (1997) *Organizational Behaviour: An Introductory Text* (3rd edn). London: Prentice-Hall

Chapman, C and Ward, S (2002) *Managing Risk and Uncertainty*. New York: Wiley

Health & Safety Executive (1998) *Risk Assessment and Risk Management*. London: HSE Books

Kirkpatrick, DLI (1998) Risk assessment in defence equipment selection, *Risk Management* Summer: 5–20

Matthews, R and Tredennick, J (2001) *Managing the Revolution in Military Affairs*. Basingtoke: Macmillan

Morris, PWC and Pinto, JK (eds) (2004) *The Wiley Guide to Managing Projects*. New York: Wiley

Mullins, LJ (2002) *Management and Organisational Behaviour* (6th edn). London: Financial Times/Pitman Publishing

National Audit Office (1984) *MoD: International Collaborative Projects for Defence Equipments* (HC 626). London: HMSO

—— (1991) *MoD: Collaborative Projects* (HC 247). London: HMSO

—— (1995) *Procurement Lessons for the Common New Generation Frigate* (HC 692). London: HMSO

—— (1996) *Initiatives to Manage Technical Risk on Defence Equipment Programmes* (HC 361). London: HMSO

—— (2001) *Maximising the Benefits of Defence Equipment Collaboration* (HC 300). London: TSO

Senge, P (1993) *The Fifth Discipline: The Art and Practice of the Learning Organisation*. London: Century Business

Wood, PC and Sorenson, DS (2000) *International Military Aerospace Collaboration*. Aldershot: Ashgate Publishing

Websites

http://www.pmi.org/

http://www.occar-ea.org/

Chapter 9

Systems engineering in the defence environment

Systems engineering is considered first in its own right, then in defence acquisition and as a practical component of defence systems engineering. Pioneering definitions introduce the concept of systems engineering and are followed by consideration of systems of systems and a description of the generic processes that facilitate both the specification of a requirement and the formulation of the optimum solution. The models and simulations that assist these activities are outlined, and there is an introduction to systems architecture in terms of the various approaches to architectural design and of the three interacting aspects of systems architecture (structure, behaviour and layout), as well as a look at some systems engineering models. Finally the need for interoperability is examined and thirteen maxims or rules of thumb are outlined that offer guidance to defence systems engineers.

1 Introduction

Systems engineering is an interdisciplinary approach to complex technical problems, which enables the engineering community to evolve, manage and verify integrated and balanced solutions that satisfy customer requirements throughout the life of the products. It encompasses:

- The technical efforts necessary for the conception, development, manufacturing, verification, deployment, operations, support, disposal and user training for the whole system and its processes.
- The definition and management of the configuration of the system and its emergent properties.
- The translation of the system definition into work-breakdown structures and their timescales.
- The development of information for management decision-making, viewing the system as a whole and in relation to its environment.

A key problem with engineering defence systems is their sheer complexity, often more than any single person can get their mind around. Systems engineering is a tool that helps to break down complex solutions into manageable human-sized chunks. Allied to modern project management (covered in Chapter 8, Section 2), systems engineering has enabled the development of today's most sophisticated types of defence equipment and will continue to serve defence systems engineers in the future.

2 Some definitions

At this stage it useful to review some definitions, but first, what is a system? A system is an integrated set of elements which, when operated together in a defined environment, successfully achieves a specified output. Systems engineering has many definitions, some of which were discussed in the introduction to this book. In order to provide an understanding of what is meant by the term 'systems engineering', the following ten descriptions of the term are offered for consideration:

1. Systems engineering is an interdisciplinary approach to evolve and verify an integrated and optimally balanced set of product and process designs that satisfy user needs and provide information for management decision-making. (US MIL-STD-499B)
2. Systems engineering is the application of scientific and engineering efforts to transform an operational need into a description of system performance parameters and a system configuration through the use of an iterative process of definition, synthesis, analysis, design, test and evaluation. It integrates related technical parameters and ensures compatibility of all physical, functional and program interfaces in a manner that optimizes the total system definition and design. It also integrates reliability, maintainability, safety, survivability, human engineering, and other such factors into the total engineering effort to meet cost, schedule, supportability, and technical performance objectives. (US MIL-STD-499A)
3. Systems engineering is the management function, which controls the total system development effort for the purpose of achieving an optimum balance of all system elements. It is a process, which transforms an operational need into a description of system parameters and integrates those parameters to optimize the overall system effectiveness. (DSMC 1991)
4. Systems engineering is the iterative, controlled process in which users' needs are understood and evolved, through incremental development of requirements specifications and system design, to an operational system. (IBM Federal Systems company definition)
5. Systems engineering is the process of building real things to solve real problems within technological, environmental, economic, legal, ethical, cultural, and institutional constraints. (DeFoe and McAuley 1991)
6. Systems engineering is an iterative process of top-down synthesis, development, and operation of a real-world system that satisfies, in a near-optimal manner, the full range of requirements for the system. (Eisner 1988)
7. Systems engineering is the transforming of an operational need into a description of system performance parameters and a system configuration. (*Field Manual: System Engineering*. FM 770-78 US Army)
8. Systems engineering is the selective application of scientific and engineering efforts to:
   a. Transform an operational need into a description system configuration, which best satisfies the operational need according to the measures of effectiveness.

   b. Integrate related technical parameters and ensure compatibility of all physical, functional, and technical program interfaces in a manner which optimizes the total system definition and design.
   c. Integrate the efforts of all engineering disciplines and specialties into the total engineering effort. (*Field Manual: System Engineering*. FM 770-78 US Army)
9. Systems engineering is a robust approach to the design and creation of systems to accomplish desired ends. (Chamberlain and Shishko 1991)
10. Systems engineering is a hybrid methodology that combines policy analysis, design and management. It aims to ensure that a complex man-made system, selected from the range of options on offer, is the one most likely to satisfy the owner's objectives in the context of long-term future operational or market environments. (P. M'Pherson, 1986)

A number of themes can usefully be picked from this list of definitions. Systems engineers need to have interdisciplinary skills and face multiple technical, economic and social constraints in their design process; a methodology that should be iterative and take a through-life approach. Systems clearly need to be balanced and optimised, their sub-systems integrated and compatible, with careful attention being paid to their interfaces to ensure their overall effectiveness. Finally, any system must satisfy user needs and meet its cost and schedule requirements. The link between defence systems engineering and some of these definitions of systems engineering can be readily appreciated. It is clear that some people view systems engineering as a technical subject, while others support the view adopted by the DEG for defence systems engineering, described in the Introduction.

In summary, systems engineering is concerned with studying a system in its entirety rather than focusing on just one sub-system or technology, as is the norm in many single-

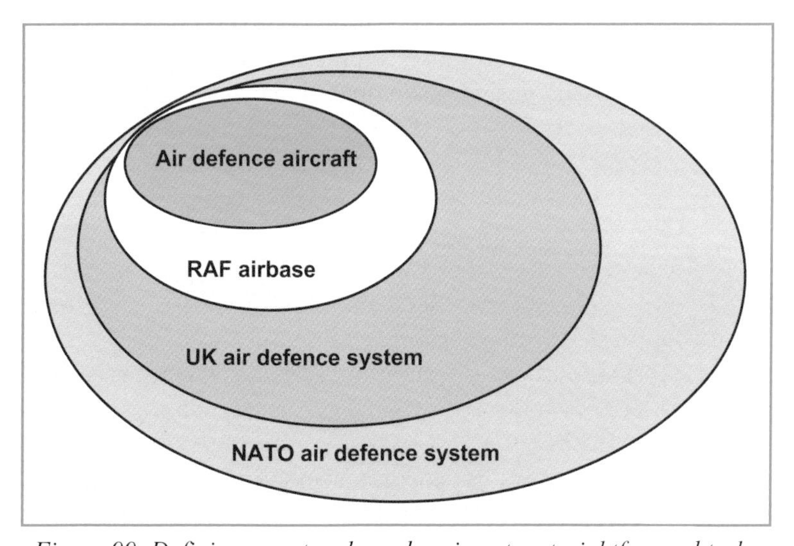

Figure 99. Defining a system boundary is not a straightforward task.

discipline engineering branches. As the entire view is difficult to grasp, the challenge is to find a way of breaking it down. However, to examine an entire system implies that the system boundary can readily be defined; in practice this can actually cause considerable difficulty. In the planning phase of any system design, it is necessary to bound the system, which involves defining and agreeing the system boundary specification that forms the external interface with the environment as is demonstrated in Figure 99. Bounding is essentially a part of the statement of the system requirements.

Defence systems engineering is systems engineering in the defence environment, and is the integration of those engineering, analytical and management activities necessary for the procurement of large and complex defence systems. It uses systems engineering philosophies and procedures to promote the achievement of performance, cost and timescale in the uncertain environment of rapidly advancing technology and evolving industrial and geopolitical circumstances. These issues have been addressed in previous chapters.

3 System of systems

The phrase 'system of systems' is often used to denote an overarching system built up from a set of other large, complex systems. The term has no agreed definition and can mean different things to different people. Most large systems can be divided into smaller sub-systems, each of which can be considered to be a semi-autonomous system in its own right. For example, a system such as a naval warship has many sub-systems (e.g. radars and

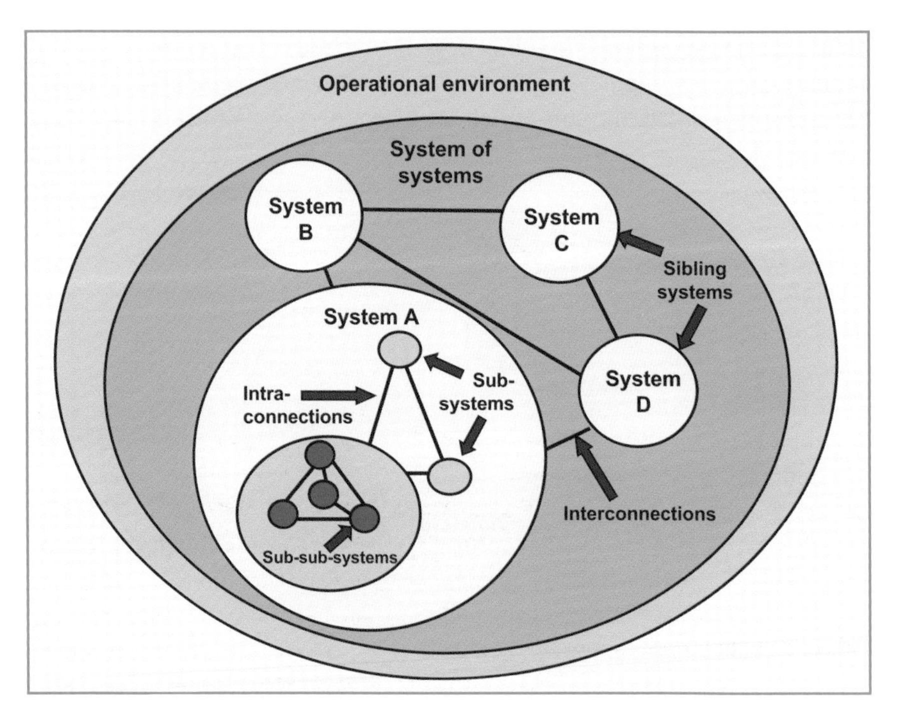

Figure 100. A system of systems illustrating the breakdown into sub- and sub-sub-systems.

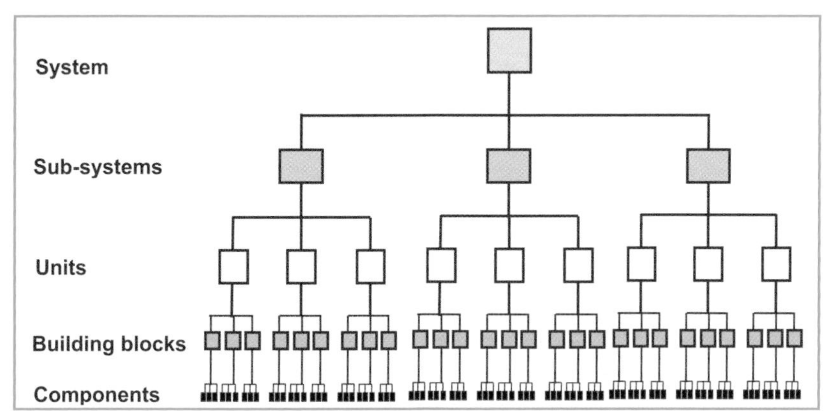

Figure 101. The smallest system shown is at building block level (e.g. a circuit board) made up from components.

missiles), which are designed, built and tested as complete systems separately from the ship and which are integrated to form the total warship system after they are delivered to the ship system prime contractor. These sub-systems have their own sub-sub-systems. The warship's radar will have a transmitter, a receiver, an antenna, a data processor and a moving mount, all of which can be treated as radar sub-systems. Thus any large system can be viewed as a hierarchy of smaller systems so that, 'one person's system is another person's sub-system'.

Various terms are commonly used to distinguish the different levels in this hierarchy and a typical set may consist of words such as 'system', 'sub-system', 'assembly', 'sub-assembly' and 'component'. Components are often assumed to be the basic building blocks, which cannot or need not be divided further. These terms relate to the system in question, and are not always defined explicitly or even treated consistently in scope or context. In a hierarchy of system entities, the term 'system of systems' implies the next level above the term 'system' and some authors have used the term 'meta-system' to mean the same thing.

However, there is one key feature of a system of systems that often distinguishes it from those systems of which it is composed, namely that the component systems were initially designed, developed, tested and accepted as separate, stand-alone systems and were subsequently brought together to form the new system of systems. In other words, the component systems already existed for other purposes and were not necessarily designed specifically with the system of systems in mind. It is sufficiently difficult to integrate or combine sub-systems that were specifically designed to work together as a system. It is much more difficult to integrate sub-systems that were not intended for incorporation in the system.

It may be argued that if the sub-systems of a system are optimised separately and independently the resultant system may be far from optimum. This implies that a system of systems composed of systems that already exist and which cannot easily be modified or changed will inevitably be sub-optimal in some respects. Provided it can adequately carry out the desired functions this may not matter, but it must be borne in mind when predicting the performance of a new system of systems, when specifying its requirement and when testing or accepting its capability.

Returning to the warship analogy, individual ships of various ages and capabilities may be required to work together, either as a national or a multinational task force. The effectiveness of a force composed of existing vessels may well be sufficient for the task in hand, but will be less than that of a specifically designed force in which the ships have been equipped with all the necessary complementary capabilities. Unfortunately, systems engineers and designers rarely have the luxury of starting with a blank sheet of paper and have to cope with the vagaries and imperfections of legacy equipment and sub-systems. The increasing emphasis on the use of COTS may exacerbate these challenges.

4 Systems engineering as a generic process

Systems engineering is a process for solving complex problems. The main steps are to define the problem, to analyse it in functional terms and to generate a cost-effective solution. Since the problem is a complex one, partitioning it into manageable portions, controlling the interfaces between them and integrating them into a final system will be key activities.

4.1 Problem definition

The systems engineering process starts by specifying the problem in solution-independent terms. It is then important to bound the problem in order to determine the scope of possible solutions and, at the same time, to identify the interfaces with external but related entities across the problem boundary. The process continues by defining the various stakeholders as well as their roles, priorities and constraints. It is essential to specify the criteria for success, including the appropriate tests and indicators. The outputs of this stage will be the user requirement (formalised within the MoD as a URD) and the acceptance test specifications.

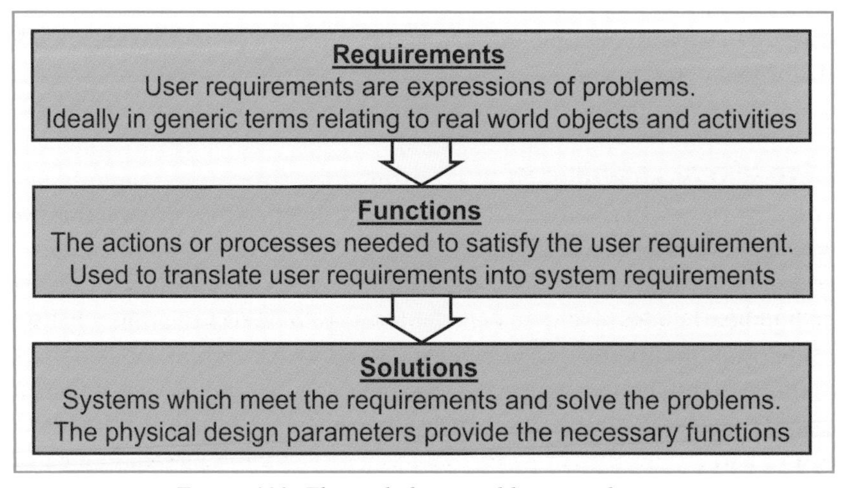

Figure 102. The path from problem to solution.

4.2 Functional analysis

The next stage is to determine the functions necessary to satisfy the requirement, again trying to avoid predicating specific solutions. It is necessary to partition the various functions as clearly and unambiguously as possible and also to understand the interactions between them that result in the emergent properties. The criteria to be met must be specified and the tests identified that are required to confirm functional operation. The outputs of this stage will be the system requirement (formalised by the MoD as an SRD) and the system test specifications.

Functional analysis is an intermediate step between the statement of requirement and the choice of ultimate solution. Functions are those actions or processes that are necessary to provide the required capability. They specify what needs to be done but not how it will be achieved. So they do not define or preclude specific solutions. Note that different function sets may be needed for different classes of solution. Functional analysis is a useful way of translating user requirements (or URD) into system requirements (or SRD), which can form the basis of competitive bidding that allows industry the freedom to propose the widest-possible range of acceptable systems, thereby ensuring that the best solution may be chosen.

4.3 Solution generation

In arriving at a solution to the system requirement, it is essential to consider all the realistic alternatives and to assess the costs and risks associated with each option. Next comes the difficult task of choosing the most cost-effective approach acceptable to all major stakeholders. The final decision may involve political issues as well as technical and commercial considerations.

In the design and development of the chosen system, it is important to focus initially on addressing the high-risk items and to partition the solution for ease of subsequent integration and testing. A decision must be made as to whether to manufacture or purchase the individual items or sub-systems. Next will come the stage of integration and test in a pre-planned and logical sequence, followed by system tests to demonstrate the emergent properties specified in the system requirement and acceptance tests in a realistic environment to validate the user requirement.

4.4 Division of responsibilities

Ideally there is a distinct separation between the three stages of this generic process. The URD specifies what military capability is needed by the MoD. It should be written and owned by the appropriate military experts in the MoD, but in practice assistance is often sought from industrial contractors or consultants. The SRD specifies the functions that the system has to satisfy in order to achieve the desired capability and is often used as the basis of a contract between the MoD and industry. It should therefore be agreed and owned jointly by both parties, regardless of who writes it. The solution, defined in industrial responses to a request to tender, specifies how the functions will be implemented in the final system design and is written and owned by the relevant contractor who designed the system.

In practice the divisions often become blurred. It is difficult to write a detailed URD without having some solution ideas in mind. The choice of words or phrases used to describe the required capability may imply certain behaviour or functions that may steer the reader or industrial bidder into certain areas of the solution domain. Similarly, the words used to describe the system functions are often associated with certain solution types, and it may be necessary to define alternative function sets in order to allow consideration of the full range of solutions. Lobbying of the customer by suppliers with specific solutions or products in mind is another obvious distortion of the ideal process. Nevertheless, attempting to follow the three stages separately and sequentially is an excellent discipline provided the problems and implications are recognised.

It is essential to involve all relevant stakeholders as much as possible at all stages. This generic systems engineering process should be applicable to all levels of the problem hierarchy.

5 From problem to solution

The acquisition of defence equipment is usually thought of in terms of a transactional relationship with the MoD as the customer purchasing military systems from industry as the supplier. It might be inferred from this that the need for systems engineering is confined to industry since it designs and manufactures the equipment to be procured. However, the real situation is much more complex than this as the MoD must be a very active customer, even for off-the-shelf items. Figure 103 indicates, during the move from problem to solution, the need for analysis, engineering and management skills.

Identify problem	Analysis	Discussion & analysis to identify true problem
Find cause	Analysis	Identify the cause(s) of problem
Create solutions	Engineering	Create number of solutions to solve problem
Assess solutions	Analysis	Consider performance, cost, time & environment
Consider whole life	Analysis	Consider short, medium & long term
Integrate knowledge	Engineering	Consider engineering, finance, politics & environment
Select best solution	Management	Use a variety of decision-making skills
Justify solution	Management	Present chosen solution & justify its use
Implement solution	Engineering	Application of solution to problem
Manage progress	Management	Monitor progress & amend implementation as necessary
Complete solution	Management	Complete solution & learn from experience

Figure 103. How analysis, engineering and management help to move from problem to solution.

5.1 A hierarchy of decisions and activities

By way of example, consider the potential need for defence against ballistic missiles, noting that many other military systems will follow the same line of discussion, require similar decisions and present similar challenges. The basic problem in the example may be expressed in its most general terms as, 'Potential enemies have ballistic missiles that may pose threats to UK assets.' The government owns this basic problem and the prime minister and the Cabinet must take the initial decisions regarding the nature of the solution on a political basis. It is not yet a problem for the MoD although the Secretary of State for Defence will be a party to the Cabinet decision. Many types of solution might be considered, of which two contrasting ones would be the negotiation of peace treaties with the potential enemies and the prevention of, or defence against, possible attack. It may be deemed prudent to pursue both options in parallel, recognising that this would require the commitment and provision of increased resources. The first type of solution would then become a problem for the Foreign Office to try to solve whereas the second would be a problem for the MoD to handle.

For its part, the MoD could consider a whole spectrum of possible solutions, ranging from sabotaging the potential enemy's factories and/or launch sites (a pre-emptive act of aggression rather than defence), through defensive action against the threats when airborne to the passive protection of the potential targets, the last possibly involving civil authorities as well as the MoD. Choosing the preferred type of solution is essentially a strategic military decision but there would be political implications if action on or over non-UK territory were

Problem	Possible Solutions	Type of Decision
Ballistic missiles	Negotiate Treaties and Alliances (FCO) **Anti-ballistic missile defence** (MoD)	Political (PM+Cabinet) May need to pursue both
How to provide defence against ballistic missiles	Attack launch sites. Attack missiles in flight **Terminal defence**. Protect targets.	Strategic/OA (MoD) Pursue parallel options?
What options exist for terminal defence?	Gun, possibly with smart shells, **missile**, directed energy weapon, novel solutions	Cost effectiveness (COEIA) Risk assessment
What type of missile?	**Autonomous**, fire and forget, semi-active, lock before launch, command to line of sight	System design, capability, cost, feasibility, risk
What type of control? What type of software?	**Fins**, thrust vector control (TVC) HLL, safety critical redundancy	Sub-system design
What type of actuation?	Hydraulic, **electrical**	Assembly design
Are there safe and reliable components?	Mil-Specs?, Def-Stans?, COTS? Guarantees and warranties	Component selection

Figure 104. The way problems and solutions flow down through the system.

proposed. The choice of direct action against airborne threats poses a problem for the military planners and the candidate solutions would include engagement by hard-kill weapons and soft-kill jamming or deception. The choice between these solutions would be an operational decision based on knowledge and assessment of the enemy assets and possible tactics. Again, it may be prudent to pursue more than one option, but this would then require either an increase in resources and funds or a redistribution and dilution of those available.

Only when the generic nature of the solution has been determined can a system requirement be properly defined. The provision of the required capability now becomes a problem for the Defence Procurement Agency (DPA) to solve and only at this stage is it appropriate for industry to be brought in to assist. (Industry would like to be involved earlier though MoD defence systems engineers would have to retain the leading role and responsibility.) The defence systems thinking required to reach this point must be done within the MoD and competent defence systems engineers with a wide experience of defence issues are essential to the process if robust and realistic decisions are to result. The MoD must, therefore, find a way to acquire, develop and maintain the appropriate high-level defence systems engineering expertise.

Thus there is an expanding hierarchy of problems and solutions flowing from the high-level decisions on policy, through strategy and operational considerations to procurement issues, and this hierarchy can be extended down through the choice of system, sub-systems, assemblies and components as shown in Figure 104, where the preferred type of solution at each level is indicated in bold green type and the type of decision is indicated in the final column. At each level in this hierarchy, solutions must be proposed to meet the problem seen at that level. The preferred solution at each level will define the problems to be solved at the lower level: 'One man's solution is another man's problem.'

Within the current policy of specifying capability requirements, rather than generic systems designs or detailed technical solutions, there is an onus on the MoD as the customer to provide potential industrial suppliers with as much detail as possible of the perceived needs and the operational and environmental constraints. Competent defence systems engineering will be required to ascertain that the capability requested is necessary and sufficient when taken in conjunction with other relevant defence systems that either already exist or are currently planned. Defence systems engineering will also be necessary to determine how well any proposed solution can provide the necessary capability and hence satisfy the perceived requirement. This will be particularly important in a competitive environment when the most cost-effective solution is desired. Only the MoD is in a position to carry out these tasks and they should not be abrogated or delegated to industry. The more detail that can be specified in the statement of the initial requirement, the smaller the range of possible solutions that will need to be considered, making the path to the ultimate solution both cheaper and quicker.

During the concept phase of a new project, brainstorming sessions involving experienced defence systems engineers and analysts within the MoD, and possibly also including systems experts from industry, will be needed before the requirement is agreed and promulgated as a user requirement document (URD). The brainstorming should have two distinct purposes. The first is to identify all appropriate options that might be considered. The second is to close off unsuitable options as quickly as possible, otherwise the resources, time and cost of the resultant work will escalate alarmingly. Both tasks require competent defence systems engineers.

5.2 Multiple customer/supplier relationships

As Figure 105 clearly illustrates, there is not a single customer/supplier relationship in the definition and acquisition of defence systems – there is essentially a similar relationship at each level of the decision-making process. At the top, political level, the government as customer puts a requirement on the MoD as supplier and provides the funding by way of the defence budget. At the strategic level, the MoD then has to determine its high-level priorities and its balance of investment. The customer is essentially the central defence staff and the supplier is the relevant service. At the capability level, the service as a customer places requirements on the DPA as the MoD supplier of equipment and allocates appropriate funds. The DPA as a customer then pays industry as the supplier for generating appropriate solutions by way of specific projects.

This is the contractual interface that is often regarded simplistically as the only customer/supplier transaction. The prime contractors in industry then negotiate customer/supplier relationships with their sub-system contractors, who in turn have to deal with assembly manufacturers who must themselves interact with component suppliers. The total

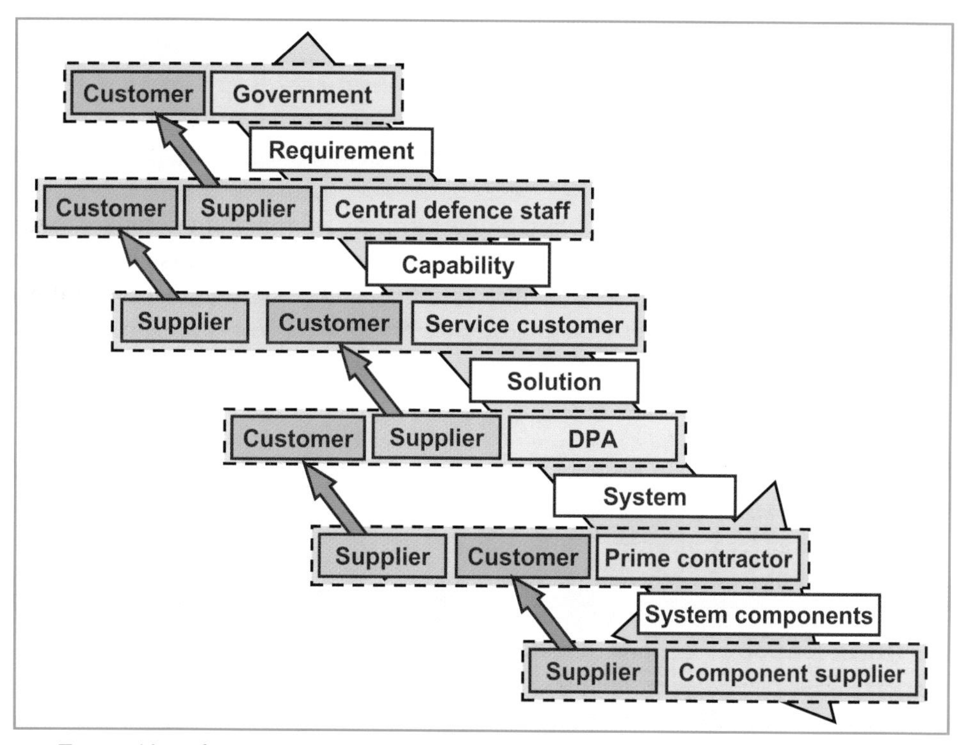

Figure 105. The customer/supplier chain from government to component supplier.

supply chain has many individual links, all of which involve defence systems engineering at the appropriate level. Therefore it is important that both the MoD and industry have sufficient defence systems engineering skills for their respective purposes.

One question raised by this hierarchy of problems and solutions is where best to draw the contractual line between the MoD as the customer and industry as the supplier in order to allow the most appropriate set of solutions to be properly considered. The high-level decisions, which must be supported by high-quality systems thinking, should only be made within the MoD, where there are multiple layers of customer/supplier relationships (e.g. between EC and the DPA). So-called independent consultants have been employed by the MoD for these tasks but can they be truly objective and independent? Their raison d'etre is to satisfy their shareholders, which means that their criteria for success are rather different from the success criteria of dedicated MoD staff. The lower levels have been progressively delegated to industry as defence companies have become increasingly able and willing to act as designers and prime contractors for large defence systems. Hence, the contractual boundary has been moving progressively upwards through the hierarchy with time. Contractual issues are dealt with more fully in Chapter 6, Section 8.

5.3 A moving contractual boundary

In the decades following the Second World War, the vast majority of systems design was carried out in the MoD research and development establishments and the resulting technical specifications were passed to industry, which was paid to produce equipment to meet them. The MoD was the system design authority as it had the necessary technical expertise, and it also specified the components and standards to be used. This was, therefore, an era of cost-plus contracts with the MoD essentially bearing both the technical and the financial risks.

In later years, the MoD tended to specify the performance requirement and the type of solution (e.g. an air-to-air missile), leaving industry to carry out the system design as well as the production. Thus the systems design and integration expertise largely resided in industry who were, de facto, the system design authority. This was an era of fixed-price, competitive contracts and while industry bore some of the financial risk, the MoD was still at risk from an unsatisfactory choice of technical solution and from delays in delivery and shortfalls in performance.

Current thinking is that the MoD should specify capability requirements in very broad and general terms, which impose minimum constraints on the possible solutions. This in itself creates a problem as the MoD's traditional force structure and support arrangements may be incompatible with some innovative solutions. It does, however, mean that industry has more freedom to propose innovative systems but will have to do much more work requiring additional resources and funding, as there will be many more options to consider. If the requirements specified by the MoD as the customer do not close off solution options, then industry as the supplier may need to pursue many parallel options in some detail in order to determine the best solution. It also implies an increasing need for defence systems engineers in industry, and a similar need in the MoD if it is to continue to act as an intelligent customer in an environment in which defence systems continue to increase in complexity and cost.

The Smart Acquisition concepts of partnering and integrated project teams (IPTs) can help in sharing the risk of defining requirements and system solutions between the MoD and industry, provided such teams are properly structured and adequately funded, and provided that the issues of intellectual property rights and competition can be resolved satisfactorily. It must, however, be remembered that the MoD and industry have different goals; the former to get the best defence value for taxpayers' money and the latter to make a profit for its shareholders and grow the company. Hopefully, these goals can both be satisfied by a successful defence project, which is where the concept of partnering is helpful.

5.4 Conclusions

In summary, defence systems engineering requires a hierarchy of customer and supplier relationships (Figure 105) and raises the question as to where best to place a mutually beneficial contract between the MoD and industry. Recent changes in attitude towards the appropriate location of requirement specification and solution generation are progressively moving the contractual division between the MoD and industry further up the hierarchy of decision-making processes.

However, regardless of where the contractual line is drawn, there will always be defence issues and decisions at the higher levels that must remain the responsibility of the MoD and therefore there will always be a need for competent and experienced defence systems engineers within the MoD to address these issues. Two essential MoD systems engineering tasks are to ensure that the right balance of military equipment is available for perceived operations and to integrate new systems with old in order to maximise capability at any point in time. As the MoD delegates more responsibility for solution selection and systems design to industry, it is essential for it to establish how it will acquire, train and maintain an appropriate cadre of defence systems engineers to meet its needs. Specifying appropriate system requirements also involves the need for MoD systems engineering expertise and this is discussed further in the next section.

6 Specifying the requirement

6.1 Divergence and convergence

'There is more than one way to skin a cat' is an apposite saying when applied to defence acquisition. A single requirement statement, for example, 'a requirement to travel under self-propulsion from A to B', will have many acceptable solutions, such as walking, running or hopping, roller skates, skateboards, pogo sticks, scooters or bicycles. Apart from the need to define more clearly the constraints on A and B, this raises three basic questions; how is the requirement best specified, how is the best solution to be chosen and who is best placed to make the key decisions at each stage of the process?

There are two conflicting pressures within the acquisition process. First, there is a need for brainstorming in order to ensure that no potentially acceptable solutions are excluded from due consideration. Secondly, there is the need to close off unacceptable options in order to converge on a single preferred solution. The wider the range of options considered, the greater the resources required, resulting in a protracted and expensive programme. On the other hand, an early assumption of the final solution may preclude better options. In order to avoid nugatory work, it is desirable to close off unacceptable options as early as possible and this process must start with the requirement statement.

6.2 Requirement specification

Taking the requirement statement given in the first paragraph of Section 6.1 above, if the need for efficient propulsion is included then several classes of potential solutions, such as walking, hopping and possibly pogo sticks (although this may need further investigation) may be quickly discarded. Other classes such as hang-gliders and sand yachts, despite being efficient and high speed, may be ruled out because of their reliance on atmospheric propulsion aids. Ice skates, also fast and economical, may be a possible solution but only if the requisite operational environment is either specified or mutually understood.

Thus it is the responsibility of the requirement specification team to define as clearly and as completely as possible the desirable features of those solutions that are acceptable to them and the disqualifying features of those that are not, together with the environmental conditions in which the desired equipment must be capable of operating. This is true whether the requirement is specified in capability or in technical solution terms. Any statement of requirements is designed to enable the relevant stakeholders, either an IPT or the military user, to focus on those solution options which can provide the desired capability and to close off quickly those which cannot and in which, therefore, there is no customer interest.

7 Translating requirements into solutions

7.1 Classical design and emergent properties

A functional specification is an intermediate step between the initial requirement specification and the solution. Dependency matrices can be used to relate the requirement statements to the functions necessary to achieve them, and to relate the functions to sub-systems or design parameters of the proposed solutions. These matrices allow the parameters and properties of the solution to be traced back clearly to specific requirements.

Classical design principles should be applied as far as possible so that, ideally, there would be a one-to-one correspondence between requirement statements, functions and solution design parameters, allowing each aspect of the requirement to be optimised separately and independently. If this could be achieved, the dependency matrices would be orthogonal with no terms other than their main diagonals, the system would have perfect partitioning and there would be no coupling between sub-systems.

Unfortunately, such independence is impossible in most real systems and indeed, if there was no cross-coupling or interaction between the separate elements, the system would have no emergent properties; it would be a pile of useless bricks rather than a functional wall. Dependency is introduced at all stages of the process. Requirements are difficult to specify independently and more requirement statements are likely to involve more dependencies. Implied solutions may also produce apparent dependencies.

The functions needed will depend on the solution type; many different sets of functions can satisfy a single requirement and several function sets may be needed to keep all sensible options open. 'Independent' functions may have secondary dependencies. Solutions will introduce further dependencies especially if common elements or sub-systems are used. Many different solutions can satisfy any given set of functions. Complexity and dependencies are introduced at each stage of the process. Whether choosing functions, sub-systems or design parameters, the aim should be to produce dependency matrices with dominant terms on the main diagonal and minor coefficients off axis. The steps are:

- Define requirements that are as independent as possible.
- Choose a function or a design parameter related to each requirement.
- Identify its influence on all the other requirements.
- Identify the relative magnitude of the influences.
- Assess all the implications, desirable and undesirable.
- Carry out iterations and sensitivity analyses as necessary.

It may be necessary to revisit and modify the initial requirements to allow a better-structured solution using systems engineering skill and experience. Translating requirements into system functions relates problems to the processes that can satisfy them. Translation of functions into practical solutions relates system design parameters to functional requirements.

7.2 Evolutionary, incremental and iterative systems

The evolutionary development of a system is all about learning from experience. It uses the knowledge gained from one system to develop the next. Experience can be applied at all stages of development and as each system in turn becomes obsolete it is discarded. It should be apparent that it is not affordable to repeat the process too frequently. Incremental development, on the other hand, is based on pre-planned stages. The whole system is planned and designed at the beginning. It may then be developed and implemented in controlled stages; each stage adding to the system capability. The attraction is that essentially nothing is wasted or discarded. Iterative development relies on rapid user feedback but often demands that both the requirement and the solution are modified. It provides a flexible approach to uncertainty and rapid advances in technology, such as occur for information systems. In an extreme case, it may be necessary just to plan a general direction and a known rate of spend. Thus it is essential that when a new system is required, defence systems engineers should decide whether an evolutionary, incremental or iterative approach is likely to be the most appropriate.

7.3 Closing off options

Figure 106 is a simple representation of the way that options are closed off by both customer requirements and supplier constraints. The curve shows a representational form of the relationship between the range of possible solutions (on the vertical axis) and the number of constraints applied (on the horizontal axis).

The more constraints applied, the fewer solutions available and vice versa. Ideally, the constraints should be independent and they must be non-conflicting, otherwise no solutions may be possible (e.g. the system must be painted black and it must be painted white). The requirement specification, in whatever form, closes off solutions that are unacceptable to the customer, constraining the solution space to the range of acceptable options. The more detailed the requirements, the fewer the solutions to be considered.

Suppliers in the market place also have constraints (for a variety of reasons) which further limit the range of possible solutions as indicated. They may have a limited range of creative ideas and will be conditioned by past experience and successes. They may be limited by their manufacturing capability or wish to reuse existing sub-systems or components. In any event, suppliers will wish to offer solutions designed to maximise their profit or return on investment. It should be noted that constraints imposed by the supplier result in a range of lost solutions, some of which may have been acceptable to the customer and which may have been better than the ones proposed. Different suppliers will have different constraints, which may lead to different classes of proposed solutions. It is, therefore, important for MoD defence systems engineers to understand the various supplier constraints in order to make a rational choice of the best solution.

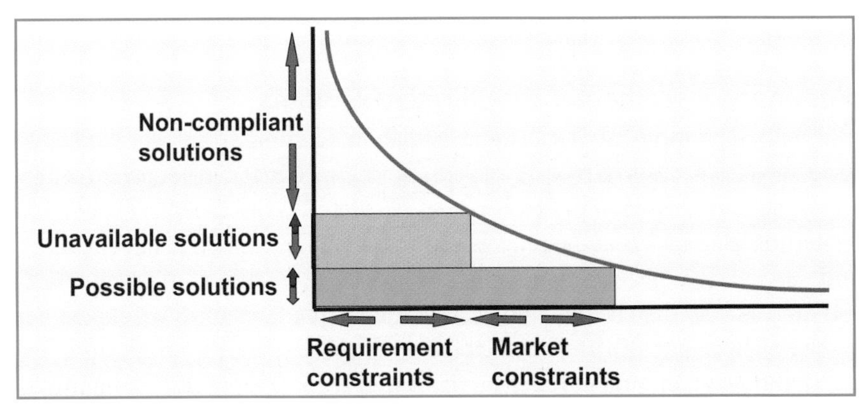

Figure 106. The range of possible solutions is constrained both by the requirement and what the market can provide.

This raises the question as to who is best placed to close off solution options, the customer or the supplier? In other words, how much or how little should the customer specify? One answer is to ensure adequate dialogue and discussion between the customer and potential suppliers at all stages of the process, so that the suppliers have a clear view of what is acceptable to the customer, who in turn gains the necessary understanding of the drivers and constraints of the suppliers. An IPT that includes systems experts from both customer and supplier can provide a valuable forum for the necessary discussions, but only if the two sides can work positively together without fragmenting into 'them and us' attitudes.

Closing off system options inevitably begins at a high level within the MoD by way of the requirement specification (URD) and ends with the choice of a detailed solution from those proposed by industry in response to the SRD. The MoD must take full responsibility for both the beginning and the end of the process. In the intermediate stages, a joint activity using an IPT and harnessing the defence systems engineering expertise of both parties may well be the best approach.

7.4 Managing interfaces

Managing interfaces was stated earlier to be a key systems engineering activity. Interfaces occur at all levels of the system hierarchy, both externally with the environment and internally within the system itself. Hence systems engineering can be practised at virtually all levels of engineering activity, whether related to systems, sub-systems or smaller assemblies.

Systems engineers have two distinct roles; first to design the right systems and secondly to design the systems right. The first role requires them to look upwards and outwards into the external environment to ensure that the system delivers the desired emergent properties across its defined boundary. The second role requires them to look downwards and inwards into the system itself to ensure that it is designed and partitioned effectively and works

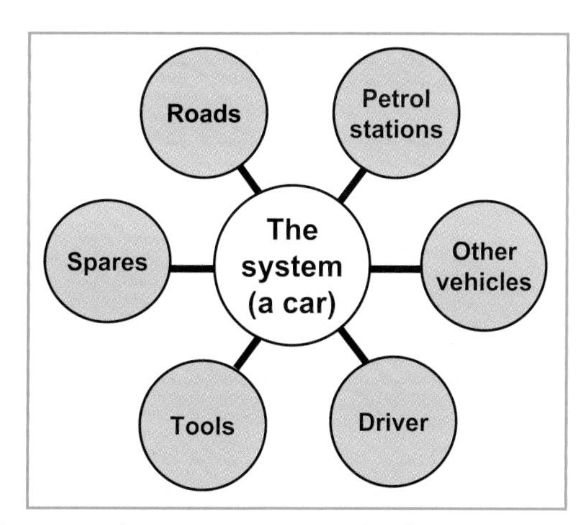

Figure 107. Context diagrams show interactions with other systems; useful in defining what is not part of the system and what is to be provided separately by others.

according to that design. Traditionally, engineers have concentrated on the second role, often to the detriment of the first one. Both roles require detailed understanding and careful management of the relevant interfaces.

External interfaces with the environment are often explored by means of a context diagram (Figure 107). A context diagram indicates all the external systems with which the system in question has to interact and can be developed to show the nature of each required interaction, leading to the writing and agreement of detailed interface specifications, which form an essential feature of the system requirement specification. It is not strictly necessary for system engineers to understand the interactions between the other systems in the environment, although it may assist in discussing alternative architectures and in reaching engineering compromises if they do.

Internal interfaces may be extremely complex and can usefully be represented by means of an interface matrix or 'N-squared' diagram (see for example Hitchens 1992). By way of illustration, an interface matrix for the high-level interfaces of a bicycle is shown in Figure 108.

The crosses in the matrix indicate that there are 26 connections to be made to the 9 elements shown, corresponding to 13 physical interfaces with a connection at each end. On average almost 3 connections will need to be made for each element. This average connectivity is an indication of the size of the integration task to be carried out to construct the complete bicycle from the 9 separate elements. Alternative partitioning schemes may lead to different connectivity numbers and, other things being equal, smaller values will mean a simpler

Front Wheel	X	-	X	-	-	-	-	-		2
X	Front Brake	X	X	-	-	-	-	-		3
-	X	Handle bars	X	-	X	-	-	-		3
X	X	X	Front Forks	X	-	-	-	-		4
-	-	-	X	Main Frame	X	X	-	X		4
-	-	X	-	X	Rear Brake	X	-	-		3
-	-	-	-	X	X	Rear Wheel	X	-		3
-	-	-	-	-	-	X	Chain	X		2
-	-	-	-	X	-	-	X	Pedals		2

Figure 108. The interface matrix for a bicycle showing the number of connections.

system with less integration to be done. If, as Leonardo da Vinci believed, everything were connected to everything else, there would be 72 crosses on the completely filled matrix. This would correspond to 100% complexity since no more interfaces or connections could be added. At the other extreme, if there were no interfaces or crosses, the 9 elements would be merely a heap of unconnected parts, not a working bicycle. This would represent zero complexity with no emergent system properties. In the matrix shown there are 26 crosses, so the system could be said to have 36% complexity (26/72). This percentage complexity can be used as an estimate of the topological complexity and is a possible alternative to the average connectivity in comparing different partitioning schemes. A refinement would be to weight each of the crosses according to the interface difficulty or risk, rather than simply using the presence or absence of a cross as a binary parameter.

The interface matrix can also indicate some of the basic system architecture if the elements are ordered so as to position the crosses close to the main diagonal (matrix diagonalisation). Figure 108 has already been diagonalised and shows the following topological features. In the top left-hand rectangle is a group of closely coupled elements forming the front sub-system of the bicycle. The remainder constitute the rear part of the bicycle with the frame, rear wheel and rear brake forming a closely coupled set, as delineated by the small rectangle in the middle of the matrix. Closely coupled sets of elements are good candidates for management and testing as discrete sub-systems. A single interface (forks to main frame) joins the front and rear sub-systems and is functionally important, as it is key to the steering requirement. Finally, the rear wheel, chain and pedals form a series set or 'waterfall' of connected components flowing down the main diagonal of the matrix.

Each element in Figure 108 can be expanded into a lower-level interface matrix showing how its constituent parts are connected, and the process can be repeated until the final components of the system such as nuts and bolts are reached. Interfaces can be traced between levels to ensure that none are omitted or forgotten; a common source of system problems. This is illustrated in Figure 109 for the single interface between a wheel and a brake.

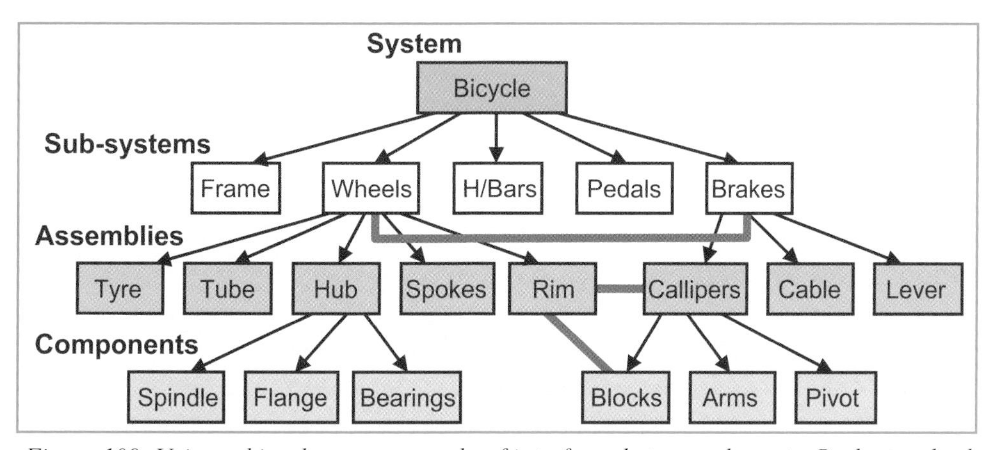

Figure 109. Using a bicycle as an example of interfaces between elements. Brake-to-wheel interfaces occur at all levels and flow down with decomposition.

If all interfaces were included and expanded down to the lower levels, this type of diagram would become very confusing and hard to interpret. A coherent set of interface matrices provides a structured way to capture all interfaces at all levels and can be used as a logical framework, common to all stakeholders, within which interface specifications can be written and filed.

An interface can be regarded as *an opportunity for testing*, since both sides have to meet the interface specification and hence can be tested against it. This can be done at all levels and should be carried out from the bottom up using the maxim of *build a little, test a little.*

For the 'wheel-to-brake' interface shown in green in Figure 109, testing would start by checking that the friction between the materials of the wheel rim and the brake blocks meets the design criteria. If not, the materials must be changed or the design must be amended – by scoring grooves in the rim, for example. Next come the assembly tests using the brake callipers and the wheel rim shape. The physical geometry and the application of even pressure must be checked. Again, any shortfalls can be remedied at this stage.

Then comes a sub-system test of the operation of the brake applied to the wheel. This may require a mock-up of part of the frame to hold the wheel and as a pivot for the callipers. Alternatively, it may be possible to use the actual frame if this is available at this stage of the development. Next come the system tests in the factory environment, involving the operation of the brakes on the complete bicycle and checking that the required retardation can be applied via the levers on the handlebars to the wheel. This may need the provision of either a simulated or a typical rider and demonstrates that the system has been built to contract and works as designed (verification tests against the system requirement). Finally, the customer acceptance tests must be performed in realistic conditions to check the stopping distance as a function of bicycle speed and road surface (validation tests against the user requirement). This raises the question, 'How much influence has the bicycle designer on the road surface?' In practice, the road surface must be clearly defined by the user at the start and treated by the supplier as an immutable requirement or constraint.

The above example has been described in some detail because it represents the generic systems engineering approach that should be applied to all integration and testing processes, showing that the earlier problems can be detected, the more quickly and cheaply they can be solved.

Interface requirements and specifications must be written at all levels of partitioning during the system design phase on the basis that *if you can't test it, it can't be a requirement.* If a requirement cannot be specified and measured satisfactorily, how will the user know that it has been met?

8 Models and simulations

8.1 Definitions

There are several factors driving defence systems engineers to turn increasingly to models and simulations. These include the increasing complexity and rising cost of new systems and equipment, declining defence budgets, the limited availability of assets, the increasing cost of operational test and evaluation, and finally the exponential growth of capability in simulation. To conquer complexity it is necessary to understand it. While interfaces are only part of the problem, these methods provide an important step towards overcoming complexity. They enable defence systems engineers to study the complexity issues and to use the methods as a foundation for other analysis techniques. There are three important definitions:

- A model – the physical, mathematical or otherwise logical representation of a system, entity, phenomenon or process.
- Simulation – the software implementation and solution of a model (usually equations and algorithms) over time within the context of a scenario.
- Modelling and simulation – the use of models, including emulators, prototypes, simulators and stimulators, either statically or over time, to develop data as a basis for making managerial or technical decisions.

In a generic model, the input includes data (parameters and interactive inputs, processes, generally algorithms or heuristics or both) and the logic and mathematics of the model. The model's output consists of results, reports or displays, which may be interactive. All output should be recorded in a comprehensive database which must include the technical environment (e.g. hardware, software and protocols) and the operational environment or real-world representation under which the simulation was conducted. Assumptions, approximations and boundary conditions should also be recorded in the interests of the credibility and reproducibility of results.

Types of simulation vary considerably. There is digital simulation where computers run models used to replicate an event. There is hardware-in the-loop (HIL) that places actual system hardware into the model/simulation and hybrid simulators, which are similar to HIL but which utilise customised hardware as well as analogue and digital systems. There are installed system test facilities (ISTF), such as anechoic chambers and electronic warfare stimulators. There is man-in-the-loop that places an operator into the simulation (often specialised ISTF) and there is threat simulation using drones and target simulators that allow systems to be operated in an approximation of their actual operating environment. Many systems use a closed-loop cycle that is common to many activities in life. A warship action information system is a good example of a closed-loop function. It requires sensors to measure the existing state of the world, computers to help assess the current situation, people to plan the best use of available assets and weapons to implement the current plan.

There are several terms used in the certification of models and simulations.

- Evaluation is the process of selecting a model or simulation for use in evaluating a specific programme and for a specific application.
- Verification is the process of determining whether a model or simulation has been constructed according to design requirements, algorithms, interrelationships and other specifications.
- Validation is the process of determining that a model or simulation is an accurate representation of the intended real-world entity from the perspective of its intended use.

- Accreditation is the certification by the intended user that the model or simulation is acceptable for use with the intended application.

8.2 Choice of model

Choosing the right model or simulation for an operational environment can be difficult. It depends on the required fidelity to reality, the correlation of the data to critical operational issues/measure of effectiveness questions, the availability of evaluation/accrediting agencies, the availability of funding, the time required for accreditation and issues of potential information overload. It begs the question 'How much modelling or simulation is enough?'

The implementation of a system will be determined by the requirements stated by the customer and any constraints imposed by the system manufacturer. Requirements relate to the impact on the environment while constraints relate to the internal working of the system. These constraints must be consistent with requirements for the system to work.

Modelling starts by considering the requirement and focusing on the interface between system and environment. This implies the modelling of factors external to the system. Only after this has been done can the system design and optimisation start. This involves modelling the internal features of the system and considering constraints such as physics, technology and cost.

As an example, consider a concept model of a radar system. Is the target part of the system? It certainly affects the system performance but the system designer has no influence on the target. Hence it must be part of the environment. Nevertheless, it must be modelled to establish system performance, showing that modelling must extend beyond the system itself. Other external factors that need to be modelled in this case include target echoing characteristics (cross-section and glint), atmospheric propagation (absorption and scattering as functions of frequency), clutter (unwanted reflections from objects such as sea, trees and buildings), multipath (coherent interference between direct and indirect returns), jamming, self-screening in main beam and stand-off in sidelobes. Validation of the modelling of external factors may be difficult and may require controlled trials in realistic scenarios.

Other model types focus on the system itself. Typical radar internal models comprise block diagrams for concepts and interconnecting components, mathematical equations for determining antenna characteristics such as beamwidth and sidelobes, digital simulation for data processing and analogue simulation using hardware-in-the-loop. Models for different system attributes include effectiveness or operational analysis models for determining the performance of the system in a simulated operational environment, where effectiveness depends on capability, availability and the opposition. These include capability models that show the system performance when working as planned, reliability and maintainability models to derive system availability, models that predict the cost of procuring, operating and supporting the system, configuration models concerned with the size and physical composition of the system and programme models that concentrate on acquisition timescales.

Availability modelling is used to determine both system effectiveness and logistic support. Availability itself is a function of the reliability and the maintainability of a system. Reliability is expressed as the mean time between failures (MTBF) and maintainability as the mean active time to repair (MART). From this, availability = MTBF/(MTBF+MART). Failure mode effects and criticality analysis (FMECA) is a key feature of reliability based on a realistic model of the system. Gathering field data to support such modelling is a perennial problem. The model includes logistic support analysis (LSA) that determines the level of support, the logistic support analysis record (LSAR) which is the result of LSA, ranging of the different types of spares required and scaling which covers the numbers of each type of spare (see Chapter 3, Section 8).

Many models will be needed and several versions of each type of model may be required, since separate models may be necessary for different aspects of the attribute in question. Each sub-system will also have its own separate suite of models. Hence a set of interconnected models can be built up, all developing in detail as the design and development progresses. Linking the many models requires systems engineering skills often overlooked until too late in the process. Unfortunately models are rarely designed as an integrated set and may thus involve different designers, different philosophies and different modelling tools. They often use different data and parameters. The solution is to plan them during initial system design and to specify all parameters that need to be exchanged.

Project management requires, in addition to the engineering models discussed above, a variety of other models including:

- Capability models that demonstrate the system performance when it is working as planned, including computer-based, combat-simulation models.
- Cost models, currently combined with capability models into COEIAs.
- Configuration models (e.g. for platform construction) that are concerned with the size and physical composition of the system.
- Programme models showing the timing and interaction between the main activities.

It must always be remembered that a model is not the real world and modelling is not an end in itself. A model is only a representation or simplification of reality and is only as good as the assumptions and approximations made for the purpose in question. Its credibility must ultimately depend on how well it can be validated using real-world data and observations, and therefore it can never become a complete substitute for trials and experiments.

9 Systems engineering process models

There are a number of process models that have been suggested to assist in the design and manufacture of complex systems.

9.1 The Waterfall model

Perhaps the simplest is the Waterfall model, a straightforward linear model. It was originally developed to assist software design and implementation. Ideally, each activity should be completed before the next is started, but in practice this is rarely achievable and some

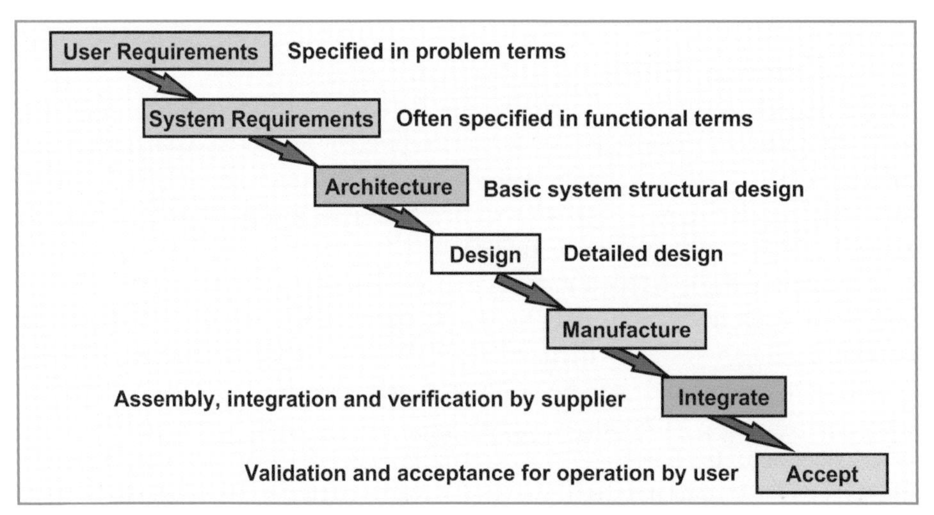

Figure 110. The Waterfall diagram: a series of discrete steps originally proposed for software.

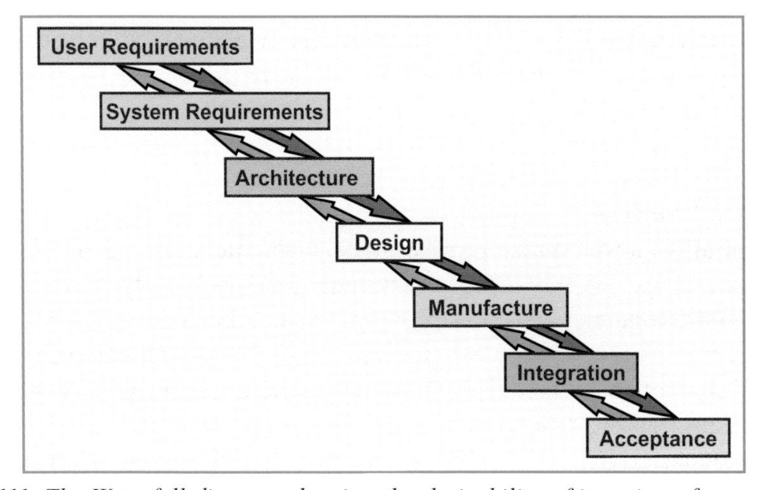

Figure 111. The Waterfall diagram showing the desirability of iteration after each stage.

iteration is necessary. The initial process plan is drawn up at the start of a project when least is known about the system, as it has yet to be built. It is hardly surprising that, as more is learnt along the way, the initial plan needs revisiting and improving. In Figure 111, the blue arrows show progression down the waterfall, while the pink arrows indicate that iteration is desirable at each stage. Assuming that time moves from top left to bottom right, it is clear that more time is needed for iteration, not less, and systems engineers must plan for this additional time.

9.2 The V-diagram

The V-diagram, shown in Figure 112 is a derivation from the Waterfall diagram and is particularly useful because it demonstrates the need for both iteration and feedback between

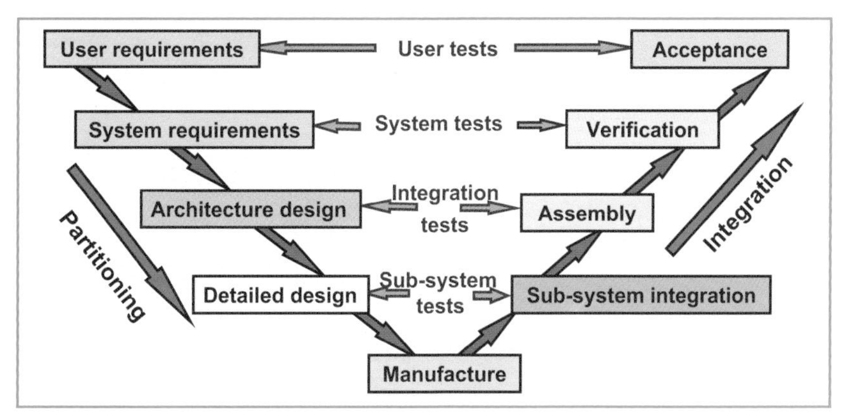

Figure 112. The V-diagram illustrating the various cross-links.

successive stages. The model, based on the same elements as the Waterfall diagram, is folded into a V form to illustrate the relationship that exists between the early design tasks and the later integration and test stages. It highlights the need for meticulous planning of the process right from the start. The figure illustrates that test and evaluation must be planned and carried out at all levels. Furthermore, test specifications must be agreed at the start of design for use at the end after the system has been integrated.

9.3 The design spiral

The design spiral is a development process model where iteration is deliberately built into the activity, which cycles through four sequential stages, namely planning, analysis, construction and testing as shown in Figure 113. It has been used successfully for many years by naval architects to design new warships. Any number of cycles may be used, but a typical approach might be to generate and evaluate a paper design on the first small circuit of the spiral, construct and test a small model during the second circuit, expand this to a prototype or demonstrator on the third, and produce and test the complete system on the

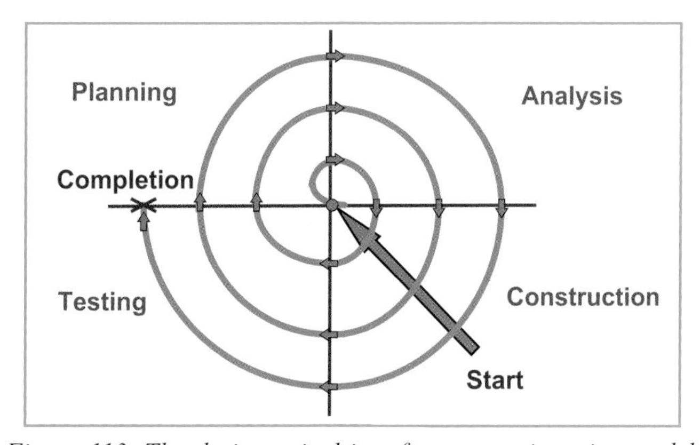

Figure 113. The design spiral is a four-stage, iterative model.

fourth pass round. Each successive circuit involves increasing detail and cost, building on the knowledge and results gained from the previous activities. This means that problem areas can be identified early in the process and remedies sought and implemented with limited nugatory expenditure. Alternatively, the basic framework of the system may be planned, built and tested on the first circuit, with more details and additional features being integrated and tested in successive cycles.

Inevitably, as with any other creative process, there will be some unplanned iteration necessary to deal with unforeseen difficulties that arise during the development, but hopefully this can be kept to a minimum and contained within the early passes round the spiral where costs are relatively low and timescales reasonably short.

9.4 The Marconi engineering process model

This was developed from the basic V-diagram by Marconi Electronic Systems in the early 1990s and was used on the systems engineering courses taught for many years at their Dunchurch Training Centre, finding fame as a T-shirt logo worn by course delegates. It is self-explanatory and introduces the concepts of continuing management, support and analysis throughout the systems engineering process. It also shows the multi-layered hierarchical nature of systems, sub-systems, etc. by way of the 'trapdoor' to the lower levels in the middle of the diagram. This so-called T-shirt diagram has been widely publicised, although the detailed systems engineering guidelines that support and underpin it are company confidential (see Figure 114).

10 An introduction to systems architecture[1]

Architectural design defines clearly in diagrammatic form what is to be built and is potentially the most creative part of the system development process. It is also the point at which the cost becomes largely fixed, so that it is extremely important to get it right. Note that systems architectural design needs inputs from system requirements and from high-level performance, cost and analysis models. It should also be remembered that the system architecture transforms system requirements into a visible form by allocating the functions to hardware, to software or to people. At this stage, each design component can be defined separately so that the group tasked to produce it can effectively implement it. The system architecture should enable system design options to be explored before going into the detail of component design, and allow reasoning about the system behaviour at an appropriate level of abstraction and generality. Finally, it endeavours to optimise the design characteristics in order to satisfy the requirements as completely as possible.

10.1 Objectives of architectural design

There are a number of aims when undertaking the architectural design of a system. These are shown in Figure 115.

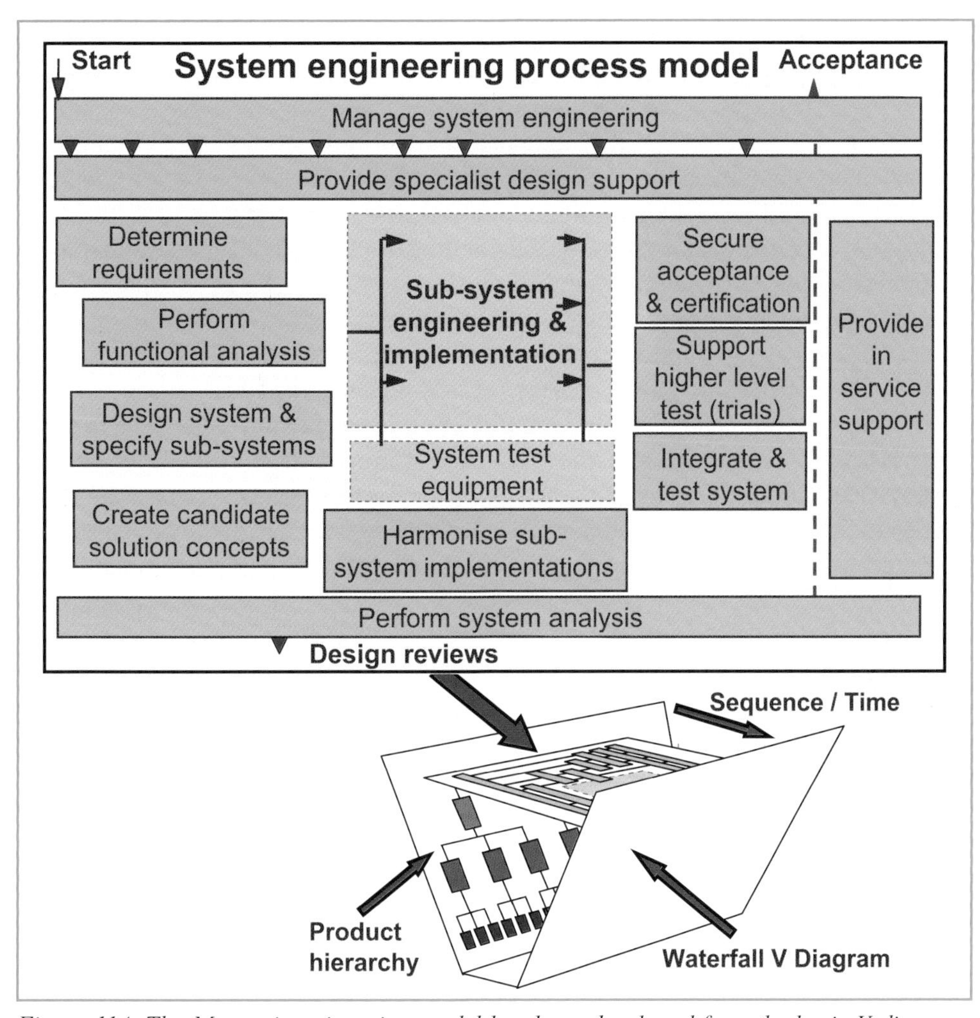

Figure 114. The Marconi engineering model has been developed from the basic V-diagram.

1. Produce a high-level design to facilitate cost and performance estimates of meeting user and system needs economically within the defined operational environment.
2. Define an implementation approach plus the core technologies to be used.
3. Define how the sub-systems interact to generate the desirable emergent properties.
4. Allow trade-off between candidate designs in order to maximise system effectiveness.
5. Generate a test strategy for proving and acceptance.
6. Partition components for allocation to implementers.
7. Define the deliverable items in order to manage them.
8. Estimate the likely cost, risks and contingency.
9. Ensure the design incorporates previous decisions.

Figure 115. Nine key objectives of system architecture design.

10.2 Rechtin's four approaches

Rechtin (1991) has described four approaches that can be taken by systems engineers:

1. Normative or solution-based method that employs formal processes such as building codes and communication standards.
2. Rational, a method that uses systems analysis and engineering.
3. Participative or stakeholder-based method that involves techniques such as brainstorming and concurrent engineering.
4. Heuristic methodology employing lessons learnt.

The first two approaches are analytic, deductive, easily followed and widely taught. They focus on solving existing problems. The last two are inductive and rely on experience in creating the art or practice of employing system architecture. They complement the first two, but are difficult to understand or teach formally. The DEG's approach to defence systems engineering is based on the first two elements of Rechtin's approach, but substantially develops the ideas of the latter two elements to create a robust philosophy for solving acquisition problems.

10.3 Three aspects of systems architecture

The key aspects of systems architecture are structure, behaviour and layout. The structure of a system is static; it defines the major components, their organisation and decomposition. It also shows the system functionality and its interfaces, as well as the link to system requirements. The system behaviour is dynamic and defines the dynamic response of the system to external events as well as providing a model for understanding and reasoning about the system. The layout of the system is topographic and defines the physical arrangement and 'packaging' of the design. The packaging shows how sub-systems are allocated to physical resources, such as the layout of a vehicle or of a printed circuit board, or how software is mapped on to hardware. Packaging also provides a basis for understanding the non-functional properties of the system, such as weight or power consumption. The layout also impacts on environmental issues such as shock, vibration or interference.

10.3.1 System structure

While the normal meaning of the word 'structure' is a physical framework, in systems engineering usage, the structure of a system links sub-systems to functions and partitioning. It is a systematic definition of what the sub-systems are, but puts no constraints on the physical layout or topology. It leads directly into a definition of the deliverable items. The principles of structural design are the same as those for functional definition. Good design should minimise coupling between parts and critical interfaces should not be dispersed across the system. The design should also be simple and easy to understand.

A suggested methodology is to define a simple structure that meets the key requirement criteria and then to add more elements for the more exotic functions or constraints. The cost of these additional functions and constraints is then more obvious and they can be 'traded'.

Any structural interface is an opportunity for testing and the interface specification is the test specification. It can be used to test in both directions, to look up and to look down, provided it has been agreed by both parties. Remember 'If you can't specify and test it, it can't be a requirement.' How else could a systems engineer know the customer's needs have been met? A loose specification results in a 'wobbly' product with possible litigation as to whose fault it is. Perhaps systems engineers should start by writing test specifications, rather than requirements! However, contracts can add engineering constraints by inhibiting changes that might benefit both parties. If change is inhibited, then so is progress. It is essential to be able to change interfaces and their specifications within the agreed contract terms.

10.3.2 System behaviour

A dynamic 'logical model' of a system will allow the system behaviour to be studied before embarking on detailed design. The interactions between architectural components can also be portrayed. Architectural designs usually address system-level behaviour, such as data rates, resilience to failure or the effect of major modifications. Furthermore, standards can be imposed, e.g. for digitisation or communication. Emergent properties depend on interactions between the system components and on the interactions with the user and with the environment. Components must be combined to give emergent properties and system testing must be done within an operational environment. Only then may undesirable emergent properties show up.

10.3.3 System layout or topography

The system layout is often explored using computer-based 3-D modelling tools. Appropriate subroutines allow physical properties to be checked, such as weight, centre of gravity or metacentric height. Packaging (e.g. boxes, frames, the exterior structures of vehicles and the internal wiring harnesses) may be a substantial part of the system. Packaging also defines certain physical characteristics: for electronics, it defines card size, connectors and rack layout: for software, it defines processors and memory. The layout can significantly affect performance due to earth-loops, electromagnetic compatibility and the like.

10.4 The relationships between the three aspects of systems architecture

The components of a system must provide both structure and behaviour, and iteration will be needed to balance design requirements against layout and component constraints. Difficulties often arise from lack of space, power or cooling. These may easily become severe design drivers in military systems. 'Installation', 'production' or 'maintenance' views of the layout are important as they allow a designer to optimise the assembly and to balance the costs of construction, development and manufacture.

10.5 Architectural style

A consistent architectural methodology offers many advantages such as a catalogue of reusable design elements or sub-systems, a set of design rules and constraints for those elements, common analyses for all systems built in that style (e.g. stress analysis for mechanical systems), and a coherent presentation of the system that allows users to build system models quickly. Finally, known solutions can be applied to new problems and the same style can be applied to a variety of projects, leading to reduced cost and improvements in performance resulting from the availability of more usage data.

10.6 Design and aesthetics

Many products are both functional and beautiful. Examples range from Samurai swords and Viking long ships to Ferraris and Concorde. A good coherent style may continue for decades, such as Rolls-Royce cars, Hewlett-Packard printers and Rolex watches. All have a design style that is easily recognisable; they represent a valuable asset for others to mimic. Aesthetics may help to sell a product but not if functional performance is compromised; this is clearly a major issue for commercial markets but does it apply to military equipment?

In the past, the external appearance of a defence system was not considered to be a high priority for designers, unless it could be shaped to affect the enemy in some way; the aim being to frighten or disturb the enemy and create an advantage. The tall mitred cap, which British Grenadiers wore in the eighteenth century, not only made them look taller and thus more fearsome to potential enemies, but also allowed unimpeded overarm throwing of a grenade. However, equipment was typically shaped by its function and the sub-systems used in the design and construction, and little attention was paid to the external shape apart from aircraft, ships and submarines where the requirements for minimum drag and/or lift affected the final form.

More recently, the requirement for minimum silhouettes, camouflage and stealth have all had an effect on the external shape of major defence systems. While aesthetics is the appreciation of shape and form for their own sake, the saying ‘what looks good, is good’ reflects a link between people’s perception of function and performance. If defence systems can be designed to look attractive, the user may have more confidence in the system. This may be an irrational connection, but if it creates a higher level of confidence and motivation in the user it is a good thing and will add to the system’s capability. Users who appreciate the aesthetics of their equipment will tend to show more care when using it, and may also undertake the maintenance in a more rigorous manner. These are very subjective matters, with little or no evidence to prove them one way or the other, but intuitively most people would support this view.

The Spitfire is still remembered, and talked of in hushed tones, as being beautiful, yet it was the Hurricane that proved a robust, stable gun platform that could sustain a lot of damage, was easy to repair, easy to fly and easy to manufacture. Equally iconic is the Kalashnikov rifle. Is that because of its looks, because it works and is tough, or both? Some people actually take a pride in the ugliness of their equipment; the A-10 Warthog aircraft is unattractive by any standards but its crews glorify its functionality. On the other hand, do some people tend to mistreat something that looks unattractive?

The defence systems engineer would be unwise to consider aesthetics as a high priority in the design, development and acquisition of defence systems, but changes in shape and aesthetics, which do not affect performance but inspire user confidence, would be an advantage worth having and, all other things being equal, systems design should aim both to be aesthetically pleasing and to look fit for purpose, after initially achieving the required performance.

11 Interoperability

While language may be one of the biggest obstacles to people interoperability, standards are the key to technical interoperability and to solving many of its problems. They can help to ensure that platforms can be replenished by allied or coalition forces away from their own bases. They can also make sure that command and control systems can 'talk' to each other. However, there are many different standards. The MoD uses UK defence standards (Def Stans). NATO uses STANAGS while ISO provides international standards. In the US, the Department of Defense (DoD) formerly relied on military standards (MIL-STDs) but has been moving away from these since the Perry initiative in the1990s. For the majority of COTS, there are open or de facto standards. Already, it is obvious that selecting the right standards to ensure interoperability when designing defence systems is something of a minefield. It is not helped by the fact that every nation thinks that its own standards are the best.

Any complex system will require interfaces between its components, sub-assemblies, assemblies, sub-systems and the outside world. The purchaser and the supplier must take great care in selecting the interface standards to provide the best possible level of interoperability. This is not helped by the large amount of legacy in-service equipment that

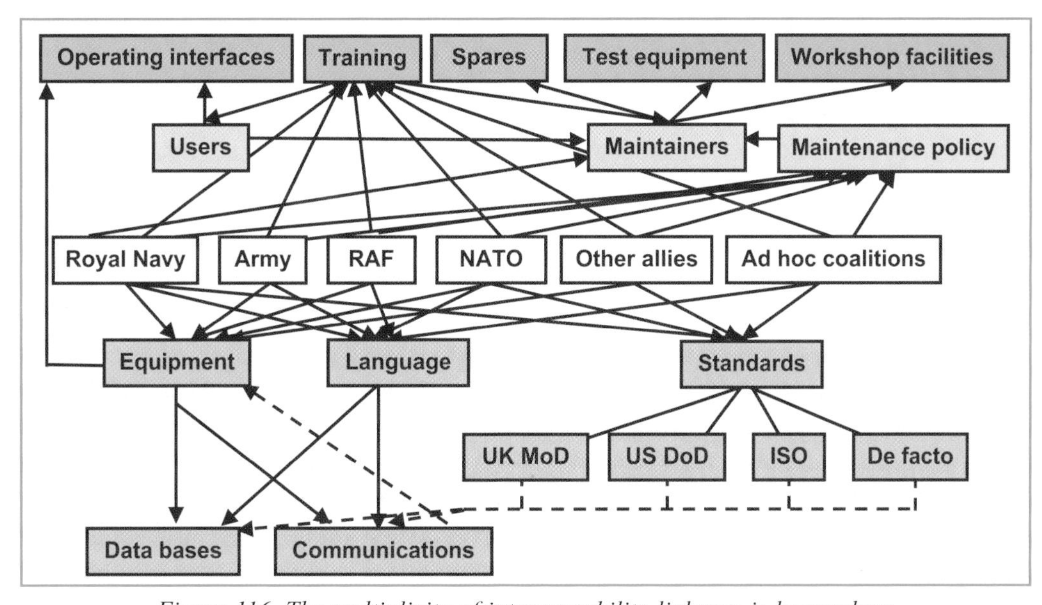

Figure 116. The multiplicity of interoperability linkages is horrendous.

is often not compatible with current standards. The MoD's Smart Acquisition initiative aims to acquire defence capability faster, cheaper, better and more effectively integrated; the latter has only recently been added to the other three parameters. Effective integration is all about equipment standards and interoperability.

Projects involving international collaboration have a potential head start in interoperability, since several nations agree jointly to develop a single equipment solution for all. Training and workshop facilities can be shared, reinforcing the interoperability message. Would that it were quite so simple! Consider a collaboratively developed platform. There will inevitably be national variants fitted, for example, with national communications packages to ensure operator and maintenance commonality with other national platforms.

Such simple factors as using the same fuel and lubricants and the same ammunition are crucial, but Europe and the US do not even use the same mains electricity; both the voltage and frequency are different! Frequency band allocation needs international agreement if the armed forces of different nations are to be able to communicate with each other, and the situation between different users within a nation can be difficult. In the incident when the *USS Vincennes* shot down an Iranian Airbus, the admiral on board the nearest US carrier later stated that he was unable to communicate directly with the *Vincennes* – and both vessels were part of the US navy! IFF (identification friend and foe) can be a real problem for ad hoc coalitions. The former Soviet Union's system is incompatible with that of NATO, and NATO's suffers from the US moving to new generations before the other member nations.

Improving interoperability with other forces, particularly the US, is seen as crucial by the MoD and the main route for this is through membership of NATO; a key forum for the development of common standards for interoperability. This will help to enable effective joint operations to be conducted when necessary. However, there are still major problems with the NATO accession states, where the first priority is to try to create interoperability with the original NATO nations. Since the UK will normally be operating as part of a military coalition, there is also a need for industrial co-operation to improve interoperability.

It is US DoD policy that military forces for joint and combined operations should employ compatible, interoperable and integrated C^3I (command, control, communications and intelligence) systems that can support operations worldwide throughout the entire spectrum of conflict and that are interoperable with allied nations' functionally related C^3I systems. The US is developing a single, joint-service, interoperable, operational battlespace picture to provide views of both friendly and enemy force locations and enable joint operational planning, co-ordination and execution.

Present UK government policy is that the nation will never enter a major conflict alone. Furthermore, single-service operations are seen as unlikely and increasingly tri-service operations are the norm. Any MoD business case for equipment acquisition submitted to the Investment Approvals Board (IAB) has to include key and user requirements for interoperability. These are normally written following discussions with the interoperability joint requirements co-ordinator, relevant DECs and the integration authority. Thus, interoperability must be regarded as one of the most important factors demanding the attention of any defence systems engineer.

12 A systems engineering strategy

Systems engineering is a demanding and complex problem-solving activity and, although humans are adaptable, they have limitations in understanding and managing complexity. Typically they find strategies that help scale complexity to an understandable level. One such strategy is to use rules of thumb, or heuristics, in problem-solving processes. Heuristics are a human response to complexity. They are rules of thumb based on the experiences and judgements of experts. They are helpful when dealing with unfamiliar problems or projects that do not easily lend themselves to rigorous analysis. They attempt to scale down problems to a simple and understandable level, while accepting that so doing sacrifices precision; the assumption is that problems arising from using heuristics can be resolved later in the design process.

12.1 Systems engineering maxims/rules of thumb

The following set of heuristics has its origin in the defence systems engineering principles taught as part of the MSc degree in defence systems engineering (MDSE) at University College London. This particular set adds to those already described by Rechtin and INCOSE's *Pragmatic Principles* (Defoe 1993). These heuristics were principally intended to 'get students thinking' about defence systems engineering issues, but they also provide useful guidelines for practising systems engineers.

The use of heuristics may be symptomatic of the relative immaturity of systems engineering as compared to civil, mechanical or electrical engineering. For instance:

- Systems engineering does not yet have a professional body.
- Systems engineering education is driven by the needs of individual employers and specific industries rather than a widely agreed curriculum.
- There is no chartered systems engineer status as yet.
- There is still much debate about systems engineering terminology.

The principles, concepts and theories encapsulated in these heuristics are intended to help students with systems engineering challenges, particularly when some ideas seem counter-intuitive. They are not intended specifically to aid the systems engineer in designing a new system, though they may be helpful in that regard. The following paragraphs describe each heuristic in the format of a title, followed by a maxim with its corollary, a paragraph of explanation, and an indication as to when the heuristic applies.

12.2 Systems engineering and project management

> *You can't engineer a complex system without managing it properly and you can't manage a complex system without understanding its engineering. Systems engineering and project management are two sides of the same coin and should be taught together in a holistic way.*

The relationship between systems engineering and project management is complex. Although they are different disciplines, they have much in common: both are management strategies for achieving specific organisational aims; both are concerned with the management of complexity; and both focus on the through-life activities of a project.

As with systems engineering, there is some difficulty in defining the term 'project management'. Bate et al (1995) recognised the close relationship that exists between systems engineering and project management. Systems engineering is concerned primarily with exploring and solving complex technical problems (product oriented), whereas project management focuses on optimising the execution of complex projects (process and task oriented).

The systems engineering community has long recognised the importance of the relationship between the two disciplines. Many papers in the INCOSE *Symposium Proceedings,* the *Journal for Systems Engineering* and other publication channels explore that relationship. Both systems engineering and project management should be co-ordinated and planned from the outset of a project.

12.3 People and systems

Systems don't go wrong. It's the people involved that do. Improve the quality of the people and you will improve the systems they build.

The corollary to this maxim is self-evident and needs little justification. Aside from the general limitations and failings of humans in terms of intelligence, judgement and ethics, the question arises, with respect to systems engineering, in what way do people go wrong and how can they be improved?

Effective systems engineering demands a combination of theoretical knowledge and practical engineering and management skills, particularly in the ability to think in a logical manner about systems. It also requires a knowledge of methods, techniques and tools, problem-solving ability, and the capability to apply and generalise the experience of systems engineering project work. At the personal level, it needs a high degree of general intelligence, creativity and imagination, enthusiasm, persistence, as well as team-working and leadership skills.

12.4 Defining the system boundary

The system is what it is defined to be. Everyone concerned must agree with the definition for the purpose in question.

A system cannot be defined in isolation from its environment and must have an agreed boundary that separates the two. For instance, considering a living organism as a system, that organism has to have an inside and an outside. A skin or membrane separates the two. Without that membrane, an organism cannot distinguish itself from its environment. *It's hard to thrive if you're just undifferentiated mush.*

The problems resulting from failure to get agreement on the purpose and boundary of systems are well documented, and the process of defining system aims and boundaries is a fundamental part of formal product design and systems engineering methods. It is essential to seek to achieve consensus amongst stakeholders on the aims of a proposed system and, in so doing, help to define the system boundary. Several different system boundaries may be defined for different purposes for the same system. Confusion and ambiguity can easily arise unless both the definition and its purpose are clearly understood by all stakeholders. Defining the system boundary is the first step in the systems engineering process, since the 'system' cannot be discussed until it has been defined and agreed as an entity.

12.5 Requirement specification

The requirement specification defines the agreed interface between the system and its environment. It must be agreed and accepted by the responsible parties on either side.

The requirement specification must define the performance of the system in its external environment. It is a formal statement of the desired functions and properties that the system must provide in its interaction with its environment across the agreed system boundary. The requirement specification is closely related to the system boundary definition and hence is an early deliverable in the systems engineering process. It may be necessary to revisit and refine the system boundary during the process of requirement specification.

12.6 The role of systems engineers

Look upwards and outwards into the environment before looking downwards and inwards into the system itself. It's no use designing a jigsaw piece that does not fit into the bigger picture.

Traditionally, engineers have been trained to focus on the internal detail of their systems and have often been constrained by a single engineering discipline. This may lead to a tendency to seek solutions before the problem has been fully explored and defined, with the subsequent risk of missing key requirements or choosing sub-optimal solutions. In this sense engineering perspectives and systems engineering perceptions differ. Systems engineering is specifically concerned with an overarching view. Therefore systems engineers need to cultivate a much wider, multidisciplinary perspective. This applies particularly to system design and solution definition stages of a project.

12.7 Hierarchy of systems

One man's sub-system is another man's system. They may have a common interface, but different priorities and perceptions.

Large and complex systems must be divided into smaller elements, which can be managed effectively. For example there is the concept of systems, sub-systems, assemblies and components. This process of division creates interfaces between the teams of people concerned and they may act in their own perceived interests, rather than those of the overall system. This idea is similar to Conway's Law, which suggests that organisations tend to design systems that mirror the management and communication structures of those organisations.

The principles of systems engineering should be applied at all levels in order to improve the understanding and cohesion across the internal interfaces. This is particularly relevant both when the system is initially partitioned and when any subsequent changes are proposed.

12.8 Partitioning systems

There is no ideal solution, but some will be better than others. Systems engineers must know how to recognise the better ones.

Professor Nam Suh has extensively explored the process of defining system function and has developed two axioms to aid the design process. His Independence Axiom states that sections of the design should be separable so that changes in one have no (or as little as possible) effect on the other. His Information Axiom affirms that the information inherent in a product design should be minimised (Suh 1990). As with system hierarchy, these concepts can most usefully be applied when the system is initially partitioned and should help defence systems engineers to distinguish the optimum solution.

12.9 Complexity

Remember that everything is connected to other things. Managing the interconnections is the key to systems engineering.

The notion that everything is connected to everything may seem, at least on the surface, to be theoretically true; an extreme, but often cited, example of which is the Butterfly Effect. This is the name given to the phenomenon whereby large-scale weather phenomena are attributed to relatively small-scale initial conditions. The idea is usually attributed to American meteorologist Edward N. Lorenz who, in 1972, gave a presentation with the title: *Predictability: Does the flap of a butterfly's wings in Brazil set off a tornado in Texas?* The challenge for systems engineering is in the prediction of the required connections and consequent interfaces; also which other parts of a system would be affected by a change to one component, and in what way? In systems engineering (as in sociology and other disciplines), small and apparently insignificant changes can have substantial and often unexpected effects on system performance. This point of view emphasises the need to understand as much about sub-system interfaces as about the sub-systems themselves. This applies throughout the systems engineering process whenever changes are proposed. Systems engineering data management tools can assist in tracking implications of change.

12.10 System integration

Build a little; test a little. Avoid the 'big-bang' solution and the 'It will be all right on the night' mentality.

At the integration stage of the systems engineering process, components should be combined and tested in small numbers rather than lumped together and tested as a much larger group. It is easier to diagnose the causes of failures if fewer contributing elements have to be considered. This has implications for the test environment; both physical and procedural. It applies particularly at the component, sub-system and system integration stages, but must also properly be considered as part of the test planning process at the partitioning stage, which is when the test specifications should be written and agreed.

12.11 Test and acceptance

If you can't test it, it can't be a requirement. If you specify a capability, you must test and accept the system in capability terms.

There is strong evidence for the value and application of formulating testable requirements. Failure adequately to plan and execute testing can have serious, even catastrophic consequences. The Ariane 5 flight 501 crash was attributed to inadequate testing of flight-control software reused from Ariane 4 (Lions 1996; Robinson 1996). The measurability and testability of requirements are critically important. If requirements are to be useful, they must be measurable. They must be given quantifiable characteristics so that testers can accurately determine whether the eventual solution satisfies the initial requirement.

The V-diagram (see Figure 112 on p. 255) specifically separates the planning of testing and the actual testing activities. In the V-diagram, test planning is closely integrated with design, whereas test execution is associated with increasing levels of system integration. For a design process following the V-diagram, planning for testing takes place in increasing detail as the system develops, and actual testing occurs later as the system is integrated. Test and evaluation is covered in detail in Chapter 7.

12.12 Emergent properties

The whole is greater than the sum of the parts. Any sane engineer would design a tricycle for stability, not a bicycle. Emergent properties can be counter-intuitive. They can also be undesirable.

Although there is some debate as to whether the concept of emergent properties is valid, it is a widely accepted phenomenon in the systems engineering community. Systems engineers typically mix the concept of hierarchy, where descending lower into the system reveals sub-system and component levels, with the concept of emergence. When viewing the system from the bottom up, that is ascending higher in the system, collective features emerge that were not apparent at the lower levels. The act of integration at a higher level leads to the definition of function, features and emergent properties. For example, the reliability of a system is a high-level emergent property.

The prediction of emergent properties is a key challenge for the systems engineer. Desirable emergent properties are defined in requirement documents, often in the form of reliability, usability, serviceability requirements and the like. These are actively pursued in the design process, but it is undesired emergent features such as earth-loops in electronic circuits or 'bugs' in software that can be the most problematic. The notion of emergence needs to be borne in mind throughout the systems engineering process, particularly the problem of unforeseen emergent phenomena.

12.13 System modelling

A fool with a tool is still a fool. Choose tools wisely and use tools wisely.

Software tools are an increasingly important part of the systems engineering process. There are tools for requirements management, systems architecture, project measurement and management – all of which are undoubtedly useful in managing and tracking complex data, but which are in themselves complex systems. Aside from designing a complex new system, the systems engineer may be faced with deciding which tool should be used, whilst giving consideration to the training required to use it properly. A tool is only as good as its operator who has to provide the necessary input data, and 'garbage in; garbage out' is still a very valid warning. Tool selection and training requirements need to be considered at project planning stages of the systems engineering process.

12.14 System optimisation

Optimising the sub-systems separately and independently will not result in an efficient and effective system. The system must be optimised as a whole.

Taking a whole-system view is central to the concept of systems engineering. Superficially, that point of view may seem contrary to the approach of taking problems 'one step at a time'. A machine can be built up from distinct parts and can be reduced to those parts without losing its machine-like character. This point of view was extremely influential, and the machine metaphor set the tone for modern science and scientific methods. The problem with the hierarchical approach is that it does not work for complex systems; it only reduces them to simple mechanisms. However, taking only a holistic view is as perilous as taking a hierarchical-only view of systems engineering. The act of partitioning into sub-systems for manageability is doomed to failure unless systems engineers continually bear in mind the interfaces and interactions between the 'separate' elements. These interfaces must be managed just as closely as the sub-systems themselves. This concept should be applied to all phases of systems engineering, from ensuring that initial sets of requirements are free of conflict and duplication to the later application of the Independence and Information axioms, mentioned in Section 12.8 above, to design solutions.

12.15 Conclusions

Additions could always be made to the set of heuristics discussed above, but those described have their basis in well-established systems engineering theory, and can be readily applied in practical systems engineering processes.

The use of heuristics is part of the general process of systems thinking, which embraces philosophy as well as methodology in that it requires the understanding and application of principles and abstract ideas as well as of well-defined processes and practices. The aim of these heuristics or 'rules of thumb' is to encourage systems engineers to think creatively and systematically about the problems in hand.

13 Summary

In most acquisition processes, there is a singular requirement to be satisfied, a plurality of function sets that might meet the requirement and a multiplicity of acceptable solutions that could provide the requisite functions and hence satisfy the customer. In UK defence acquisition, it is current policy for the MoD as the customer to specify the requirement in terms of military capability, allowing the global defence industry as the suppliers to offer the widest possible range of solutions, from which the preferred one will be selected competitively.

The capability required of a new system at any particular time is only a small subset of total defence capability, and the nature of the capability gap to be filled will inevitably depend on what other military assets exist or are planned. Thus any statement of requirements must rest on a thorough analysis of relevant capability and only expert defence systems engineers and systems analysts within the MoD can do this. There is creative tension and potential conflict between the need for brainstorming to identify a wide range of possible solutions and the need to close off undesirable options as early as possible in order to reduce the manpower, time and cost required. Hence, the user requirement document (URD) must contain as much detail as possible in order to minimise nugatory work on solutions unacceptable to the customer. This is equally important for a requirement specified in generic capability terms as for a traditional requirement written as a detailed technical specification.

Functional analysis is often used to assist in the translation from the URD to a system requirement document (SRD), which usually forms the basis for a competitive contract. The resultant functions define the actions required to provide the capability but not the details of how they are to be implemented. It may be necessary to have more than one set of functions to describe the operation of different classes of solution, but keeping multiple options open will be very resource-intensive. It may be helpful for industry to assist in the generation of the SRD but it must be remembered that industry will impose additional constraints on the solution, some of which may close off options that would have been acceptable to the customer. 'A missile manufacturer will always see the solution as a missile!' Thus it is essential that the MoD takes the lead in writing the SRD and has sufficient defence systems engineering expertise to do so.

Finally, only the MoD can judge between the candidate solutions offered by industry and, if the requirement is specified in capability terms, the solutions must be evaluated in capability terms. A fair and objective evaluation of the capability of disparate solutions within the context of other defence equipments is by no means easy and this is possibly the most demanding defence systems engineering task that the MoD has to carry out.

The bottom line is that the MoD requires an excellent cadre of defence systems engineers if it is to achieve the cost-effective acquisition of complex, new defence equipment.

Note

[1] The section draws on and acknowledges the description of systems architecture in the book by Stephens et al (1998), chapter 4.

Further reading

Achenbach, J (2003) Strange life, *National Geographic Magazine* January: 24–51

Alexander, I (1999) Migrating towards co-operative requirements engineering, *Computing and Control Engineering Journal* February: 17–22

Anscombe, E, et al (1954) *Translation of Rene Descartes Philosophical Writings: Rules for the Direction of the Mind* (pp 153–80). London: Nelson

Augustine, N (1983) *Augustine's Laws*. New York: American Institute of Aeronautics and Astronautics Inc

Bate, R, et al (1995) *Systems Engineering Capability Maturity Model. Version 1.1.* Pittsburgh, PA: Software Engineering Institute, Carnegie Mellon University

Bertalanffy, L von (1969) *General Systems Theory: Foundations, Development, Applications*. New York: George Brazziler

Chamberlain, R and Shishko, R (1991) Fundamentals of systems engineering at NASA. In *Proceedings of the INCOSE Conference*, October 1991 p23. Chattanooga: International Council on Systems Engineering

Checkland, P (1998) *Systems Thinking, Systems Practice*. Chichester: Wiley

Conway, ME (1968) How do committees invent? *Datamation* 14(4): 28–31

Currie, W (1994) The strategic management of a large scale IT project in the financial services sector, *New Technology, Work and Employment* 9(1):19–29

DeFoe, J (ed.) (1993) *An Identification of Pragmatic Principles*. Final Report to the INCOSE SE Practice Working Group, Subgroup on Pragmatic Principles.Washington, DC: International Council on Systems Engineering

DSMC (1991) *Systems Engineering Management Guide*. Fort Belvoir, VA: Defence System Management Centre

—— (1999) *Systems Engineering Fundamentals*. Fort Belvoir, VA: Defence System Management Centre Press

Eisner, H (1988) *Computer Aided Systems Engineering*. New York : Prentice-Hall

Forsberg, K and Mooz, H (1991) The relationship of system engineering to the project cycle. In *Proceedings of the INCOSE Conference*, October 1991, pp 57–65. Chattanooga: International Council on Systems Engineering

Gelb, MJ (1999) *How to Think Like Leonardo da Vinci*. New York: Dell Publishing

Hitchens, DK (1992) *Putting Systems to Work*. Chichester: Wiley

Holder, I (2002) *MSc in Defence Engineering Syllabus*. London: UCL

IEE (1997) *Building Integrated Systems. Report of the Foresight Panel Technology Working Party*. London: Institution of Electrical Engineers

Kaposi, A and Myers, M (1996) *Systems for All*. London: Imperial College Press

Lions, JL (1996) *Ariane 5 Flight 501 Failure*. Report by the Independent Enquiry Board. Paris

Lorenz, EN (1972) *Predicatability: Does the Flap of a Butterfly's Wings in Brazil Set Off a Tornado in Texas?* Talk given to the American Association for the Advancement of Science, Washington DC in December 1972

M'Pherson, P (1986) Systems engineering: a proposed definition, *IEE Proceedings 133*: 330–31

O'Connor, T and Wong, HY (2002) Emergent properties. In the *Stanford Encyclopedia of Philosophy* (Winter 2002), Edward N Zalta (ed.)

Ramo, S and St Clair, R (1998) *The Systems Approach: Fresh Solutions to Complex Civil Problems through Combining Science and Practical Common Sense*. Anaheim, CA: KNI

Reason, J (1990) *Human Error*. Cambridge: Cambridge University Press

Rechtin, E (1991) *Systems Architecting: Creating and Building Complex Systems*. Upper Saddle River, NJ: Prentice-Hall International Inc

Robertson, J and Robertson, S (1997) Requirements made to measure, *American Programmer* X(8): 27–32

Robinson, K (1996) *Ariane 5, Flight 501 Failure: A Case Study*. Sydney: Department of Software Engineering, School of Computer Science and Engineering, University of New South Wales

Stevens, R, et al (1998) *Systems Engineering: Coping with Complexity*. Hemel Hempstead: Prentice-Hall

Suh, NP (1990) *The Principles of Design*. New York: Oxford University Press Inc

Waring, A (1996) *Practical Systems Thinking*. London: Thompson Business Press

Websites

www.incose.org/

www.deg.meng.ucl.ac.uk/SYLLABUS_2002-_ISSUE_1_3,PDF

http://plato.stanford.edu/archives/win2002/entries/properties-emergent/

Chapter 10

Looking to the future

The next few decades are likely to involve many changes to defence systems acquisition in the UK. The dawn of the information age and the explosion in global communications are both facilitating the realisation of unmanned autonomous systems. Industry continues to reorganise and this will have an impact on defence companies and their relationship with their customers. With no superpower confrontation, and as pressure increases in the industrialised nations to provide pensions and health care for a growing aged population and to improve education for the new generations, the inevitable casualty will be the defence budget. The aim of acquiring systems to provide best value for the through-life cost of the equipment will force systems engineers to take a more holistic view in their design approach.

1. The impact of information technology

1.1 Revolution in military affairs

The armed forces of the world, particularly those of the industrialised nations, have been facing a 'revolution in military affairs' over the last two decades. This has been caused primarily by the impact of the information technology revolution that has affected the vast majority of both military and civil systems. In the defence field, this technology has resulted in smart weapons, the automation of many platform systems resulting in reduced manpower to operate them or even unmanned solutions, and the digitisation of the battlefield with data and images being rapidly transmitted and readily available to those that need them.

This technology can also link all combat and support units operating in a land/sea/air battlespace within an information network, providing them with a shared awareness of the current situation and with the ability to co-ordinate and synchronise operations to achieve their overall objectives. The information network should vastly reduce the traditional 'fog of war' which in former times limited a commander's visibility of enemy forces (and even of his own), and should vastly increase the agility and responsiveness of networked forces by accelerating the detect-consider-act command cycle. In consequence, future network-centric warfare (or warfare using network-enabled capabilities) will be radically different from war in preceding centuries, unless and until ingenious enemies devise effective countermeasures targeting the hardware or software on which a network will depend.

This rapid and widespread change in techology will continue its impact on the effectiveness of much of the world's defence equipment. With the threat faced by nations continually altering, trying to predict what the UK requires in terms of defence equipment is difficult, especially if looking up to 30 to 50 years ahead (the typical life of a defence system). The long lifetime of defence equipment in a world where civil equipment lives are continually reducing is becoming a major problem. It might be easier if defence equipment were designed to last 10 years, so it could be replaced by something more suitable, rather than adapting equipment expected to remain in service for 50 years. But that in itself would introduce a different set of problems; those of reducing the timescale from concept to in-service date.

1.2 The information explosion

Information technology (IT) seems set to continue its rapid pace of development for the foreseeable future. Moore's Law, established by one of the founding fathers of the microprocessor company Intel, predicts future progress with processors and has held for more than 30 years; there is confidence that it may continue to do so, though there are signs that the rate may accelerate. Thus systems engineers will carry on enjoying increased performance of IT-based sub-systems. Similar advances have been made in the computer peripheral field where the amount of data that can be stored has increased more than ten thousand fold in the last decade while data transfer speeds have also risen. Thus the performance of IT systems seems likely to continue its rapid progress allowing more complex software to be run and thus driving improvements in weapons and platform modelling, as well as providing ever more realistic virtual reality for use in training and simulation. Unfortunately, the lack of a similar growth rate in communications capacities may limit networking capabilities. Furthermore, the problems of producing bespoke military IT, both in terms of the availability of resources and in financial terms, are driving system engineers to find ways of configuring COTS IT sub-systems to provide the required military capability.

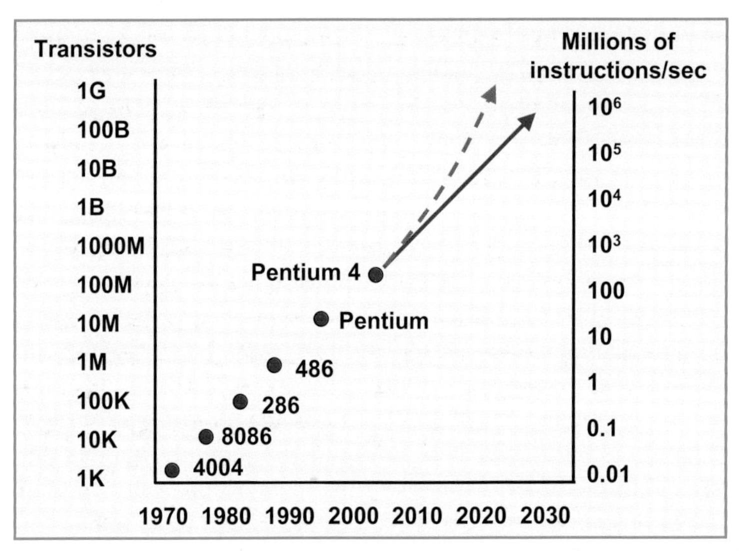

Figure 117. Moore's Law predicts a doubling of processor speed every 18 months, though technology breakthroughs may accelerate the rate of increase.

Use of the Internet provides an example of the revolution in IT and the growth of communications that started at the end of the last century. It has worried democratic governments in terms of combating terrorism and organised crime, while dictatorships have been equally concerned about the freedoms it brings. A nation can be divided by the multitude of different reports and 'spins' put on news. Democracies will find it more difficult to undertake unacceptable (and usually unpopular) military policy when their populations use the plethora of information in different ways to express their views. Defence systems engineers, like other professionals, will have to absorb a surfeit of information of varying validity, and derive from it cost-effective designs and efficient acquisition policies.

At the same time, the need to transmit huge quantities of information has increased pressure on communications. Cables, radio links and satellites carry the vast amount of data that computers store and process, and in the future technology will improve the speed and quality of communications. But available bandwidth always seems to lag behind demand and the use of wireless computer peripherals increases the pressure on bandwidth. This problem faces military users, who wish to transmit still and video images (often infra-red, radar or electronic warfare). The lowliest infantry soldiers want as much information as possible about the threats around them. Sensing assets such as airborne early warning, maritime patrol and battlefield surveillance aircraft need their real-time pictures downloaded and distributed to interested users without delay.

1.3 Networks

Early in the twenty-first century the ongoing development of the revolution in military affairs (based on the increasing power of modern computers to assemble, transmit, analyse and display prodigious quantities of information) will link military units into ever wider and more complex networks. These networks will link military combat units such as warships, aircraft, armoured vehicles and even individual infantrymen with each other and with supporting reconnaissance and logistic units. They will probably extend to political organisations and media groups, which can significantly affect the final outcome of military operations, albeit indirectly. Since the number of interfaces grows more rapidly than the number of nodes in a network, there will be a greater role for systems engineers who can manage them effectively. Management of these networks will involve sophisticated filtering and data fusion to reduce the plethora of available information to the minimum required by field commanders to carry out their allotted tasks without being swamped with information which is only appropriate to higher or lower levels in the organisation's area of responsibility.

1.4 Autonomous systems

As long ago as 1957, the UK Secretary of State for Defence, Duncan Sandys, cancelled the development programmes of existing manned fighter aircraft, predicting their rapid demise and replacement by rockets and missiles. He was clearly wrong, but half a century later there has been significant growth in autonomous systems. Surface-to-surface, surface-to-air and air-to-surface missiles are already largely autonomous, and the recent proliferation of cruise missiles and unmanned air vehicles for attack and reconnaissance have reduced the risks that were faced by the crews of their manned predecessors. Now development work is underway in the US on unmanned air combat vehicles.

Missiles, unmanned aircraft and torpedoes are now widely deployed, but progress has been less dramatic for movement on the ground. The US competition for unmanned land vehicles has resulted in unpromising results so far, though Martian rovers have been successful. However, the growing capability and relatively low cost of rugged computing power and memory, allied to increasingly capable software and sensors, make it likely that significant progress will be made; autonomous systems will provide a major field for defence systems engineers.

2 Industrial changes

2.1 Consolidation in the defence sector

The capacity to develop major defence systems will be developed increasingly in China and India, but the UK will probably continue to procure its defence equipment from prime contractors based in the NATO nations. The number of such prime contractors has fallen sharply since the end of the Cold War and will probably be driven by economies of scale down to about half a dozen (primarily US-based but having a significant presence in the UK and other European nations), at which level competition to supply most types of equipment can be maintained. It is possible, due in particular to pressure from France and Germany, that there may be attempts to maintain a complete defence systems capability in Europe which can challenge the US, in the same way that Airbus has successfully challenged Boeing in the civil airliner field.

Apart from the US, a few NATO nations may choose to sustain one or more domestic prime contractors with expertise in some important defence systems, but since these contractors would not have access to the technology arising from the vast research programme funded by the US government (which spends ten times more on defence research than the French), it is unlikely that their products could be competitive. Other European nations may choose to sustain some specialist parts of their defence industrial base, which could not survive in a free market but which have nostalgic value or which are perceived to contribute to national economic or social goals. Support for these cherished companies through formal or informal partnering with government (balancing between market forces and nationalisation) will impose additional constraints on the equipment design, project scheduling and work-share allocation. These constraints will affect defence systems engineers working on future projects.

Does the UK want an industrial policy to enable its home industry to survive, or does it want the best value for money? Is value for money to be defined by best value for the MoD or for the nation? If the UK is the system, then getting best value for money for the MoD is optimising the sub-system, not the system. How will the UK react when BAE Systems is hunted by one of the US defence industrial giants such as Boeing or Lockheed Martin? The MoD bases its definition of the UK defence industry on the economic value that it brings to the UK, by creating employment, technology and intellectual property in this country. UK industry is therefore defined less by ownership than by considering:

- Whether investment is being undertaken in the UK.
- Whether intellectual property will be created and retained within the UK.
- The number and quality of jobs sustained and created within the UK.
- Whether skills and expertise are utilised or developed within the UK.

Whether the government and Parliament would feel the same way about UK ownership if BAE Systems were to be acquired by a foreign company is another matter.

2.2 Balance of power

The decline in the number of prime contractors producing major defence systems relative to the number of customer governments has shifted, and will continue to shift, the balance of power in the market for such systems. Formerly, each customer government had several domestic and foreign contractors eager to supply its needs for each class of defence equipment, but in the twenty-first century there will be only a few large prime contractors supplying many sovereign nations in a global market. These contractors will have to rely more on exports and less on orders from their host governments.

It follows that fewer individual nations will be able to specify their military requirements and to commission a chosen contractor to produce a bespoke system to meet that requirement. Instead a nation may have to select the system that best meets its requirement from a limited range of systems available off-the-shelf. As and when UK defence acquisition tends towards the latter situation, there will be a change in the competences required of UK defence systems engineers engaged in acquisition.

International collaboration has been a cornerstone of MoD policy for several decades and it supported the formation of OCCAR (Organisation Conjointe de Coopération en Matière d'Armement), established to improve European co-operation in armaments and to provide less costly, more modern, common equipment. It provides Europe-wide research, programme management, technology, investment and test centres for its founding members: UK, France, Germany and Italy.

Its aims are to improve cost effectiveness and through-life costs on co-operative programmes, to co-ordinate requirements and common technology programmes, to improve the competitiveness of the industrial and technological base and to give up juste retour. OCCAR is open to other nations and already runs a number of European collaborative programmes such as the A400M transport aircraft and Cobra weapon-locating radar. The UK might decide to merge its defence equipment acquisition activities with those of other nations with similar requirements and thereby create an organisation, like OCCAR, able to negotiate on more equal terms with the remaining large prime contractors. If so, the UK defence systems engineers working in that international organisation would require additional competences in bureaucracy and diplomacy.

In former times governments could impose their preferred acquisition policies on subservient suppliers. In future, the change in the balance of power may force governments to accede to supplier demand for partnering arrangements, so that industry may obtain assured workload and satisfactory profits instead of competition and fixed-price contracts. In this future world, defence systems engineers will require a much greater ability to negotiate, based on an understanding of a contractor's situation and aspirations.

2.3 PFI in the defence sector

One result of the UK use of PFI in defence acquisition is that the resulting contractorisation is likely to be a growing feature of UK defence expenditure. With the increasing use of contractors, the interface between the military and the contractor needs to be rigorously defined. This is difficult for equipment used in the UK, but is much harder for equipment deployed in the front line – perhaps it requires a different type of contract rather than the 'specification/payment' type currently used. A contract for capability, rather than equipment, may be the way forward, but the UK will need to overcome the impression of 'hiring mercenaries' as contracting for capability includes all the elements of capability: command and control, doctrine, training, equipment, logistics and the like.

3 Financial issues

3.1 Limited defence budgets

If no conventional military threat to the UK homeland or its interests overseas emerges in the coming decades, and if the UK government's budget then faces heavy demands from a rapid growth in pensions, increasing medical treatment for an aging population, dealing with hospital superbugs, a dramatic increase in the number of asylum seekers or economic migrants, the onset of global warming, and the expense of 'homeland defence', there will be almost inexorable pressure to reduce the UK defence budget by one of the following:

- Reducing the scale of the UK armed services and creating a small elite force which would be capable of operating alongside US forces and hence would similarly be transformed by the revolution in military affairs; it would therefore be trained to US standards and largely equipped with US weaponry.
- Shrinking the size of the UK armed services and incorporating them into a European rapid reaction and peacekeeping force, with integrated planning and budgeting.
- Downgrading the combat capability of the UK armed services relative to those of allies and potential enemies, yielding a 'gendarmerie' with B-list weaponry which would be suited to peace support roles.

The evolution of one of those alternatives would arise from parallel decisions by the UK, the US and the EU governments; the US government could preclude the first option by declining to make first-rate equipment (see Section 3.3 below) and training available even to its closest allies and thus avoid a marginal extra risk of any breach in arms control. But any of the options would significantly affect the future activities of UK defence systems engineers.

Even if the pressure for reduction in the UK defence budget were less severe, and the present size and character of UK forces could be preserved in a recognisable form, the increasing unit cost of first-rate defence equipment will make it progressively more difficult to fund major projects (such as Tornado, Trident, Typhoon and CVF) and will strengthen the current trend towards incremental acquisition, i.e. increasing the capability of current systems progressively by technology insertion. However, successful technology insertion to meet a military requirement depends on the preceding success of a research programme, launched several years earlier, of appropriate scale and scope to bring the relevant technologies to an acceptable level of maturity. Without research results to guide assessments of performance and risk, technology insertion projects are doomed to disappointment. UK defence systems engineers already have some experience of managing mid-life updates to extend the life of equipment or to enhance its performance, but will need to enhance their understanding of technology maturity, of open systems architecture and software, of the issues involved in incremental contracting, and of the dangers of interface obsolescence in legacy systems.

With the reduction in spending on defence research and the enormous amounts of money being invested in the commercial IT field by companies such as Microsoft and Intel, there is every reason to believe that military equipment will continue to become more and more reliant on COTS IT. The performance of IT seems set to continue its rapid progress and the digitisation of the battlefield is a key target for both the UK and the US military, so its importance in battle winning is certain to increase. Thus defence systems engineers will increasingly have to find ways of building COTS IT into their solutions in a way that provides the necessary ruggedness, reliability and through-life supportability.

3.2 Reduction in defence research

While the above paragraphs are largely speculative, it is already evident that MoD defence research spending, after rising in real terms until a peak in 1995/96, fell by about a third over the following six years. Will research spending in the twenty-first century continue to reduce? If it does (unless the MoD's new research management arrangements have succeeded in getting a quart out of a pint pot), it will continue to diminish the ability of the MoD to act as an intelligent customer and will also reduce the ability of UK industry to produce competitive equipment. UK defence systems engineers will have to adapt to this challenge by enhancing their ability to manage risks and uncertainties and assessing the conflicting claims of rival contractors.

Research partnership between the MoD and industry is being fostered by two complementary MoD initiatives. To facilitate the pull-through of particular technologies into new defence equipment, 'towers of excellence' (set at system or major sub-system level) have been set up. They seek to build upon a new level of co-operation and interaction between the MoD and the equipment supplier base, and improve the technological excellence in key high priority areas. They also draw upon the particular strengths of UK academia. The first tower of excellence to be set up was for guided weapons, followed by radar, underwater sensors, synthetic environments and COTS/HMI (commercial off-the-shelf/human-machine interface). Defence technology centres are collaborative arrangements between industrial and academic experts jointly funded by the participants and the MoD, to generate and exploit future technologies. The first defence technology centres are for electromagnetic remote sensing, data and information fusion, and human factors integration, followed by systems engineering and integrated systems for autonomous and semi-autonomous vehicles. This leaves a problem. If the MoD only researches a subset of technologies, it can only be an intelligent customer for this limited set of technologies rather than for the complete range of technologies involved in an equipment project. What happens if one or more key project-related technologies are missed from the list and how will this impact on defence systems engineers?

3.3 The consequences of unit cost growth

The unit cost of successive generations of defence equipment has been rising rapidly since the end of the Second World War. The scale of the increase was dramatically illustrated by Norman Augustine's (formerly Chairman and Chief Executive Officer of Martin Marietta) observation that *In the year 2054 the entire US defence budget will purchase just one tactical combat aircraft.* Other studies have shown that the rapid growth of unit cost affects many types of defence equipment (the unit cost of tactical combat aircraft has grown at about 10% per year in real terms; the unit cost of other types has grown at 5–15%), that this unit cost growth has persisted for decades, and that similar growth affected the key instruments of military power in medieval as well as in modern times.

In recent decades, the unit cost growth of many types of defence equipment has significantly exceeded the concurrent rates of economic growth in the UK and in other developed nations, and accordingly has also exceeded the sustainable rates of growth of their defence budgets. In response, these nations have funded equipment acquisition programmes less frequently, and in successive programmes have procured fewer units of each type of equipment. Their defence forces have tried to maintain broadly the same military capability against potential enemies while evolving towards smaller forces with greater individual combat effectiveness. Ultimately, when the unit cost of a particular class of equipment becomes so large relative to a nation's defence budget that it can no longer afford a viable force, the nation must forgo that class of equipment and the military capability it would provide (today few nations operate strategic bombers and New Zealand plans to operate no combat aircraft whatsoever). Of course national priorities can change with geo-political circumstances; in the Cold War the UK ceased to buy and operate large aircraft carriers for conventional take-off and landing aircraft in order to allocate more of its resources to large armoured forces in Central Europe, but today those armoured forces are being cut back to fund the acquisition of two aircraft carriers to support expeditionary warfare.

The increase in the unit cost of defence equipment arises inevitably from military rivalry and from advances in technology, and as long as these persist unit cost growth seems likely to continue for the foreseeable future. As military forces shrink, defence systems engineers must concentrate on getting the greatest possible military capability from them by:

- Making each class of equipment capable of several roles in varied scenarios.
- Ensuring that the equipment's reliability and maintainability, and the provision of logistic support, yield high availability.
- Reducing the equipment's mass and/or bulk and its logistic footprint to facilitate rapid strategic redeployment.

Furthermore, as successive acquisition programmes involve fewer units, and as the fixed costs of concept plus assessment plus demonstration tend to rise relative to the variable costs of manufacture plus operation plus support, the UK (and other nations with similar or smaller budgets) will conclude that national equipment projects are increasingly uneconomic. It follows that for such nations, most future equipment projects (except perhaps warships where the fixed/variable cost ratio is unusually low) must adopt collaborative or off-the-shelf acquisition strategies, and hence that defence systems engineers must develop their understanding of foreign contractors, languages, legal systems, and political organisations in order to conduct future acquisition projects successfully.

4 Multiple lines of development

It seems also virtually certain that in the twenty-first century defence systems engineers will have to pay increasing attention to all six lines of development (equipment, support, training, personnel, doctrine and infrastructure) whose delivery must be synchronised to provide an enhancement in military capability. Good defence systems engineers have always addressed their equipment's requirements for peacetime support and infrastructure, and the need for sufficient training equipment, as essential inputs to a through-life approach. In future they will need to consider plans for the deployment and support of the equipment for combat operations in far-off countries, and to assess potential trade-offs in reliability and maintainability to reduce the logistic footprint. They will also have to understand better the interface between the equipment and its human operator, and the resulting implications for the recruitment and organisational policies of the operating service. Future defence systems engineers will need the professional knowledge, management responsibility and budgetary authority to manage all six lines of development coherently.

MoD guidelines on equipment acquisition have only recently included explicit emphasis on the importance of co-ordinating and synchronising all six lines of development, but this policy only reflects the well-established holistic approach which has always characterised defence systems engineering. For more than a decade, students of defence systems engineering at the DEG have been taught that the acquisition of new defence equipment must consider carefully all of the external interfaces between that equipment and its environment, as well as resolving any problems with the internal interfaces between components and sub-systems within the equipment itself. It is gratifying that this fundamental principle of defence systems engineering has now been more widely recognised, in the MoD's *Acquisition Handbook.*

5 Summary

It is clear that UK defence systems engineers in the twenty-first century will have to address a wide range of complex issues. These include:

- Bigger systems incorporating more complex networks and autonomous platforms, requiring more emphasis on information technology, information management and on interoperability between the UK services and between the armed forces of UK and its allies.
- Complex partnering arrangements between the MoD and parts of the UK defence industry, due to an altered balance of power between governments and global defence contractors, requiring more knowledge of corporate economics.
- A significant increase in international collaborative defence programmes.
- More procurement off-the-shelf and more technology insertion, demanding understanding of capability-based military requirements and how they might be satisfied sufficiently if not always completely.
- Greater emphasis on managing programmes including all six lines of development, requiring a broader range of knowledge and skills than were needed in former times for equipment-only projects.

These challenges will have to be met by a professional cadre of well-educated defence systems engineers who are trained to look upwards and outwards into the environment before looking downwards and inwards into the system itself. They must also try to look forwards into the future but, as the physicist Neils Bohr appositely remarked, 'Prediction is very difficult, especially about the future.'

Further reading

Albert, DS, Gartska, JS and Stein, FP (1999) *Network Centric Warfare*. Washington, DC: US Department of Defense

Clark, M and Sabin, P (1993) *British Defence Choices for the 21st Century*. London: Brasseys

Hain, P (2001) *The End of Foreign Policy*. London: Royal Institute of International Affairs

Matthews, R and Tredennick, J (2001) *Managing the Revolution in Military Affairs*. Basingtoke: Macmillan

Sandler, T and Hartley, K (1999) *The Political Economy of NATO: Past, Present and into the 21st Century*. Cambridge: Cambridge University Press

Conclusions

There have been many MoD initiatives and changes to processes and procedures since the Chair of Defence Engineering was established at UCL in 1991, but the systems engineering principles and practices taught by the Defence Engineering Group have stood the test of time and remain as valid today as they were more than a decade ago. Both the MoD and the UK defence industry will continue to need high-quality and experienced systems engineers to conceive, provide and support sophisticated and complex defence equipment which is capable of dealing with an ever-increasing range of threats, some well established and understood, others relatively unknown and unpredictable.

Defence systems engineers assigned to lead equipment acquisition projects must understand all the technological, military, industrial, financial and political issues affecting the project, and must respond constructively to the pressures of changes in the geopolitical environment

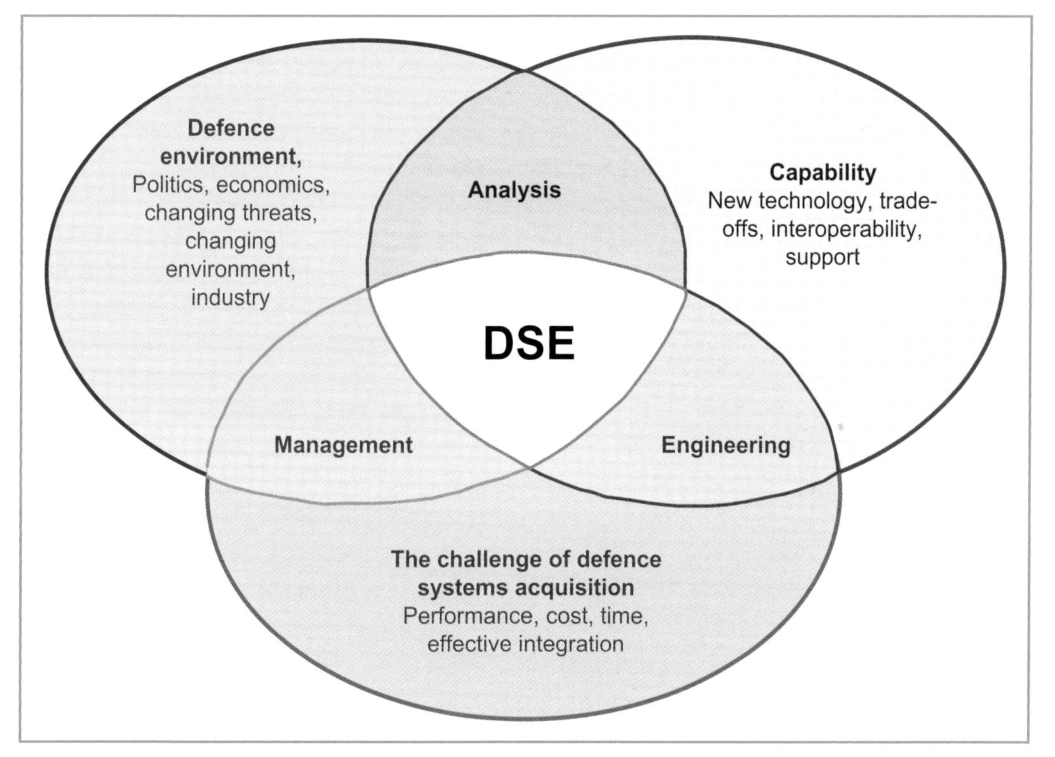

Figure 118. The challenges of defence systems result from the defence environment, the capability required and the acquisition process.

and the rapid development of relevant technologies. They must take account of the interactions of their project with its operating and support personnel, of its networked interfaces with other current and future equipment operated by UK and allied military forces, and of industrial and economic policies. They must be able to apply a blend of engineering, analytical and management skills (two out of three is not good enough), accommodate the concerns of a multitude of disparate and sometimes disruptive stakeholders, and integrate effectively a team drawn from several organisations (and often nations) with a wide range of professional skills, traditional cultures and prejudices.

This book summarises the key areas of knowledge, and the applicable methodologies, which should assist defence systems engineers to conquer the complexities of their multi-dimensional tasks. It provides them with a broad perspective of the difficulties that might beset their projects, with sufficient appreciation of current acquisition processes, procedures and methodologies to communicate effectively with the responsible specialists, and with sufficient understanding of the dynamic relationship between their projects and the military/industrial/political environment to respond quickly and constructively to changing circumstances and unforeseen difficulties. In particular, the book illuminates the philosophy and methods of systems engineering and indicates how these can be applied to facilitate the acquisition of defence systems.

No one text can provide the answers to every challenge facing defence systems engineers, but *Conquering Complexity* supplies the insights which should enable its readers to avoid most of the pitfalls and to ask most of the right questions. Success, as always, will depend on the ability of the practitioner to draw lessons from academic study and from personal experience, and to apply those lessons effectively in supplying the nation's armed forces with the necessary equipment to help maintain world peace and to defend UK interests whenever and wherever they are called upon to do so.

Appendices

Appendix 1 Education in defence systems engineering

This appendix reviews the appropriate syllabus and delivery process for the education of a defence systems engineer who is like a really good engineer, only more so.

1.1 Introduction

We train for the expected but educate for the unexpected. We train for the present, we educate for the future.

The Introduction to this book and Chapter 9 explain that defence systems engineering is the application of systems engineering (and other contributing disciplines) in the defence environment and includes:

- Technologies, legacy/future systems and networks of systems.
- Management, analysis and finance.
- Military, political and industrial issues.

It follows that defence systems engineering is broader than systems engineering and so the syllabus for a course in defence systems engineering must include a wide range of subjects, blending those traditionally found in MSc, MEng and MBA courses.

An education in defence systems engineering is valuable for all executives, managers and designers in UK industry, and for those military officers and civil servants in the MoD who are involved in the acquisition of defence equipment as members of an integrated project team (IPT) or of organisations within the MoD supporting equipment acquisition. This education is essential for the IPT leaders who direct multidisciplinary teams and who must interface effectively with other stakeholders in the MoD and beyond. The Smart Acquisition initiative in 1998 specifically emphasised the need for the MoD to develop a better-educated corps of acquisition personnel and identified systems engineering as one of the key strategies required to manage modern defence equipment projects.

However, the delivery of an education in defence systems engineering presents a difficult challenge. Defence systems engineers must have not only a sound knowledge of a broad range of engineering, analytical, management and military topics relevant to their equipment projects but also an overarching understanding of how these topics and their multiple interactions affect the acquisition process. This understanding is a vital foundation for the selection of an optimal acquisition strategy for an equipment project and for taking subsequent decisions (as the project evolves through an uncertain environment of rapidly advancing technology and of changing political and economic priorities), which lead it to a successful conclusion.

1.2 Syllabus of the Defence Engineering Group (DEG) MSc course

1.2.1 Range of subjects

The 52-week MSc course on defence systems engineering run by the DEG was designed for MoD acquisition personnel, and included taught modules on:

- National defence policies and planning.
- UK government funding, accounting and acquisition policies.
- International military and economic relationships.
- Military operations, support and logistics.
- Corporate finance, accounting, law and contracts.
- Organisational analysis and behaviour.
- Engineering technologies relevant to defence systems.
- Project management principles and practices.
- Cost-effectiveness analysis and forecasting.
- Risk analysis and management.
- Equipment test and evaluation.
- Systems engineering concepts and procedures.
- Systems architecture, modelling and partitioning.

Modules on these subjects provided an overview of the military, political, financial and industrial environment within which defence equipment must be procured, operated and supported, an introduction to the analytical methods and project management techniques used in defence equipment projects, and an understanding of the systems engineering approaches which can facilitate the transition from a service need for enhanced military capability to the entry to service of a cost-effective system providing that enhancement. Each module contained an appropriate mix of lectures, case studies, assignments, debates and games (such as the acquisition game described in Section 1.5 below) to develop the students' understanding, supplemented by visiting speakers with expert knowledge and practical experience of the subjects considered.

Because the course included a broad range of topics, it could not provide complete mastery of all of them, but it did give the students a sufficient understanding to communicate effectively with specialist staff in the relevant areas of expertise and an adequate awareness of potential pitfalls.

It should be noted that other systems engineering courses related to defence (at University College London, at the Royal Military College of Science and at the universities of Bristol and Loughborough) are tailored to the requirements of their various customers and accordingly

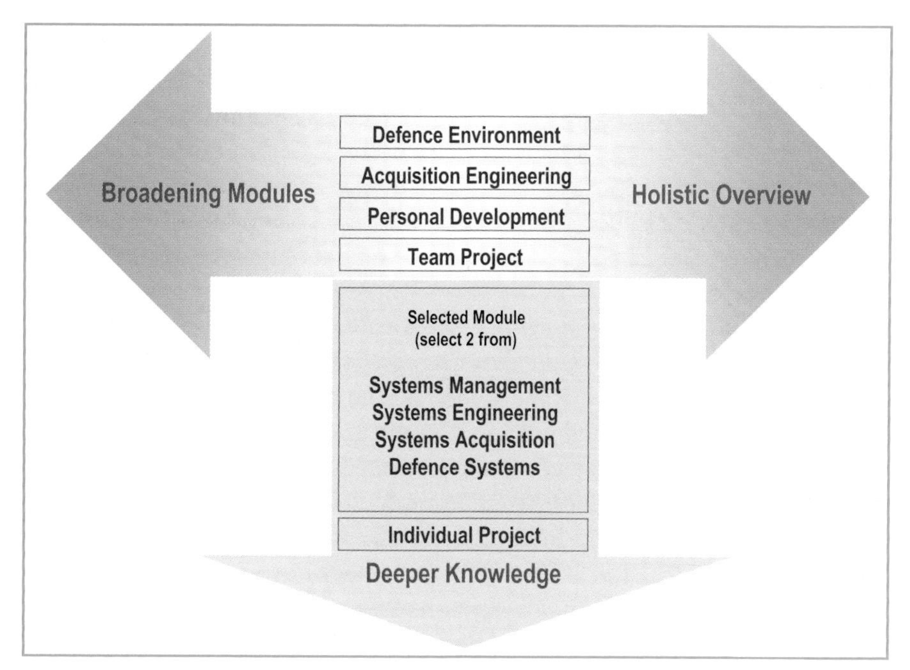

Figure 119. Breadth and depth are essential in defence systems engineering.

tend to put more emphasis on the practical application of systems engineering techniques and tools (and rather less on military, political and financial issues) than the DEG course.

1.2.2 Project work

It is essential that an education in defence systems engineering provides a student with opportunities to develop a practical understanding of the subject and to demonstrate the capabilities obtained. In the DEG's MSc course such opportunities were provided by a series of projects, two done by the students working in groups of about half a dozen and one by students working individually. The 'design and build project' required students to create an item of equipment (such as an amphibious vehicle) to perform a task specified by the staff. The development and construction of the equipment were constrained by inviolable upper limits on cost and timescale, and the project concluded with a formal trial to demonstrate the equipment's performance. Successive cohorts of students learnt to establish effective arrangements for group management, to subdivide their project into sub-systems and sub-tasks, to evolve their design to overcome unexpected difficulties, and finally to integrate their separate efforts to achieve a reliable and effective system. Many groups discovered the enduring truth that not everyone can work on an engineering system simultaneously, and that diagnosis of a system failure is facilitated by earlier test and evaluation of the individual sub-systems.

In the group project, a similar number of students addressed a current issue in defence equipment acquisition, or a comparable problem in civilian management, which was suggested by an interested sponsor organisation in government or industry. The students were required to research the problem, to organise and analyse the information collected, to derive credible recommendations, and to prepare a written report and an oral presentation describing their work. In this project, the students experienced the benefits and difficulties of working in a non-hierarchical group to attain a collective goal. Both the design and build project and the group project demonstrated the students' capacity for teamwork and their ability to apply the principles of defence systems engineering. Recent group projects included the impact of current defence policy on the achievement of network-enabled capability, a new multiple stores carrier for future stores on legacy aircraft, and future infantry systems technologies.

In the individual project, each student took personal responsibility for a research task suggested by a sponsor organisation and sometimes undertaken on its own sites. This task allowed a student to demonstrate individual abilities in the planning and risk management of a discrete mini-project, and sufficient initiative and self-discipline to complete the project successfully. Each individual project was concluded by a 10,000-word report and a 45-minute presentation delivered on predetermined dates. Recent individual projects included the management of system interfaces for the CVF and the JSF, barriers to technology insertion in defence equipment, risk-based safety assessments, and cost-capability trade-offs during project assessment.

1.2.3 Communications

An important part of the DEG's syllabus was the development of the students' ability to communicate their ideas effectively through presentations and reports. There would be little value in its well-educated graduates being right (like Cassandra) if they were unable to convince others to take the right decisions. The ability to communicate requires competence in the composition, word-processing and illustration of reports, and in the delivery with appropriate visual aids of presentations. It also requires the judgement to formulate a coherent and balanced structure for the report or presentation, the insight to present the message in terms that match the audience's pre-existing knowledge and culture, and the imagination to devise effective ways of achieving impact. The students who started on the course initially had varying levels of eloquence and literary skills but they all improved during the course as a result of tuition, practice and feedback.

An education in defence systems engineering must enable students to:

- Recognise all aspects of a problem and take account of all potential solutions.
- Exploit the complementary talents of a multidisciplinary team.
- Surmount barriers between stakeholders with different disciplines and cultures.
- Take the holistic view necessary to direct a major project successfully.

Part of the scope of the course was to create people who could lead and manage defence projects in the twenty-first century. Leadership is a challenging subject to teach; there are natural leaders and some people who adapt well to a leadership role, but rather than trying to teach leadership in a military or formal manner the DEG approach was through the management element that included motivation and management practices, along with organisational design and development.

The DEG added a personality assessment to the course to enable each student to understand their own personality and how their personality and character related to the average of their professional group. This was designed to enable them to capitalise on their strengths and use these when developing professional relationships and leading teams. It also enabled them to work on those areas of their personality which did not provide strong leadership skills, either through further development during the year's course, or by recognising their limitations and adopting alternative approaches such as building a team with the right balance of personalities to suit their style of management and leadership.

1.3 Timing of systems engineering education

It has been argued that schoolchildren have a natural understanding of systems engineering until their imaginative approach to problems is eroded by a curriculum of separate subjects. It has also been argued that the tendency of undergraduates to focus on a single speciality should be offset by multidisciplinary courses including systems engineering. However school and undergraduate courses are already overcrowded, and most schoolchildren and undergraduates lack the real-world experiences which facilitate understanding of the principles of systems engineering. The DEG believed that the principles and application of defence systems engineering could be most easily understood by post-graduate students who had an honours degree in a scientific or engineering discipline (though occasionally students from other disciplines have also succeeded) and about 5 years of relevant experience in government or industry posts dealing with defence equipment acquisition. Such students are aware of the depths and complexities of their own disciplines and therefore appreciate that others can be equally demanding. They recognise that technical excellence in their own discipline is an insufficient foundation for a successful career and have become receptive to other technical and management disciplines, which affect their projects. They have already encountered the interface problems and confusing complexities of real projects where there is no textbook answer and where the issues are obscured by a grey fog of uninformed speculation and conflicting interests. Their experience thus provides useful case studies of the successful (or unsuccessful) application of defence systems engineering, and these case studies accelerate the understanding of themselves and their classmates. An ideal class would contain about a dozen post-graduate students from different disciplines and with varied career experiences that enrich class discussions.

It is true that many professionals never stop learning, and the educational development of an individual is a long process; post-graduate education it is not completed until the individual is a mature and experienced adult. The educational process continually stretches the individual. At school and in the initial stages of first degrees, assumptions are made to provide the student with the opportunity to understand the principles involved. These assumptions are progressively removed during a first degree to enable the students to appreciate and deal with the challenges they will face in their career. The DEG's MSc course removed all of the assumptions about defence and presented the student with all the issues and challenges. Students, with the aid of the teaching staff, can develop their own way of dealing with the complexities of defence acquisition. It is important that students adopt their own way of dealing with the problem as each individual has a personal learning style, a different personality and strengths, and a different background and experience.

1.4 Delivery of education in defence systems engineering

Alumni of the DEG course are unanimous that an education in defence systems engineering can be delivered most effectively by a full-time residential course at a well-equipped university with access to an extensive library (as was done by the DEG in 1991–2004). A part-time course, in which students intersperse short periods of study within their normal workload, must be spread over several years and risks being disrupted by unsympathetic managers or remote postings. Furthermore, part-time students cannot avoid being preoccupied with their normal work, and accordingly give less attention to their academic studies. A residential course detaches the student from the usual pressures of domestic and social life, and allows valuable mutual interchange and support between classmates with different talents and experience. The DEG staff always recommended that potential students should opt for full-time residential study whenever possible; some students did perforce study part-time and some successfully graduated the course, though none received distinctions.

Other MSc courses have adopted a compromise arrangement with several discrete weeks of intensive residential teaching supplemented by private study and project work undertaken in parallel to the student's normal work. This arrangement is attractive to employers, on the simplistic basis that it involves fewer weeks away from the workplace, but it is less popular with students and may deliver less satisfactory outcomes.

The 52-week duration of the DEG's MSc course was driven partly by the volume of material which the MoD included in the syllabus and partly by the time needed for students to immerse themselves in the philosophy of defence systems engineering. The residential phase might in principle be shortened by distance learning of factual material in advance of the course, with a qualifying exam to ensure that the students had mastered it before the residential phase. In practice, no such distance-learning material on the relevant subjects is available and it would be inordinately expensive to develop and update it.

The characteristics of alternative methods of delivery are:

- **Full-time** – interrupts the student's career with up to a year away from the workplace, but allows full concentration on academic study and achieving professional and personal development.
- **Part-time** – presents difficulty in balancing the demands of work and study and in reconciling schedules, and it is more difficult for the student to integrate knowledge from different modules or to achieve culture change.
- **Distance learning** – needs a large up-front investment to create and upgrade study material, demands long-term commitment from the students, inhibits interaction

between students, and between students and staff, which is an essential input to education (the invention of printing did not abolish medieval universities).

Unlike a traditional MSc course, in which post-graduate students advance their knowledge through an ever-narrower stovepipe to reach the leading edge of a specialist topic, a course in defence systems engineering must include both deepening and broadening elements. The broadening elements improve the students' understanding of the world beyond engineering and the deepening elements take students to the limits of current knowledge in some aspect of defence systems engineering and encourage them to look beyond.

Graduates of a defence systems engineering course must have the confidence and insight to tackle effectively the current challenges which beset UK defence equipment acquisition, but additionally must have the overarching understanding and mental agility to address the unknown challenges of the future. The DEG's MSc course tried to develop those qualities in successive selected groups of the MoD's acquisition personnel, and some others from industry and from allied nations.

1.5 Acquisition game

DEG students developed an acquisition game. It represents the CADMID cycle and enables players, who represent the IPT leader, to learn about the processes of systems acquisition and the impact of decisions made at each stage of the CADMID cycle. Having made a decision, the subsequent progress of a player, or of a team of players, is advanced or hindered as a result of the impact of that decision in the later stages of the CADMID cycle and the systems acquisition processes.

The Acquisition Game is designed to:

- Aid students in identifying the fundamental elements of the CADMID cycle, including initial gate, main gate, contracts, in-service date and out-of-service date.
- Provide an overview of the principles and processes of Smart Acquisition and how these are applied within the CADMID cycle.
- Aid students' identification of stakeholders for each phase of the CADMID cycle.

The Acquisition Game is played by making decisions on the use and allocation of resources such as money and personnel during each stage of the CADMID cycle. The tabletop game is played on a board to allow visibility of progress, and uses a computer-based assessment package to provide analysis of the players' decisions and inputs. The game also has random inputs to provide additional challenges for the players to overcome; these represent typical technical, financial and personnel risks. The players cannot influence random events, but effective risk management will help to mitigate the risks and to optimise the performance, time and cost scores associated with the risks.

Appendix 2 Origins of defence systems engineering

This appendix reviews the growth of defence systems engineering in the Defence Engineering Group at University College London and the development of a Masters course in defence engineering.

2.1 The early days

The Defence Engineering Group (DEG) was created in 1991 to meet the Ministry of Defence's (MoD) need for a cadre of competent systems engineers to manage the acquisition of the complex defence systems in the twenty-first century. These systems engineers would need the knowledge and competence to deal with the technological, political and commercial aspects of defence projects in an integrated and through-life approach.

The concept of the DEG stemmed from a number of initiatives and ideas in the late 1980s. The primary sponsor was Sir Donald Spiers in his role as Head of Profession for MoD scientists and engineers, and the initiative was implemented by the civilian management personnel group responsible for specialist civilian staff in the MoD.

The MoD employed standard procurement practices to establish the DEG. It produced a formal statement of requirement; it ran a competition to host a Chair of Defence Engineering; over 30 academic organisations expressed interest and in April 1991 a joint bid by University College London (UCL) and King's College London (KCL) was selected. In May 1991 the establishment of a Chair of Defence Engineering was announced in Parliament, and Mr Ian Holder was seconded to UCL from the land systems area of the MoD to start initial planning and development work for the Chair. In July 1991, Mr Ken Hambleton, then a Director General in Air Systems Procurement in the MoD, was selected competitively and appointed as Professor of Defence Engineering. Over the next few weeks the DEG was formed, and Professor Ken Hambleton and Mr Ian Holder as the 'founding fathers' developed the MSc in Defence Systems Engineering (MDSE). A part-time secretary and a lecturer recruited from industry formed the initial staff, and the first MDSE started in late September 1991 after a summer of intense activity.

2.2 MDSE

The DEG initially concentrated on the MDSE course, a unique blend of politics, technology, management and analysis with a core of systems engineering principles to draw the subjects together into an integrated skill set. As an academic subject, defence systems engineering took the 'big-picture' view of defence starting with world politics and defence policy (ably provided throughout the life of the MDSE by Professor Lawrence Freedman's War Studies group at KCL) before identifying the need for current and future defence projects within the UK defence missions and tasks. The basic concepts of systems engineering, such as requirements definition, systems architecture, partitioning, interface control and integration were taught in some detail, in close conjunction with analytical, management and commercial practices. The integration within the MDSE of defence policy and defence technology with the 'MBA' modules covering management, financial and commercial issues were the key to its success.

2.3 Centre of excellence

Once the MDSE was progressing smoothly, with about a dozen students successfully completing the course each year, the DEG was able to develop the other elements of its charter, namely research work and the creation of a centre of excellence in defence systems acquisition. Two research fellows were recruited in 1993 and several mature PhD students joined over the next few years, most of them already having had successful careers in either the MoD or the defence industry. These experienced people, together with the use of senior MoD and industrial personnel as visiting lecturers and the employment of retired experts as part-time consultants, gave the DEG a powerful and credible workforce, able to relate its teaching to current defence issues, to tackle difficult research topics and to provide support, guidance and input to many MoD, academic, industrial, professional and government groups. Over the years, the DEG has made active contributions to Foresight, the House of Commons Defence Committee, the Royal United Services Institute, the Royal Academy of Engineering and several MoD studies.

2.4 Maturity

By the late 1990s the DEG had become well known internationally as a centre of excellence and had expanded significantly. Its MDSE was supplemented by shorter teaching courses for the MoD and industry, it had a number of research contracts and it was playing an increasing role within UCL. The full-time staff had increased to two professors, two lecturers, three research fellows, four mature PhD students, a business manager for external work, a short course administrator for specific short training courses and an overworked secretary.

Dr David Kirkpatrick, a director in the MoD with experience in aircraft technology and cost-effectiveness analysis had joined as a senior lecturer in 1995, becoming Professor of Defence Analysis shortly afterwards and adding considerably to the depth and breadth of the group's capability. Professor Ken Hambleton, Mr Ian Holder and Professor David Kirkpatrick have been the driving force behind the DEG for most of its life, although Mr Ian Holder had a brief spell back in the MoD at the turn of the century, returning to the DEG as its Director. Professor David Kirkpatrick took over as academic Head of the DEG in 2000.

2.5 UCLse

By 1996 the DEG had developed and run many short systems courses for industrial clients, often tailored to specific requirements. These courses stimulated a wider interest in systems engineering and in 1997, UCL created a Centre for Systems Engineering (UCLse) to provide appropriate education to a broader customer base and to encourage an integrated systems approach across many separate UCL departments. UCLse began by creating a bespoke

MSc in Systems Engineering for a major defence industrial organisation with whom the DEG had worked for several years. This was followed by a general MSc course. The DEG played a major part in developing the early UCLse activities and former DEG staff continue to support the venture as it expands.

2.6 Defence capability and technology course

In 1998 the DEG won a competition to supply four-week training courses for science and engineering graduates joining the MoD and has taught 19 such courses to some 300 students over a period of 6 years. Also in 1998, the MDSE was made available in a modular format to allow part-time attendance over several years and was expanded to include specialist options such as Test and Evaluation, Defence Systems Acquisition and Defence Systems Support.

2.7 MoD's Defence Engineering and Science Group

Over the 13 years of its existence, the DEG has enjoyed the support of successive heads of profession, manifested through the MoD civilian personnel management group. Mr David Ibberson in particular deserves recognition for his enthusiastic support for the DEG and his tireless efforts to attract and encourage a cadre of suitable MSc students each year.

2.8 Conclusions

In summary, the DEG educated over 140 graduates of the MDSE, most of whom are enjoying successful careers in the MoD, although some have since left to exploit their skills in other government departments and in the commercial world. In addition to teaching the principles of systems engineering, analysis and management, the DEG staff sought to provide a stimulating and interactive environment in which students could contribute significantly, bringing their own knowledge and experience and sharing it with others in discussions and group activities. The aim of all DEG activities was to help the students to become what are known as 'T-shaped' engineers, having a broad understanding of all the disciplines that are required to manage complex defence projects as well as a deep knowledge in their own specialist area. The acquisition of this knowledge base, together with the opportunity to develop and practise communication skills, equips MDSE graduates for future roles as project team leaders for complex defence systems.

Appendix 3 Abbreviations/acronyms and glossary

3.1 Abbreviations/acronyms

AFV	Armoured fighting vehicle
AMS	Acquisition management system
ASTOR	Airborne stand-off radar
AWACS	Airborne warning and control system
BC	Business case
BOI	Balance of investment
BSE	Bovine spongiform encephalopathy
C^3I	Command, control, communication and intelligence
CADMID	Concept, assessment, demonstration, manufacture, in-service and disposal
CDL	Chief of Defence Logistics
CER	Cost-estimating relationship
CIS	Command information system
CLS	Contractor logistic support
COEIA	Combined operational effectiveness and investment appraisal
COTS	Commercial off-the-shelf
COTS IT	Commercial off-the-shelf information technology
CPA	Contract price adjustment
CPS	Cardinal points specification
CV	Aircraft carrier
CVF	Fleet aircraft carrier
Def Stan	Defence Standard (UK)
DEFCON	Defence contract conditions (UK)
DEG	Defence Engineering Group
DESO	Defence Export Services Organisation (UK MoD)
DLO	Defence Logistics Organisation (UK MoD)
DMA	Defence Manufacturers Association (UK)
DoD	Department of Defense (US)
DPA	Defence Procurement Agency (UK MoD)
DSE	Defence systems engineering
Dstl	Defence Science and Technology Laboratory
DT&E	Development test and evaluation
DTI	Department of Trade and Industry (UK)
EADS	European Aeronautic Defence and Space Company
EC	Equipment Capability
EMC	Electromagnetic compatibility
EP	Equipment plans
EU	European Union
EW	Electronic warfare
FCO	Foreign and Commonwealth Office (UK)
FEI	Federation of Electrical Industries (UK)
FLC	Front-line commander
FMECA	Failure modes effects and criticality analysis
FSC	Future surface combatant
GOTS	Government off-the-shelf
HMI	Human/machine interface
HSE	Health and Safety Executive
IA	Investment appraisal
IAB	Investment Approvals Board
ILS	Integrated logistic support
INCOSE	International Council on Systems Engineering
IPR	Intellectual property rights
IPT	Integrated project team
IRA	Irish Republican Army
ISO	International Standards Organisation
IT	Information technology

ITEAP Integrated test evaluation and acceptance plan
JCA Joint combat aircraft
KCL King's College London
LSA Logistic support analysis
LSAR Logistic support analysis record
MART Mean active repair time
MBA Master of Business Administration degree
MDAL Master data and assumptions list
MDSE Master of Science degree in Defence Systems Engineering
MEng Master of engineering degree
MIL-STD Military Standard (US)
Milspec Military specification
MLRS Multiple launch rocket system
MMC Mergers and Monopolies Commission (UK)
MoD Ministry of Defence (UK)
MoE Measure of effectiveness
MOTS Military off-the-shelf
MSc Master of Science degree
MTA Maintenance task analysis
MTBF Mean time between failures
NAO National Audit Office (UK)
NASA National Space and Aeronautics Administration (US)
NATO North Atlantic Treat Organization
NBC Nuclear, biological and chemical
NEC Network-enabled capability
NPV Net present value
OA Operational analysis
OCCAR Organisation Conjointe de Coopération en Matière d'Armement
OE Operational effectiveness
OR Operational research
OTS Off-the-shelf
PC Personal computer
PCS Policy and Capabilities Studies department (of Dstl)
PD Project definition
PERT Program evaluation research technique
PFI Private finance initiative
PPP Public/private partnership
PT&E Production test and evaluation
RAB Resource accounting and budgeting
RAF Royal Air Force (UK)
RCM Reliability centred maintenance
RDT&E Research, development, test and evaluation
REME Royal Electrical and Mechanical Engineers (UK)
RFA Royal Fleet Auxiliary (UK)
RMA Reliability, maintainability and availability
RN Royal Navy (UK)
ROCE Return on capital employed
ROI Return on investment
RSI Repetitive strain injury
SAM Surface-to-air missile
S&TE Support and test equipment
SAS Special Air Service (UK)
SBAC Society of British Aerospace Companies (UK)
SCM Supply-chain management
SIPRI Stockholm International Peace Research Institute
SRD System requirement document
SSBN Nuclear submarine with ballistic missiles
SSN Nuclear attack submarine with torpedoes
STOVL Short take-off and vertical landing
STP Short-term plan (UK MoD)
T&E Test and evaluation
TLC Through-life costs
TLMP Through-life management plan
TRL Technology readiness level
UAV Unmanned air vehicle

UCL	University College London
UCLse	UCL Centre for Systems Engineering
UK	United Kingdom
UN	United Nations
UOR	Urgent operational requirement
URD	User requirement document
US	United States
USSR	Union of Soviet Socialist Republics (split up in 1991)
VAT	Value-added tax
VTOL	Vertical take-off and landing
VV&A	Validation, verification and accreditation
WBS	Work-breakdown structure
WIP	Work-in-progress

3.2 Glossary

Chinese wall	Any means of separating teams of people to ensure that no intercommunication is possible.
COEIA	A formal comparison, on a cost-effectiveness basis, of particular equipment options (or combinations of options) for satisfying an operational requirement.
Commonwealth	A loose association of nations formerly within the British Empire.
COTS	Products or services designed for and available on the commercial market.
Disposal	The efficient, effective and safe disposal of equipment, together with its spares and consumables, at the end of its life. Disposal should consider the possibilities of redeployment, sale, waste disposal, environmental impacts and the possible disposal of recovered material by sale.
Equipment capability customer	The individuals responsible for developing a balanced, coherent and affordable equipment programme to meet the current and future needs of the armed forces.
Interoperability	The ability of equipment and systems to operate and interact together.
Legacy	A term describing existing equipment that is already in service.
LSA	A supportability analysis that is conducted iteratively, as an integral part of the design process, with the aim of influencing the design by stimulating trade-off decisions to optimise TLC.
LSAR	A database, which is used to record resultant data from the LSA process. It should be used as the single source of information for the design and development of support resource requirements.
Methodology	An approach to exploring problems.
Model	Physical, mathematical or otherwise logical representation of a system, entity, phenomenon or process.
Modelling	The use of models, including emulators, prototypes, simulators and stimulators, either statically or over time, to develop data as a basis for making managerial or technical decisions.
MOTS	Products and services already developed for use in the military domain.
Reliability and maintainability	The probability of equipment working correctly when required, and the ease of putting it right, once a failure has occurred. The R & M of equipment are two of the key drivers of its support costs and its availability and also encompass the areas of safety, testability and durability.
Second customer	The front-line commander responsible for in-service equipment operation.
Simulation	Software implementation and solution of a model (usually equations and algorithms) over time within context of a scenario.
Warsaw Pact	An alliance of the Soviet Union and Eastern European nations during the Cold War.
Through-life	The life cycle of equipment from concept to disposal.

Appendix 4 About the authors

Ken Hambleton, MA, FEng, FIFE, FRAeS

Emeritus Professor of Defence Engineering, he studied physics at Cambridge University and his MoD career began with research into semi-conductor materials. Later he worked on radar and ship-borne weapons before leading a group responsible for research and technical support of naval systems. His last MoD post was as Director-General for procurement of radar, command and control systems, air weapons and avionic systems for the UK armed services. Professor Hambleton created the DEG in 1991 and was its head until 2000. His knowledge and experience of systems engineering is widely recognised, and he has supported many national committees on the use and application of systems engineering.

David Kirkpatrick, PhD, MSc, BSc (Hons), MSc (Econ), CEng, FRAeS, AFRUSI

Emeritus Professor of Defence Analysis, he studied aeronautical engineering before starting a career with the MoD, which initially comprised research into aerodynamics and operational analysis of air systems. Following a PhD in aeronautics and an MSc in economics, he undertook cost analysis and forecasting for aircraft and weapon systems. After a period as defence attaché in the US, he returned to lead the MoD's aerodynamic research, before becoming Director of the MoD's centre of expertise on cost forecasting and risk management. He joined the DEG in 1995, and was head of the group from 2000 until 2004. His career and experience includes many of the multidisciplinary subjects that are relevant to successful defence acquisition, and he is a major contributor to national and international forums on systems engineering. He has written over 60 papers on aerodynamics, the effectiveness and cost of military equipment, defence procurement, defence economics and military history.

Ian Holder, BSc (Hons), AMIMechE

He started his carreer by joining the MoD and studying mechanical engineering. His experience includes the design and testing of armoured fighting vehicles, reliability analysis of ground and air vehicles, air-launched weapons, and operational analysis of joint and combined force structures. His systems engineering skills are derived from over 10 years experience of designing and testing complex vehicle systems, and providing solutions to the problems associated with interfacing weapons onto UK combat aircraft. During his career he has dealt with over 30 MoD project managers and acquired a comprehensive knowledge of the problems of defence project management. He made a major contribution to the development of the DEG, designed and managed the MSc in defence systems engineering for 6 years, and became Director of the DEG in 2002. He currently works for the DLO at Andover.

David Kimberley, BSc

His career began in the MoD where he initiated and led a number of aircraft, avionic, operational analysis and procurement activities, reaching Director-General level. Later he was Managing Director for the test and evaluation division of DERA (Defence Evaluation and Research Agency). He was Director of the DEG Systems Engineering Team (DEG-SET) promoting the use of systems engineering through bespoke courses, using world-class tutors to deliver current best practice. He also developed, organised and contributed to an MSc in system test and evaluation. He has a wide range of skills and experience in modelling, testing, evaluation and a broad view of the problems of using defence systems in operational situations.

Lt Col Mike Bragg (retd), BSc, MIEE

He studied electronic engineering before beginning a career in the army, where he served in the Corps of Royal Electrical and Mechanical Engineers. Most of his career was involved with the front-line support of armoured fighting vehicles, and planning the support arrangements for new vehicles entering service. He also undertook roles involved with operational analysis, and MoD policy and planning. He joined UCL in 1990 to plan and manage a scheme for service personnel to gain degrees at the end of their service careers, and later joined the DEG to run courses and contribute his expertise on NBC defence.

Stephen McInally, PhD, BSc

He started his career working in the communications industry, before joining Philips Medical Services as an installation, test and commissioning engineer. He subsequently studied industrial and business systems before becoming a requirements manager for Philips Innovation Group. He commenced a PhD (methodology for interdisciplinary complex instrument design) at UCL in 1995 and, after graduating in 2002, became a full-time member of the DEG staff. His research interests include the underpinning philosophy of systems engineering, and the application of systems engineering to design and support processes. He is currently a technology teacher at the Chalfonts Community College in Chalfont St Peter.

Alex Weiss, PhD

He served in both the army and the Royal Air Force. The major part of his service career was as a fast-jet pilot and flying instructor. After the RAF, he worked in several electronics companies before becoming Sales Director of Thorn EMI Electronics. After retiring he wrote a number of books and started a research project that led to a PhD thesis on the use of commercial off-the-shelf equipment in defence systems. He is currently researching the interpretation and meaning of the term 'value for money' as perceived by the MoD.

Tim Williams, PhD, MA, BA

He joined the DEG in 1996 bringing knowledge of economics and defence supply chain management. Initially he did research work for DERA, developing research and technology forecasting methods. He subsequently became a leading contributor to the EPSRC-funded Manufacturing Infrastructure Development for the Aerospace Sector (MIDAS) project working with Exeter and Cambridge universities. Tim is a co-founder and a Director of the Defence Engineering and Management Institute (DEMI), an organisation created to help nations to reduce their offset obligations through training and education. He has also completed research for Cranfield and the Open University. His published research on defence industrial restructuring has appeared in journals such as *Defence and Peace Economics, Interdisciplinary Economics, Long Range Planning and Defence Analysis.*

Index of main subject entries

Folds in Fashion

The art of pleating in clothing design and construction

Rosa García Prieto &
Adriana Muñoz Laverde

FIREFLY BOOKS

Published by Firefly Books Ltd. 2014

First printing

Publisher Cataloging-in-Publication Data (U.S.)

Prieto, Rosa García.
Folds in fashion : the art of pleating in clothing design and construction / Rosa García Prieto ; Adriana Muñoz Laverde.
[120] pages : ill. (some color), photos. ; cm.
Summary: Detailed instructions for professional dressmakers, designers, wtailors and experienced home sewers for making 24 basic projects that create sophisticated embellishments for contemporary fashion pieces. Only basic sewing tools are required.
ISBN-13: 978-1-77085-444-4 (pbk.)
1. Tailoring. 2. Clothing and dress. 3. Dressmaking – Pattern design. I. Laverde, Adriana Muñoz. II. Title.
646.404 dc23 TT520.P6438 2014

Library and Archives Canada Cataloguing in Publication

Prieto, Rosa García, author
Folds in fashion : the art of pleating in clothing design and construction / Rosa Garcia Prieto & Adriana Muñoz Laverde.
ISBN 978-1-77085-444-4 (pbk.)
1. Pleats (Sewing). 2. Fashion design. I. Laverde, Adriana Muñoz, illustrator II. Title.
TT715.P75 2014 646.2 C2014-900898-8

Published in the United States by
Firefly Books (U.S.) Inc.
P.O. Box 1338, Ellicott Station
Buffalo, New York 14205

Published in Canada by
Firefly Books Ltd.
50 Staples Avenue, Unit 1
Richmond Hill, Ontario L4B 0A7

Printed in China

Conceived by
LOFT Publications
c/ Domènech, 7-9, 2º 1ª
08012 Barcelona, Spain
Tel.: +34 93 268 80 88
Fax: +34 93 268 70 73
loft@loftpublications.com

For LOFT:
Publisher: Paco Asensio
Editorial coordinator: Claudia Martínez Alonso
Assistant to editorial coordination: Ana Marques
Art director: Mireia Casanovas Soley
Editor, texts and pleats: Rosa García Prieto
Illustrations: Adriana Muñoz
Photos: Rosa García Prieto and Adriana Muñoz
English translation: textcase

STOCKMAN

INTRODUCTION

There is real magic in the pleasure of traditional sewing — sitting patiently, caringly and imaginatively shaping fabrics to develop personal creations that defy production line fashion.

Folds in Fashion is a book for all lovers of the craft of sewing. It consists of basic projects, which are illustrated step-by-step and require only a few basic tools.

In these pages you will find traditional techniques as well as projects with an element of innovation that provide different ideas for clothing. These ideas can be applied to small details or to the entire garment.

New designers will find this book especially helpful. Illustrated final results help you grasp the basic concepts for each project and allow you to play around with the initial idea, giving it your own touch. In some of the projects, we show you how to create classic pieces and then invite you to give them your own twist, starting your own trends.

This book is about working with the natural characteristics of fabrics, creating three-dimensional shapes with suitable textures and even imitating nature to convey an idea or tell a story through a garment and its details.

ORIGAMI RECTANGLES WITH STRIPS

This project is based on the Japanese technique of origami and consists of forming well-defined pleats in a rectangular strip. It is ideal for creating entire garments, such as skirts or even jackets, as the final result is uniform and structured.

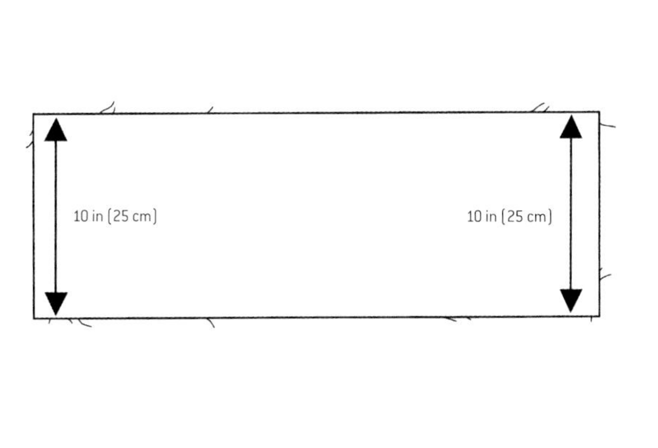

1

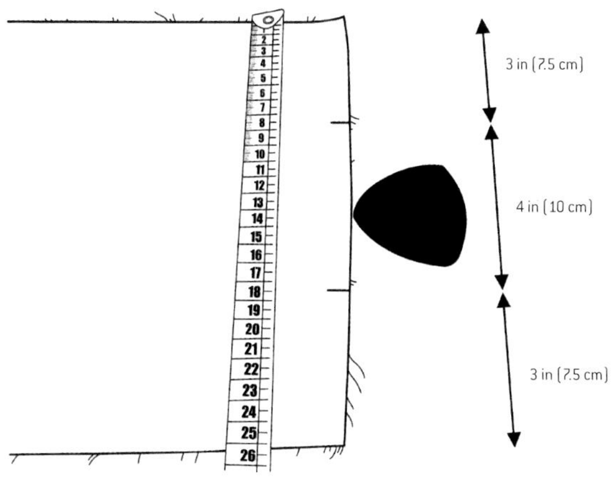

2

Cut and iron a 10-inch-wide (25 cm) strip, long enough for the garment that you are working on. Starting with this size, you will end up with a 4-inch-wide (10 cm) finished strip.

Divide the width into three parts, marking the first at 3 inches (7.5 cm), the middle one at 4 inches (10 cm) from the first and the last at 3 inches (7.5 cm) from the second. Repeat the process on the other end.

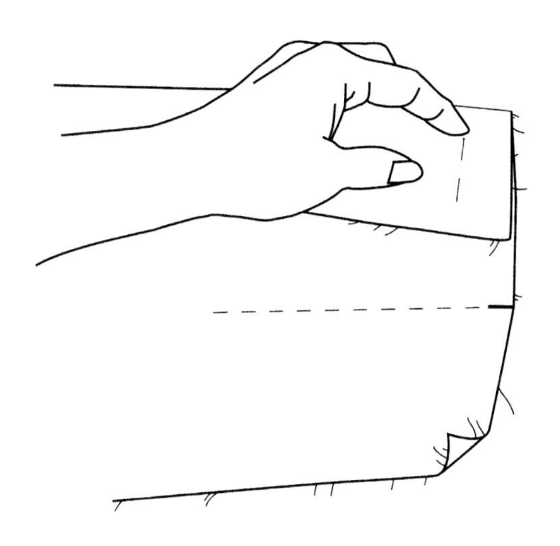

3

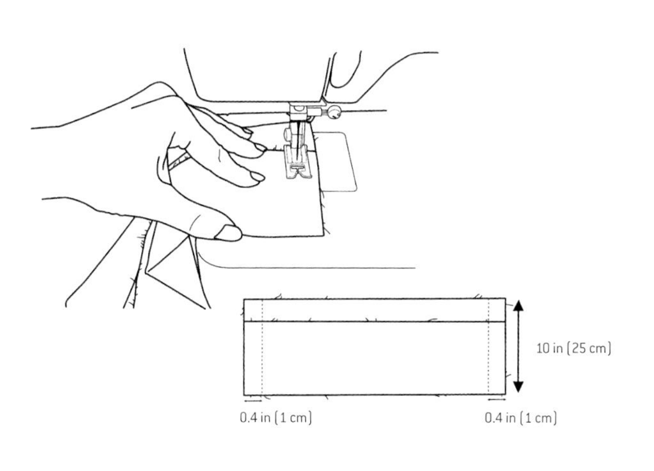

4

Fold the first section over and fix it with a pin. Next, fold the other 3-inch (7.5 cm) section, pinning it on top of the one that has already been folded. Repeat the process on the other end. The resulting width will be 4 inches (10 cm), the center section.

Use the sewing machine to fix the two ends with a straight stitch approximately 0.4 inches (1 cm) from the edge.

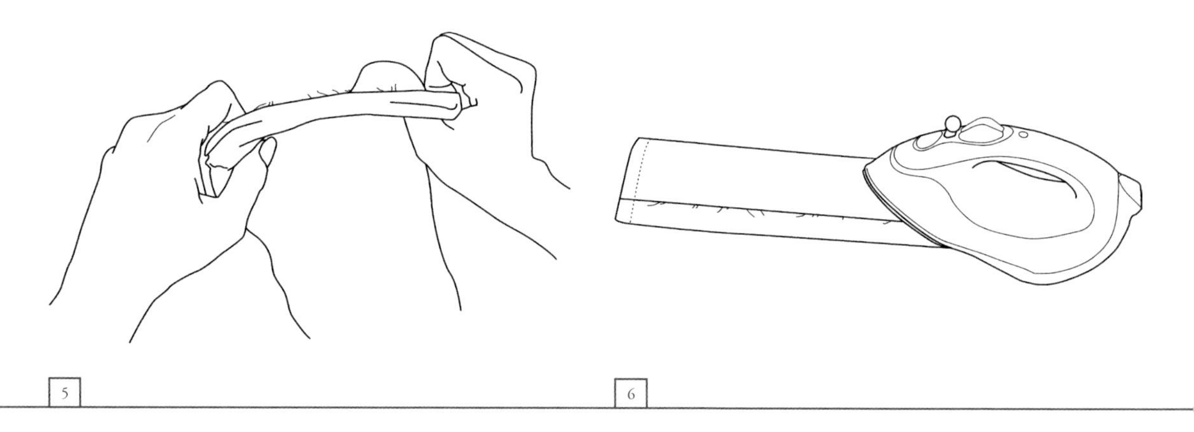

After the edges have been straight stitched, turn the piece over.

Iron the piece well to set the pleats.

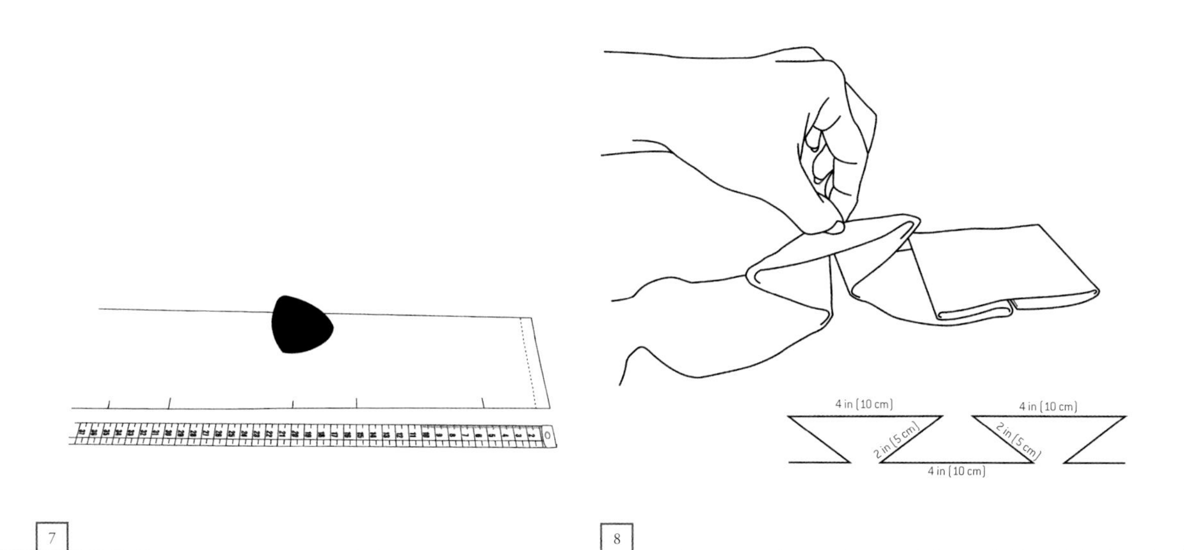

Turn the piece and divide the total length into alternate 2-inch (5 cm) and 4-inch (10 cm) sections. Mark them with tailor's chalk.

Fold the first 2-inch (5 cm) section down. The 4-inch (10 cm) section stays on top. Again, fold the third 2-inch (5 cm) section down, and repeat. The fourth section must stay down, like a zigzag. Don't forget to secure each fold with pins.

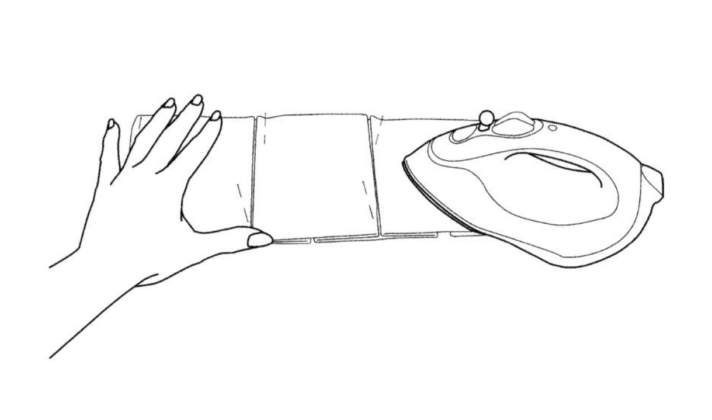

9

Once the pleats have been folded and fixed with pins, set them firmly with the iron.

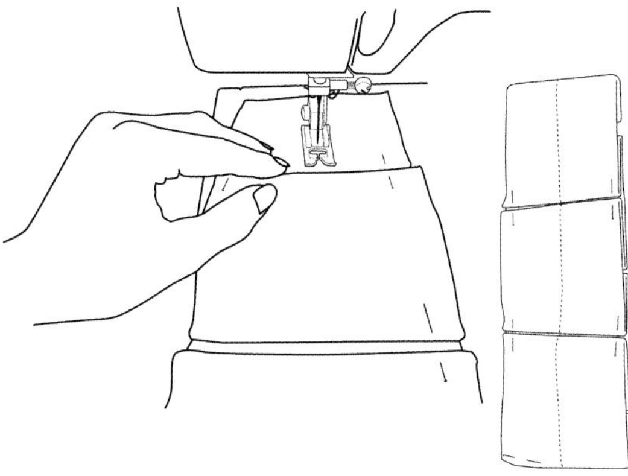

10

A straight stitch along the exact middle of the strip using the sewing machine will hold all the pleats in place. This straight stitch will also attach the strip to the garment. Now you can remove the pins.

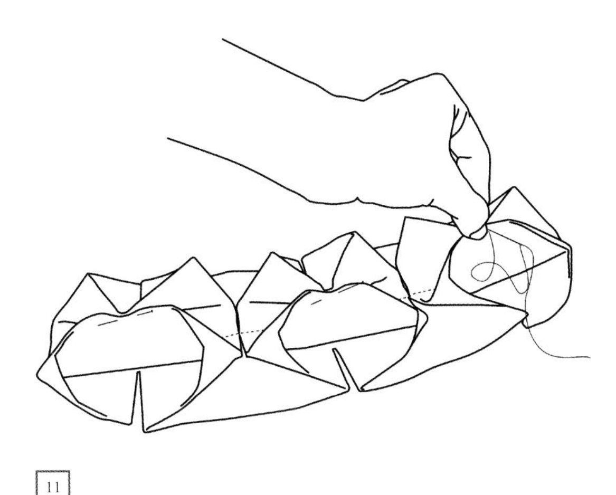

11

Finally, with needle and thread, use a tiny hand stitch to join the two ends of each pleat to achieve a three-dimensional origami effect.

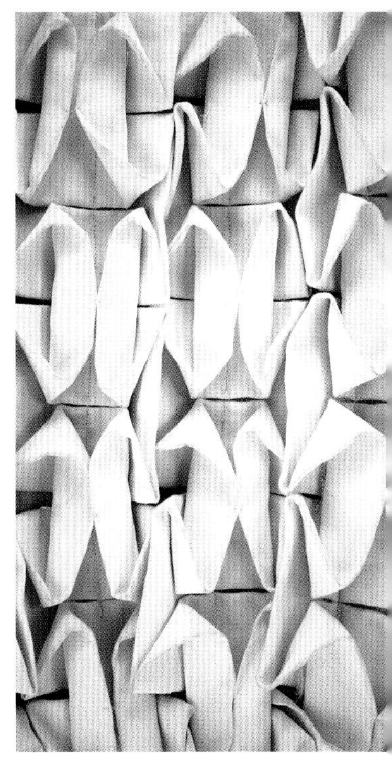

3-D HEART

Using only a basic heart shape, this project demonstrates a simple and effective way of adding three-dimensionality to a garment.

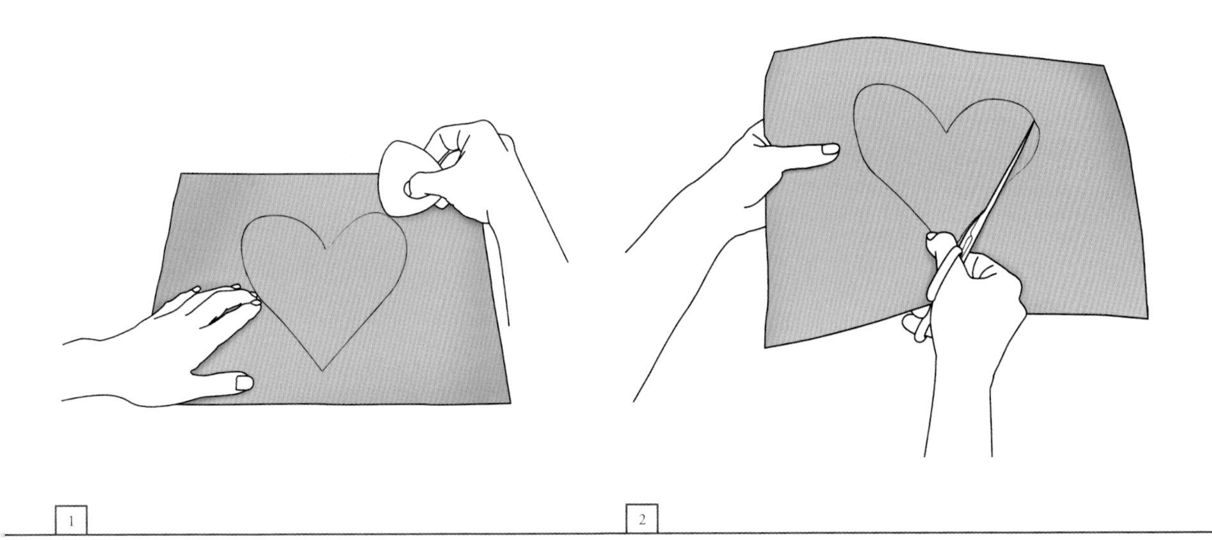

Use tailor's chalk to draw a symmetrical heart shape on your fabric, with an outline of about 24 inches (60 cm).

Cut it carefully, making sure the scissors follow the rounded tops as well as the pointed bottom so that there is no irregularity. The fabric should be sufficiently rigid.

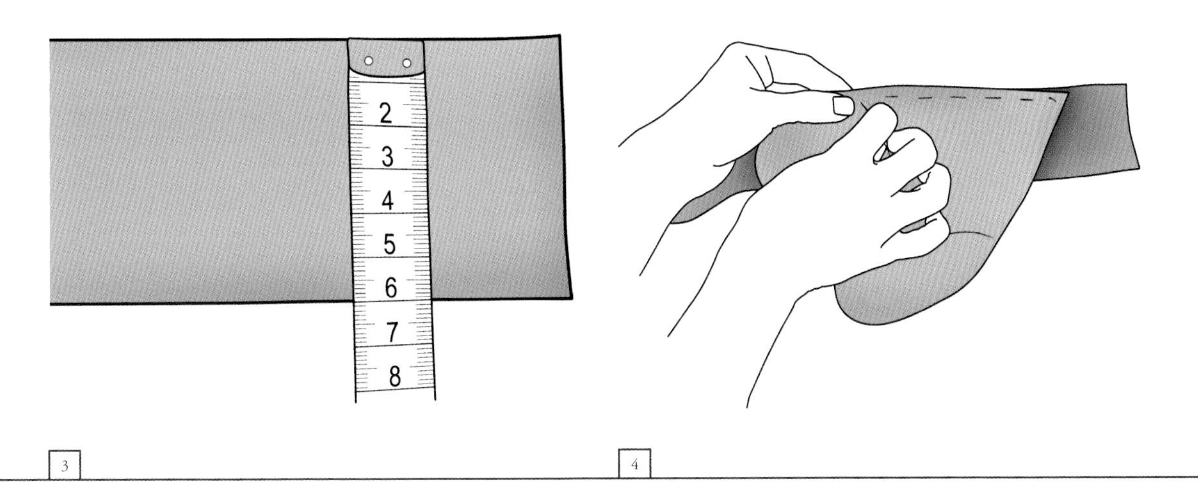

Cut a straight strip of the same fabric, approximately 2.5 inches (6 cm) wide and 26 inches (66 cm) long (2.5 inches [6 cm] more than the total outline of the heart). This strip will serve as the sides of the heart to give it a three-dimensional effect.

Tack the heart to the strip leaving about 0.8 inches (2 cm) of the strip protruding at the pointed end of the shape. This tacking will serve as a guide when it is time to machine sew both parts together.

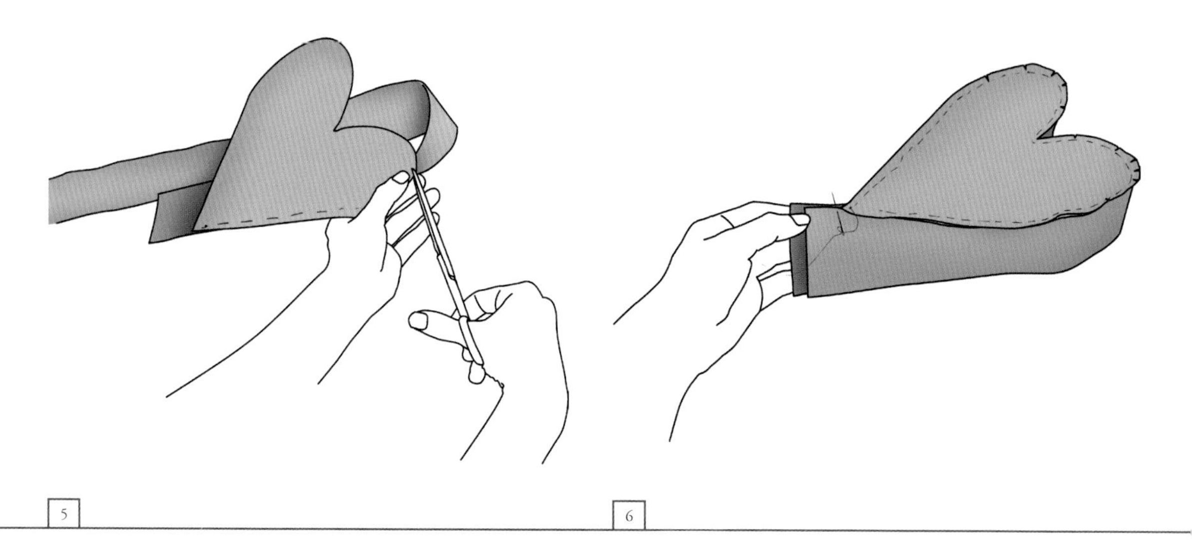

Because of the roundness of the heart, you will have to make small cuts — notches — in the edges of the seam. This will enable the fabric to smoothly adapt to the curves without becoming misshapen and wrinkled.

When you've tacked all the way around the outline, you should have 1.5 inches (4 cm) of one end of a strip left over that will join with another 0.8 inches (2 cm); this adds up to the extra 2.5 inches (6 cm) that you cut earlier for the 24-inch (60 cm) heart shape.

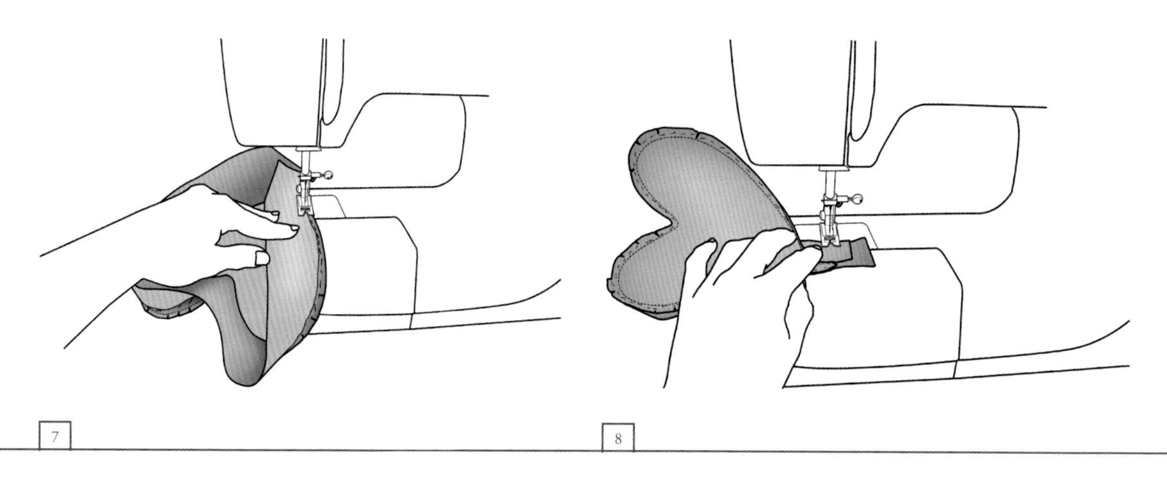

With the tacking as a guide, use the sewing machine to straight stitch around the outline until you come to the bottom of the point.

Here you should straight stitch to join the two ends of the strip and completely close the shape.

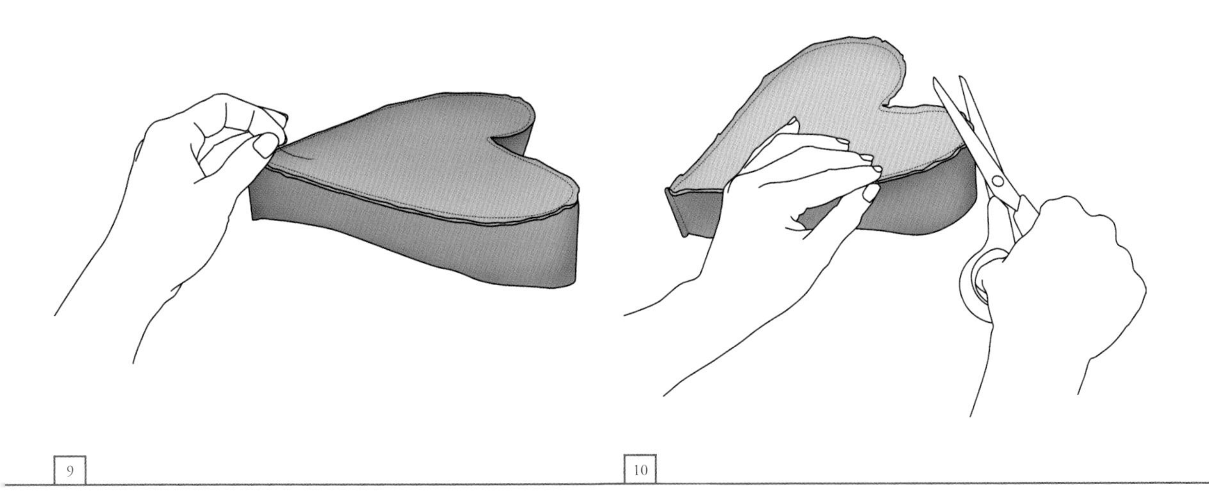

Remove the tacking.

Trim all the seams so they will be as small as possible when it is time to turn the heart the right way out.

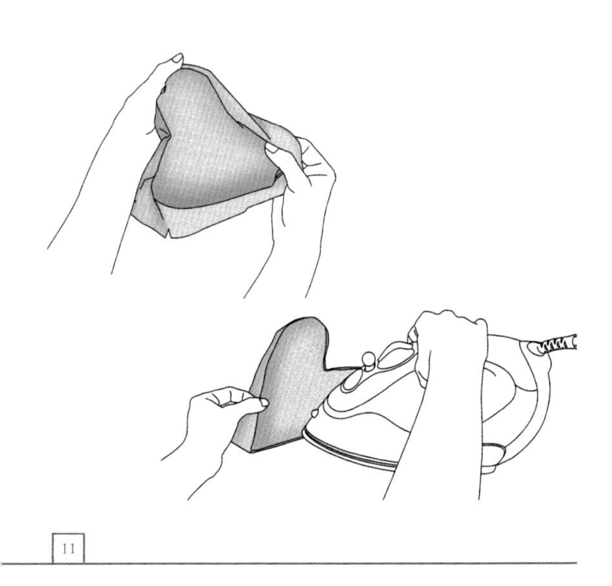

Turn the heart the right way out and slowly iron the seams to achieve a perfect shape when sewn to the chosen garment.

WIRE SNAILS

This spiral shape is a nod to Jean Paul Gaultier and the shapes in his bodices. The hidden wire adds rigidity to a simple folded strip of fabric, evoking the golden age of this great creator.

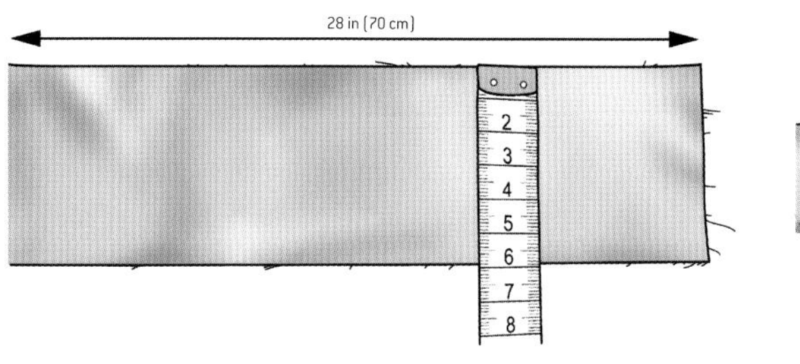

1

Cut a strip approximately 28 inches (70 cm) long by 2.5 inches (6 cm) wide. These are the measurements we are going to use for the medium-sized snail project, which can be used as an adornment on bodices, shoulder pads and even pockets. A bright silk satin will work well here, especially with the nature of the project, as it is ideal for party clothes.

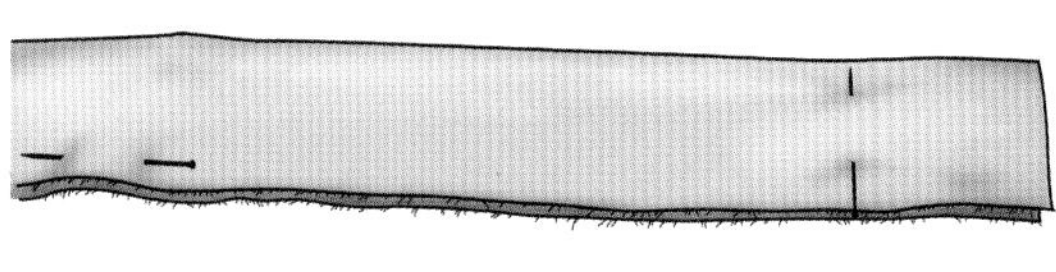

2

Fold the strip in half along the middle so that the reverse of the fabric is visible. Pin each of the two ends of the strip.

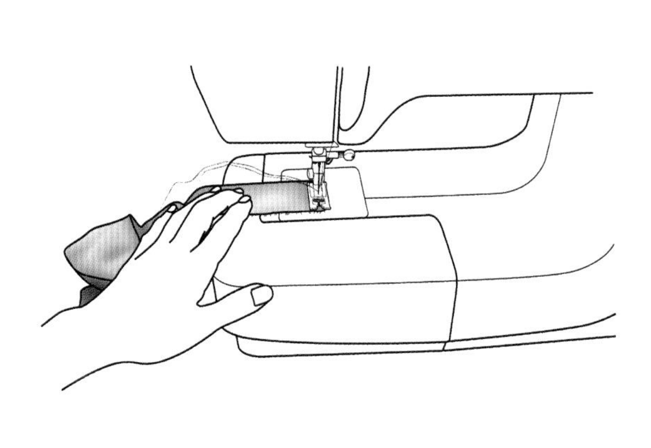

3

Straight stitch them using the sewing machine.

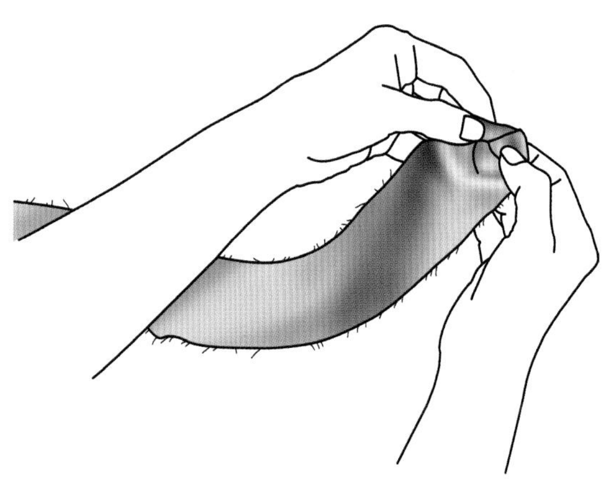

4

After straight stitching the ends, turn the fabric strip the right way out.

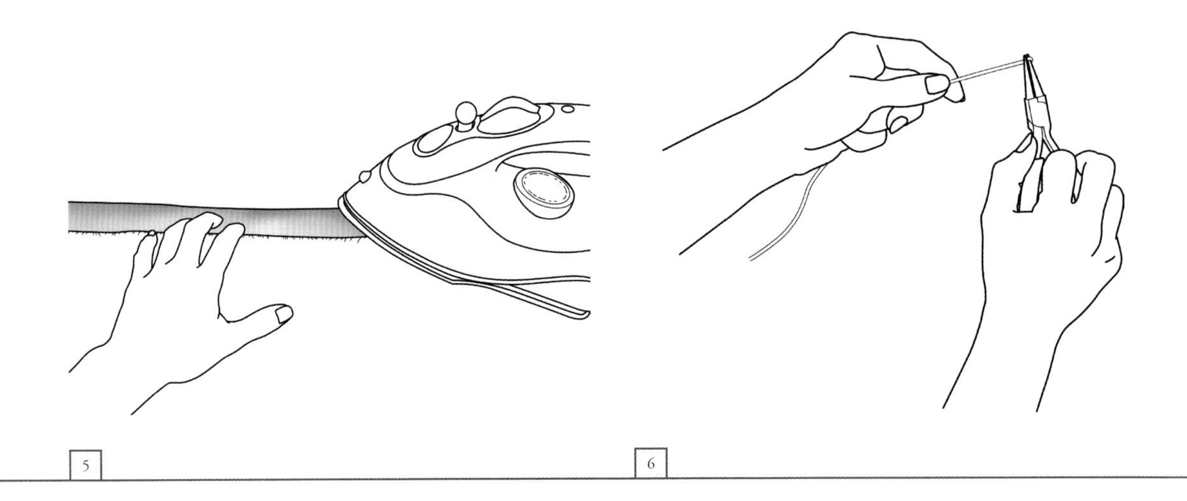

5

Iron it along the middle.

6

Take a length of fine wire and trim it to fit the strip. Use round nose pliers to soften the ends of the wire, rounding them so that they will not pierce and poke through the fabric.

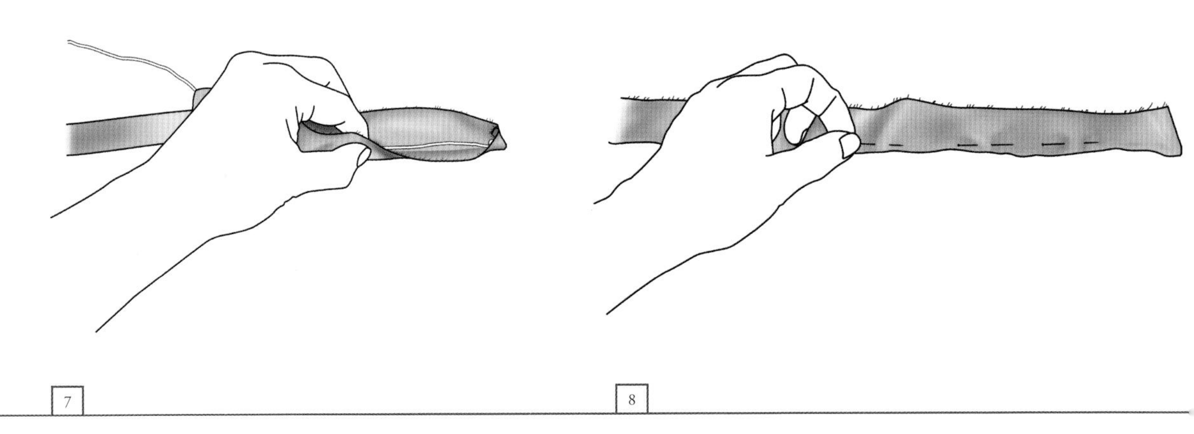

7

Place the wire along the length of the strip and ...

8

... pin it in place.

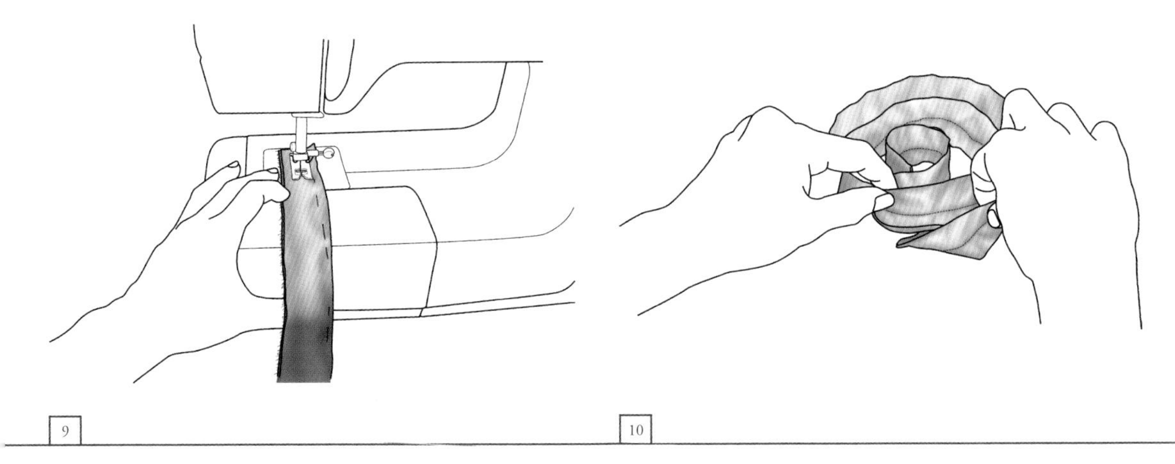

9

Straight stitch along the strip, 0.6 inches (1.5 cm) away from the edge; you will now be able to use this space as a seam to insert the wire into the strip.

10

Slowly shape it with your hands to get a perfect spiral with a rigid, three-dimensional aspect provided by the wire.

POINTED SHOULDER PADS

In this project we give basic shoulder pads a futuristic look by adding pleats that are then changed into pintucks using the sewing machine.

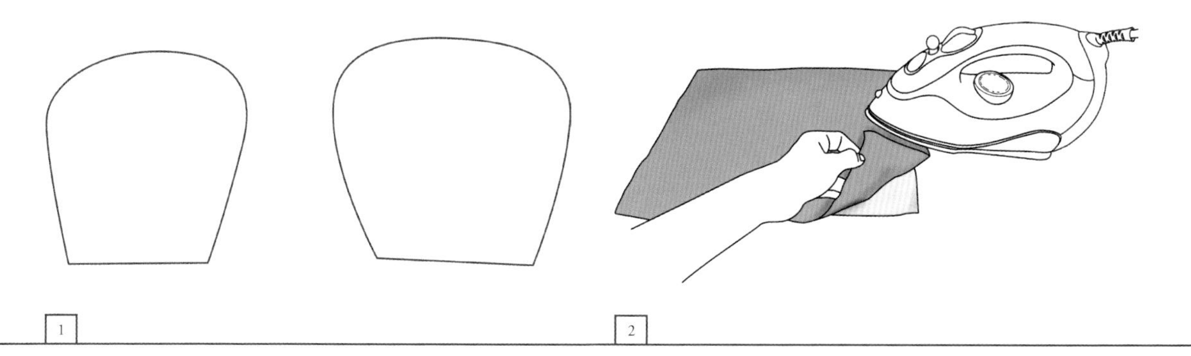

Trace two shoulder pad patterns onto manila paper or pattern card — one of them will be smaller, since it will be the base, while the larger one will be the one on which we will be doing almost all the work in this project. It is important for the difference in size between the two to be about 0.6 inches (1.5 cm) equally around the outline.

Cut a chosen fabric and iron it with a thick lining fabric between two pieces to make them more rigid.

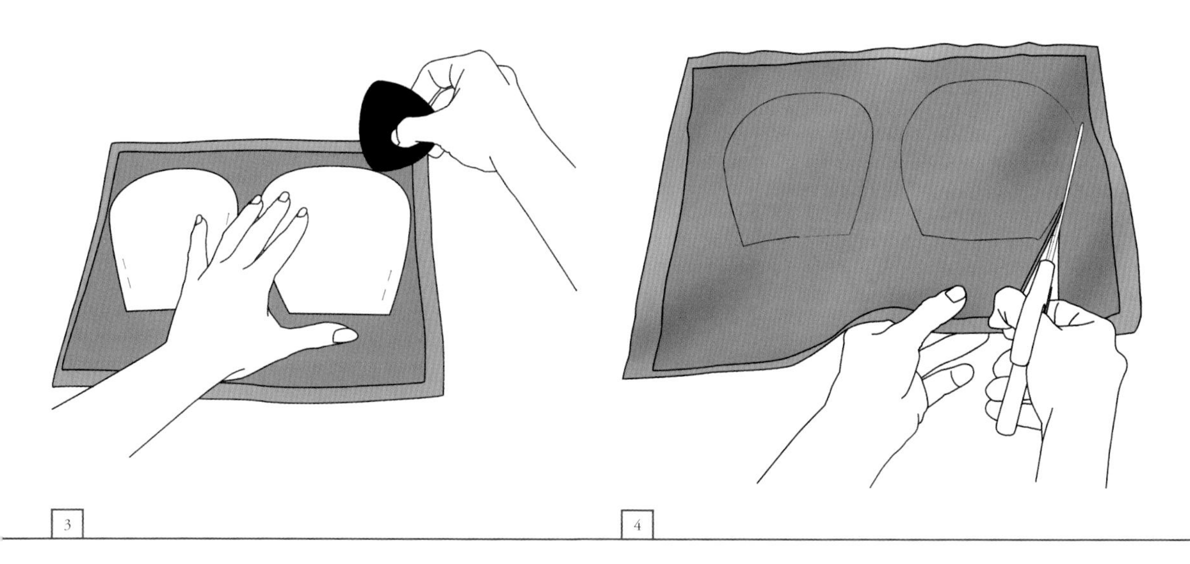

Use tailor's chalk to mark out the two shoulder pad patterns on the fabric.

Cut them out carefully.

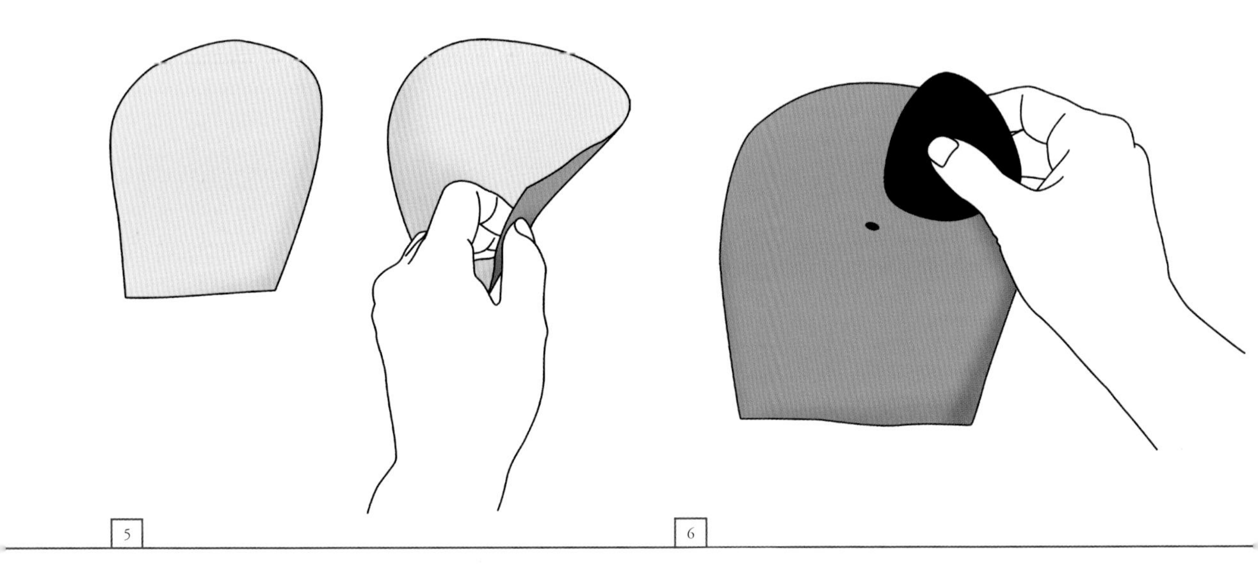

Turn the larger piece over so its reverse side is facing up.

Use tailor's chalk to mark the center point.

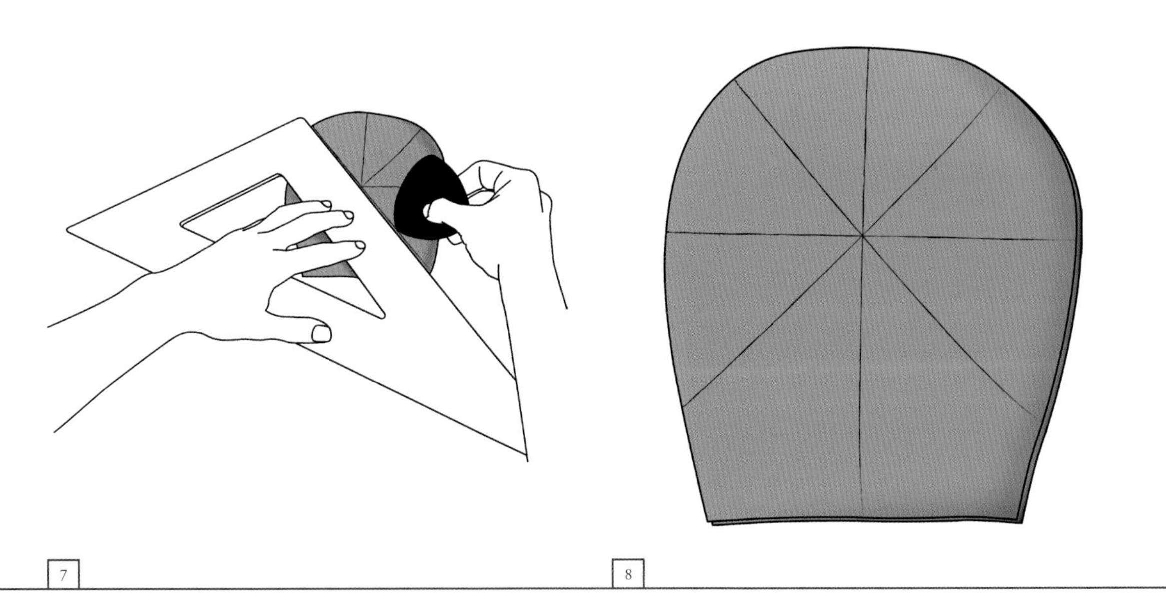

Starting from that point, draw lines radiating across the width, the length and both diagonals.

This is what your work should look like by now.

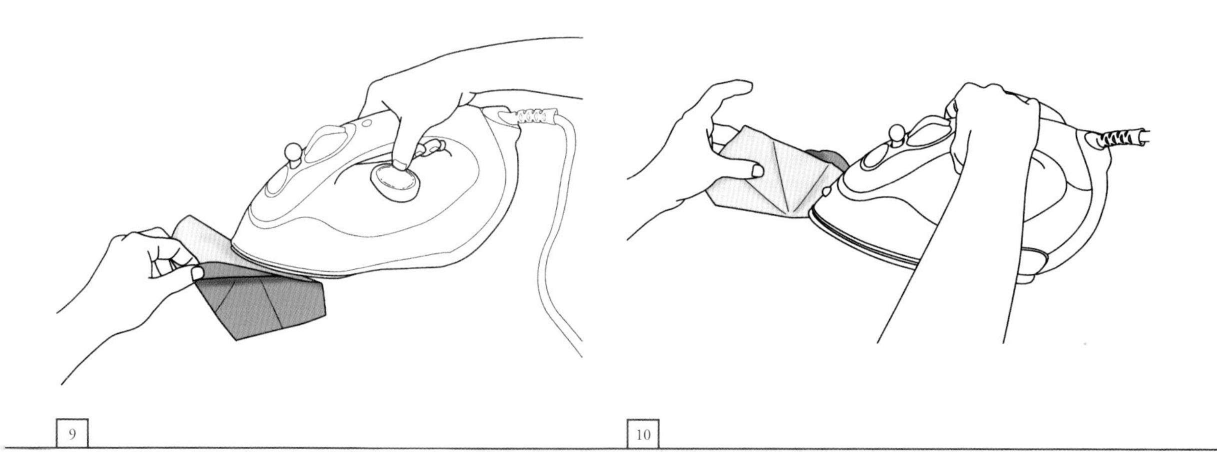

9

Iron the shoulder pad using those lines as a guide.

10

Set the lines with the iron on the right side of the fabric.

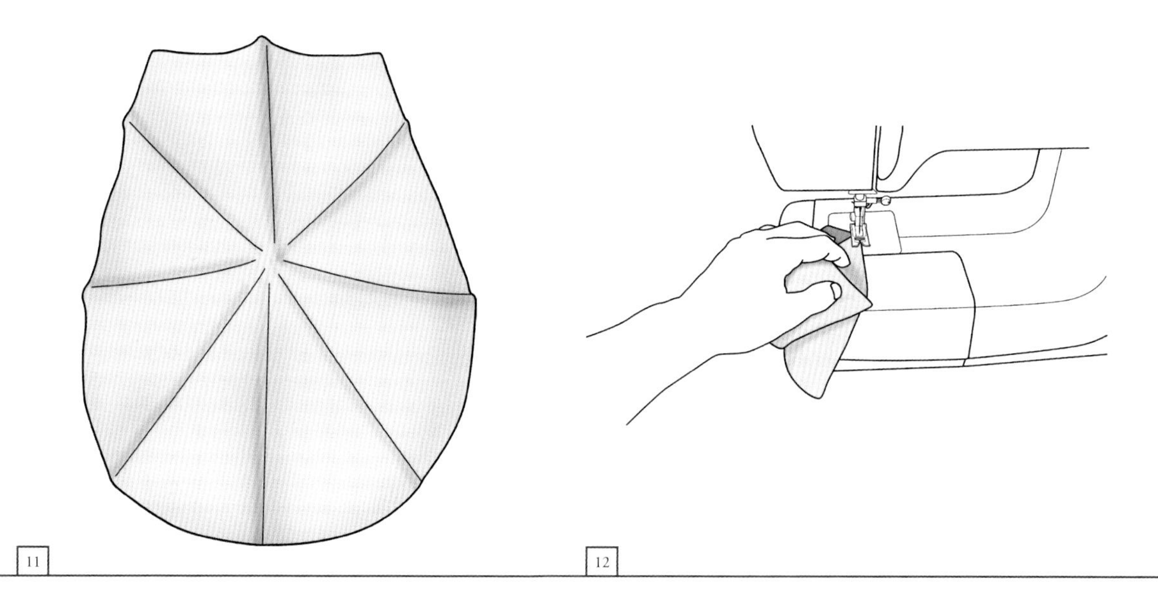

11

The final result resembles a shield or badge.

12

With the sewing machine set to a short stitch, straight stitch the pleats until they look like pintucks to enhance the shape.

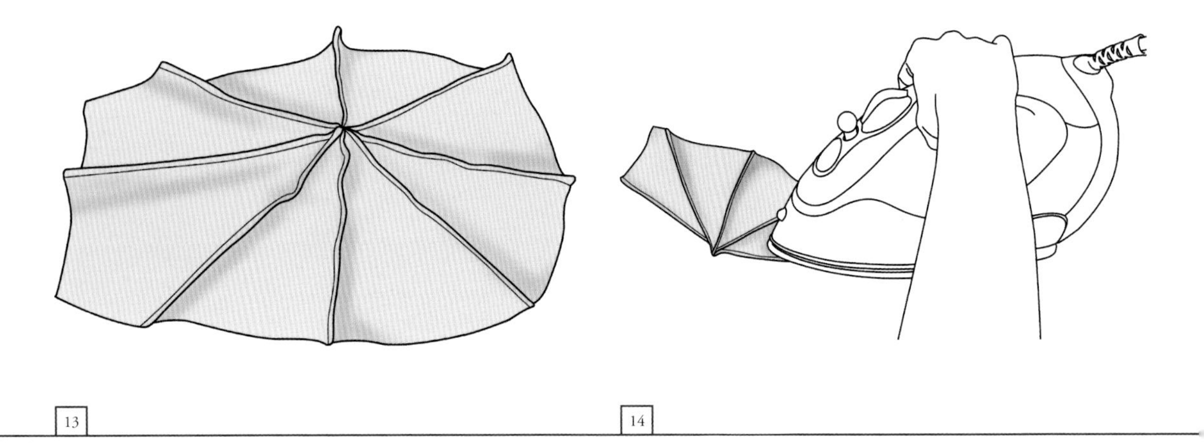

13

When finished, the piece should look like this.

14

Iron these pintucks so that they are firmly set.

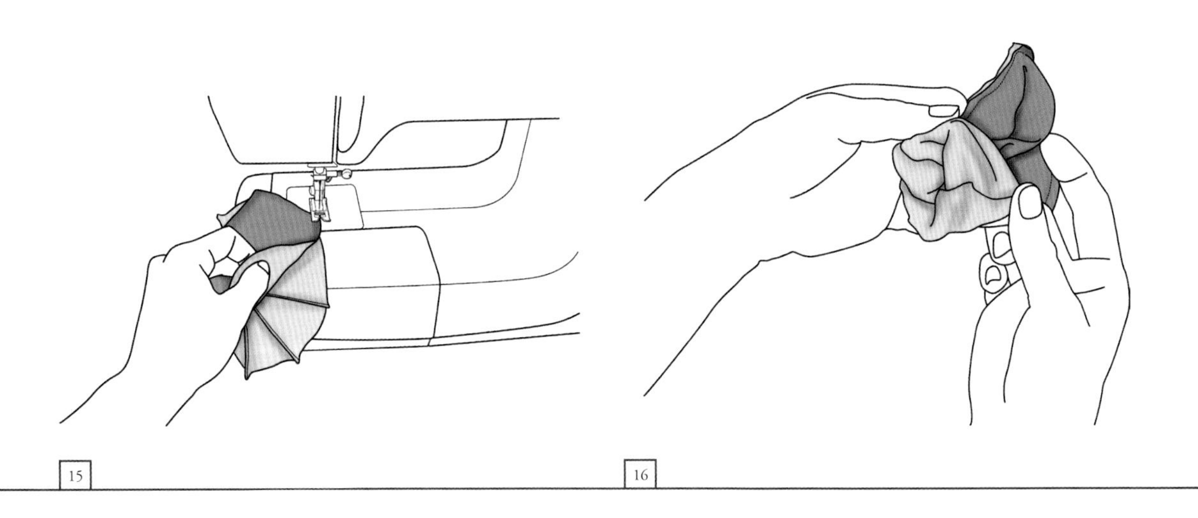

15

Now join the two pieces together using the sewing machine, with their right sides facing inward. Don't forget to leave one part open — the area that will be nearest the neck — so that the pieces can later be turned the right way out.

16

Now carefully turn the two pieces, which have now become one shoulder pad, the right way out.

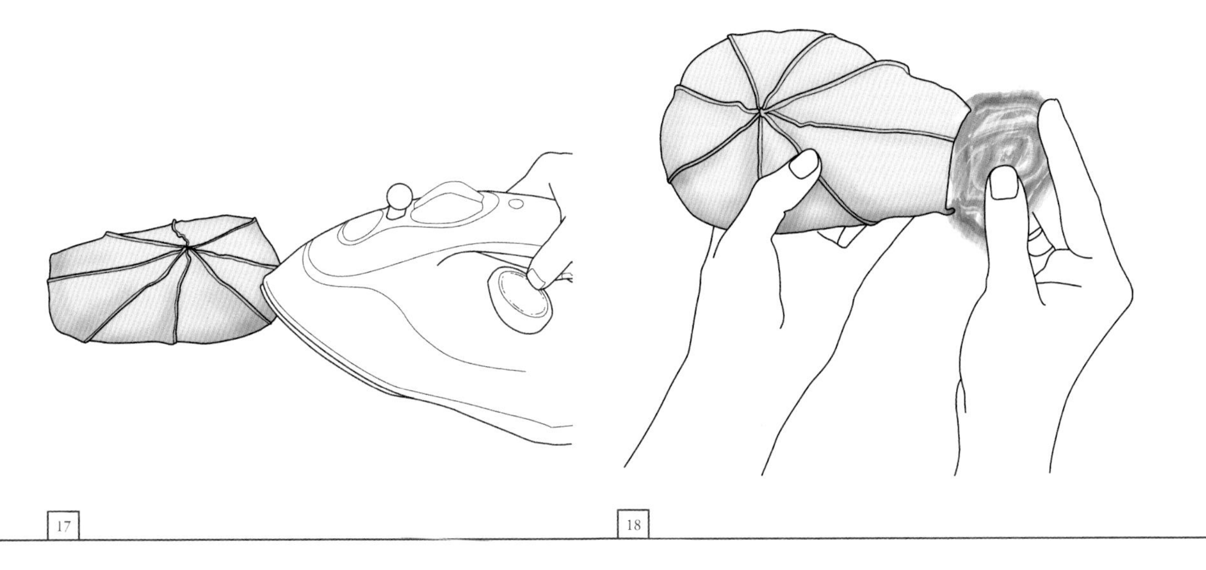

17

Use the iron to add definition to the outline.

18

Fill the interior with kapok to give the shoulder pad its final shape.

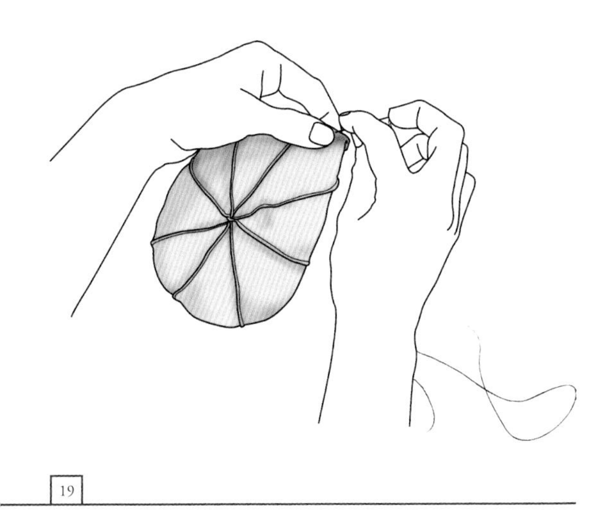

19

To finish, close the part you left open with a needle and thread by hand. In doing so, the result will be sophisticated shoulder pads that can be used as individual pieces or incorporated directly into a pattern, enhancing the shoulders and giving the garment a lovely East Asian look.

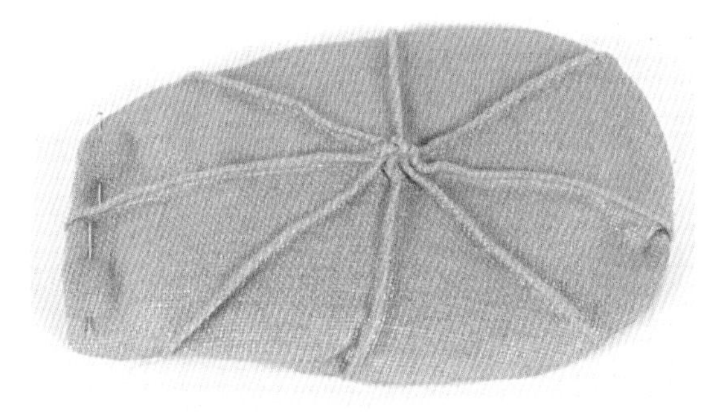

THE WHEEL OF FORTUNE

This project adds a dramatic touch to any garment, either as a decorative piece or as part of its design. This project consists of triangles pleated at their sides, which brush against each other to create a wheel that could adorn the most fashionable garment or add the final touch to a party dress.

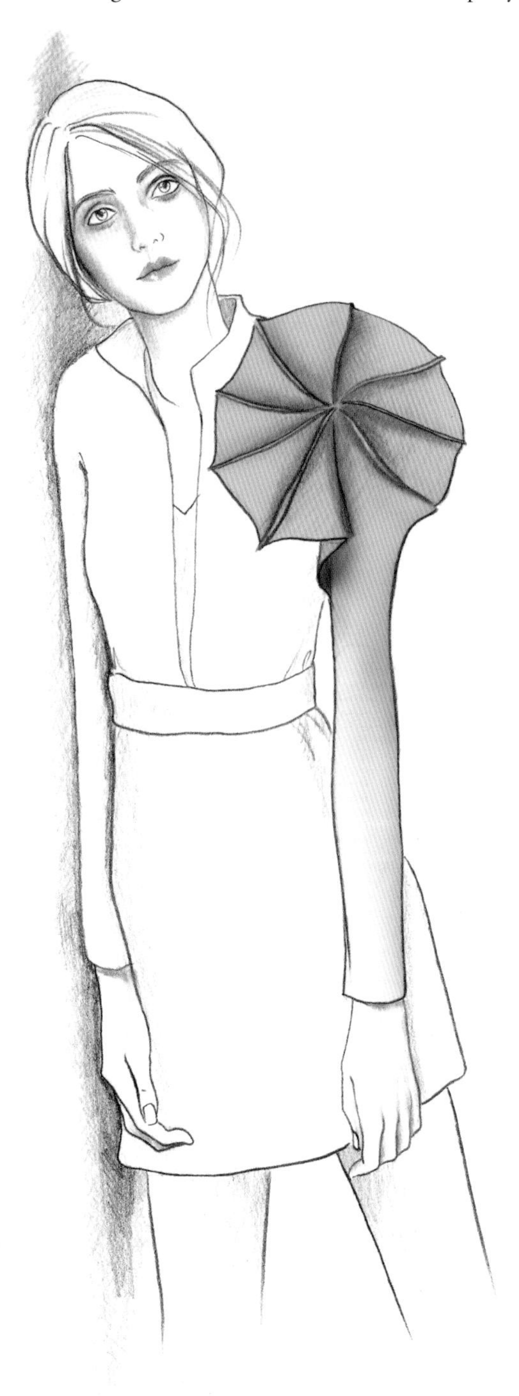

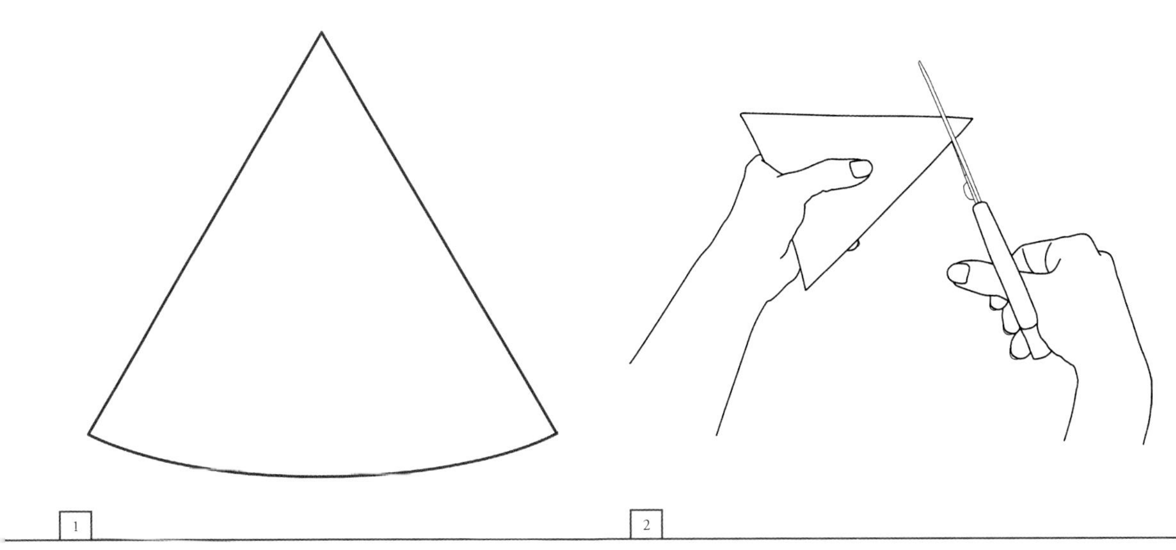

Cut a triangle on brown paper or pattern card measuring 5 inches (12 cm) across the base and 5.5 inches (14 cm) for each side.

With a straight cut, trim 0.4 inches (1 cm) from the top point of the triangle. Using these measurements will give you an 8.5-inch (22 cm) diameter wheel.

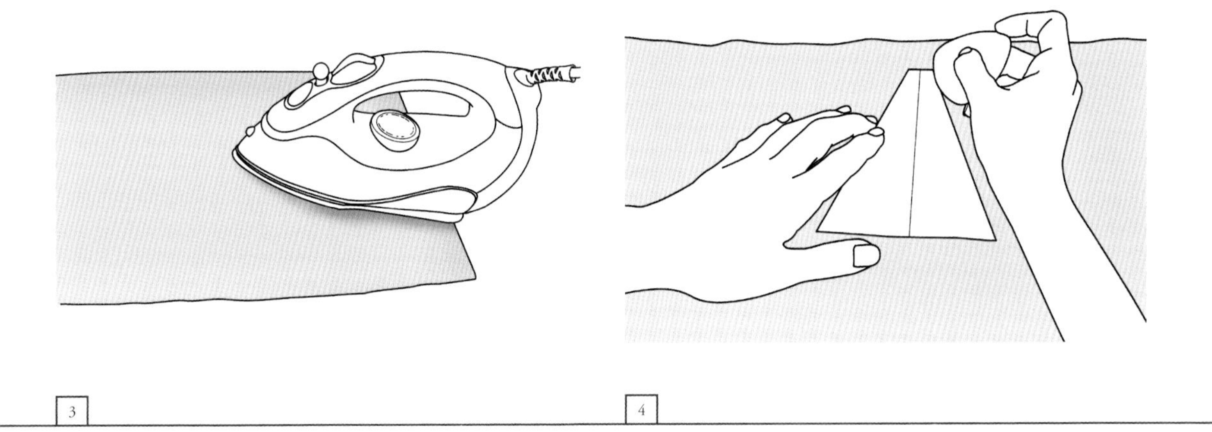

Iron the section of the fabric that you are going to use. It is best to use a thick fabric as this project requires a high degree of rigidity.

Use tailor's chalk to mark the outline of the triangle on the fabric. Repeat the process until you have marked a total of seven triangles on the section of fabric.

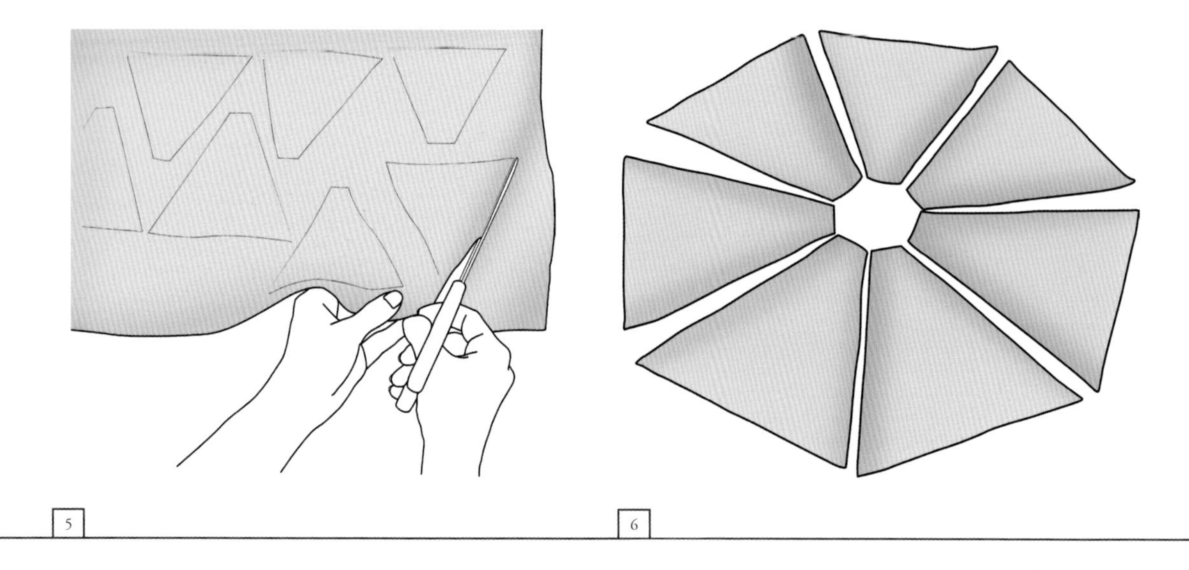

Cut all the triangles using scissors.

Arrange the triangles in the final form to check that they match.

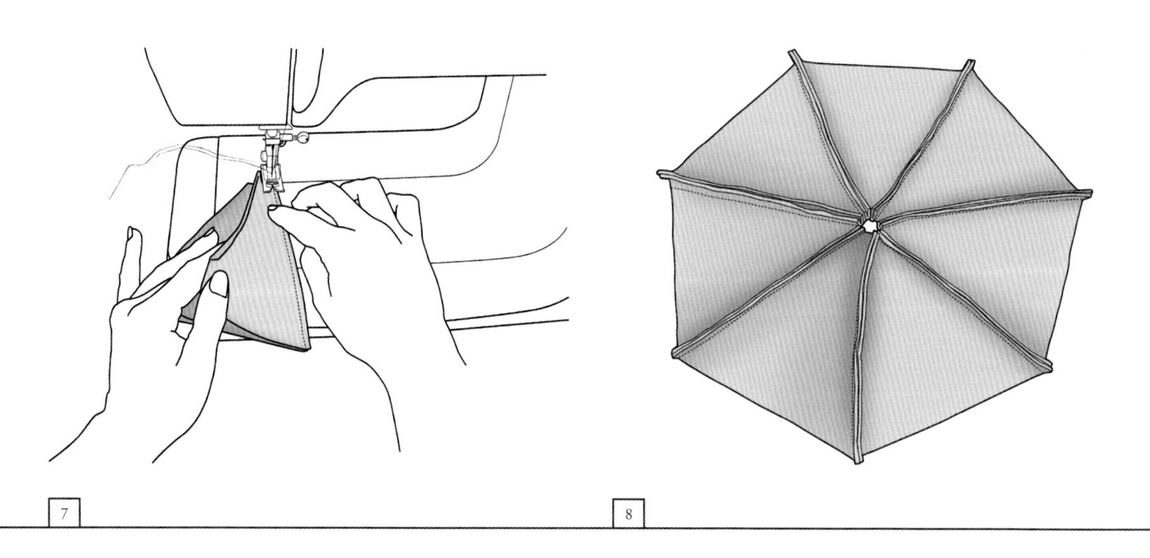

Using a sewing machine, join the triangles along their sides, leaving a 0.4-inch (1 cm) allowance toward the outside of each seam.

Once all the pieces are joined edge to edge, you will have a polygon consisting of seven pieces. Iron all the seams well so that they are facing upward when you stretch the wheel out.

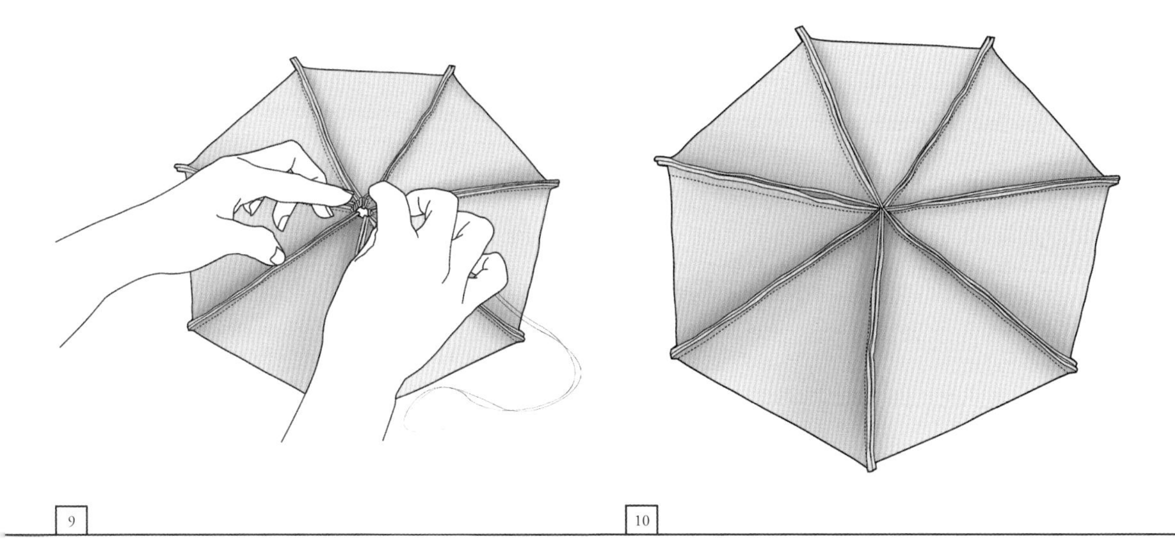

With a needle and thread, join the center of the wheel, where all the seams meet.

Now that you know the technique, you can leave the wheel open by trimming a triangle off and instead join it to a piece of the pattern; this way, it will be an extension of the pattern. The illustration on page 24 shows how the wheel of fortune has been joined to the pattern of a sleeve.

WINDMILLS

By pleating the edges of a square in an original way, we create a cute windmill that is perfect for adding a sweet touch to a garment.

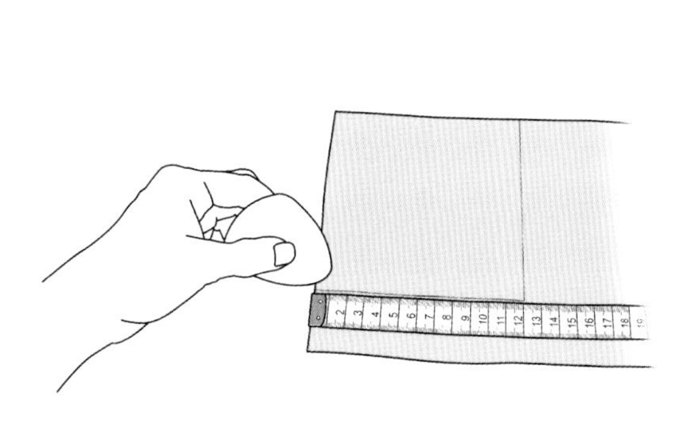

1

Here we will use mid-weight felted fabric (or similar). Mark a 5 x 5-inch (12 x 12 cm) square using tailor's chalk.

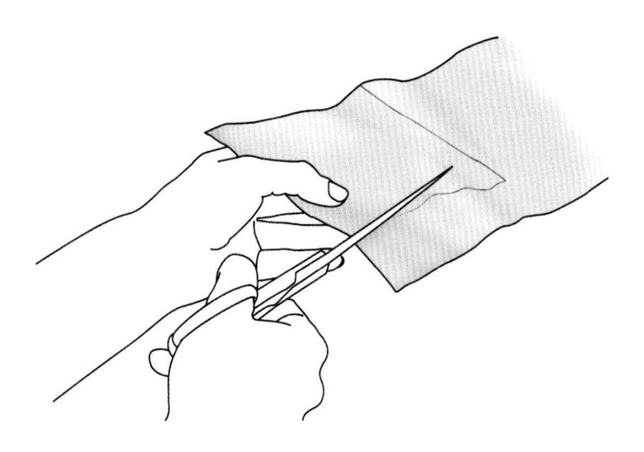

2

Cut out the square with scissors using straight, clean cuts to obtain a perfect square.

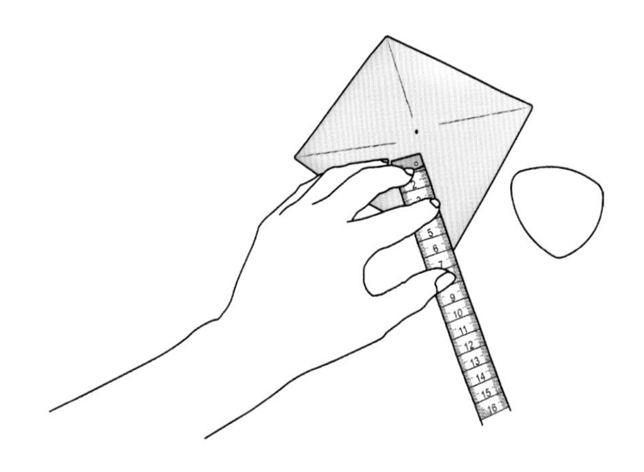

3

Mark the exact center of the square with tailor's chalk and draw a 3-inch (7 cm) diagonal line from each corner toward the center.

4

Use scissors to cut along each diagonal, leaving 0.6 inches (1.5 cm) between the end of the cut and the center. After the diagonals have been cut, the square will now be a cross shape.

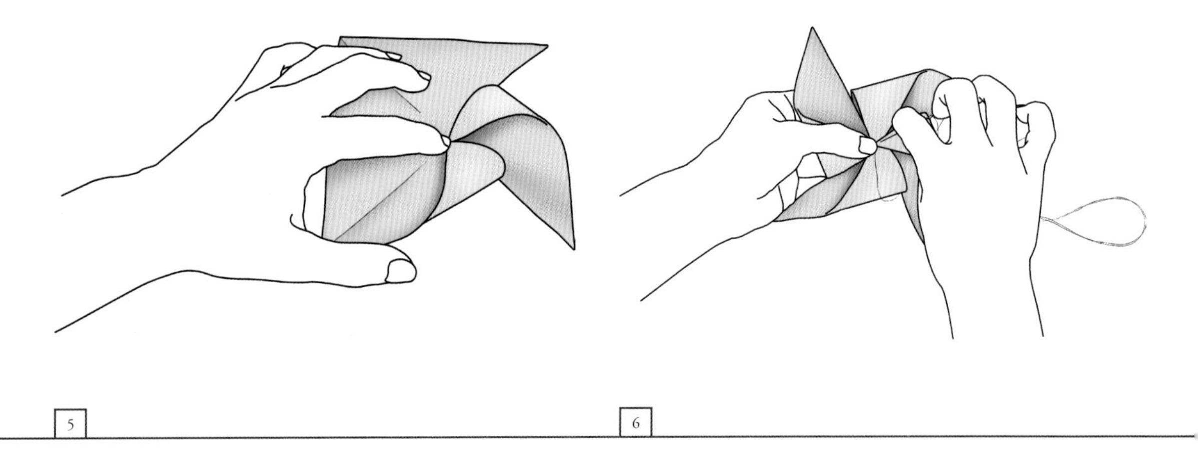

5

6

Fold alternate corners toward the center until the square is complete.

Use a needle and thread to join the corners.

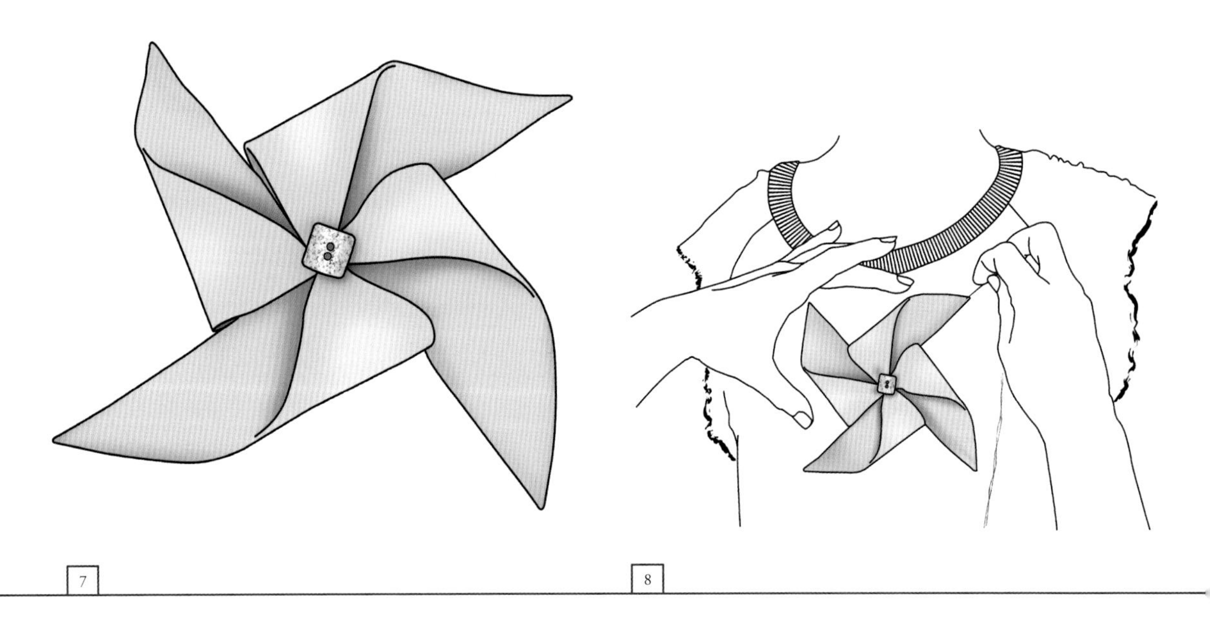

7

8

Decorate the center with an attractive and distinct button in a size appropriate to that of the windmill.

Once the felt windmill is finished, use a mannequin to sew it to your favorite shirt, making small, invisible stitches in the corners and in the center.

FILIGREE PLEATS

For this project, we are going to use the ancient and detailed art of filigree on colorful, pleated fabrics to make fanciful shapes for decorating garments in an exaggerated baroque style.

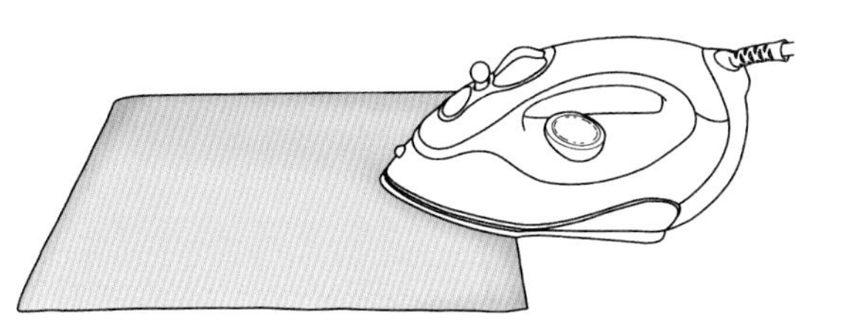

1

Iron a section of the fabric that you are going to use. On this occasion, we'll use a 26 x 26-inch (65 x 65 cm) square of satin chiffon.

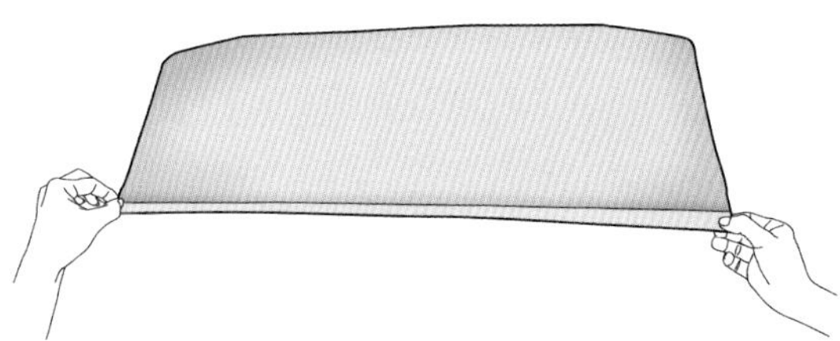

2

Slowly make zigzag-shaped pleats, approximately 0.6 inches (1.5 cm) deep, on the ironing board. Fold the first pleat upward and fix it by ironing, using quite a lot of steam.

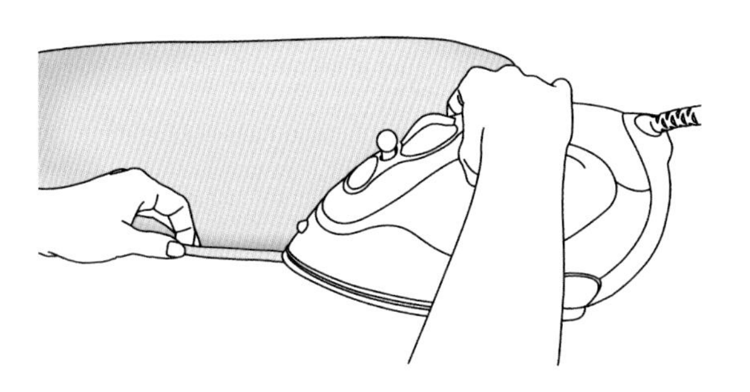

3

Repeat the process, changing the direction of the pleat; this will produce the zigzag pleats we mentioned earlier.

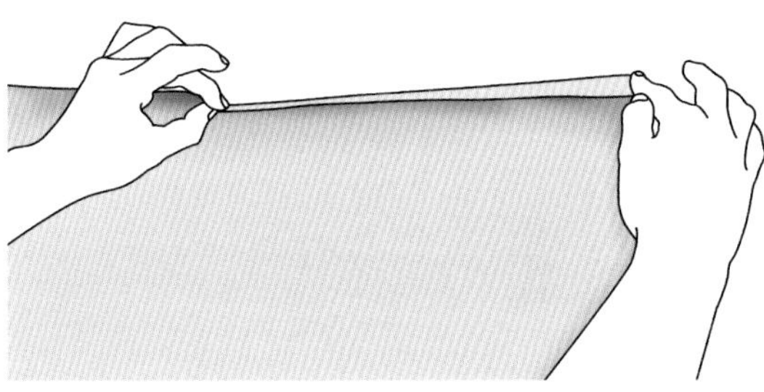

4

Apply this method cleanly and symmetrically over the entire surface of the fabric until it is completely pleated.

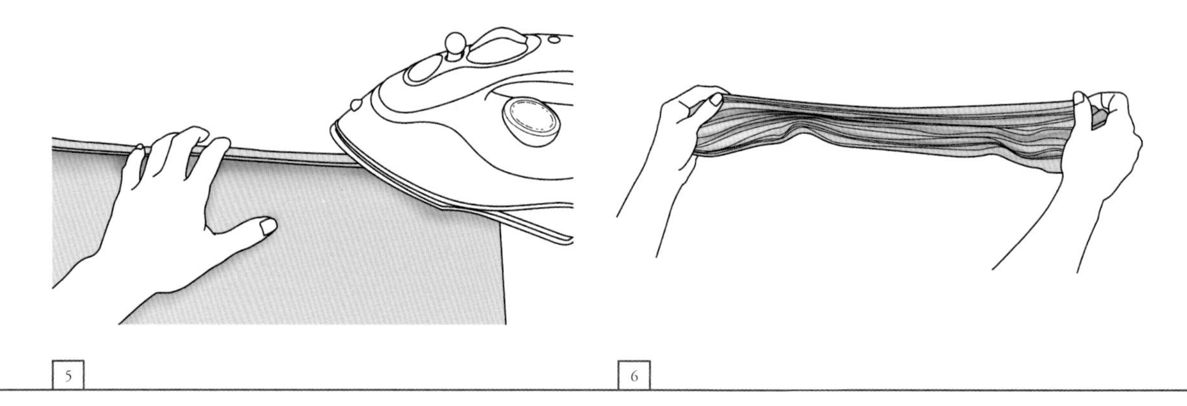

5

When finished, the piece should look like an accordion.

6

With needle and thread, make stitches in strategic areas, such as the edges and some in the center, to prevent the pleats from opening too much. Try to hide the stitches as much as possible.

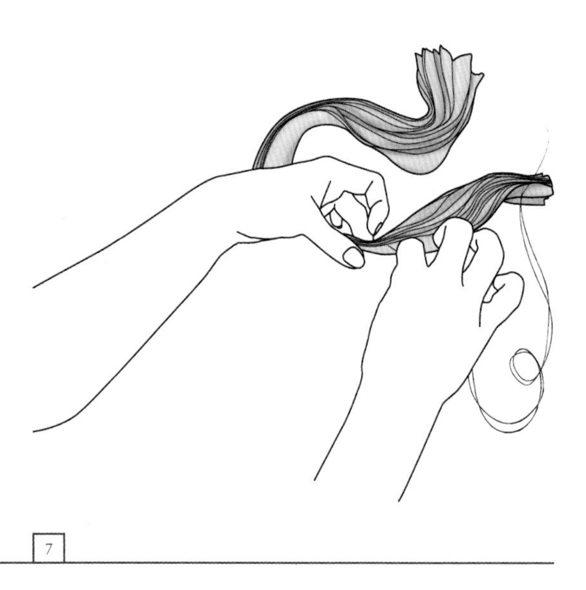

7

Twist and play with the shape of this piece, attaching it to a rigid surface or directly on the garment as an appliqué — you will achieve a very interesting effect that is deserving of the filigree name.

STOCKMAN

FORTUNY PLEAT

This project, which involves pleating fabric horizontally then waving it, is a version of the technique patented under the name of Spanish artist Mariano Fortuny. Belonging to the Fortuny-Madrazo family, he worked in various artistic disciplines. His taste for ancient Greek-style clothing led him to experiment with pleating fabrics imported from the Far East. To perform this technique he invented a secret method, which remains a mystery to this day. His most famous garment is the Delphos dress, created from fine fabrics. What makes this type of pleat so special is the way it softly hugs all body shapes.

1

For this project, we took inspiration from the Fortuny technique to make a strap for an evening dress. Start by cutting a 14 x 18-inch (35 x 45 cm) rectangle from a very light fabric, such as silk chiffon.

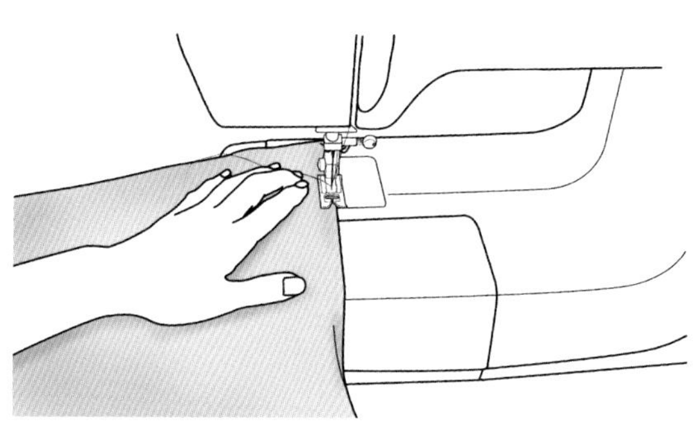

2

Iron it and use a sewing machine to finish all the edges with a small hem to avoid fraying when the garment is completed.

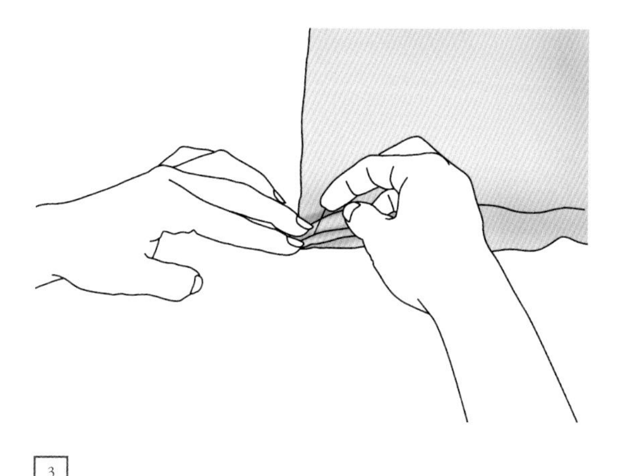

3

Place the piece on the ironing board and pin one of the ends. Fold irregular horizontal pleats, iron and spray the piece with specialty spray starch.

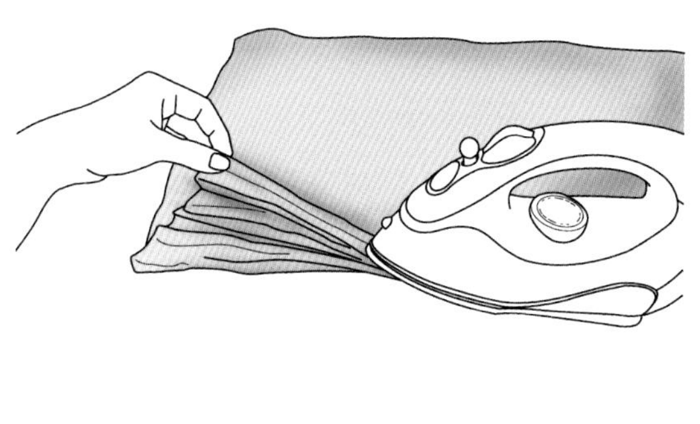

4

This will set the pleats and make them more durable.

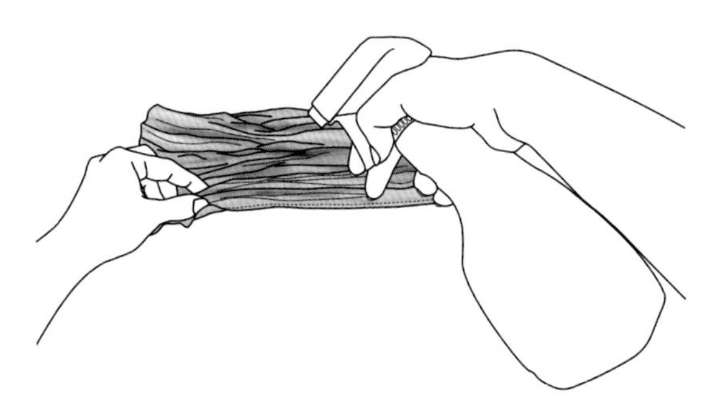

5

Once the piece is completely pleated, set the pleats with the help of the spray and the iron.

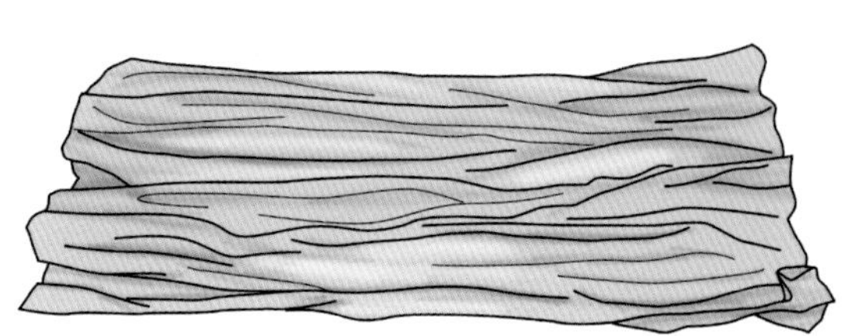

6

The result should be a rectangle of irregular horizontal pleats.

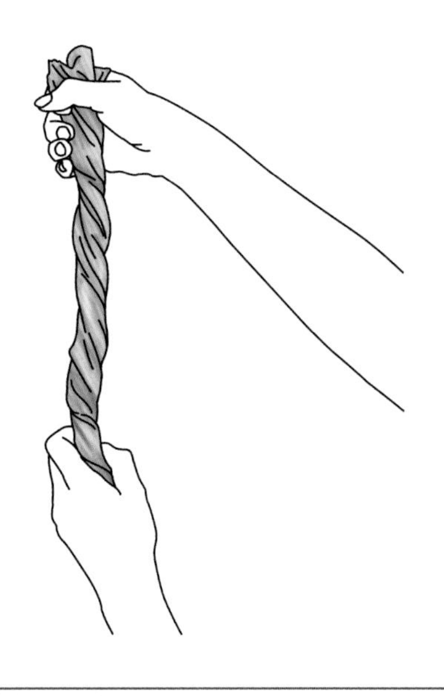

7

Now, with the piece in a vertical position, proceed to twist it firmly, holding the ends of the fabric with your hands.

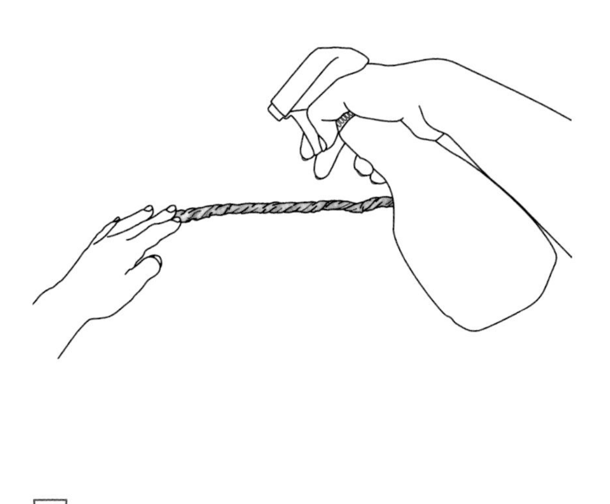

8

Spray again with starch.

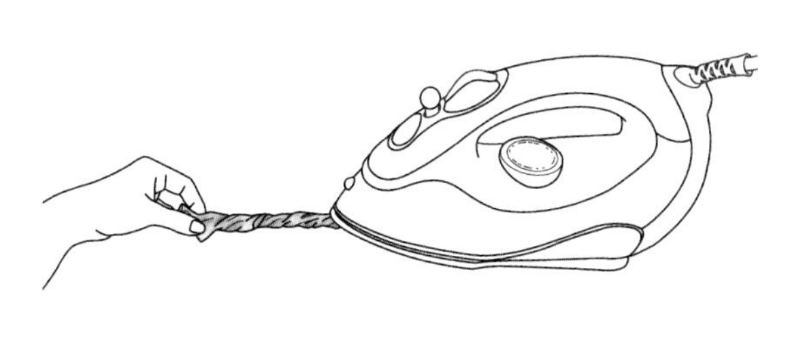

9

Iron it thoroughly. This will set waves in the fabric because of the way in which it was twisted.

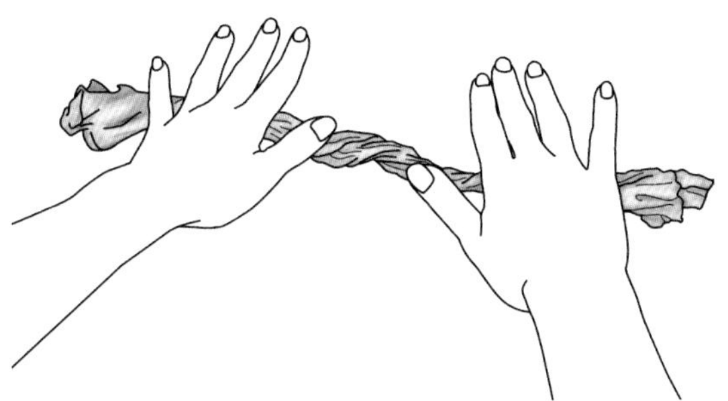

10

Slowly unroll the fabric with both hands.

11

Stretch it carefully from both ends. You will now have a pleat that is inspired by the Fortuny technique — one that is distinct in the way it adapts to the shape of the body. Pleating it horizontally in a disorderly way gives it a unique and casual look.

CRINKLED TIES

In this project we create a cheerful bow by pinching the center of a pleated rectangle. The bow can then be sewn to a garment, adding instant charm to any outfit.

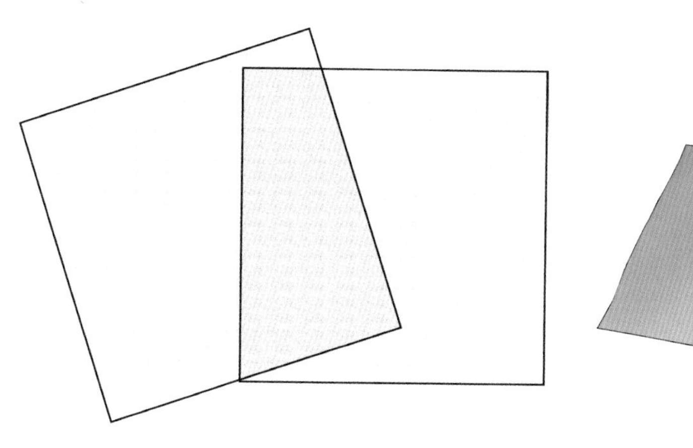

1

Cut two identical squares from manila or silk paper. They must be the size you want the finished bow to be.

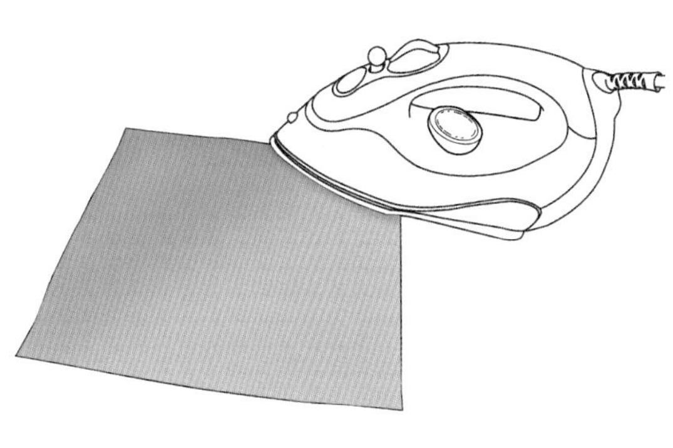

2

From the fabric you are going to use, cut the same squares plus an extra 0.4-inch (1 cm) allowance for the hem. Fold that extra fabric over, iron it and straight stitch the hem on all four sides.

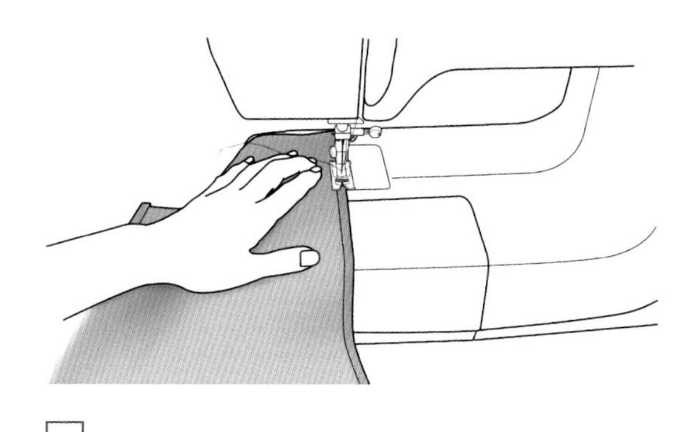

3

This is very useful and should always be done to avoid the fabric fraying.

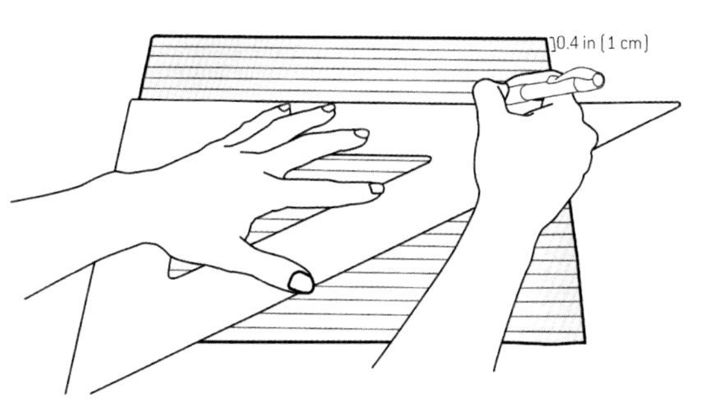

4

With a pencil and ruler, draw parallel lines along the length of one of the sections of manila paper. These lines must be 0.4 inches (1 cm) apart, dictating the depth of the pleat.

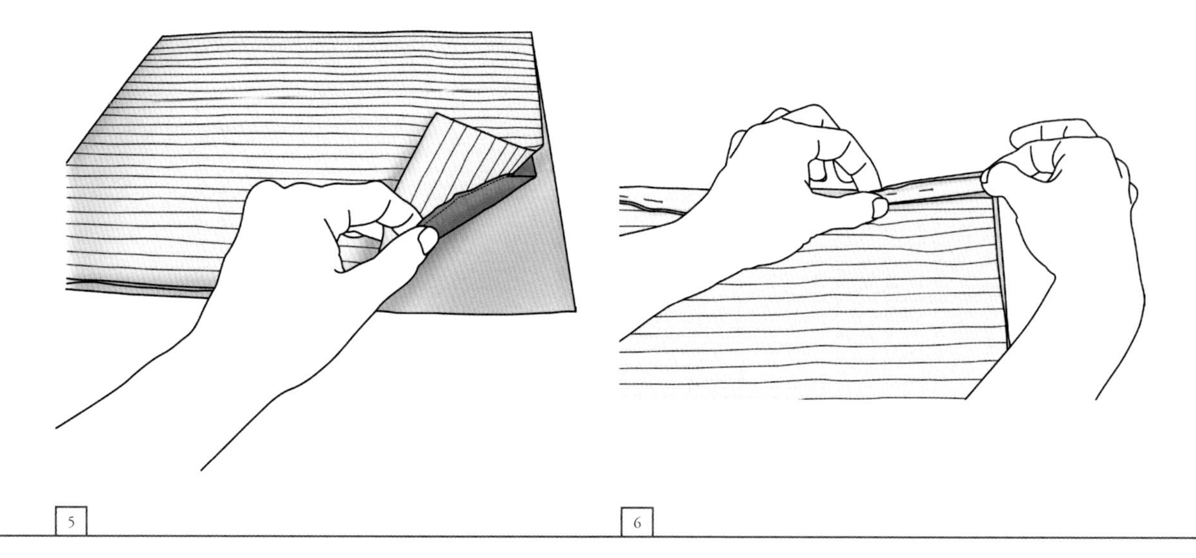

Place the three pieces together, centered and straight. Put the piece of fabric on top of the unlined piece of manila paper, then the manila paper you marked with lines on top of both. Pin the three pieces together.

Line up line one with line three, leaving line two folded inward. Repeat the same process by folding line four and lining it up with line six. Continue in this manner along the whole surface, so that the pleats form a type of zigzag.

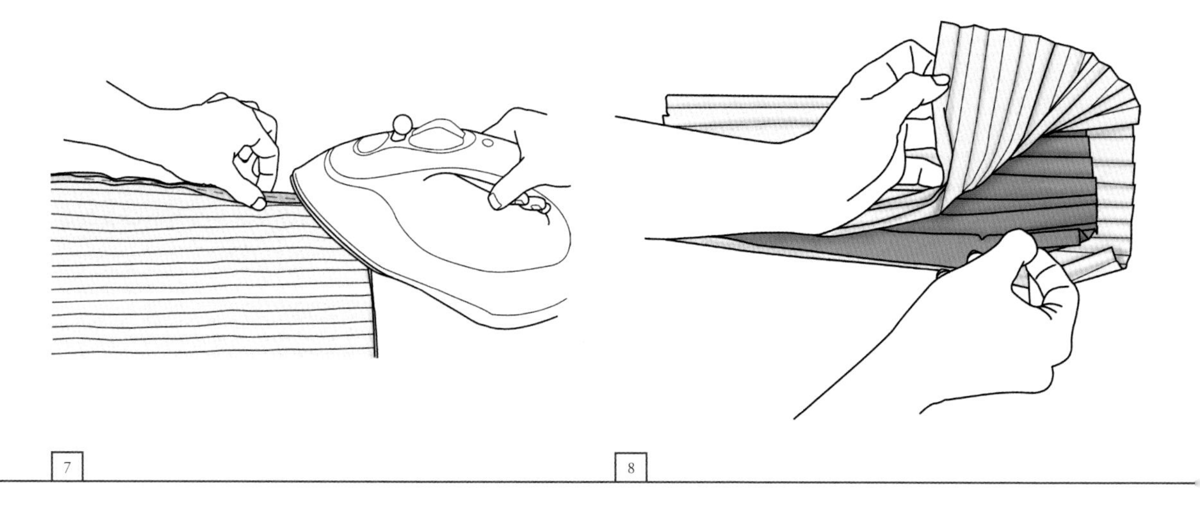

As you fold the pleats, iron them painstakingly to set them firmly. Fix each pleat with pins after ironing it to avoid the fabric moving.

Once the entire surface is pleated, slowly separate the pieces of manila paper from the fabric, which will now be fully pleated.

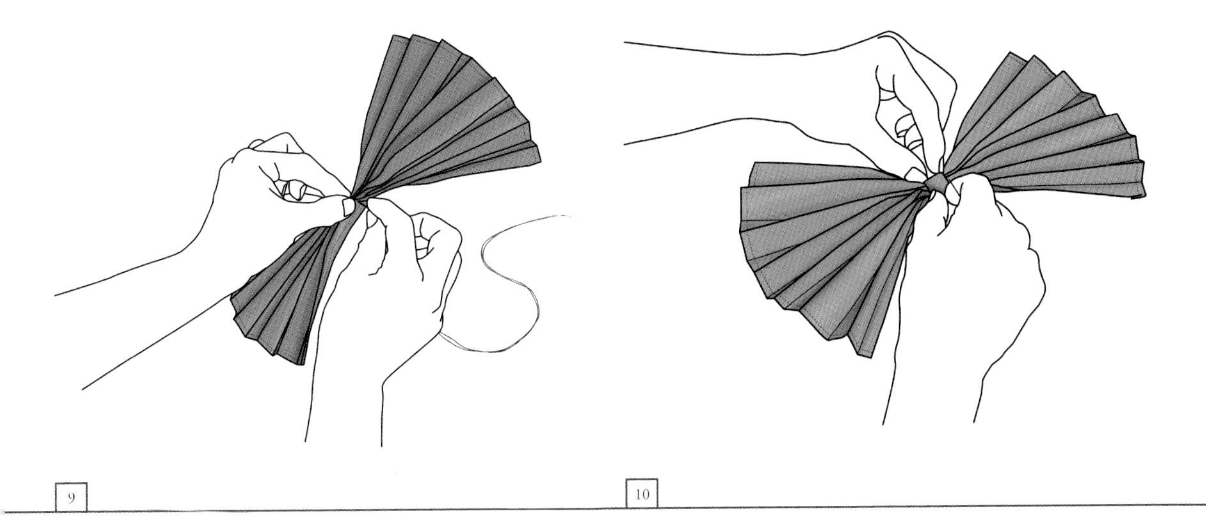

Sew the exact center of the pleated fabric with strong stitches using a needle and thread. This will give you a bow shape.

Cut a strip of the same fabric and sew it around the center of the bow to cover the central stitches.

Now you have a pleated bow ready to attach to a garment. To do this, sew it at the central part and at the ends so that it remains open, showing all the pleats.

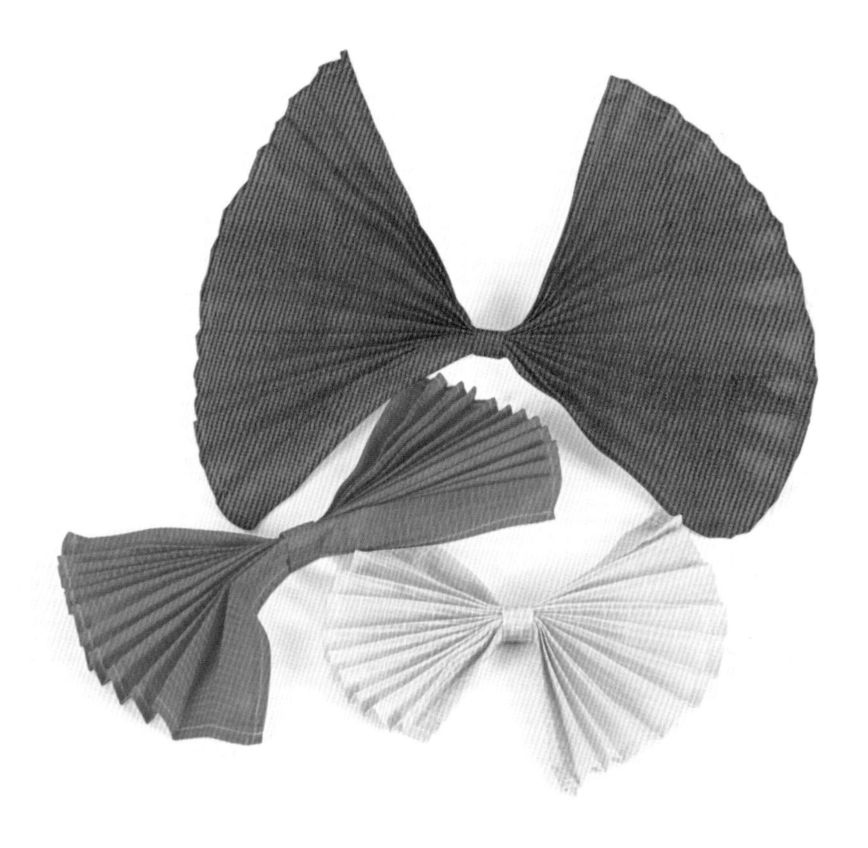

SYMMETRICAL TUCKS FOR SKIRTS

This technique allows us to create symmetrical tucks in skirts and dresses. Once the straight stitching is finished and lined up with the bottom of the garment, it can then be modified with a few small appliqués depending on the style you wish to create.

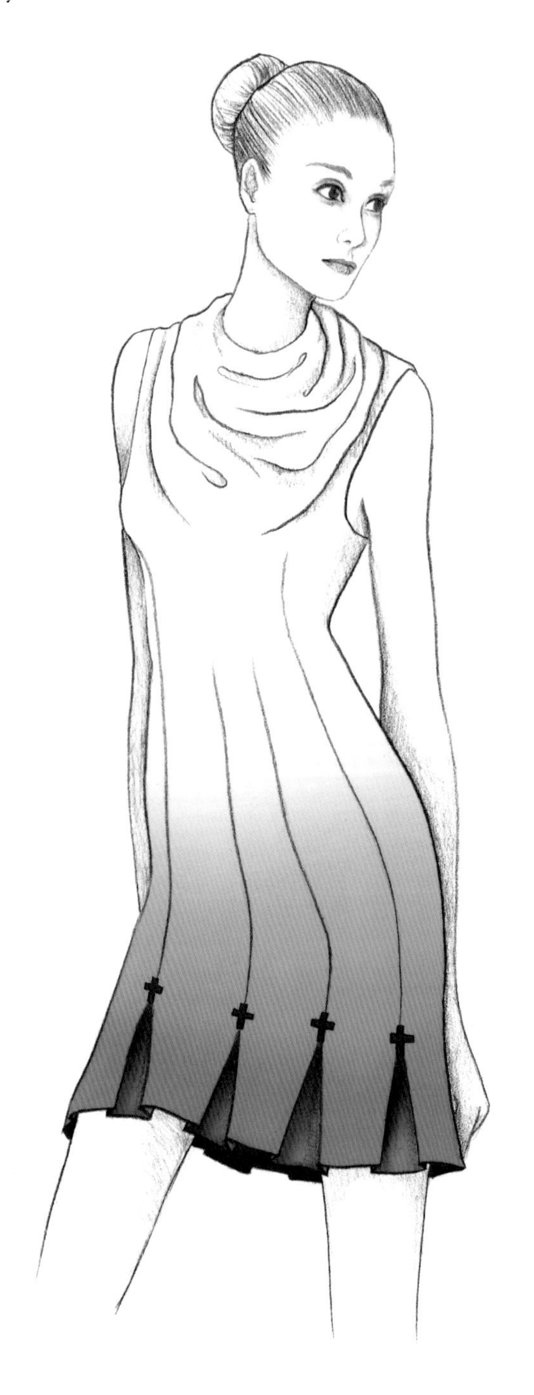

1

Iron a section of the fabric that you are going to use. Here we will show you a small square piece as a demonstration of this technique, which can be applied to the entire length of a straight skirt or even a dress.

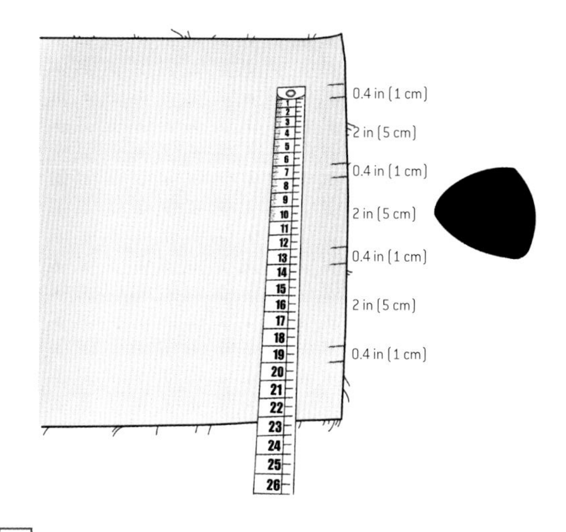

2

Using a ruler and tailor's chalk, make a pair of marks every 2 inches (5 cm) along one side of the fabric. Each mark should be 0.4 inches (1 cm) from its partner. Remember to center them well in the fabric and don't mark the first pair too close to the edge.

Repeat this process as many times as permitted by the size of the pattern piece that you want to work. In this case we have marked four pairs.

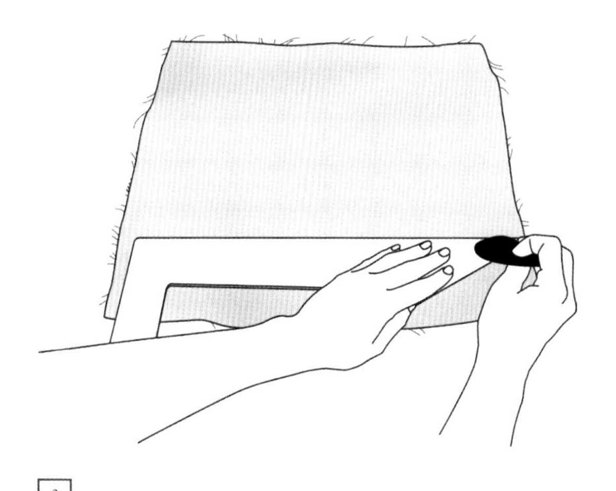

3

Use a ruler to draw identical marks on the other side of the fabric, parallel to the ones you have already made.

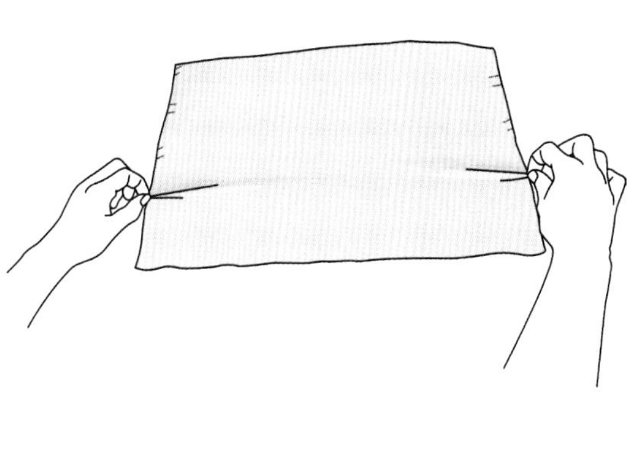

4

Pinch the first 0.4-inch (1 cm) mark and place the fabric so that the ridge you made by pinching the mark becomes a straight end-to-end pleat. Use an iron to set it.

Repeat the process, transforming the four marks into perfectly defined pleats.

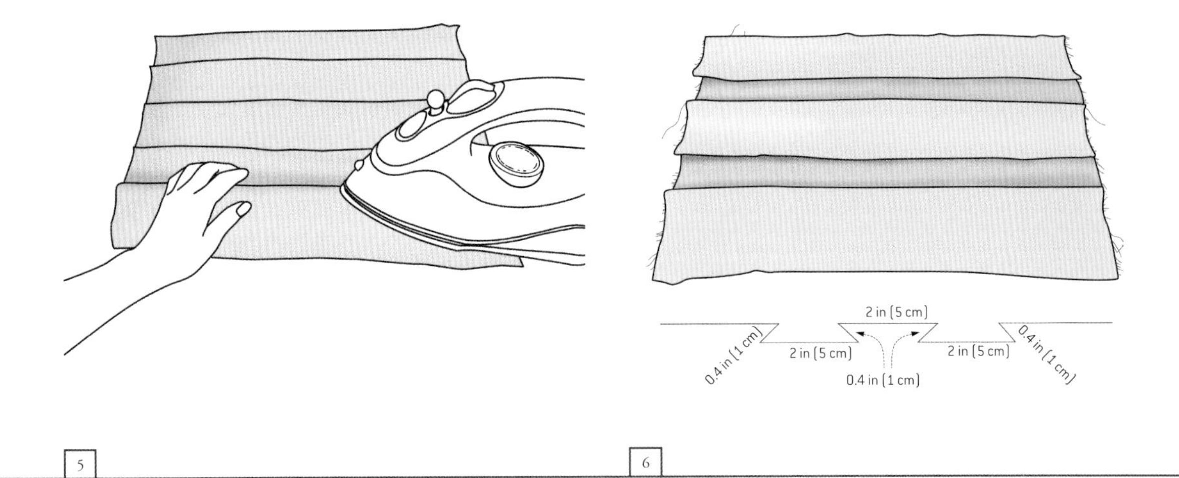

Take the first fold and loosen it upward, ironing it with a depth of approximately 0.4 inches (1 cm).

Now loosen the second pleat, this time downward, thus ensuring that the two are facing each other.

Repeat this process with the rest of the pleats, remembering that you should alternate loosening pleats upward and downward. Now repeat this process over all of the fabric that you have marked.

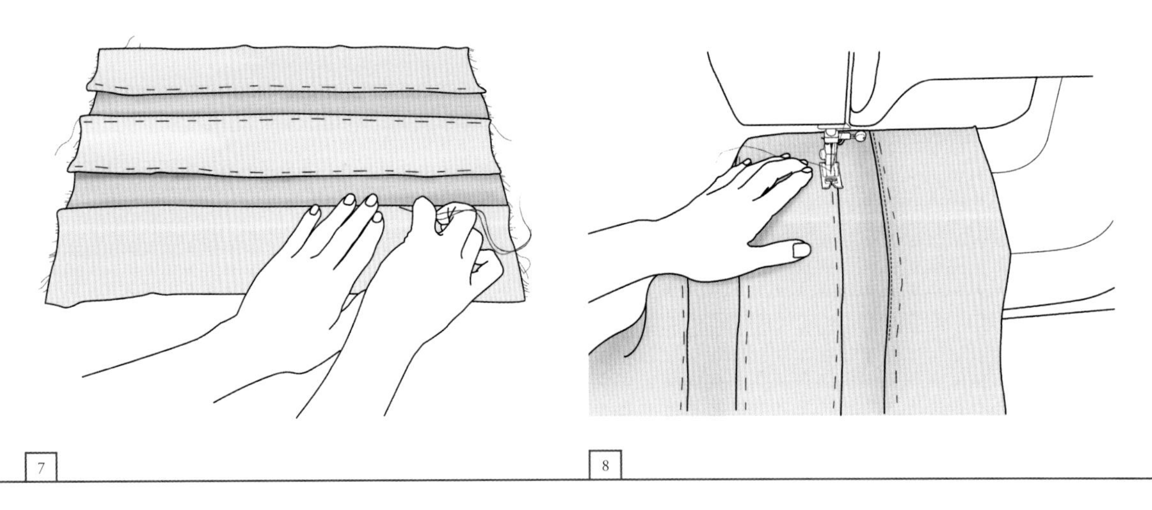

With needle and thread, firmly tack each pleat so that none of them can move and lose their shape.

Using the sewing machine, straight stitch the pleats at about 0.1 inches (3 mm) from the edge to make them into small tucks. Do not stitch a section of about 3 inches (7 cm) up to the hem of the fabric in all the tucks; this section will reach from the end of the straight stitch to what will be the bottom of the skirt.

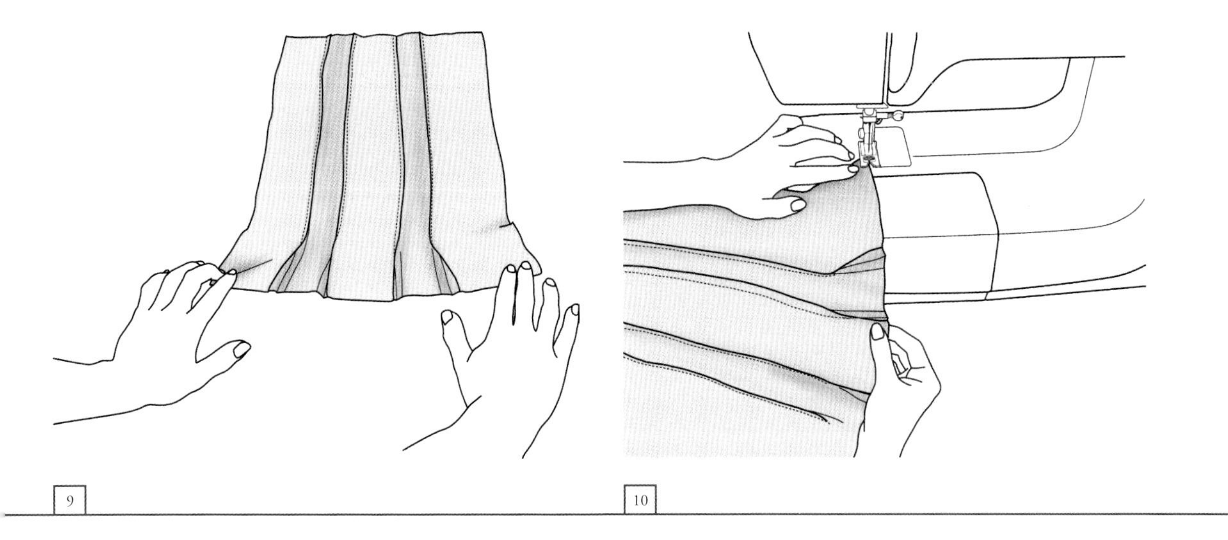

When finished, the piece should look like this.

Fold 0.2 inches (0.5 cm) of the fabric from the bottom of the piece and use the machine to hem it with a small zigzag. This will become the bottom of the skirt.

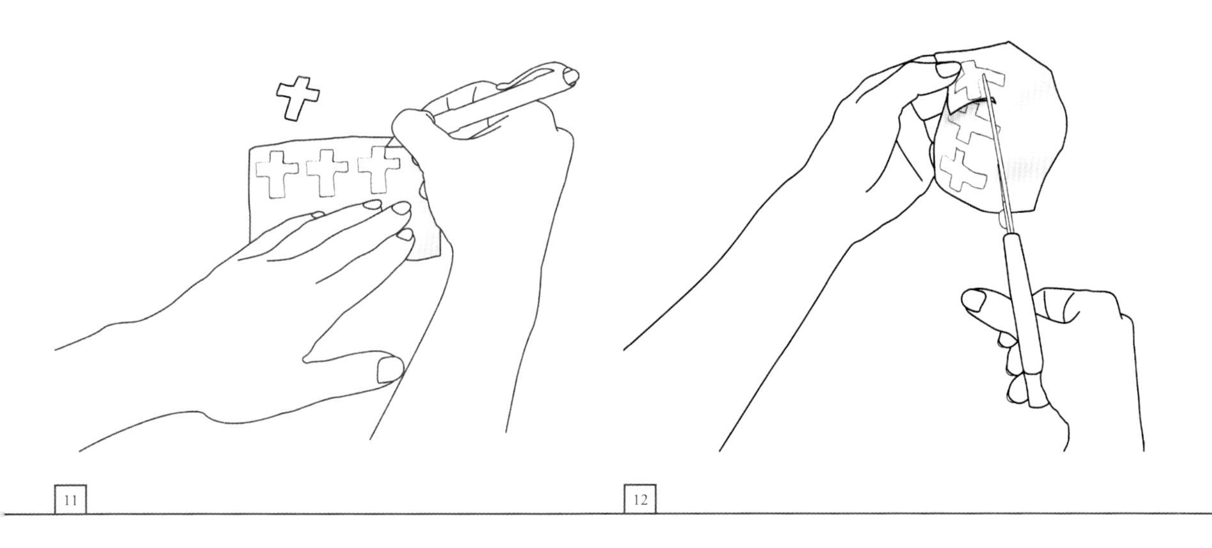

Now take a small swatch of suede or suedette in the same color as the fabric and mark some small crosses on it with a pen. This cross shape is a nod to the punk style of the 1970s.

You can, however, mark whatever shape you want on the suede to give it your own style.

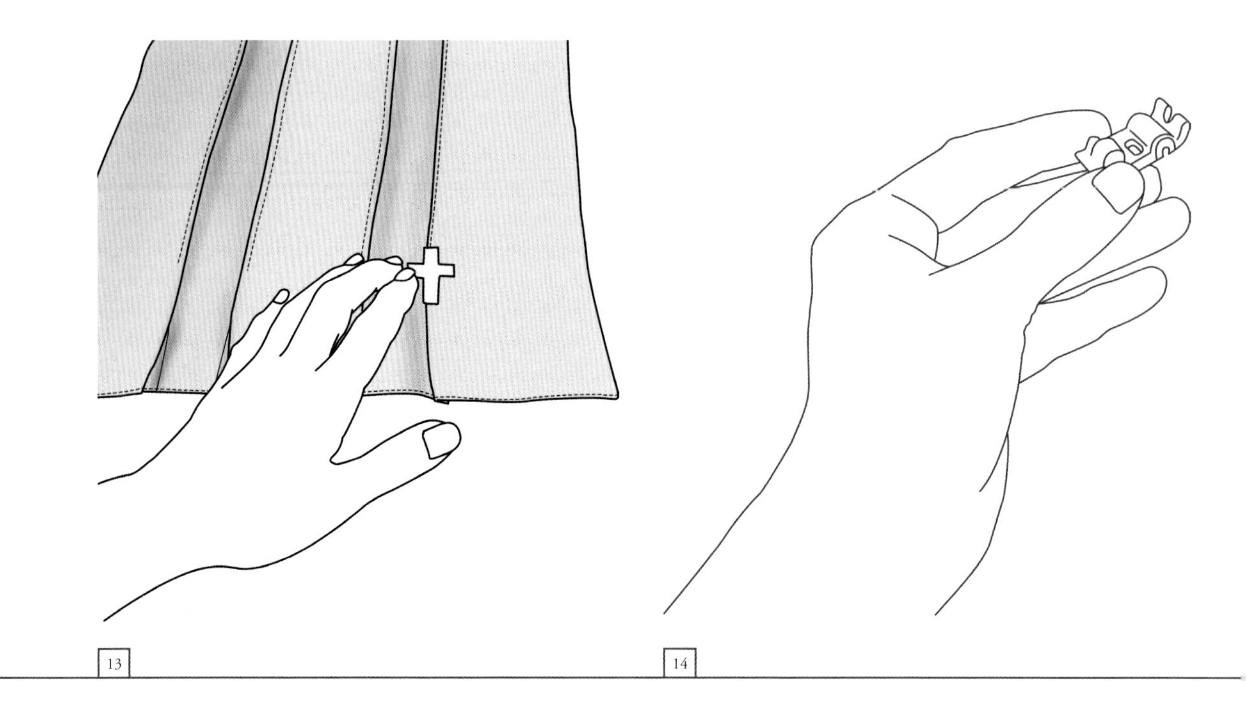

Place the crosses where the straight stitch of each tuck finishes.

Put the presser foot for sewing leather onto the sewing machine. Use small straight stitches to fix the small crosses to the skirt. These add-ons provide additional flair to the symmetrical tucks in your skirt or dress.

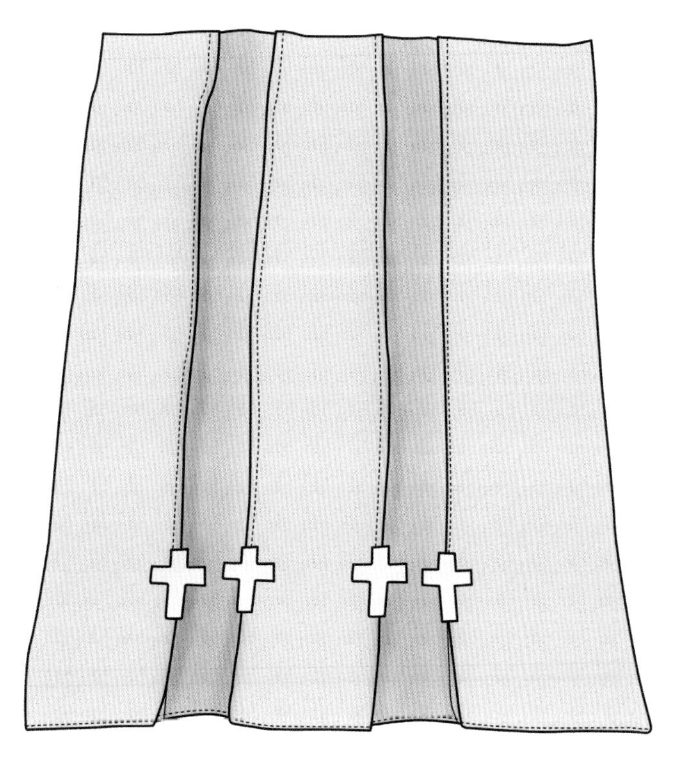

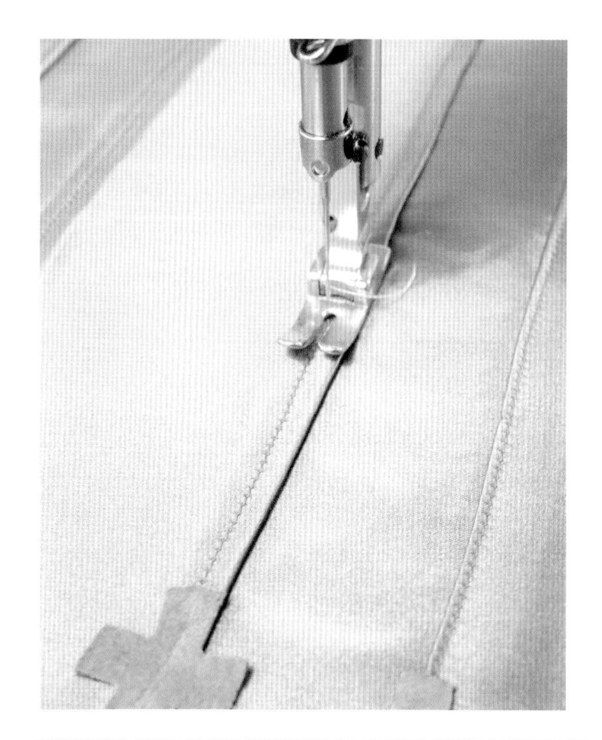

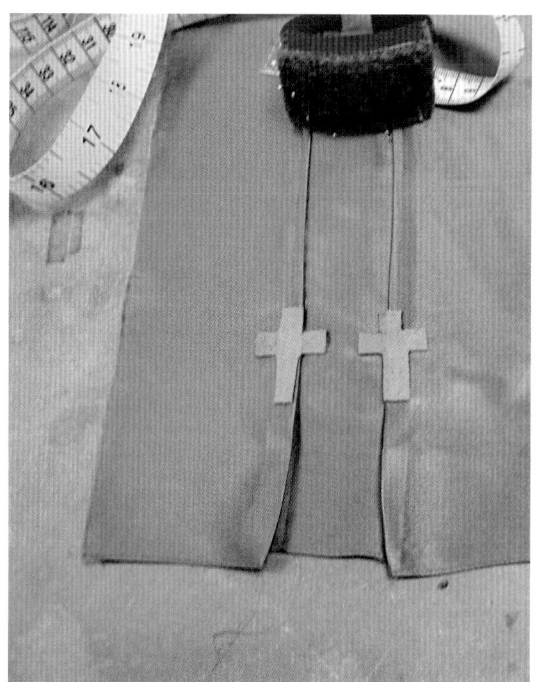

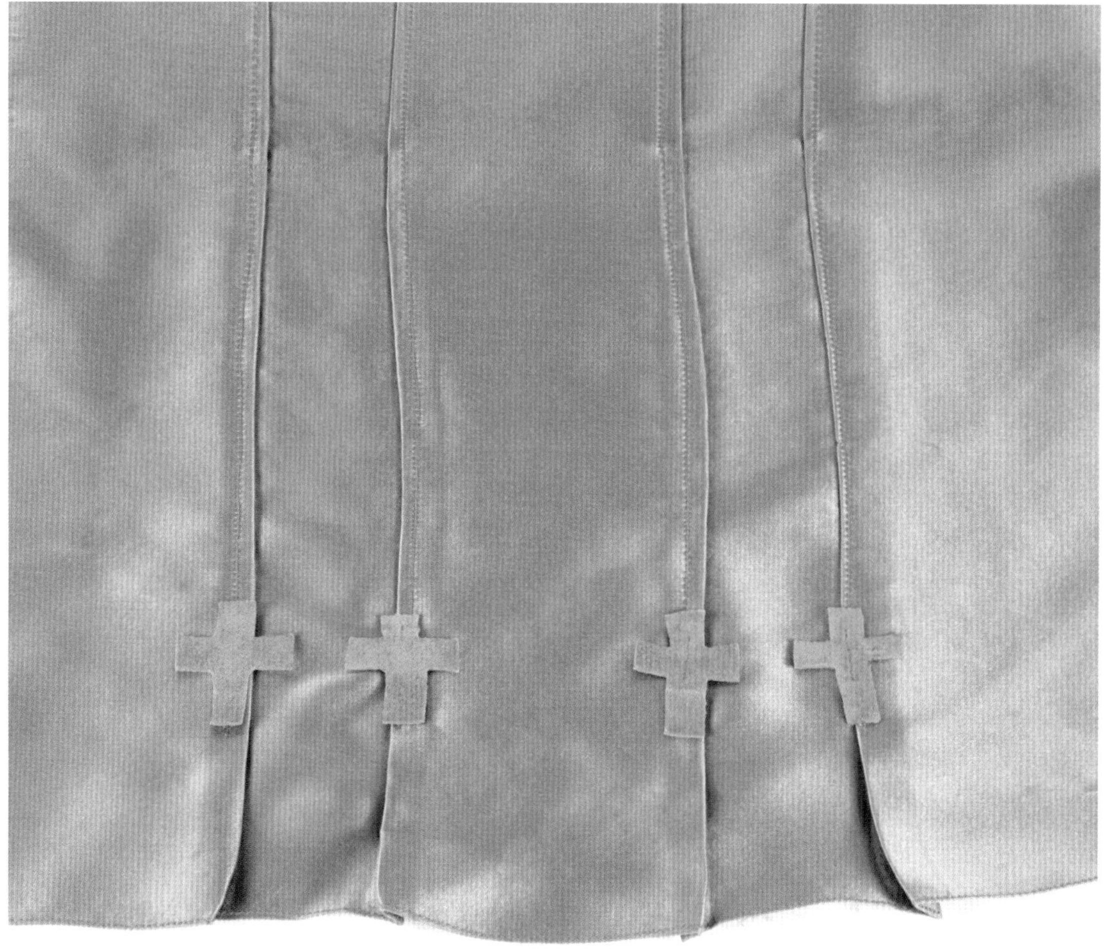

GATHERED FLOWERS ON A CIRCULAR BASE

For this project we are going to make an elegant accessory — a romantic and wispy flower — from gathered and twisted strips of fabric on a rigid, circular base.

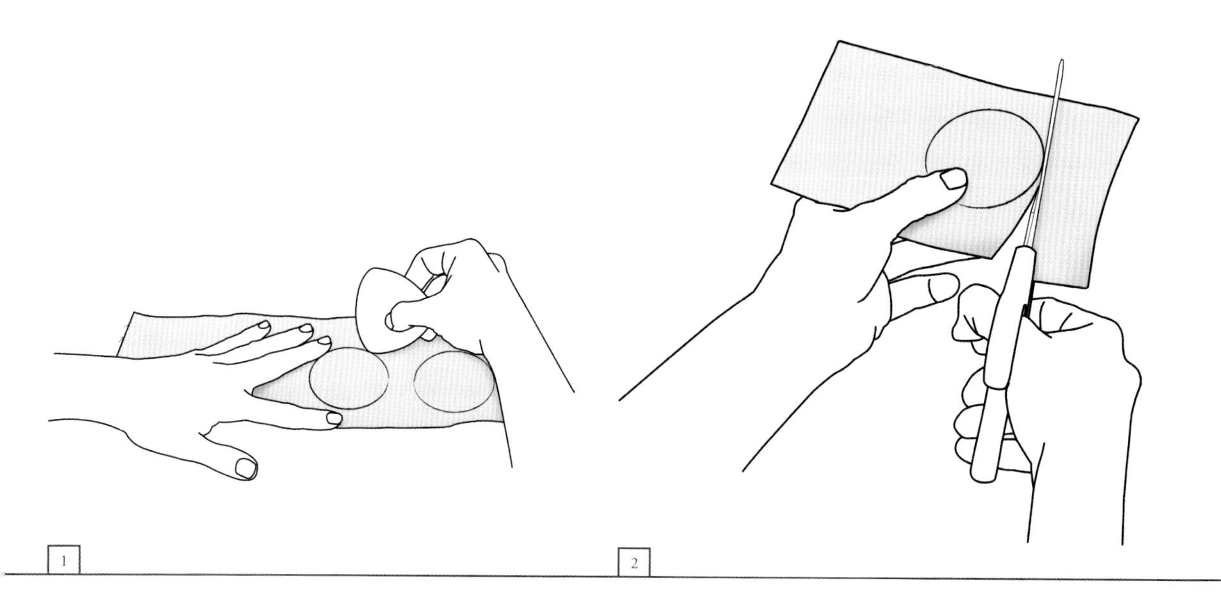

1

2

Use tailor's chalk to draw two 3.5-inch (9 cm) diameter circles on the material that you are going to use, which you have already ironed. It should preferably be quite a thick fabric, like a mid-weight cotton.

Use scissors to cut around the circumference of both circles, making sure that they end up exactly the same.

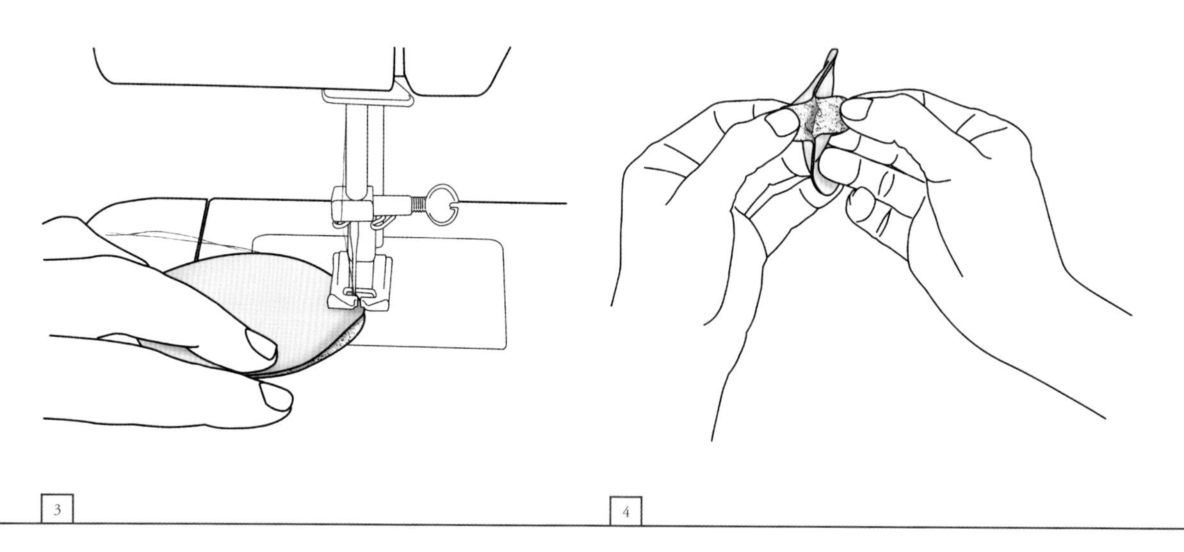

3

4

Put the two circles together so that both right sides are facing inward. Use the sewing machine set to a short stitch to slowly join the circles, sewing at approximately 0.4 inches (1 cm) from the edges until the circle is almost complete. Remember to leave 0.8 inches (2 cm) open so that the piece can be turned the right way out.

Carefully turn the two joined pieces the right way out through the open 0.8 inches (2 cm) for this step. We now have a single circle with hidden seams, and the right side of the fabric facing outward.

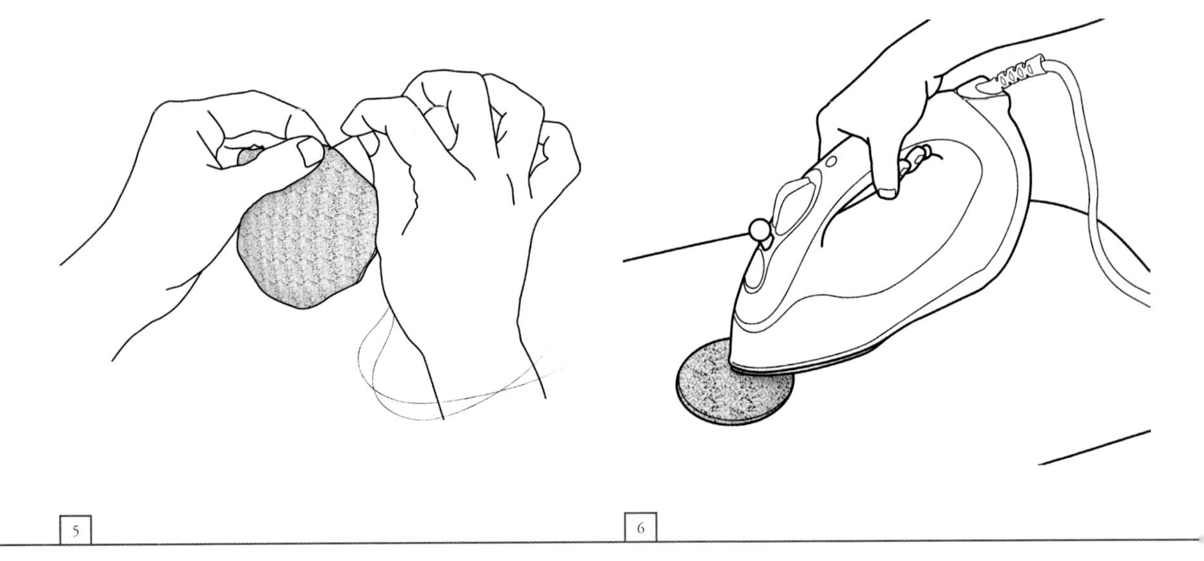

Now, by hand, stitch the 0.8 inches (2 cm) that you left open, folding the edges toward the inside so that the result is a perfectly sewn circle.

Iron the circle well so the shape is perfect.

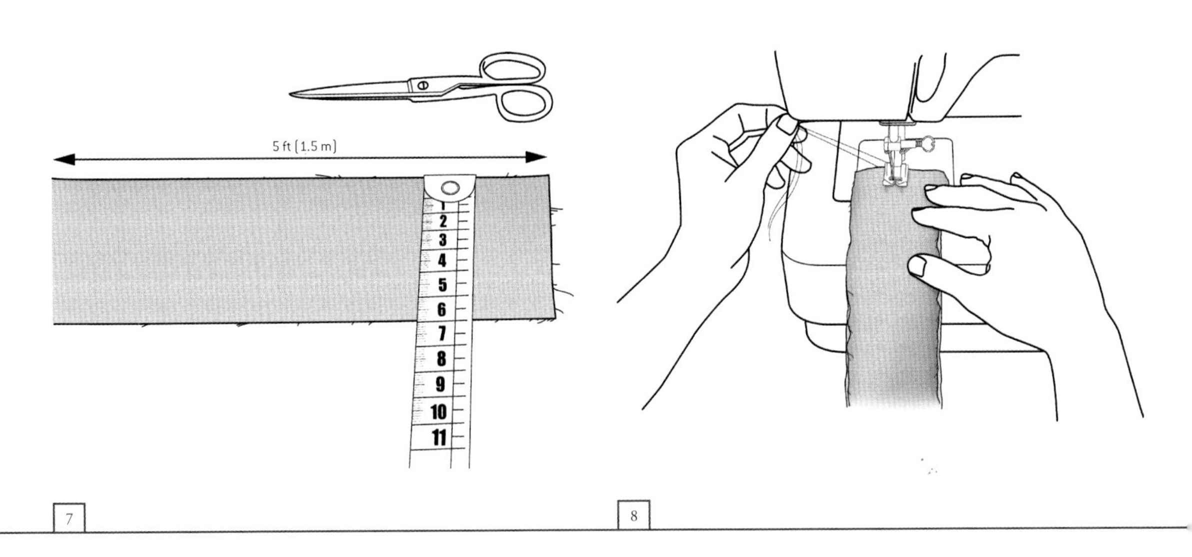

Cut a 2.5-inch-wide (6 cm), 5-foot-long (1.5 m) strip of fabric, preferably something wispy such as georgette or muslin. It is advisable to use this type of fabric because it will be much easier to gather and once the flower is finished the fabric will closely resemble delicate petals.

With the machine set to a long stitch and leaving the first strands of thread quite long, begin to straight stitch the strip right along the middle of its width.

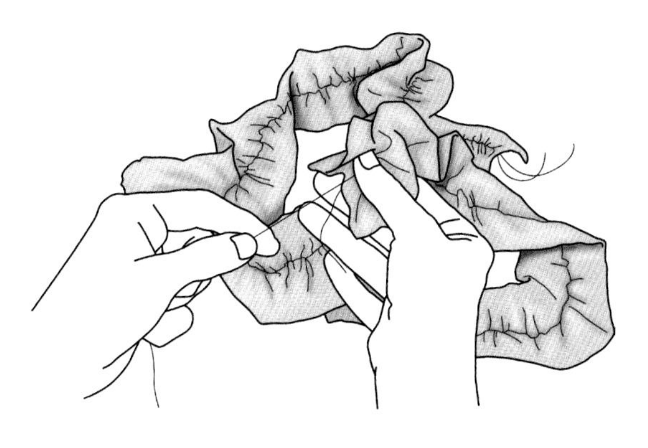

9

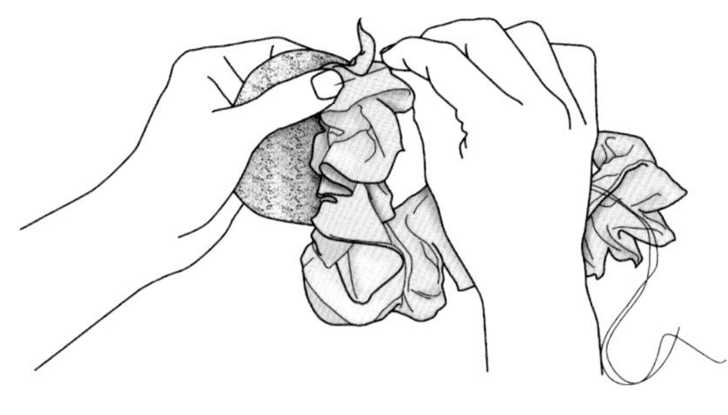

10

After straight stitching along the entire 4-foot (1.5 m) strip, gather it by hand by pulling, with the utmost care, one of the threads that you left long when you straight stitched with the machine. Little by little you'll see how the fabric gathers up easily and softly.

Once the strip has been gathered, make sure it is uniform, with ruffles that are distributed evenly. Its finished length should measure 14 inches (35 cm).

Taking the circle you made earlier, hand sew the gathered strip in a spiral starting from the edges and finishing in the center. Sew the center of the strip, so you will not mistakenly sew any of the ends of the gathered fabric. At this point you should use your creative flair — while you sew, try to make the fabric look like a flower, simulating its shapes.

11

Following the previous steps will give you a flower. Thanks to its rigid and circular base, you can attach the flower to garments either individually as a brooch or in groups, using several different sizes and colors as decoration. This will provide a splash of originality for your garment.

FRILLS INSERTED INTO PLEATS

The end result of this project showcases two different textures and shapes. Basic pleats set off delicate ruffles that, when arranged vertically and horizontally, provide a luxurious detail to accessorize any garment.

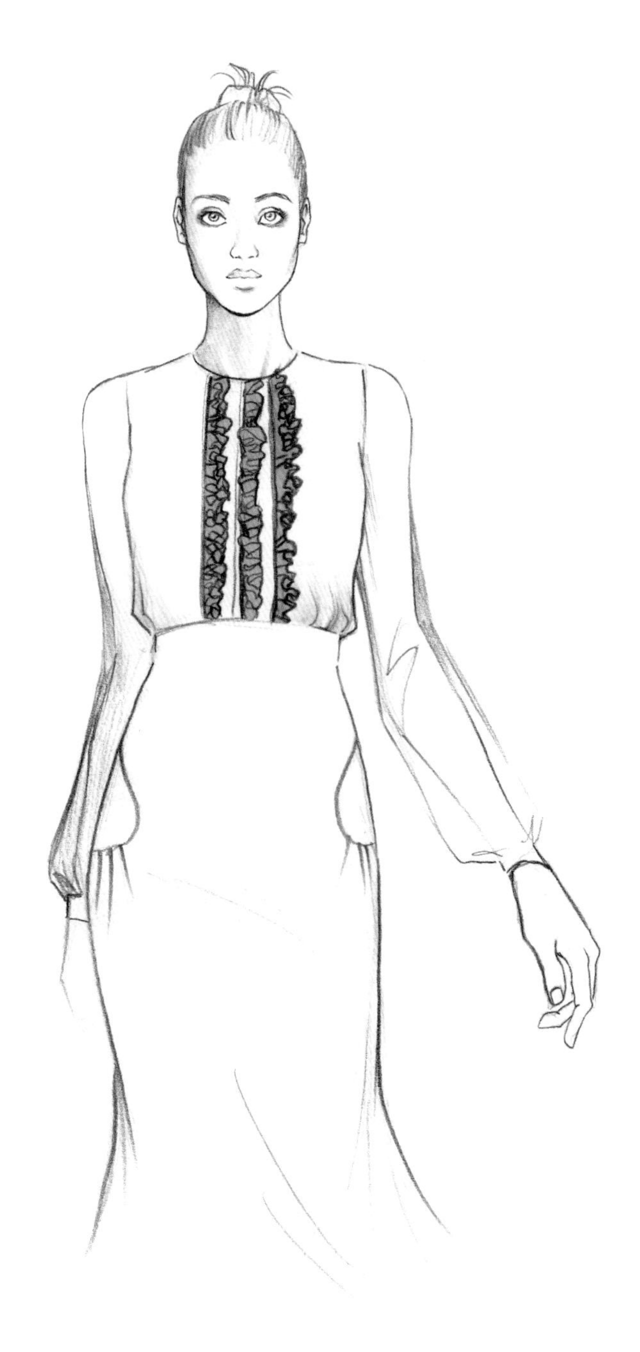

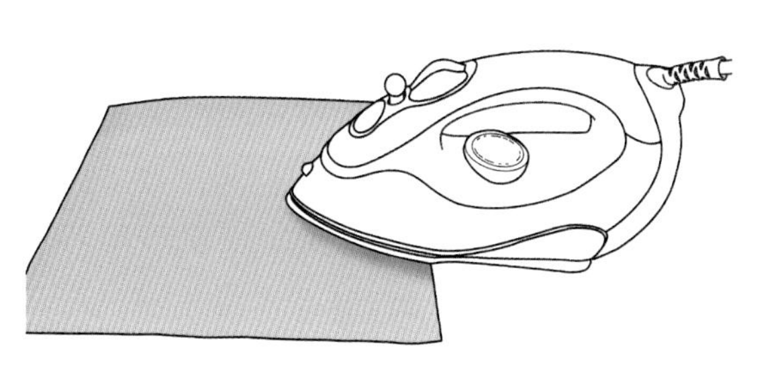

1

Iron a section of the fabric that you are going to use, keeping in mind that this project is ideal for decorating shirts and shirt dresses. It is basically a frill inserted into a pleat; for this reason you should use a light fabric for the ruffled strip, contrasting it with another more rigid one for the pleats, for example a crepe de Chine.

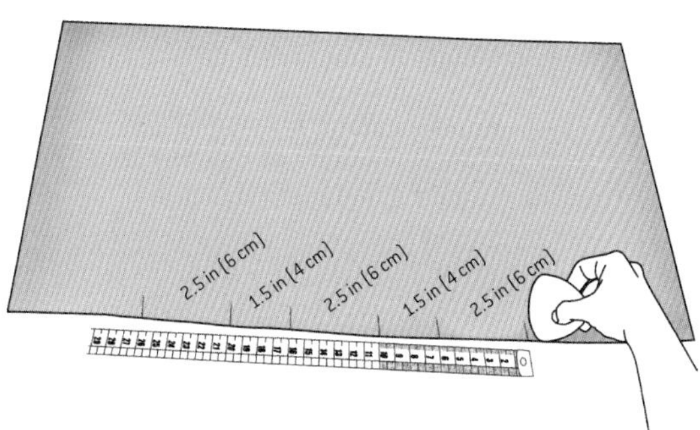

2

Use a ruler and tailor's chalk to mark the upper and lower ends of the material with two small marks, 2.5 inches (6 cm) apart. Leaving a distance of 1.5 inches (4 cm), make another two marks, also 2.5 inches (6 cm) apart. Repeat the process a third time, again leaving 1.5 inches (4 cm) in between.

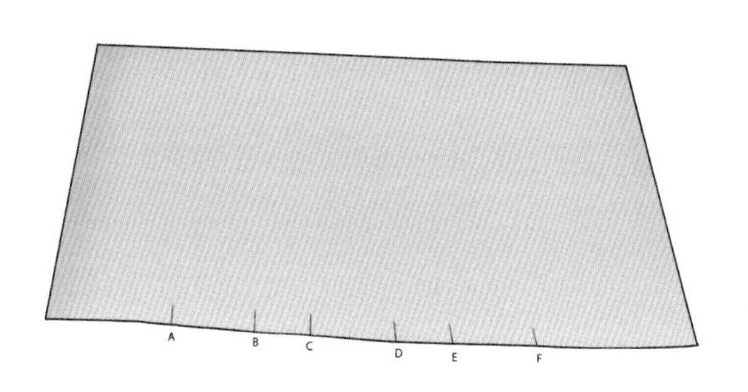

3

Don't forget to make the marks toward the center of the fabric, and bear in mind the measurements of the garment that you are going to make. Remember that these measurements are just for guidance and you can play with different variations based on the garment that you are going to decorate using this project.

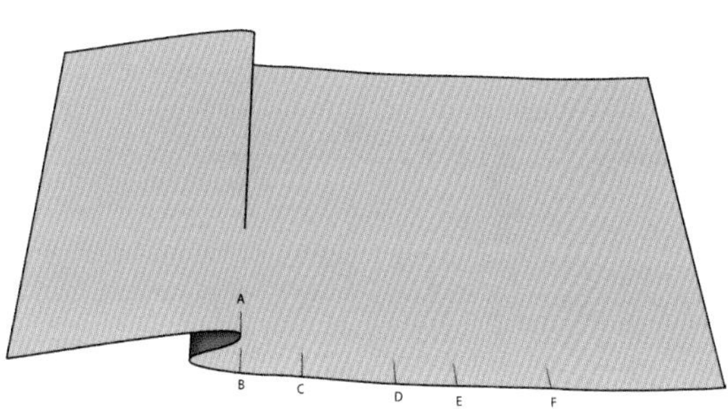

4

Beginning on the left, lift the first parallel mark and fold it so that it lines up with the second.

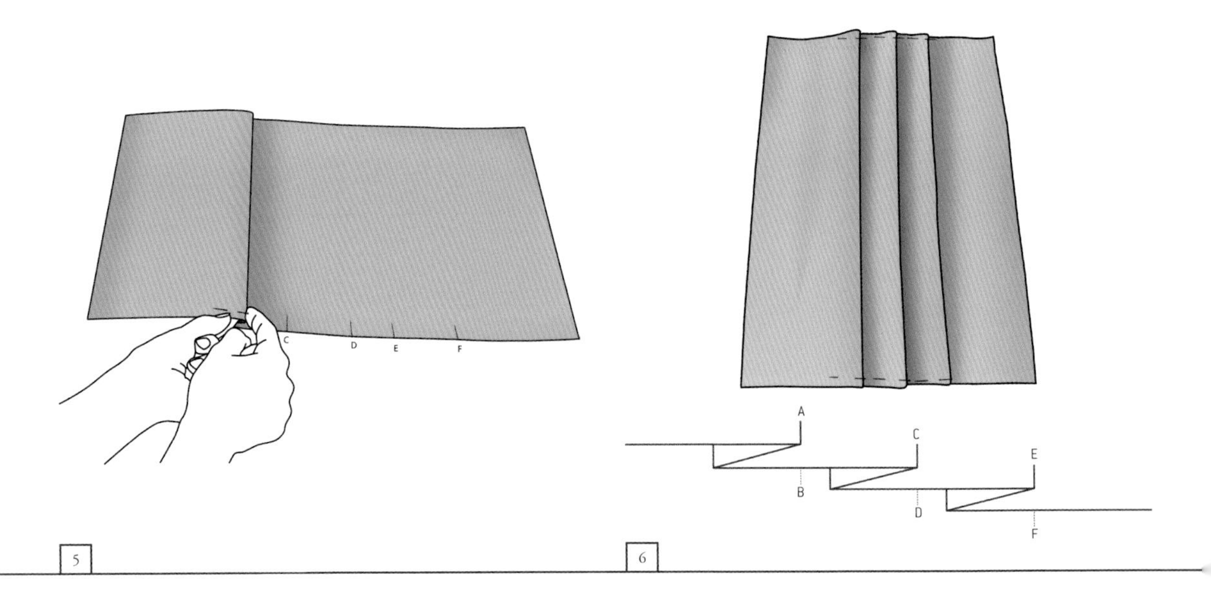

Repeat this process with the third mark, making it line up with the fourth and lastly, the fifth with the sixth. Pin each pleat.

Now you have created three equally sized pleats.

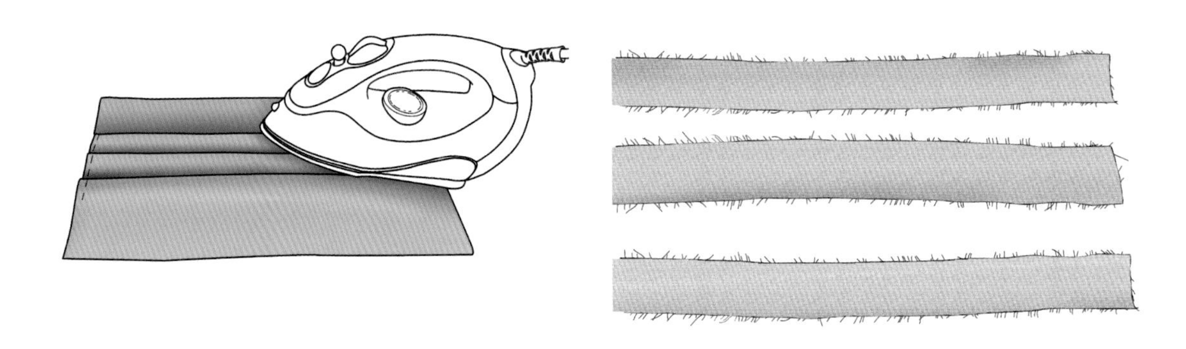

7

Iron the three pleats without removing the pins to make sure that the pleats are well set.

8

Cut strips from a light fabric, such as tulle or muslin; they should be about 1.5 inches (4 cm) wide.

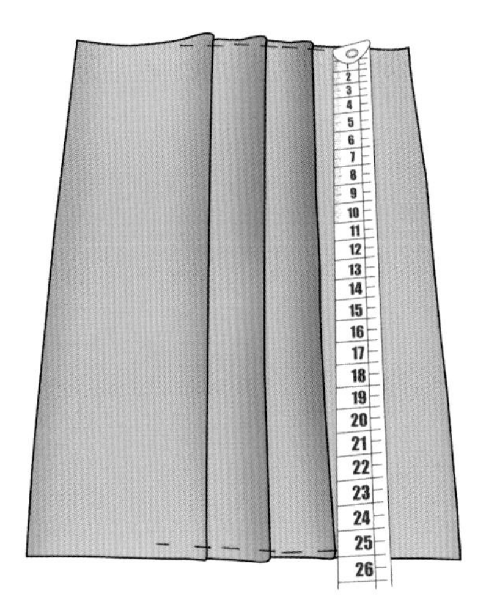

9

To calculate the length of these strips, measure the length of the pleats and multiply this by three. For example, if the length of each pleat is 12 inches (30 cm), you should cut a 35-inch-long (90 cm) strip because when it is ruffled it will be shorter. You can always calculate the measurement you need for making ruffles by multiplying the length of the garment by three.

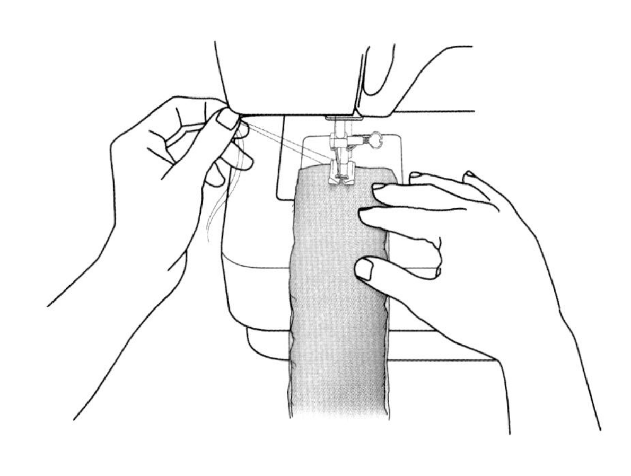

10

Now use the machine to straight stitch the middle of each strip; remember to leave sufficient strands of thread to allow you to gather the strips easily.

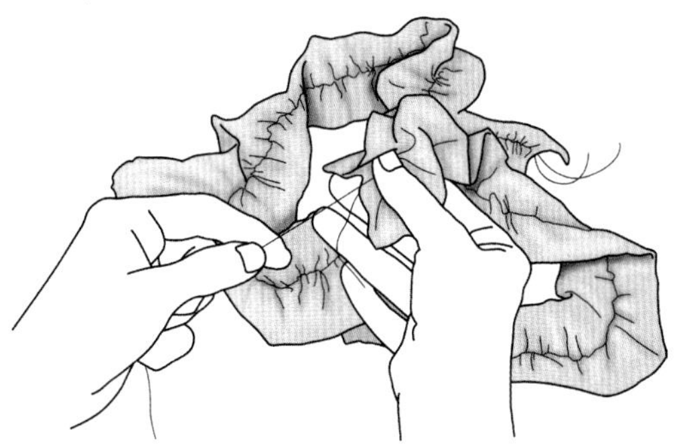

11

Gather the three strips, making sure they are exactly the same length as the pleats.

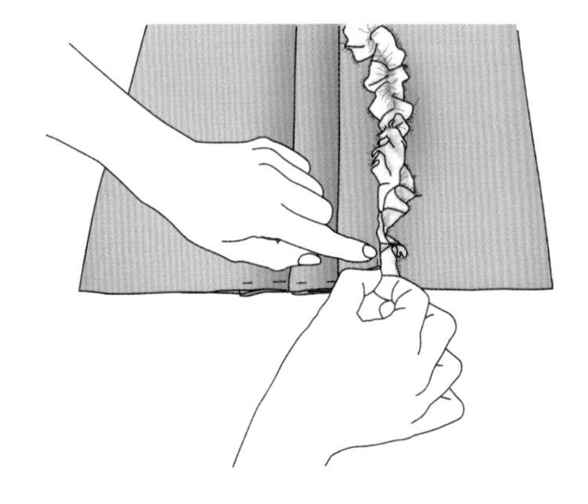

12

Insert the middle of the strips into the inside of the pleats, pinning them in place.

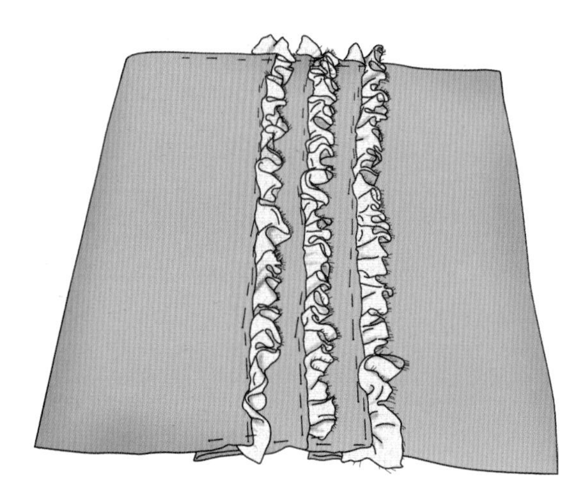

13

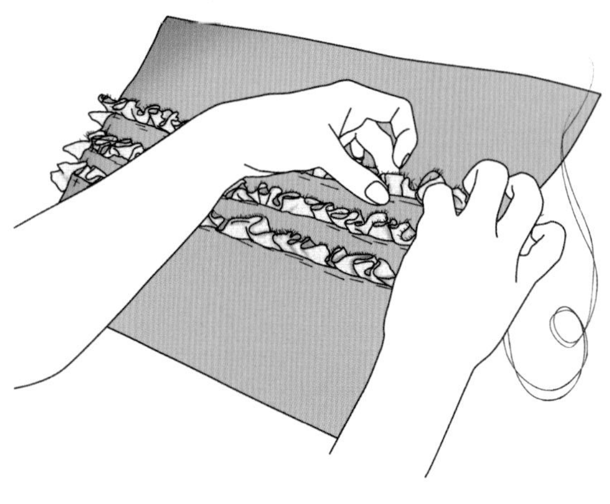

14

This is what the pleats with the ruffles should look like when pinned.

Tack the pleats to the ruffles very carefully, so that only half of the strip protrudes from the pleat.

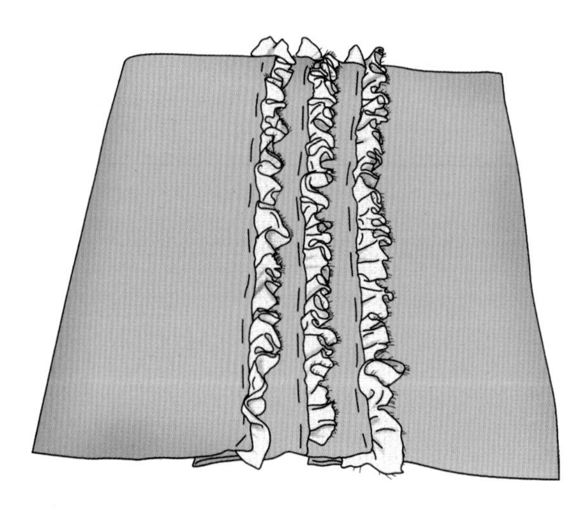

15

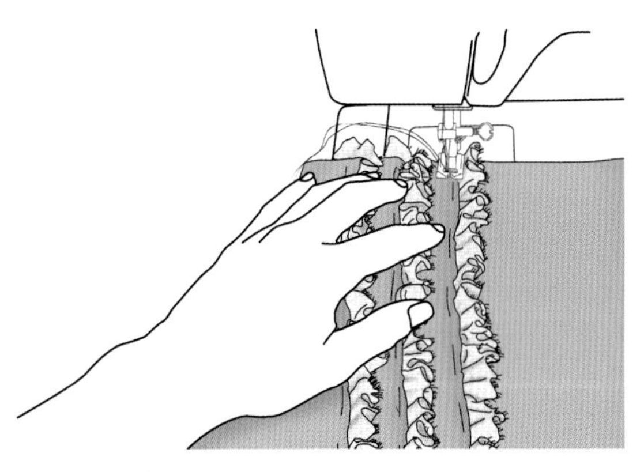

16

This is what the pleats with the ruffles should look like when tacked.

Once the three pleats are tacked, straight stitch them to firmly fasten the gathered strip and the pleated fabric. Carefully removing the tacking will leave you with three ruffles inserted into pleats. You can use them for decorating camisoles, sleeves and even accessories, such as belts.

PLEATS AND RUFFLES COMBINATION FOR NECKLINES

To adorn the most delicate of necklines, try this combination of pleated and ruffled materials. It is sure to add a feminine touch to any outfit.

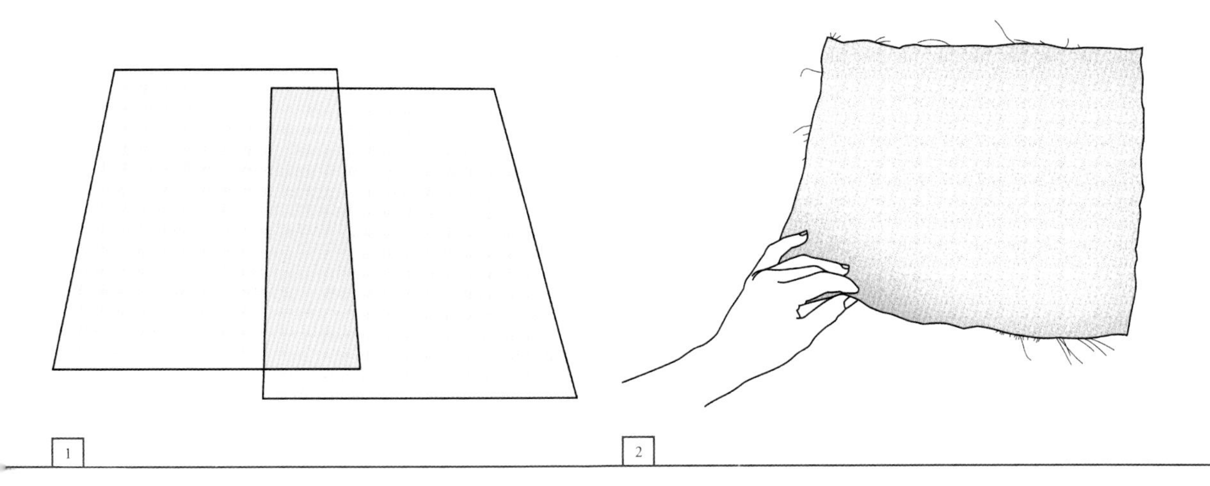

Cut two identical pieces of manila or silk paper along with a piece of fabric with the same measurements.

It is preferable to use silk muslin as this project is ideal for adorning bodices and necklines to give them a delicate and romantic appearance.

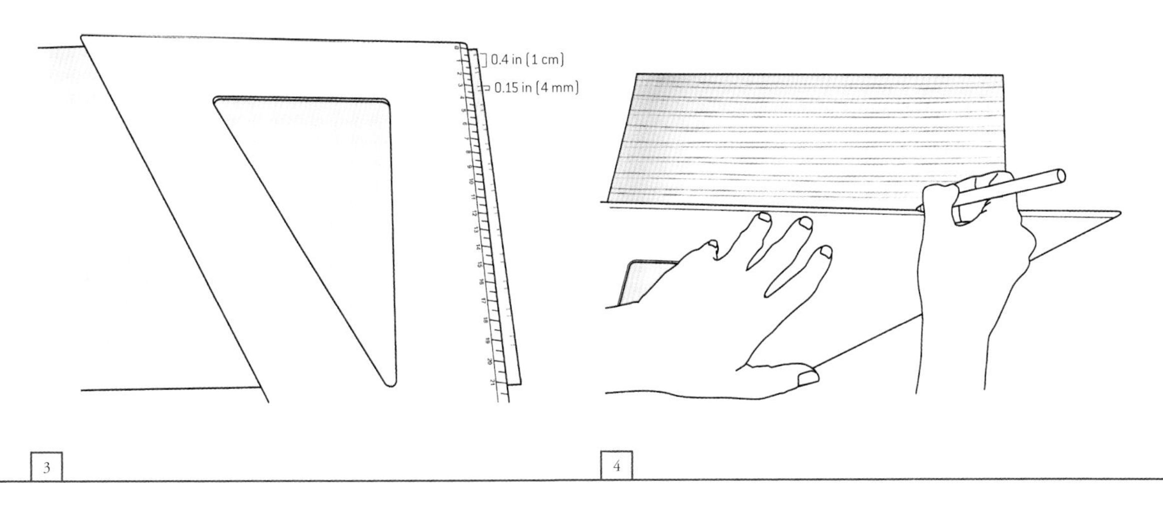

Use a pencil and ruler to draw horizontal marks on both sides (left and right) of one of the pieces of manila paper. The first mark should be 0.4 inches (1 cm) from the upper edge; the second, 0.15 inches (4 mm) away from the first and so on, alternating 0.4 inches (1 cm) and 0.15 inches (4 mm) between lines.

Once you have marked both sides, join the marks with lines, filling the entire surface of the paper.

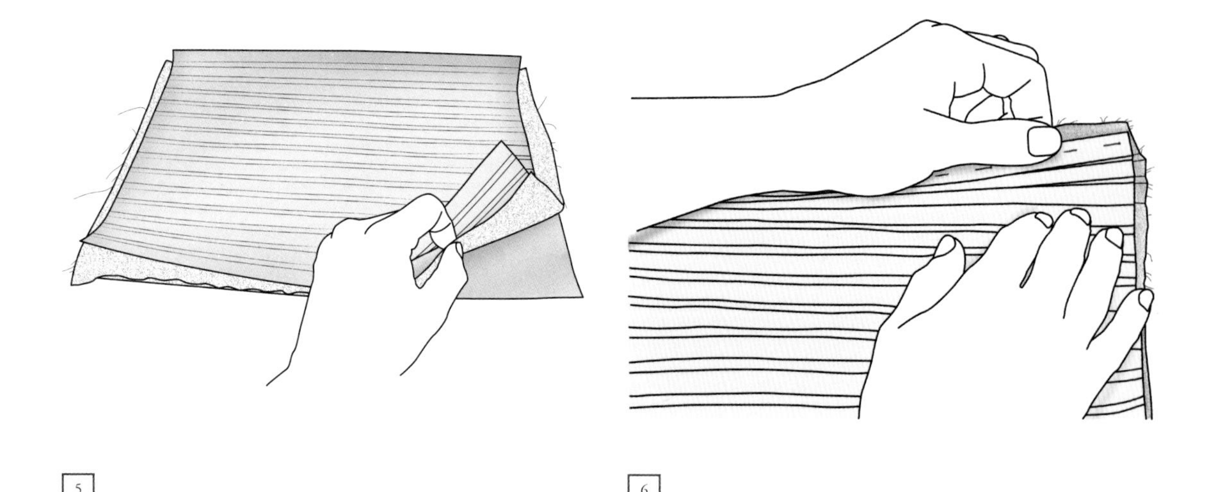

5

Use the unlined piece of paper as the base, place the piece of fabric on top of it and then place the manila paper marked with the lines on top of them both. Pin the three pieces together.

6

Slowly fold the lines to form pleats — fold line one over line two, line three over line four and so on. In this case, when you have a 0.15-inch (4 mm) pleat that rests on 0.4 inches (1 cm), the result will be a small 0.25-inch (6 mm) pleat.

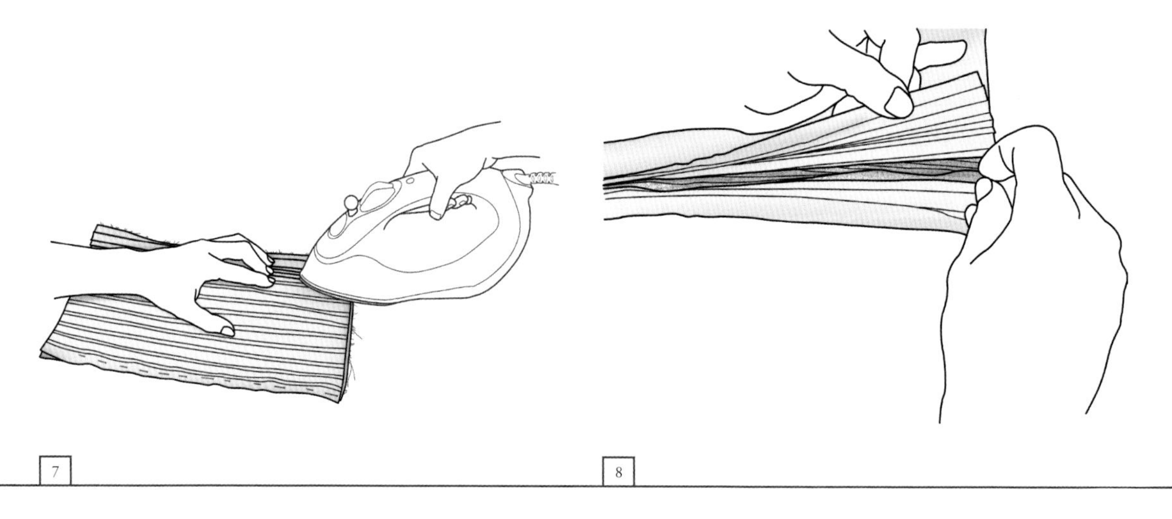

7

As you are folding lines and forming pleats, iron them carefully so that the pleats set well.

8

When you have folded all of the lines, carefully separate the paper sections from the fabric.

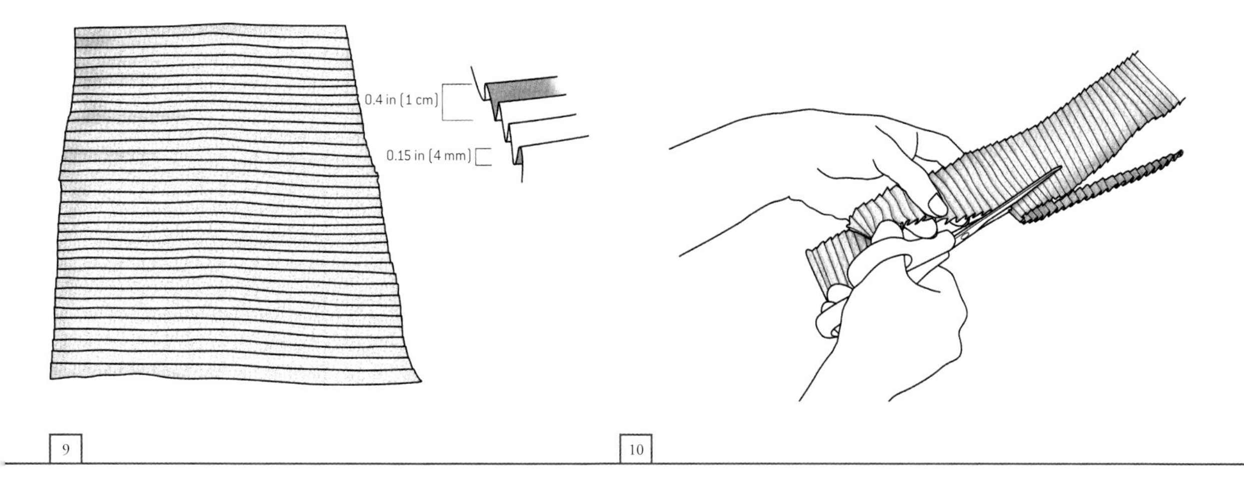

You now have a fully pleated section of fabric. Remember that folding your lines neatly, keeping the correct distances between them, will give you a better result.

Carefully cut the fabric into 2-inch-wide (5 cm) strips; you will probably get at least three strips from the first section.

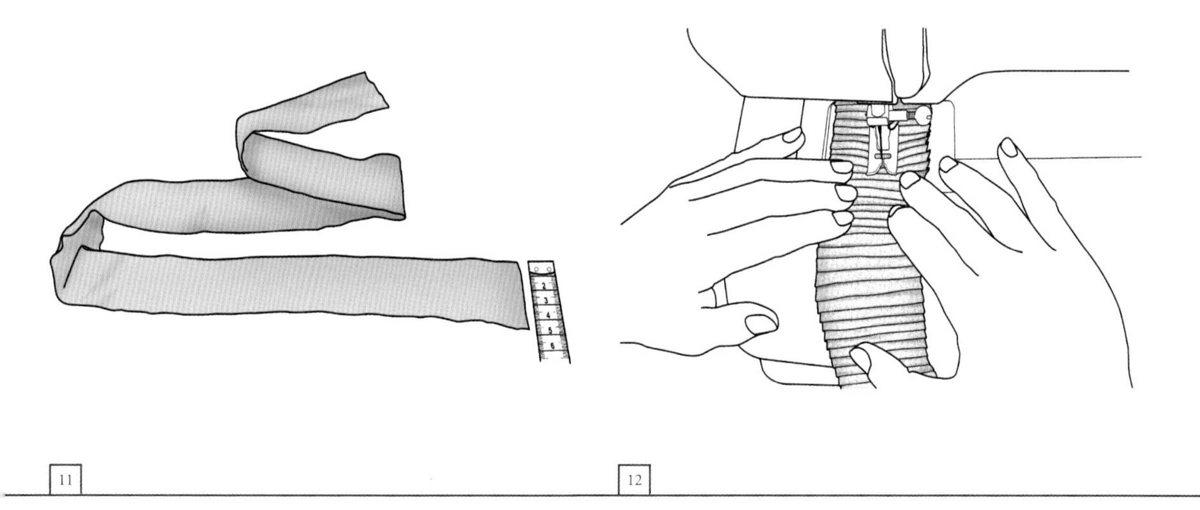

Cut identical 2-inch-wide (5 cm) strips from smooth fabric, preferably the same texture (but a different color would be fine). They should be at least three times longer than the length of the pleated strip. These strips will be gathered, so they must be longer as they will be shortened by gathering.

Now straight stitch the pleated strip right down the middle of its width and along its entire length. You must be very careful not to open out the pleats — hold the strip with both hands and straight stitch it slowly. The result should be as perfect as possible and the straight stitch must be equal on all of the pleats.

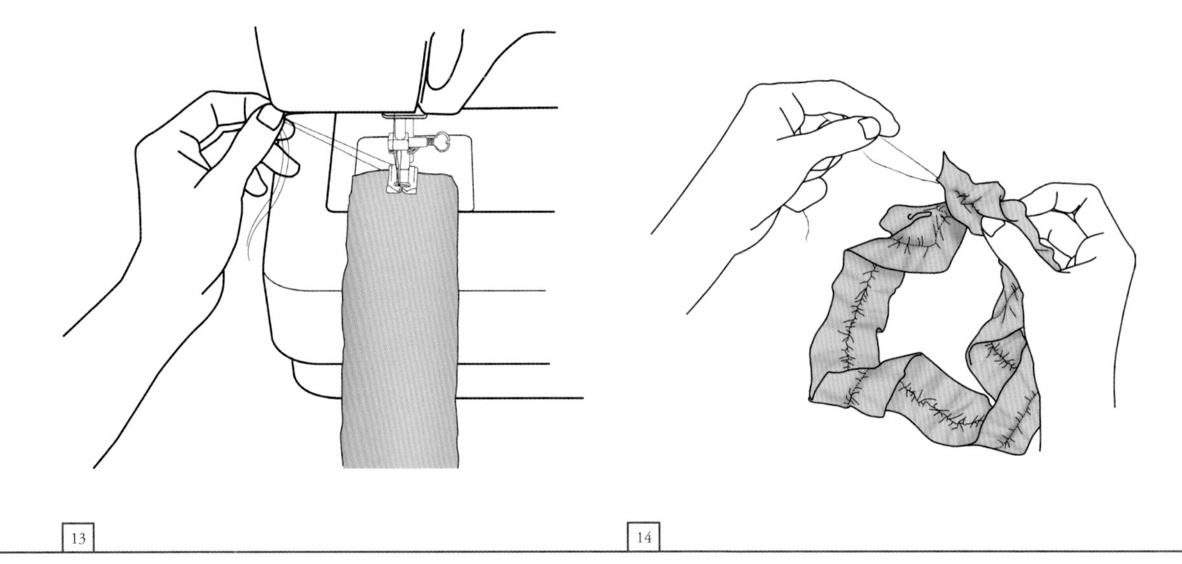

13

Take the strip of smooth fabric and straight stitch along the middle of its width, with a long stitch. You should leave the first strands of thread sufficiently long enough to use for gathering the strip.

14

After straight stitching along the entire length of the smooth material, gather it by hand by pulling the strands of thread that you left longer. Try to make the ruffle soft and uniform, and ensure that once it is finished its length is the same as the pleated piece.

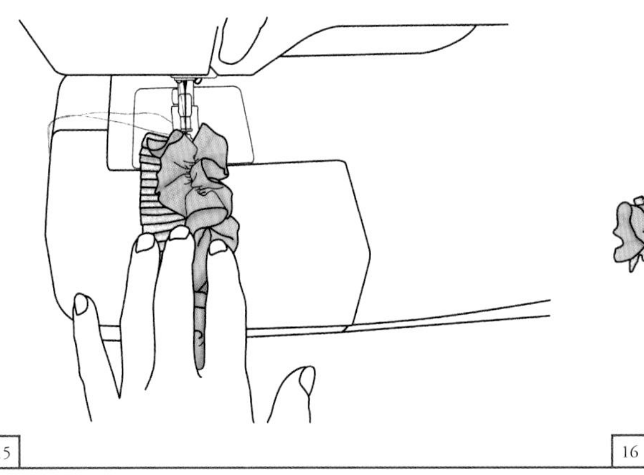

15

When you've finished the pleated strip and the ruffled strip, join them with a short straight stitch on the sewing machine. Place the entire ruffled strip in the right-hand end by lining it up with the right-hand end of the pleated strip so that once they are joined with the straight stitch, half of the pleated strip will peek out from the surface of the ruffle.

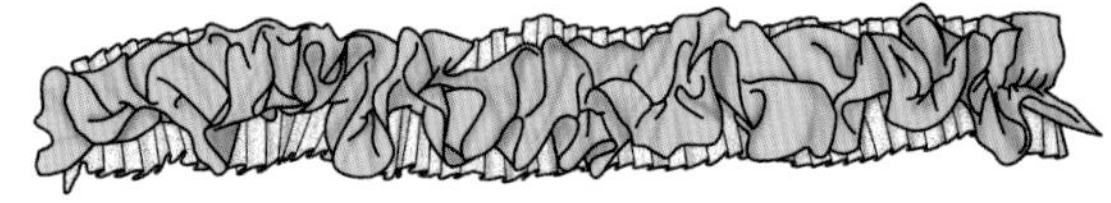

16

Calculate the length of the neckline that you are going to decorate and make the necessary amount of strips to cover it, joining them together.

PLEATS AND RUFFLES INSERTED INTO A NECKLINE

Follow the previous steps, using enough strips to go around the neckline. By placing them exactly between seams in the neckline you will obtain an original finish made up of finely pleated strips combined with romantic ruffles.

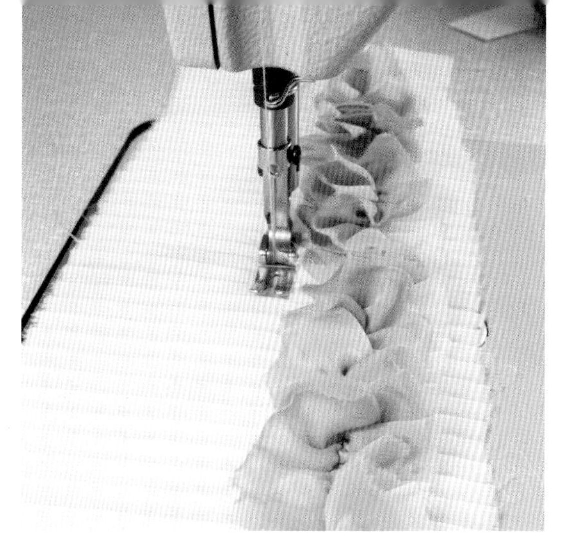

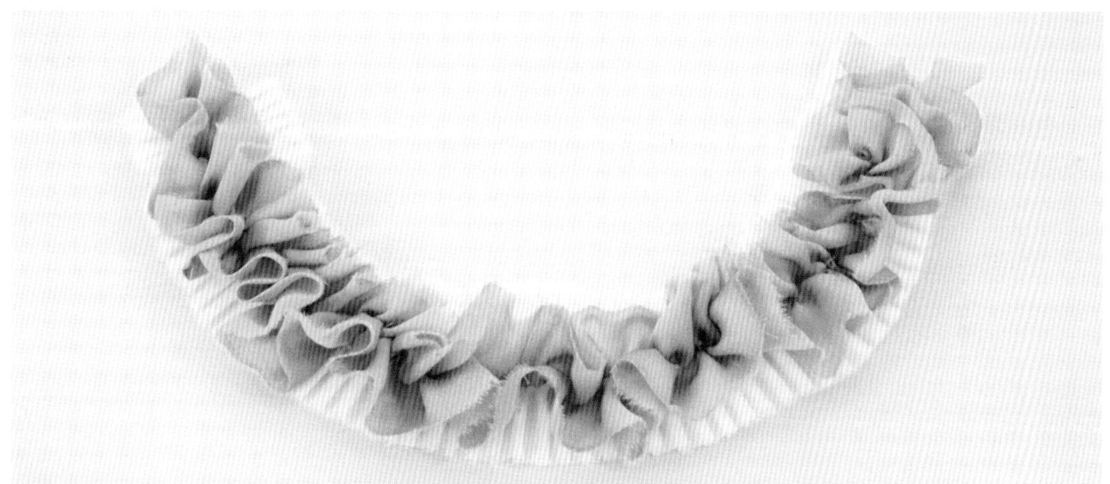

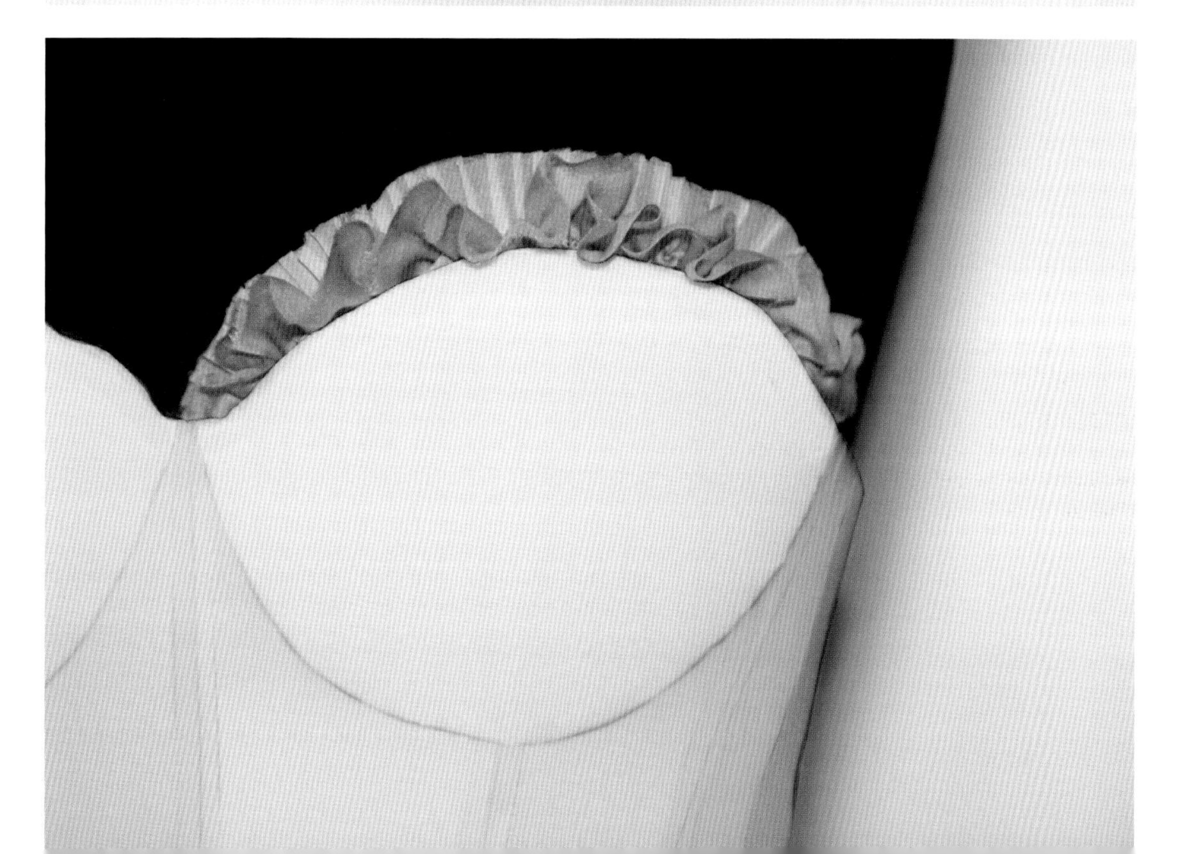

GODET PLEATS WITH TULLE RUFFLES

Godets can be used to adjust the volume of a garment. If we decorate them with delicately ruffled strips of pretty fabric, the result is truly original. For inspiration, think of a flamenco dress.

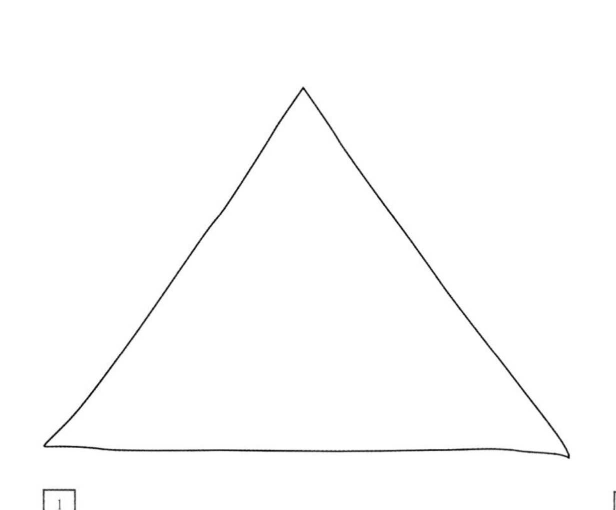

On brown paper or pattern card, trace the actual dimensions of a godet or flounce for the garment that will be made and carefully cut it out with scissors. In this project we are going to show you step-by-step how to assemble a single godet — repeat all the steps for each one of the godets that will give shape to the skirt.

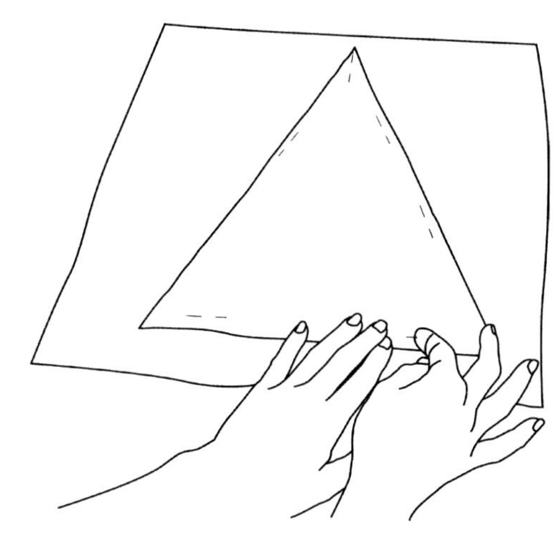

Place the pattern on the fabric and pin them together.

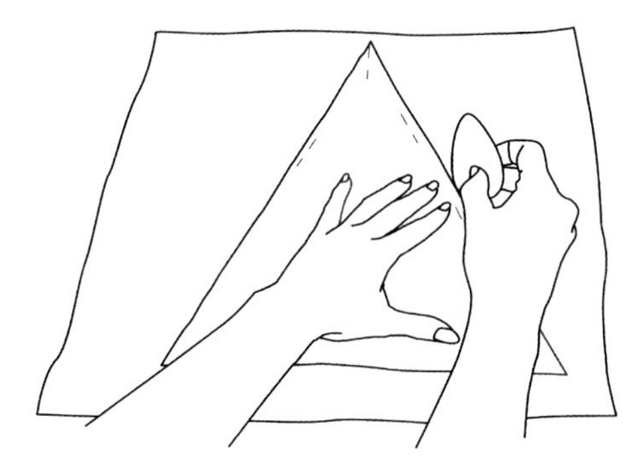

Mark the outline of the godet on the fabric with tailor's chalk.

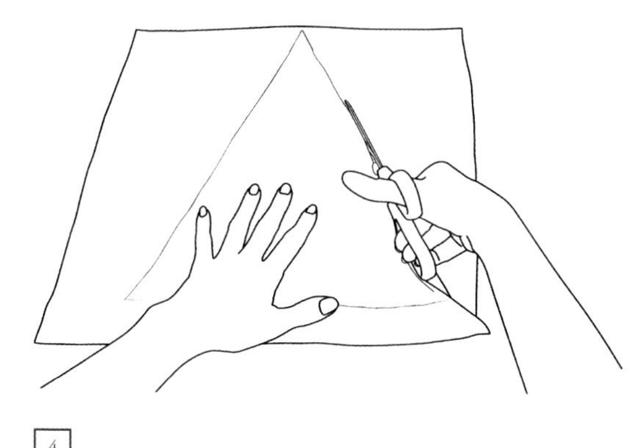

Carefully cut around the outline of the godet with scissors.

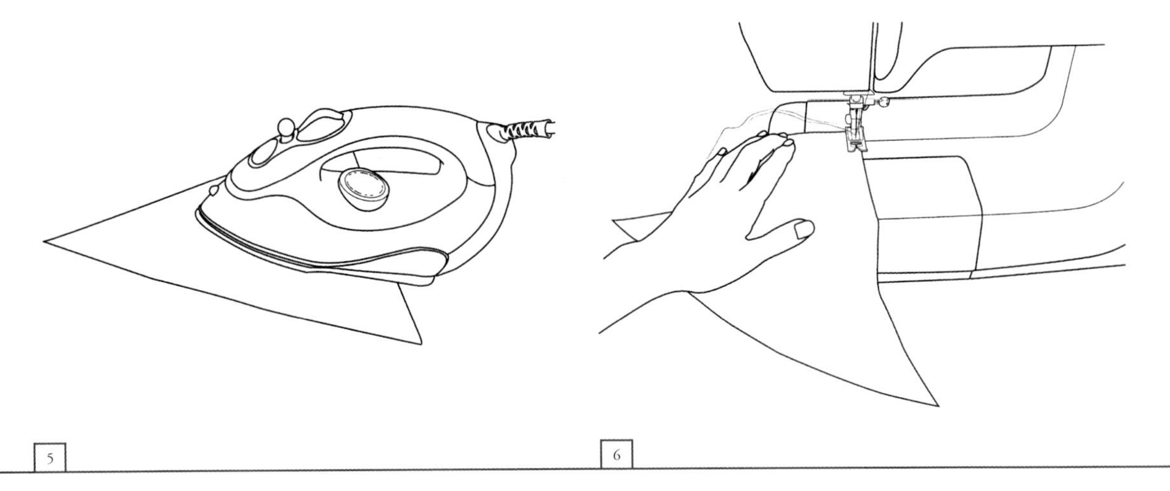

5

Iron the godet well after cutting it and finish the actual bottom of the garment, using the machine to make a small hem. This hem is the base of the triangle.

6

Take a section of tulle in the required color and begin pleating it following steps three to nine of the Pleats and Ruffles Combination project on page 60. As indicated in these steps, cut and pleat some strips, which, when joined, form one piece measuring the same as the combined length of the two equal sides of the triangle (multiplied by three, as it will be shorter when gathered).

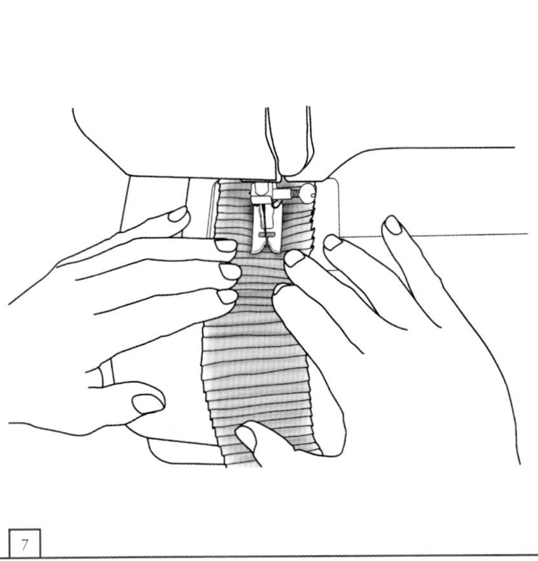

7

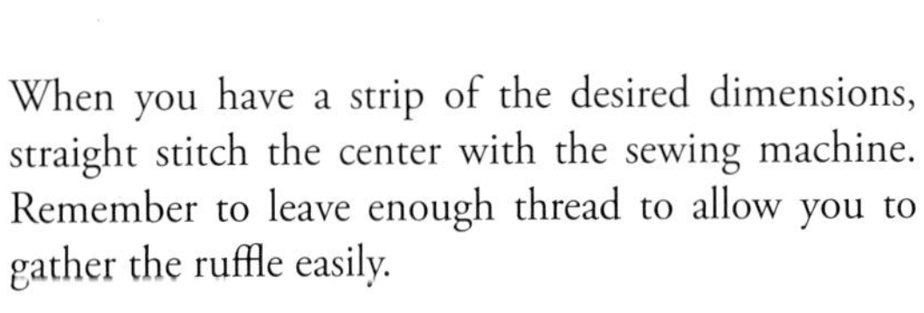

When you have a strip of the desired dimensions, straight stitch the center with the sewing machine. Remember to leave enough thread to allow you to gather the ruffle easily.

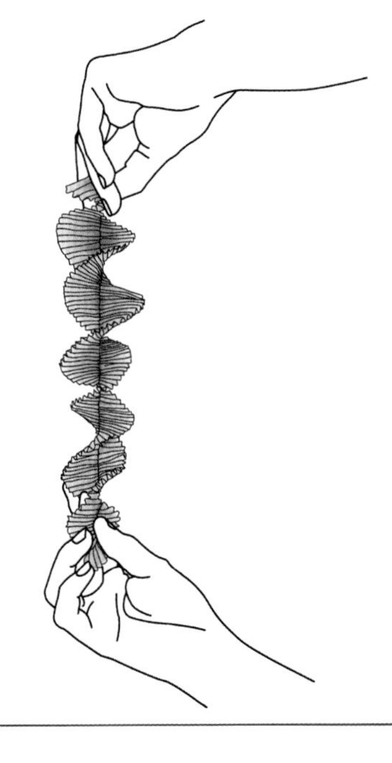

8

Slowly gather the strips of pleated tulle with both hands. Here you are going to gather over pleats, which is more difficult than a simple ruffle. Twist the strip with your fingers to give it an original, cork-screw look.

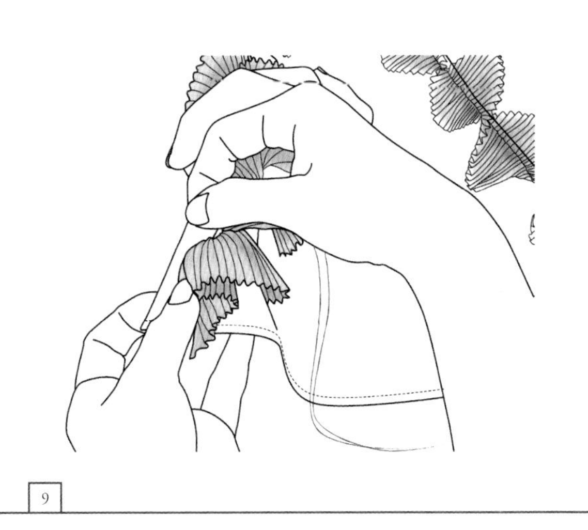

Leaving at least 0.4 inches (1 cm) for the seam that will join the godet to the skirt, sew the tulle strip on the two equal sides of the triangle with strong stitches.

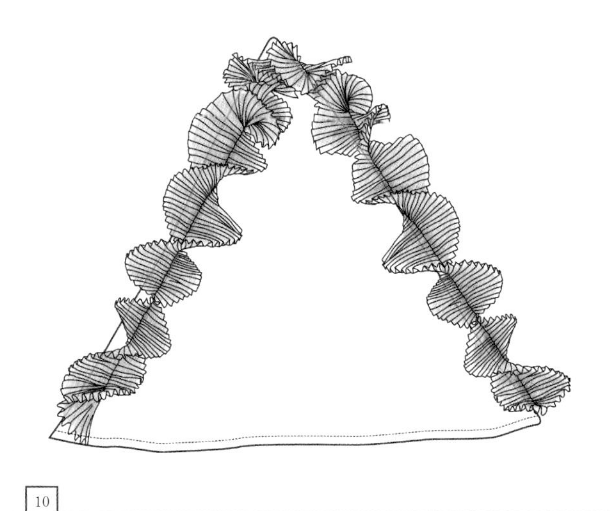

Leave the base of the triangle free.

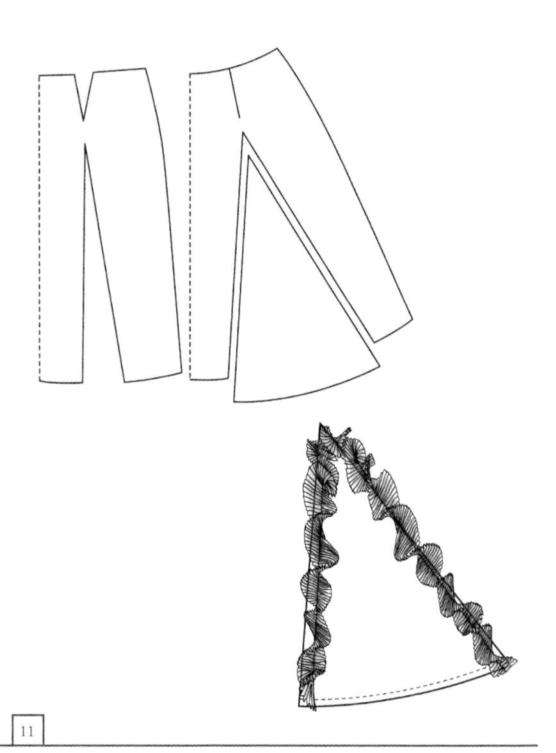

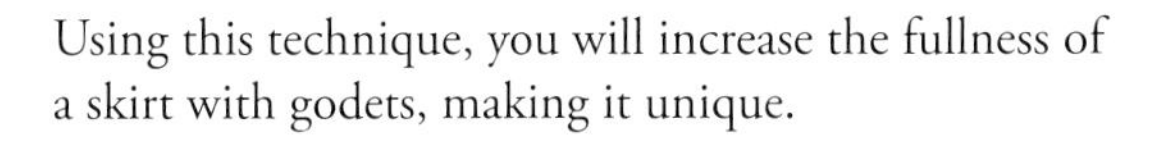

Using this technique, you will increase the fullness of a skirt with godets, making it unique.

LOUIS XV JABOT

This fun jabot is a twist on the Versailles classic. It can be used to accessorize any shirt, whether it be made from a classic material or a modern denim.

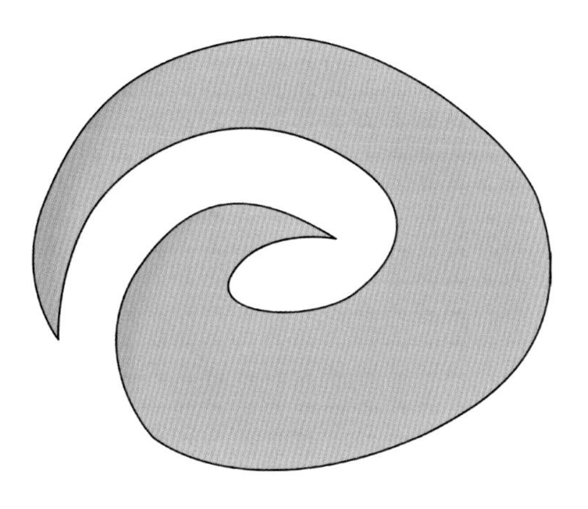

1

Mark a spiral on brown paper or pattern card; it should be wider at the center. Then proceed to cut around the outline. In this case, we have traced a spiral onto a 7-inch (18 cm) diameter circle.

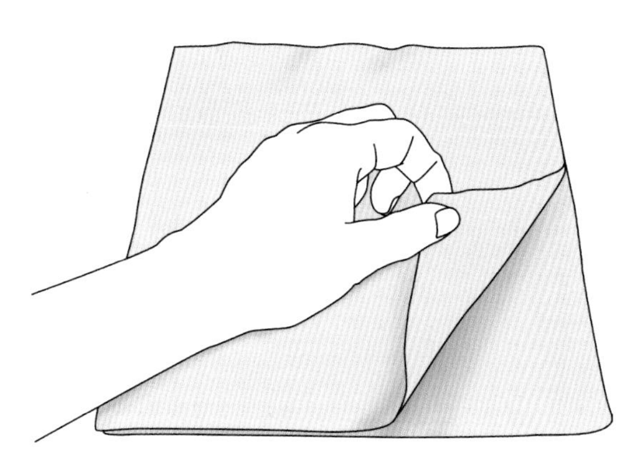

2

Cut and iron your fabric. You will need two pieces of fabric that are exactly the same.

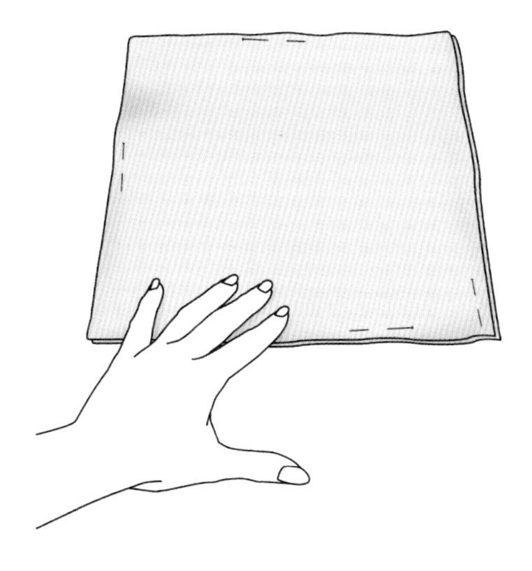

3

Place the two sections of fabric one above the other, and pin them together so that they are perfectly aligned and all the ends are together.

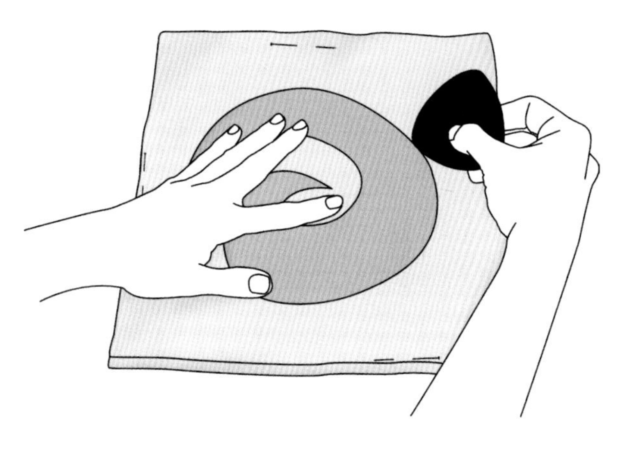

4

Place the spiral pattern on the fabric and mark its outline with tailor's chalk.

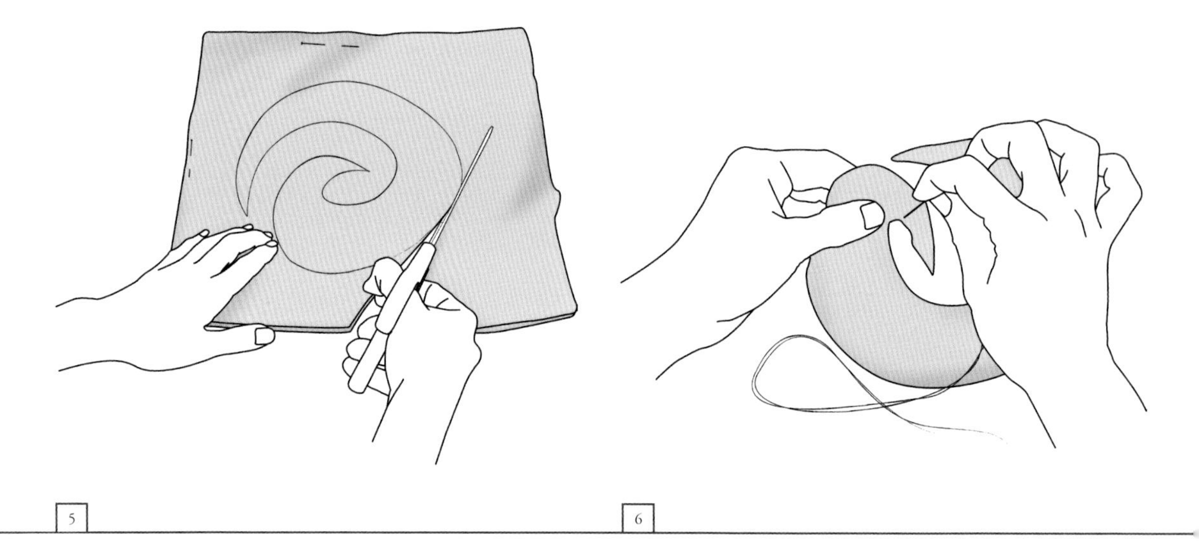

5

6

Carefully cut the spiral with scissors, using the chalk lines as a guide and avoiding imperfections.

With needle and thread, use large stitches to tack the inside of the spiral. Do this with a thread in a color that contrasts with that of the fabric to avoid problems when it is time to remove the threads.

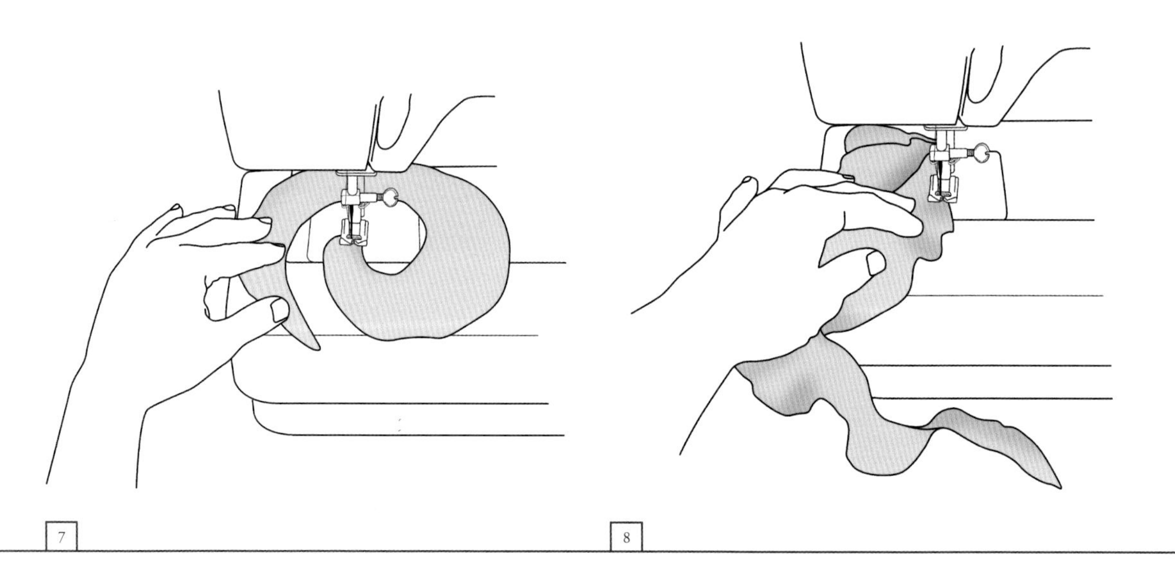

7

8

Join the two fabrics with the sewing machine, using the tacking stitches for guidance. When you have finished joining the two pieces, remove the tacking stitches; they are no longer needed.

You should then finish the jabot with the sewing machine, making a small zigzag straight stitch around all the edges.

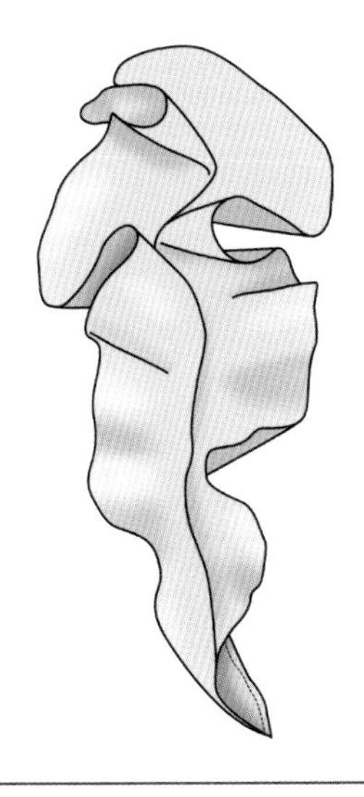

9

When you have sewn the two pieces, you will get this shape.

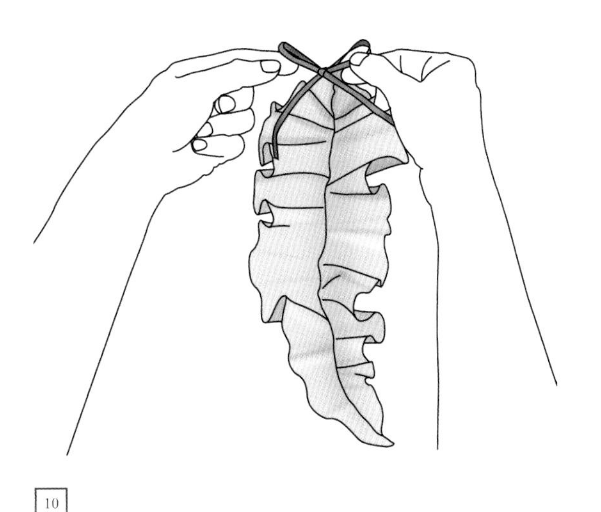

10

Take a satin ribbon of the same shade, approximately 0.2 inches (5 mm) wide, tie it into a bow and sew it with a needle and thread to the upper part of the piece.

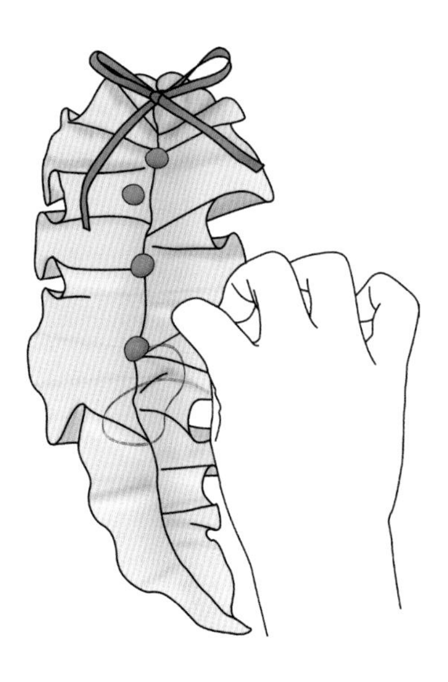

11

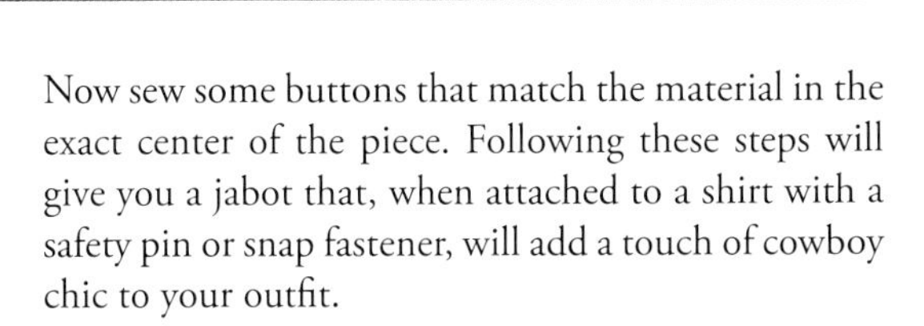

Now sew some buttons that match the material in the exact center of the piece. Following these steps will give you a jabot that, when attached to a shirt with a safety pin or snap fastener, will add a touch of cowboy chic to your outfit.

FRAYED FABRIC ROSES

This project uses fraying to play with fabric's natural tendency to rip. Fabric strips sewn into spirals are transformed into frayed flowers, which are great for giving clothes a quaint, rustic look.

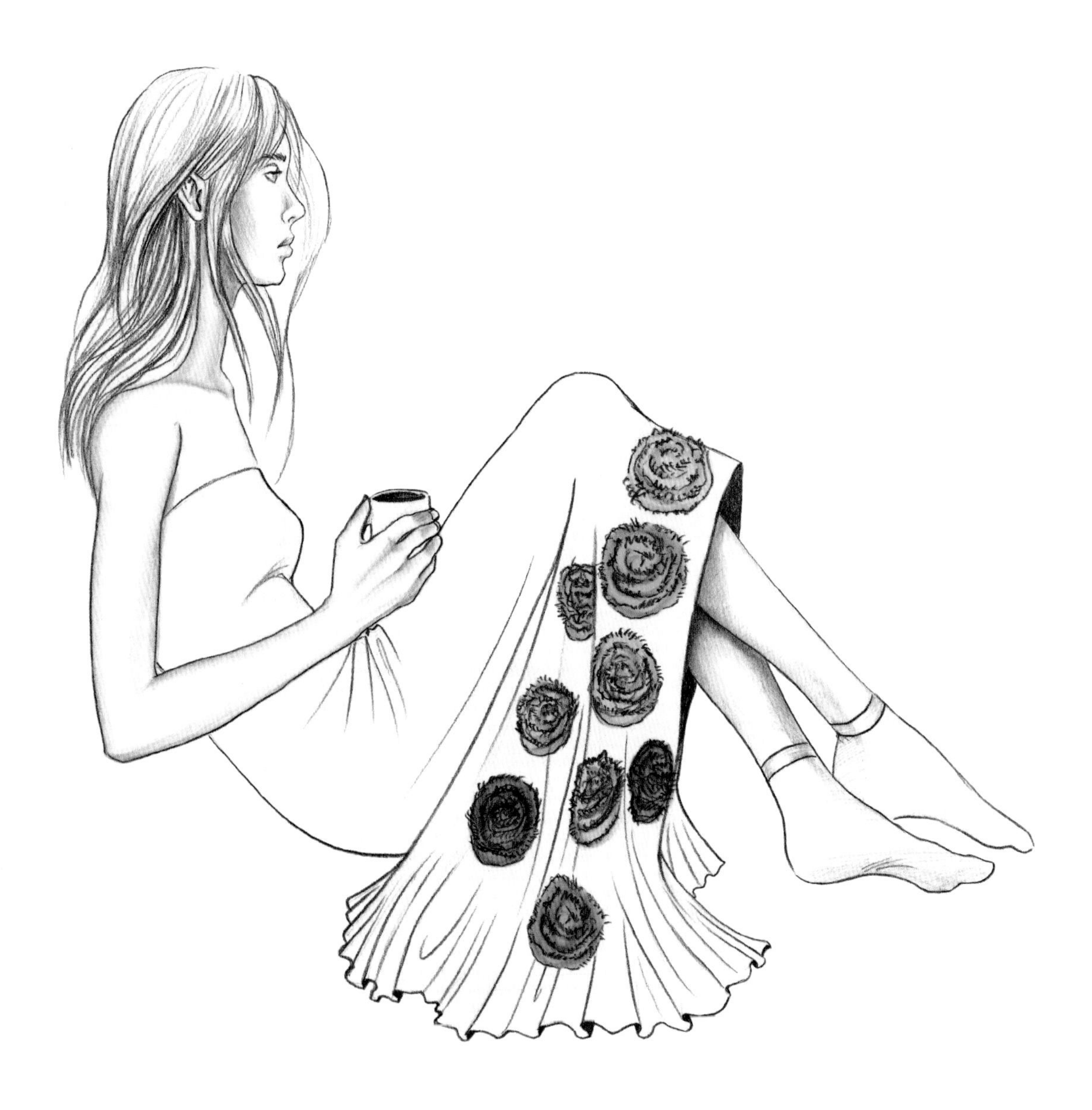

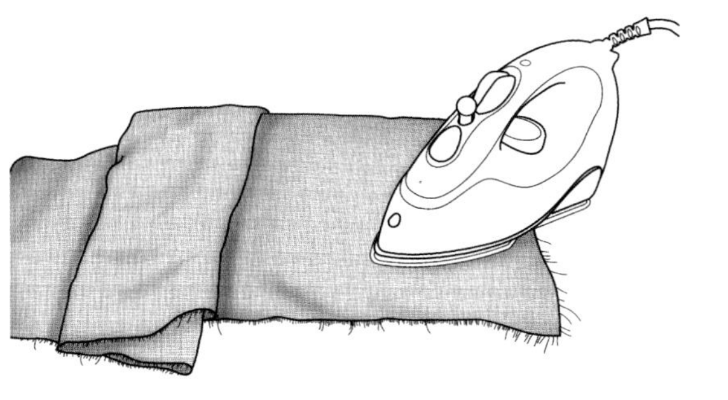

1

Cut and iron the fabric that you are going to use. The fabric should be wispy and should tear easily, since most of the charm of this project is its frayed effect.

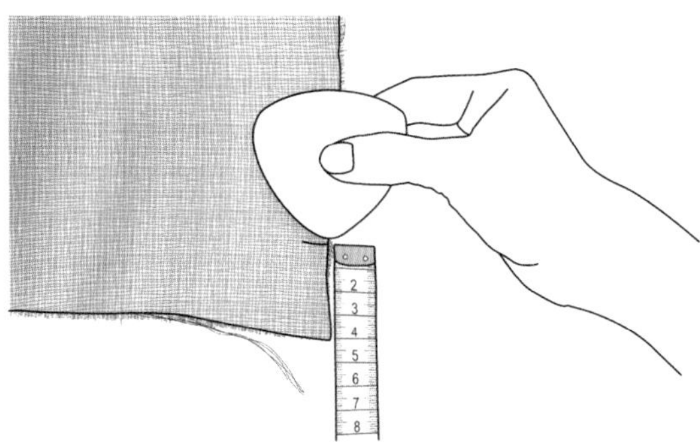

2

Use tailor's chalk to make a small mark on the fabric, about 1.5 inches (4 cm) from the edge.

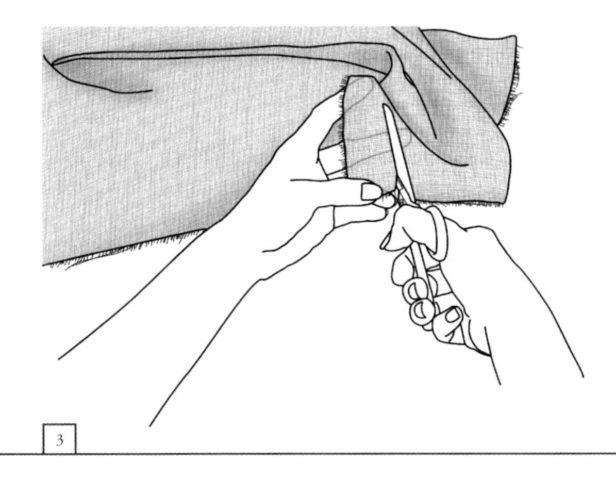

3

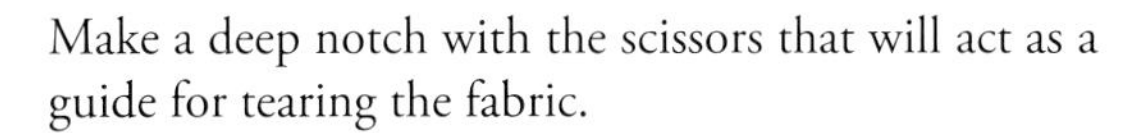

Make a deep notch with the scissors that will act as a guide for tearing the fabric.

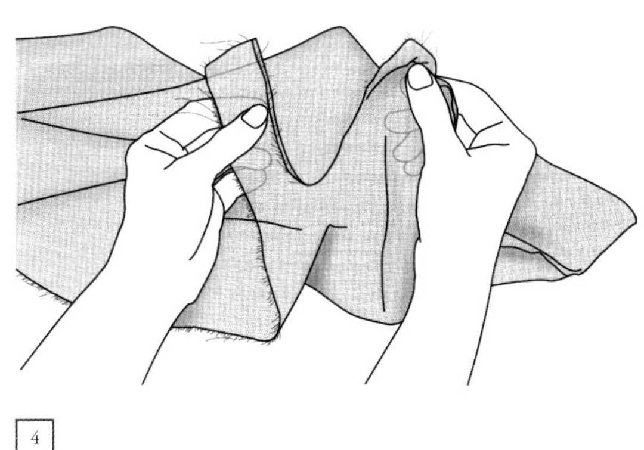

4

Firmly, using both hands, rip the material from the marked notch. This method gives a straight and uniform tear.

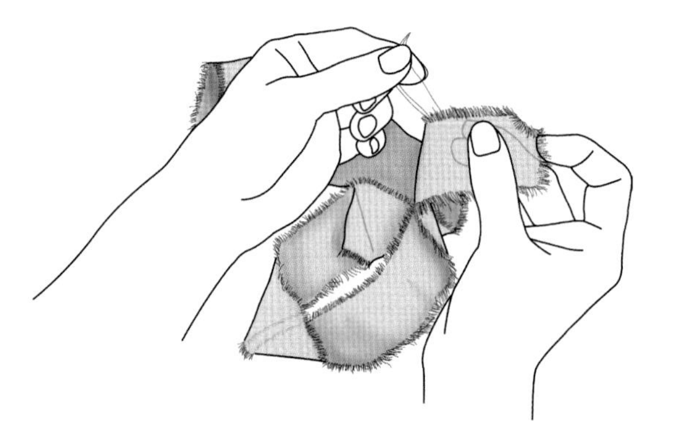

5

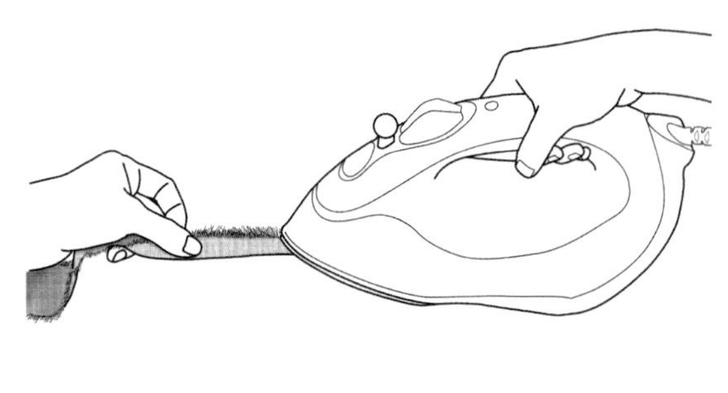

6

Next, fray both sides of the strip. You can do this by carefully pulling on the threads by hand or with the help of a pin.

After fraying the strip, fold it in half and iron along the center of its width.

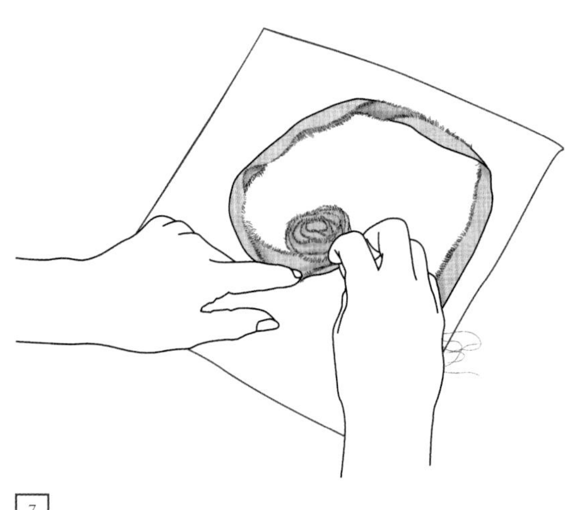

7

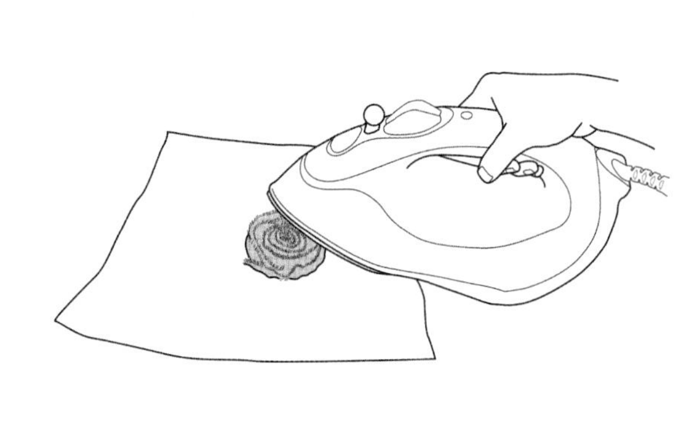

8

With small, strong stitches, hand sew the spiral that will form the rose along the center of the strip. Though you could sew it to a small piece of fabric that could then be sewn onto the garment, it is advisable to skip this step and sew it directly onto the garment for a more beautiful, artisanal look.

Once the spiral is finished, crush and steam it with an iron. You now have a beautiful rose accessory to decorate items such as the hem of a wedding dress.

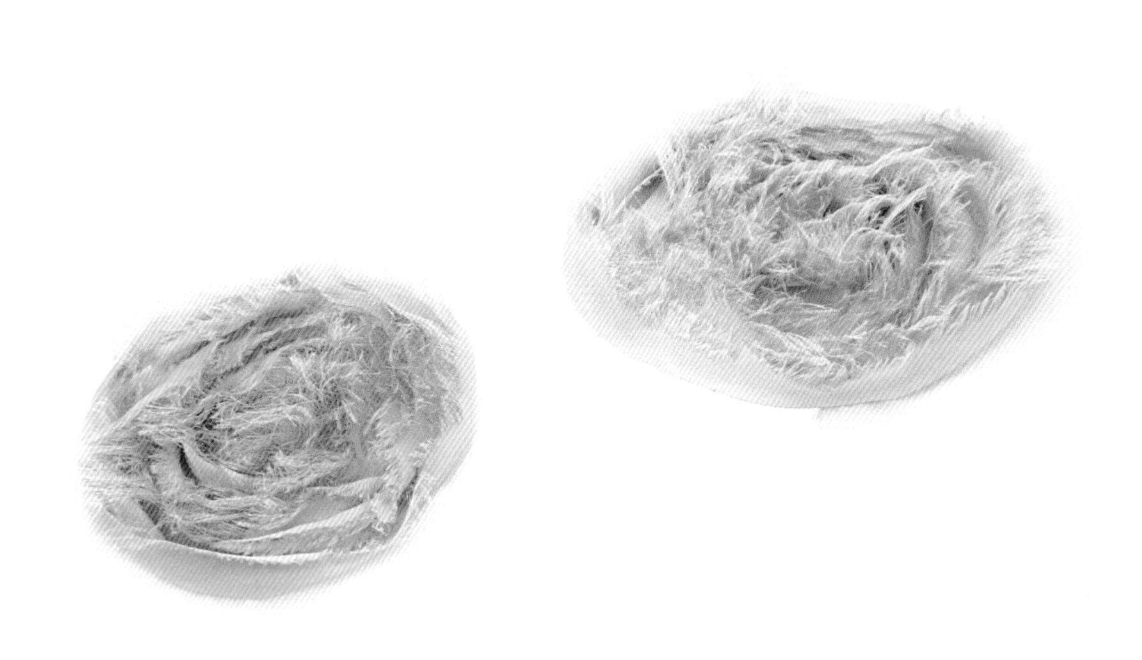

FRILLED BELT

Adding frills made from different fabrics to the edges of a lined sash, and knotting it at the back, will grace your waist with a distinctive belt without the need for buckles and rivets. This subtle and dreamy project achieves elegance through the simple softness of the fabric.

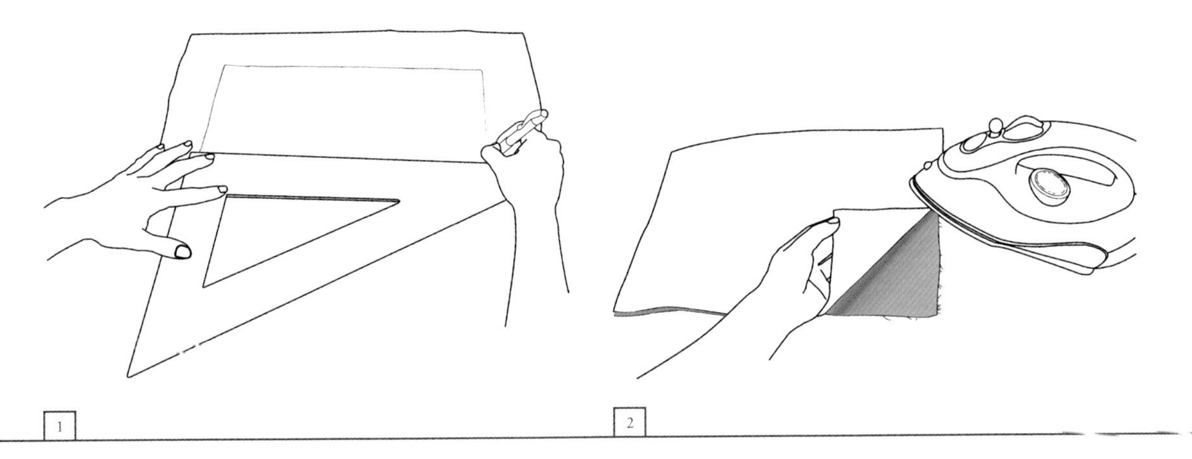

Use a ruler to trace a 12-inch-long (30 cm) and 5-inch-wide (13 cm) rectangle on pattern card. These are the dimensions for the front of a sash or belt for a waist measurement of about 26 inches (65 cm). You can adapt the measurements to suit any size you want. Cut it out with scissors.

Iron the piece of fabric and line it with a thick lining. You should allow for enough lining fabric to cut two rectangles with the same measurements as the previously traced pattern.

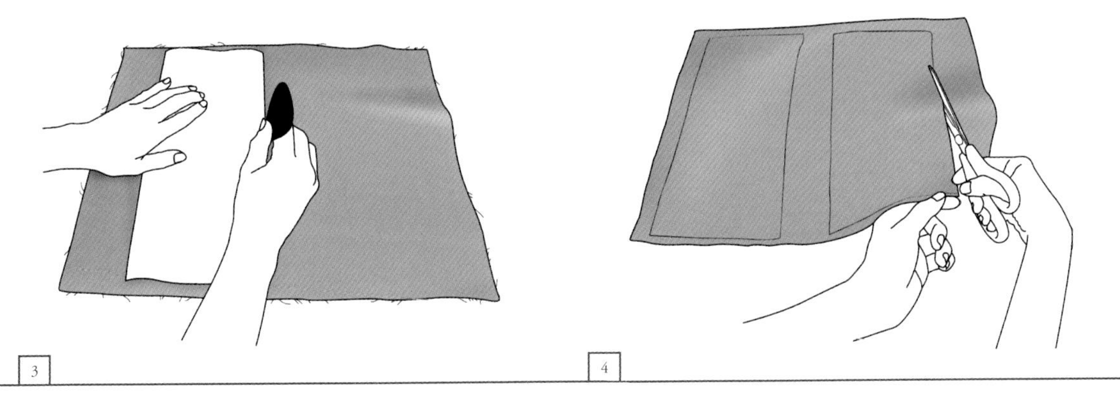

Now mark out the pattern of the rectangle using tailor's chalk on the fabric. You need to mark it out twice.

Use scissors to cut the two rectangles from the fabric.

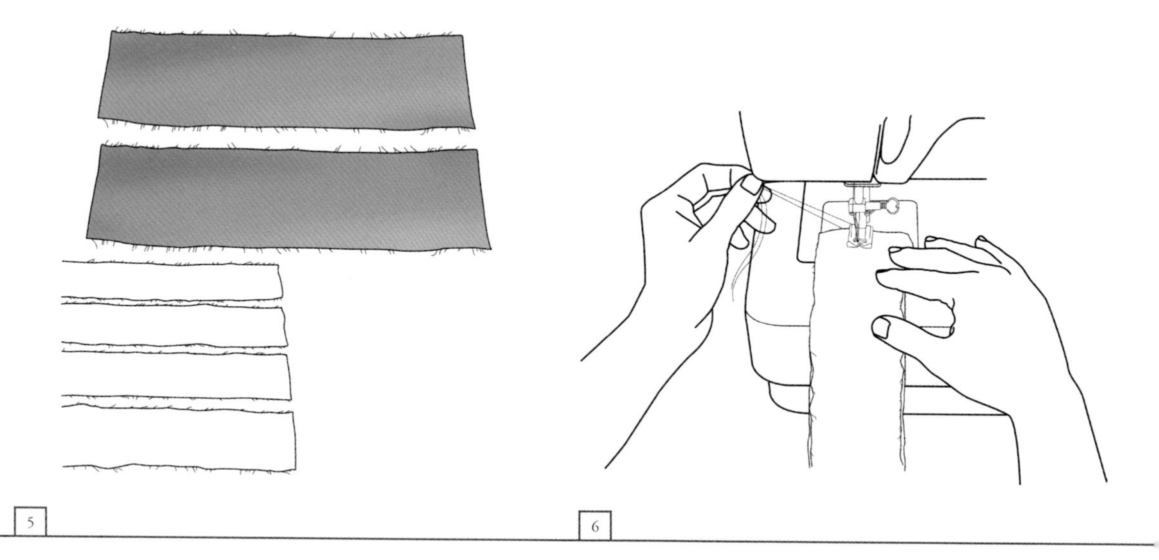

5

6

Now cut two straight strips from the same material you used for the rectangles; they should measure 4 x 28 inches (10 x 70 cm). Also cut four strips of muslin or similar material, which should be as light as possible as it will be used to make ruffled frills. Two of the strips should be 35 x 2.5 inches (90 x 6 cm) and two of the strips should be 15 x 2.5 inches (39 x 6 cm).

Using the machine set to a long stitch, straight stitch exactly along the middle of the strips.

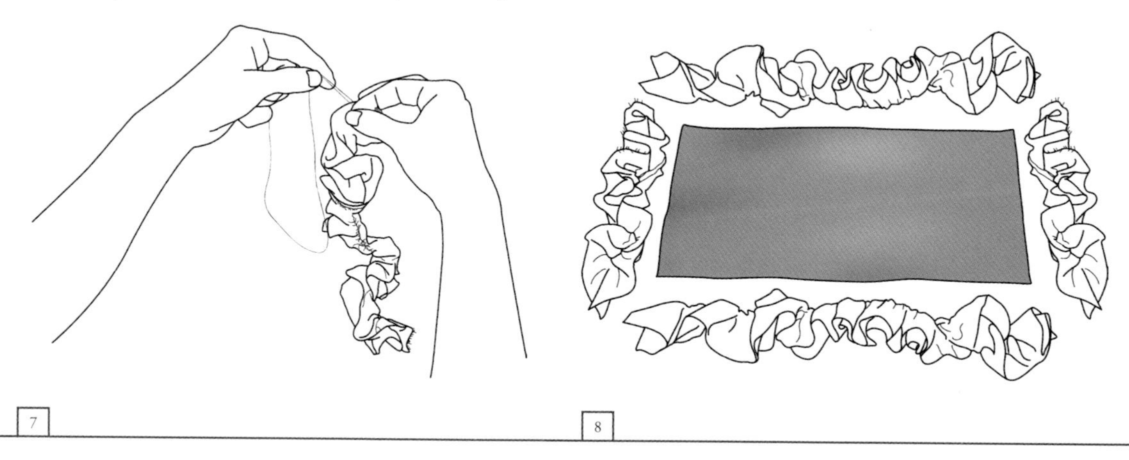

7

8

Then carefully gather them by hand, distributing the frills evenly.

Make sure that they are the same size as the sides of the rectangles (12 x 5 inches [30 x 13 cm]).

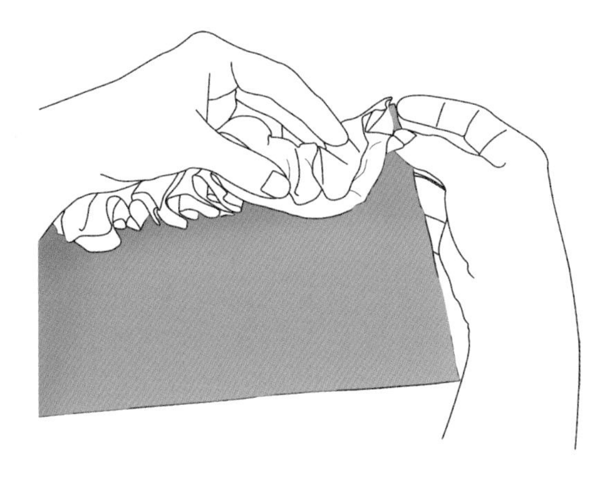

9

Sew the four frilled strips to one of the rectangles.

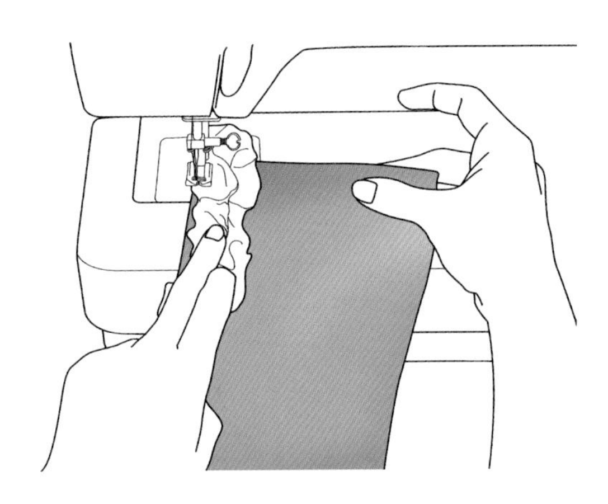

10

Join these strips to the piece with the sewing machine, sewing all the frills toward the inside.

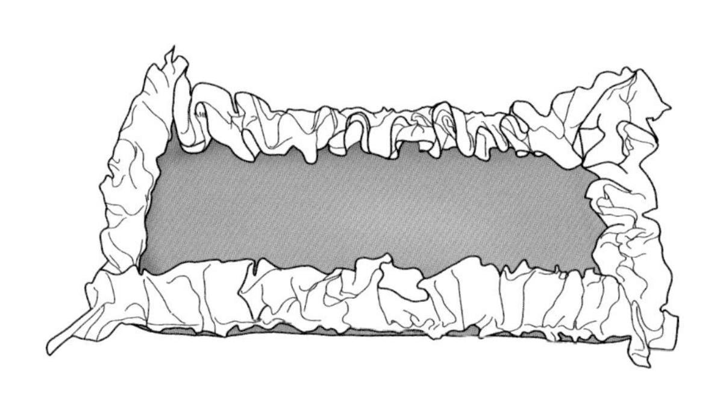

11

When finished, the piece should look like this.

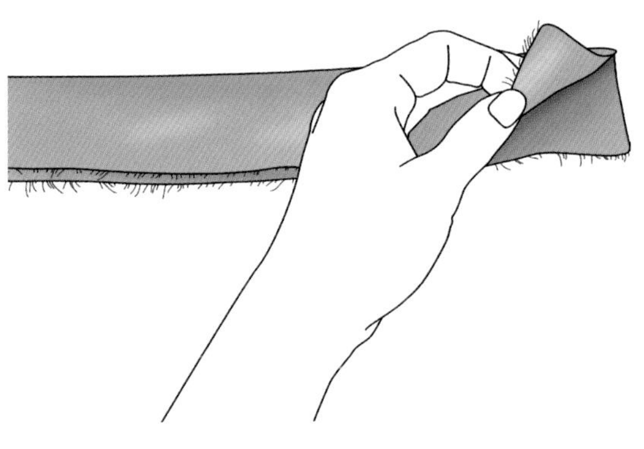

12

Take the two strips that are made from the same fabric as the rectangles that you already cut and fold them exactly in the middle, leaving the back of the material visible.

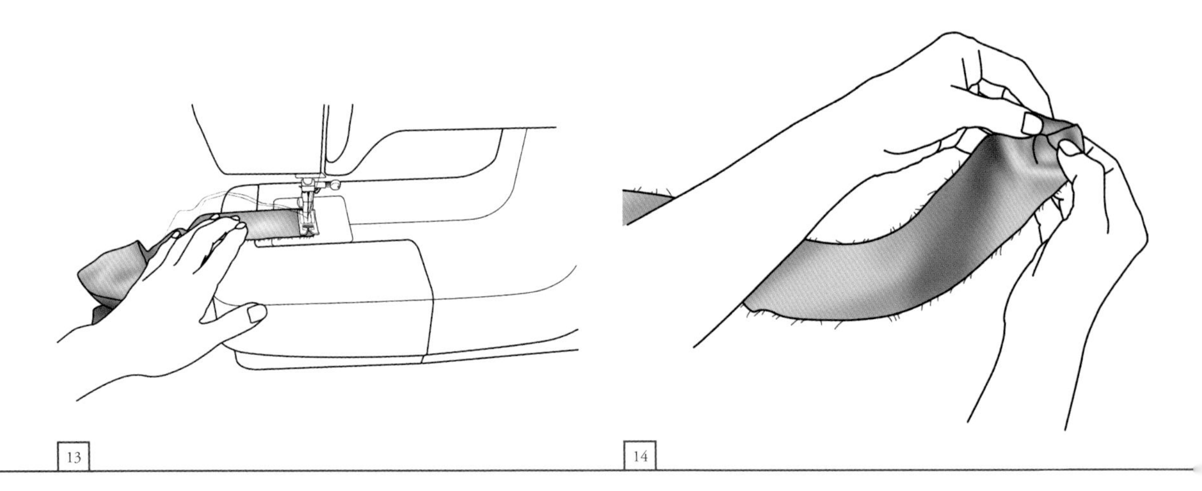

Straight stitch the strips along the whole area that is left open and on one of the ends. Remember to not close the other end as we will use that to turn the pieces the right way out.

Once the pieces have been straight stitched, use the open end to turn them slowly the right way out.

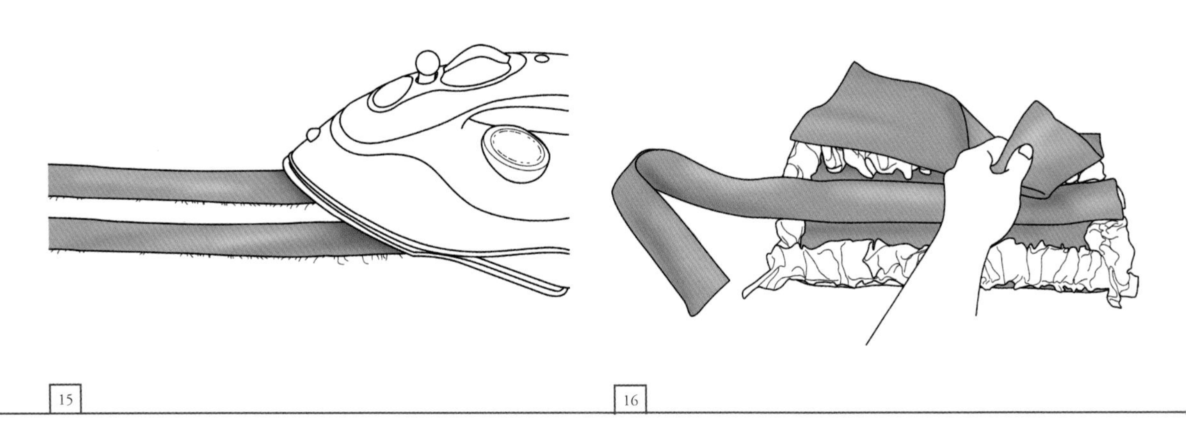

Iron them well so that they are totally flat. These will be the two laces that we will use to knot the belt at the back.

Now close the belt by sewing the other rectangular piece to the one with the frill trim. Face both parts on the right side of the fabric, leaving the ruffled strip inside. Straight stitch the upper side of the rectangle using the sewing machine. When you straight stitch the sides in the middle, insert the strips that form the ties and sew the three pieces together.

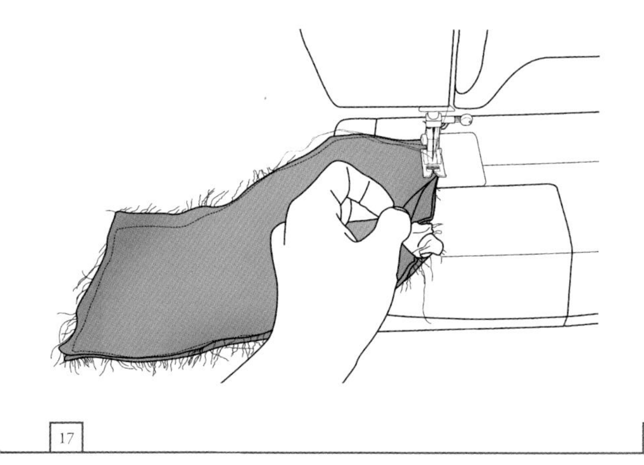

17

When you have almost finished closing the entire rectangle, remember to leave about 2 inches (5 cm) so that you can turn it the right way out when sewn.

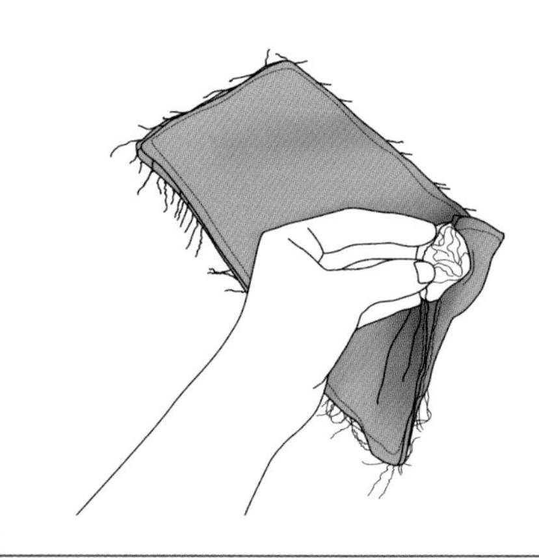

18

Turn the piece the right way out through the open 2 inches (5 cm).

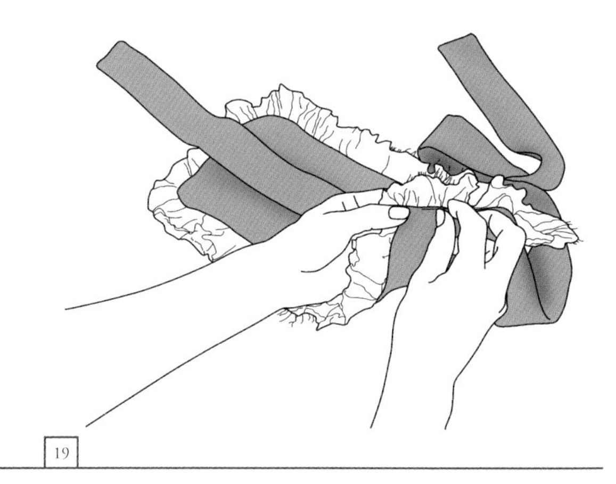

19

Use a needle and thread to close the piece with invisible stitching.

Once it has been ironed, the rectangle will become the front of the sash, which, when knotted at the back with an elegant tie, will hug the waist of any dress.

SIXTEENTH-CENTURY RUFF

Ruffs hit their peak in the sixteenth century, although they were still being used in the seventeenth century. We can reproduce the classic ruff, a relic of other ages, by strategically pleating a circle of rigid fabric.

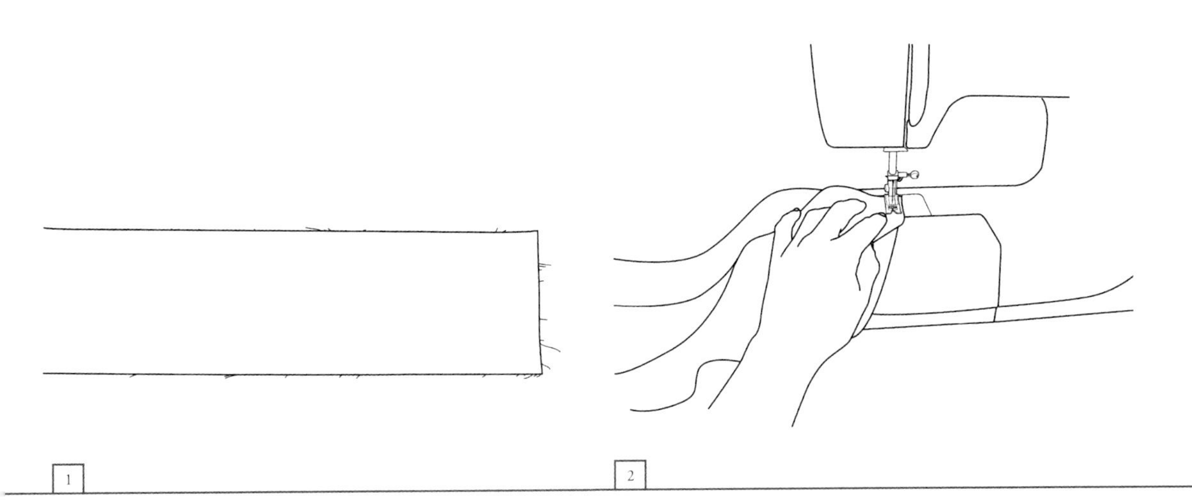

Cut and iron five strips 5 feet (1.5 m) long and 4.5 inches (11 cm) wide from a rigid material that has a starchy texture, such as organza.

With the sewing machine, join the five strips to get a single piece that is 25 feet (7.5 m) long. This measurement will be used to make a ruff for an average-sized neck.

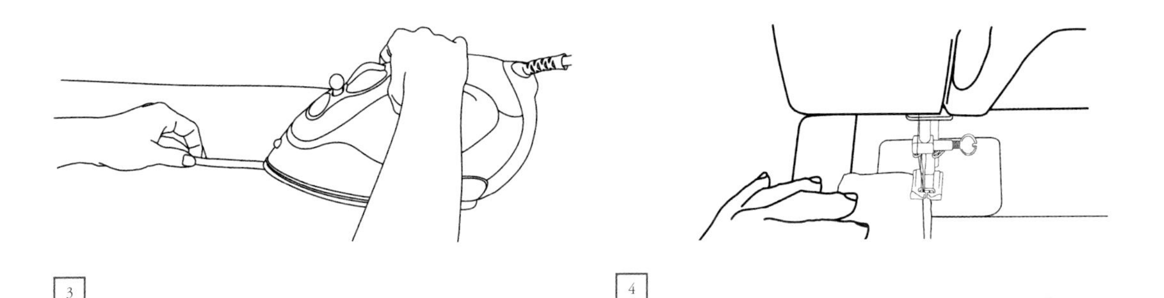

Make a small 0.4-inch (1 cm) fold along all the edges of the strip and set it using an iron.

Use the sewing machine to straight stitch the fold to finish the entire length of the strip.

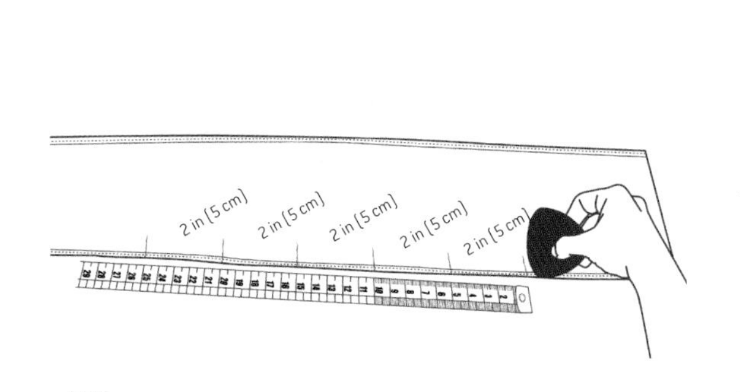

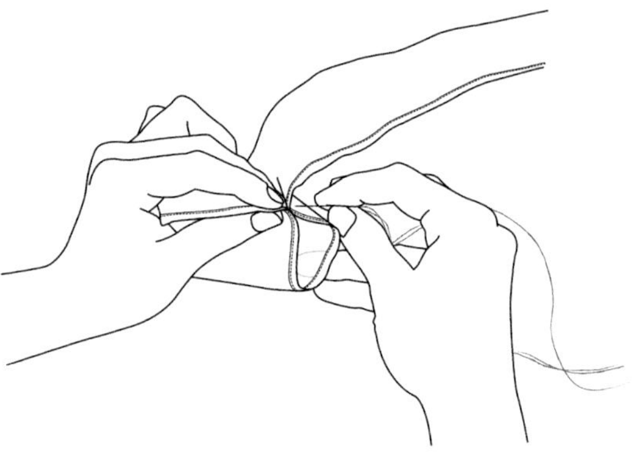

5

With tailor's chalk and a ruler, make small marks, 2 inches (5 cm) apart, on one of the sides along the whole length of the strip.

6

Starting at the side of the neck, join the marks with small hand stitches so that the first mark joins the third and the second remains underneath, forming a wave.

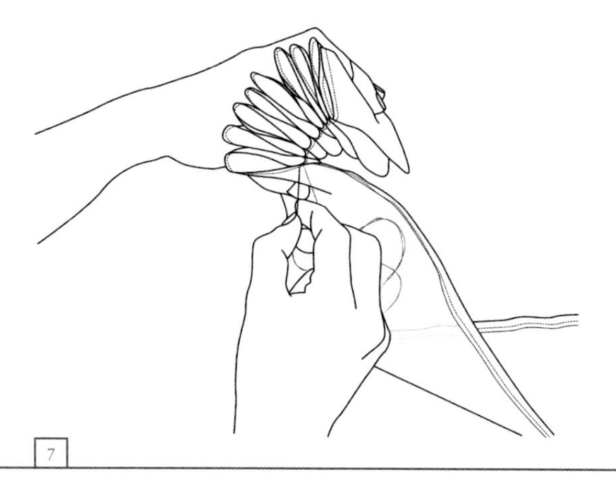

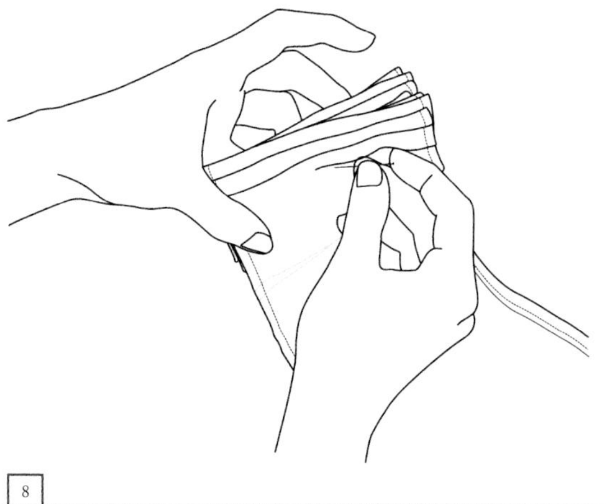

7

Repeat the process to complete the length of the strip.

8

Before stitching the waves, pin them as they are created so that you can work more comfortably.

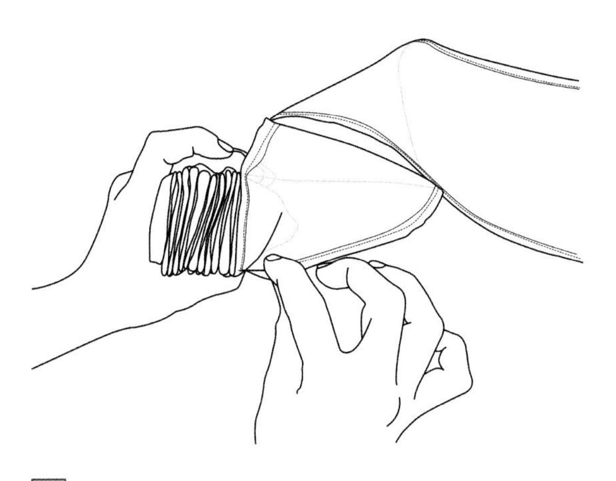

9

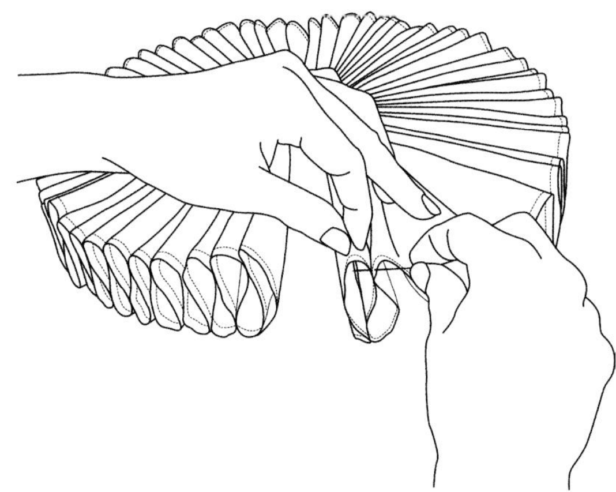

10

Now join the lower part of the waves with the same stitches. It is important that you apply these stitches to the surface of the wave with care, with neither too much nor too little fabric in the same stitching order, to give movement to the neck area.

Now move to the other end of the ruff, where the waves are more obvious and open. With small stitches and a lot of patience, you should now join them one by one, starting at the top.

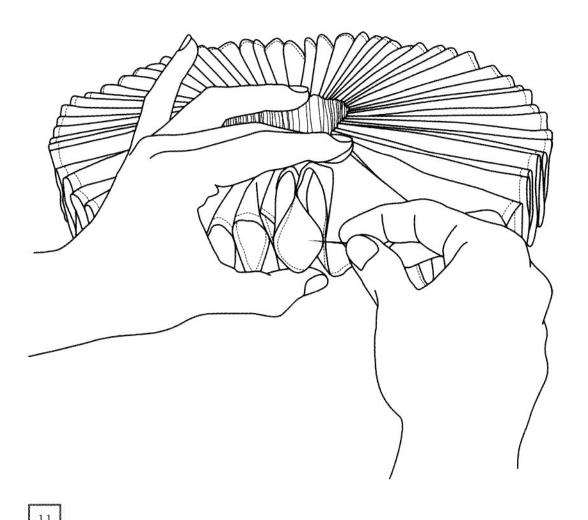

11

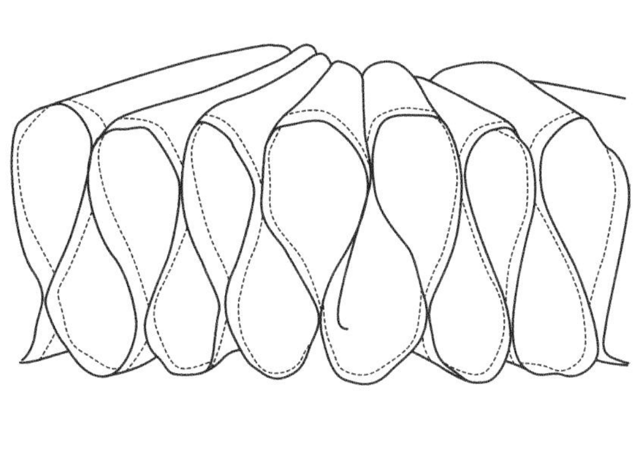

12

Once the first waves are joined at the top, join them at the bottom and so on.

When finished, the piece should look like this.

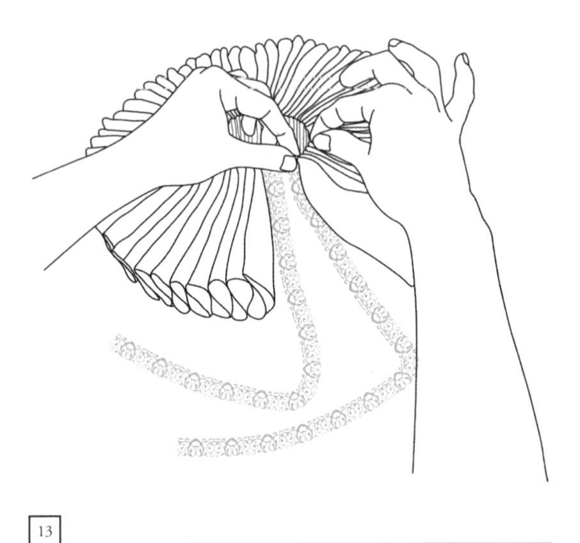

13

Sew a delicate ribbon onto the ruff so it closes with a classic bow. The ruff, also known as a "harlequin collar," is now ready to be used as a daring accessory.

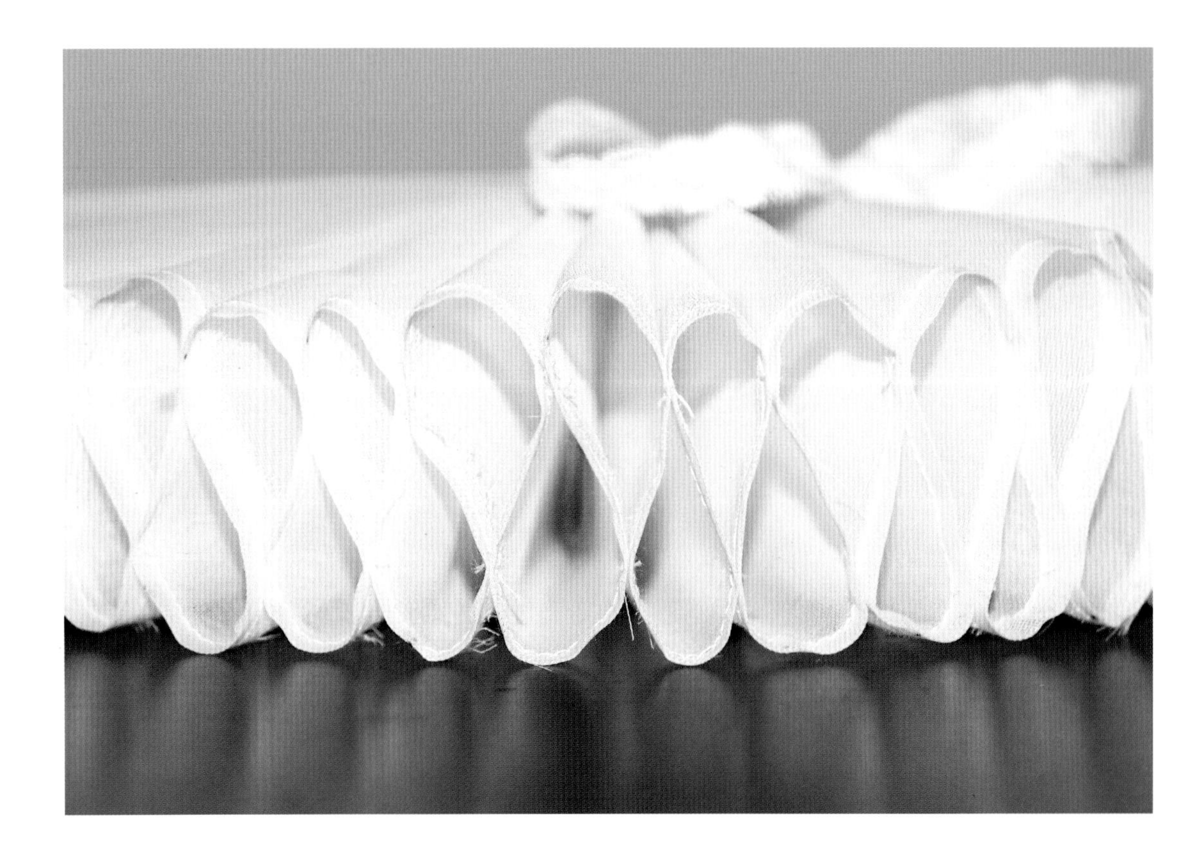

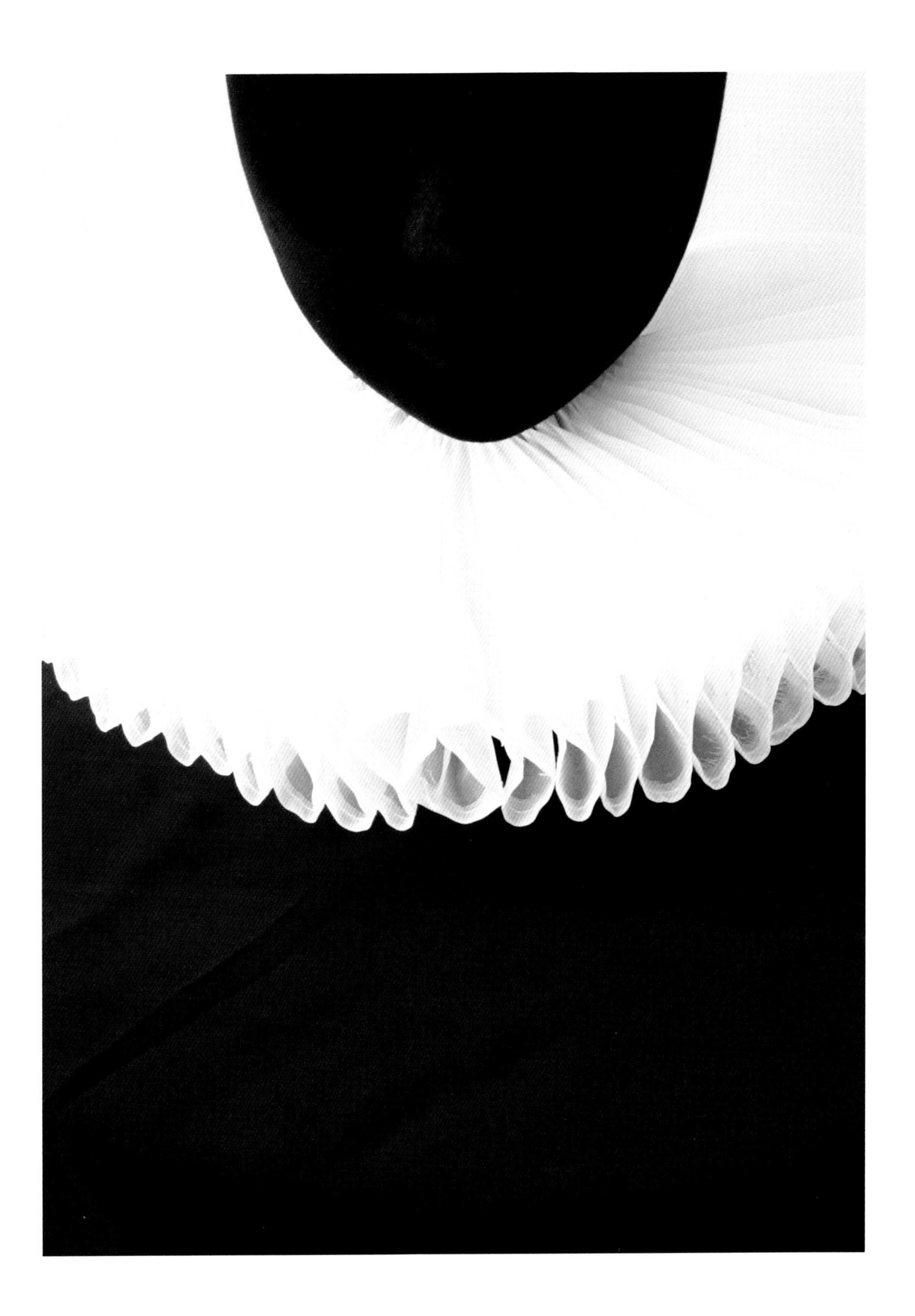

QUILTING WITH KAPOK

Padded quilting is the inspiration behind this project. We will use kapok to achieve a look that is ideal for decorating winter clothes.

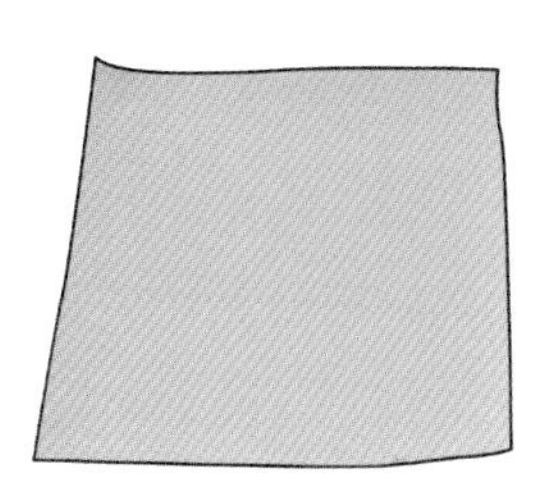

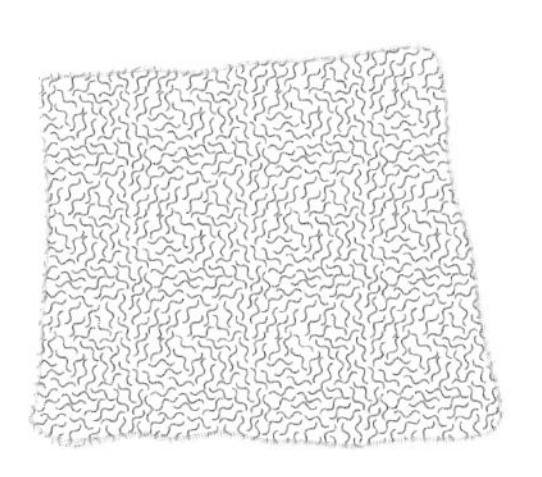

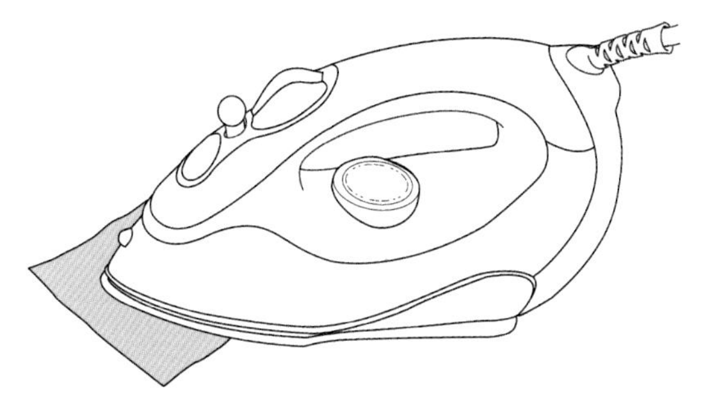

1

Cut a square of fabric and an equal measure of kapok. Using fabrics such as linen or woolen cloth will allow you to highlight the three-dimensional quality of the quilting.

2

Iron the piece of fabric.

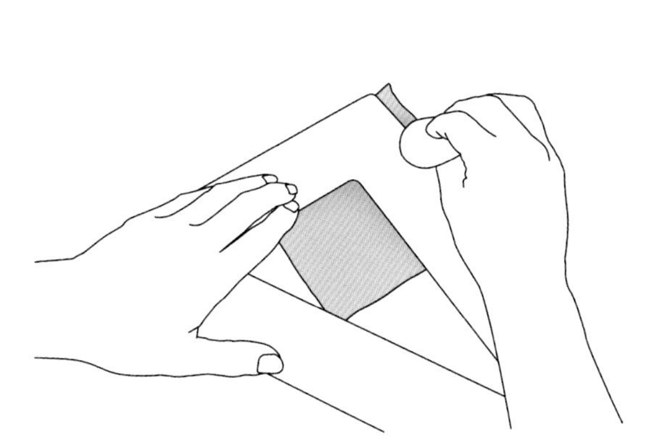

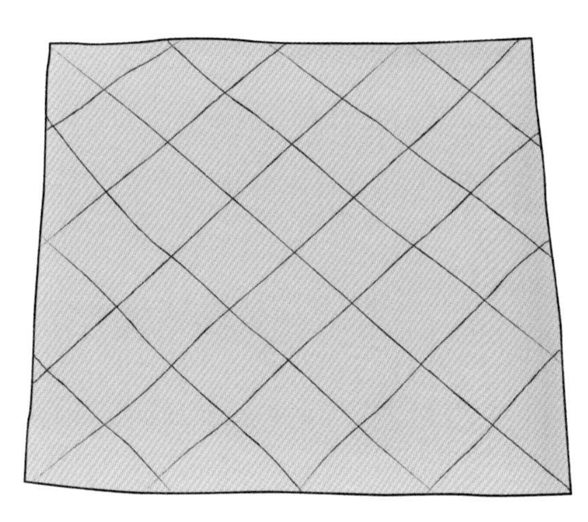

3

Taking the square of fabric, use a ruler and tailor's chalk to divide each side of the square with small equidistant marks. For example, if you were using a 5-inch (12 cm) square, as if making a pocket, you would divide each side with four marks, 1.2 inches (3 cm) apart.

4

Once the marks are drawn, join them diagonally, making a kind of grid so that the material is divided into small diamond-shaped cells.

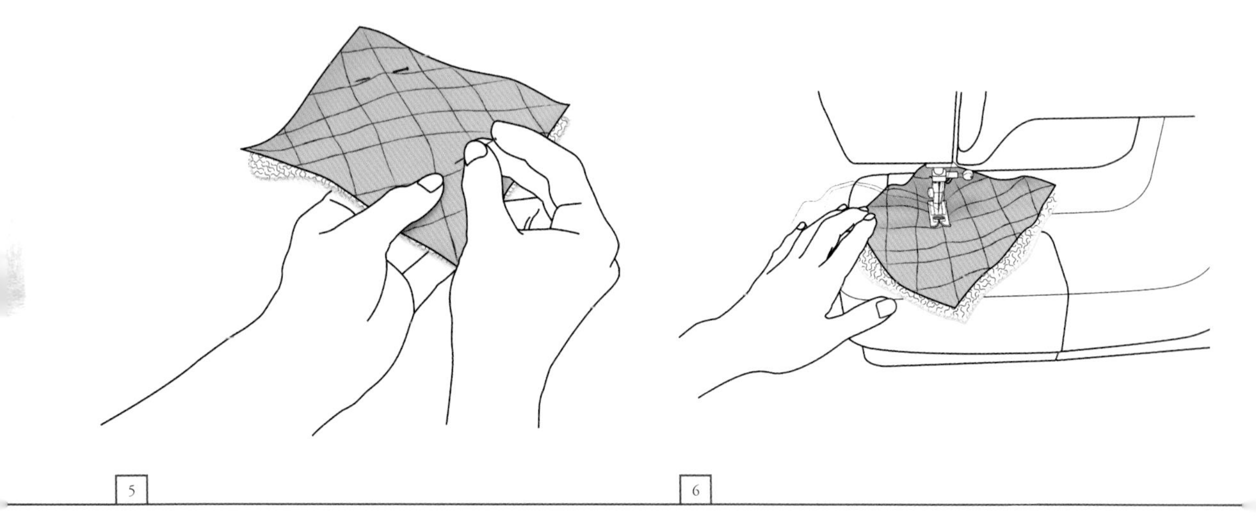

5

6

After marking the fabric, place it over the portion of kapok and firmly pin the pieces together.

Straight stitch the lines you drew on the material with a sewing machine. You could use a different color than the material so that the straight stitch stands out.

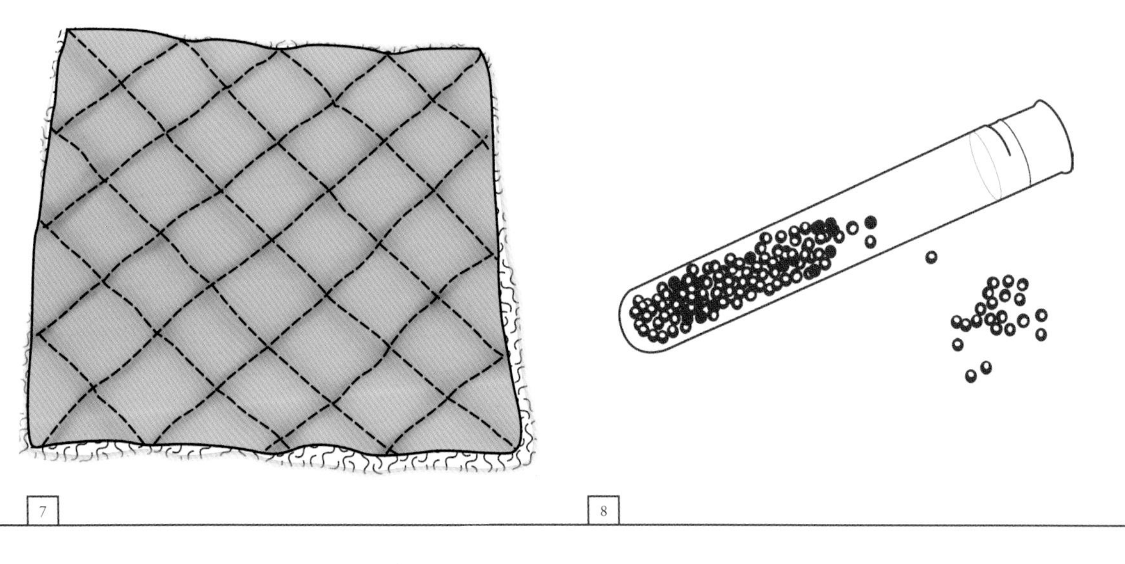

7

8

In doing so you will join the fabric with the kapok, achieving a cushioned look.

Once all the cells are straight stitched, embroider the fabric with a set of beads in the same shade. Remember that the size of the beads should be appropriate for the size of the piece that you want to work.

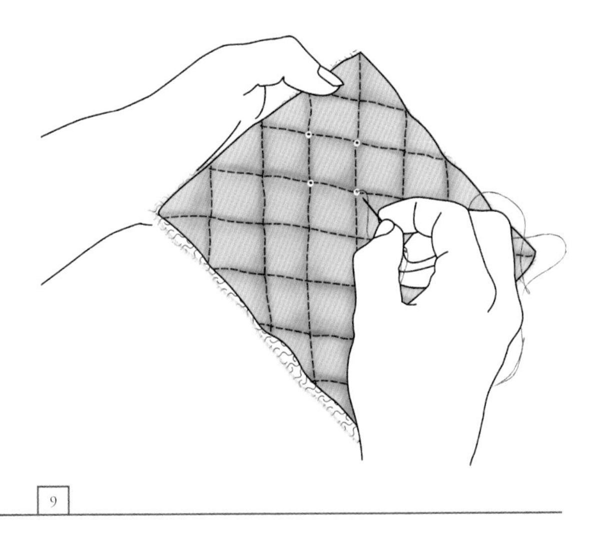

9

Sew a bead in the corner of each diamond. This imitates the buttons that are added to quilted items such as upholstered sofas. Tighten the thread to further highlight the cushioned effect produced by the kapok, hiding the bead in the corner of the diamond.

MICRODRAPERY

The drapery technique consists of gathering fabric to form pleats. It is achieved by attaching fabric to a lined base and meticulously, pin by pin, making tiny pleats around the body. Drapery is one of the most elegant sewing techniques.

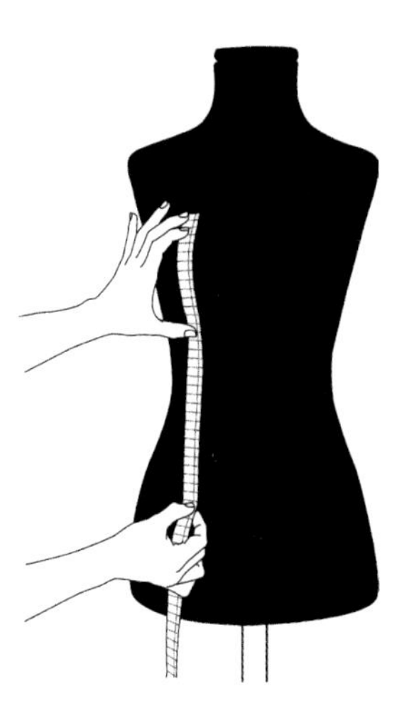

1

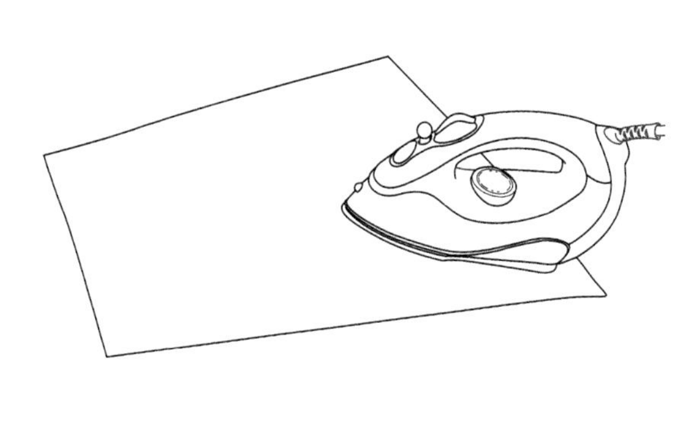

2

This technique is the most delicate kind of drapery. It is somewhat laborious and requires a lot of patience, but if we use the mannequin for draping we can work on intricate shapes, such as those for the chest. On the mannequin, measure the length to be draped.

For this project, we will drape the area corresponding to the cup of the left breast. We are using a measurement of 5 inches (12 cm) from the top — from the neckline to the lower chest area.

3

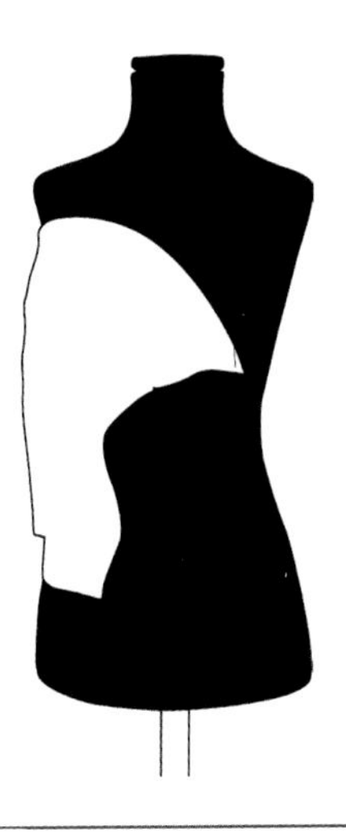

4

Cut the material to be used on the bias. In this case we have used a mid-weight silk crepe. Multiply the initial measurement you took by three because, as you know, when you drape the material the length of the material will shorten. If you measured 5 inches (12 cm) on the mannequin, you should cut the piece 14 inches (36 cm) wide; the length should reach from the side to the center of the chest.

Cut the piece to this shape, so that the sharp peak of the upper right area fits over the center of the chest when the project is finished.

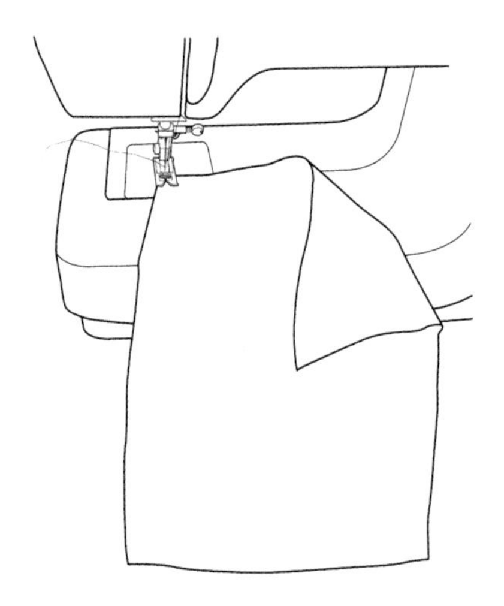

5

With the sewing machine, use a long straight stitch in the left-hand side so that the piece can then be gathered. This straight stitch will help us to define the pleats of the drape.

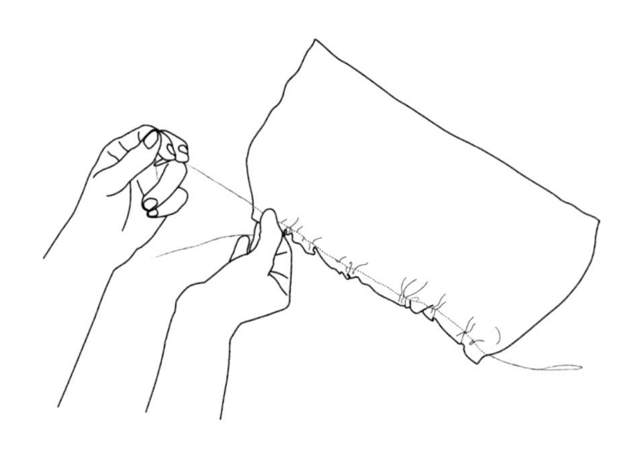

6

Slowly gather the straight stitched area with both hands. This will define the tubular pleats that will later become the draped material.

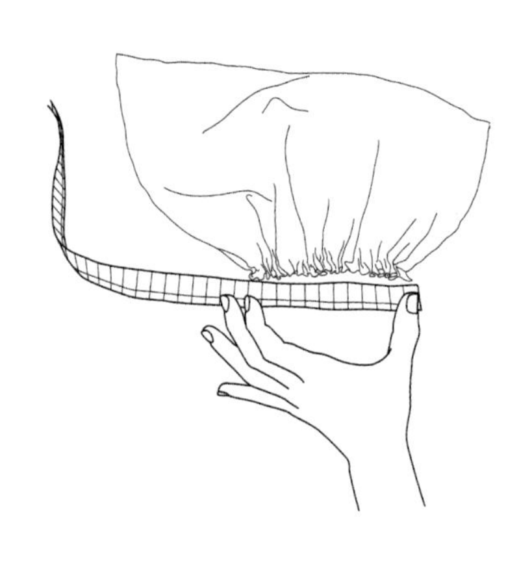

7

Remember that once gathered, the length must be the initial measurement we took on the mannequin; in this case, the 5 inches (12 cm) we measured for the chest area.

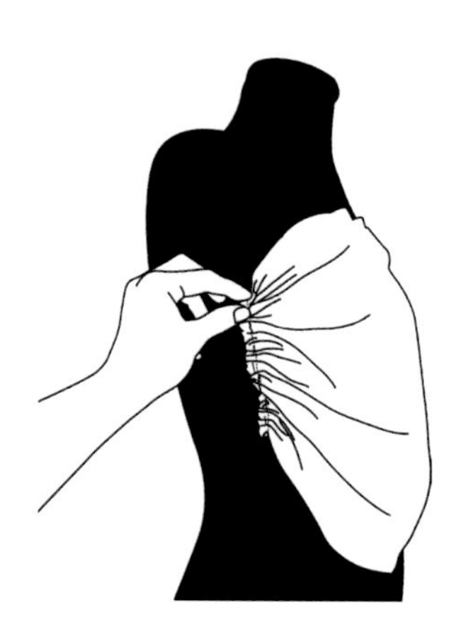

8

Pin the piece on the mannequin, lining up the gathered area with the side so that it is held firmly. This will allow you to work comfortably.

9

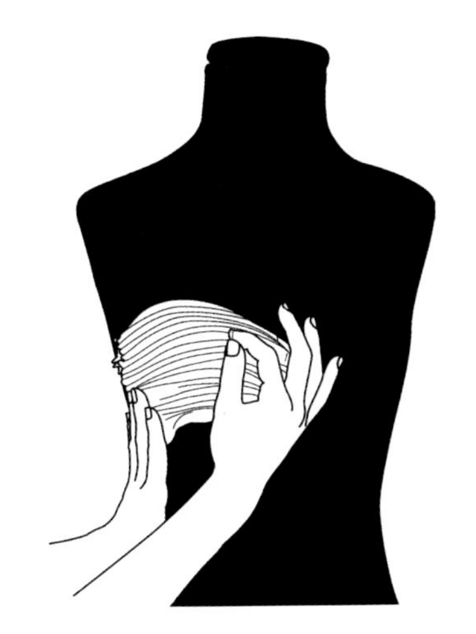

10

Begin to pinch the rolls that were defined during the gathering process, stretching them firmly and pinning them on the mannequin. Ensure that they are all identical.

Repeat this process over the surface of the entire cup, draping all the fabric, pleat by pleat, making sure they all finish at the center of the chest in a slightly arched shape.

11

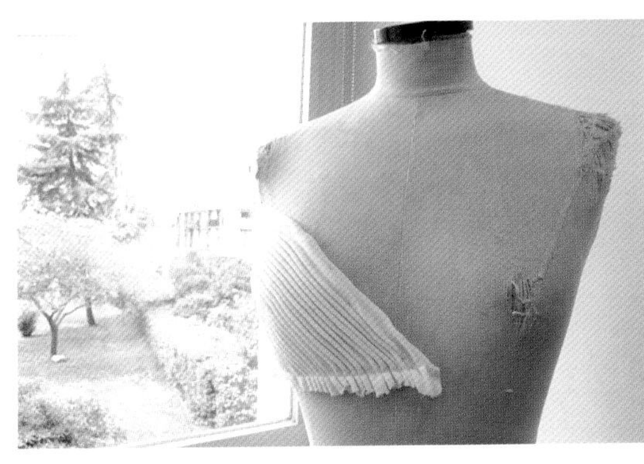

Once you have finished draping the fabric, use a needle and thread to set each pleat with an invisible stitch so that they are attached to each other and keep their shape. This way you will have one perfectly draped breast. You should apply this method to each piece of the fabric for the garment that you are making.

IRREGULAR PLEATED BODICE

The bodice, also known as the corset, has as many lovers as it does enemies. In this project you will learn one of the many techniques for adding irregular pleating over the framework of a bodice.

1

Cut and iron a section of fabric. Because of the nature of this project, we recommend you use a rustic material, such as a rough linen or silk, which is reminiscent of the old-fashioned bodices that were once used as underclothes. It is important that you always cut on the bias, resulting in a better fit for the curves of the body.

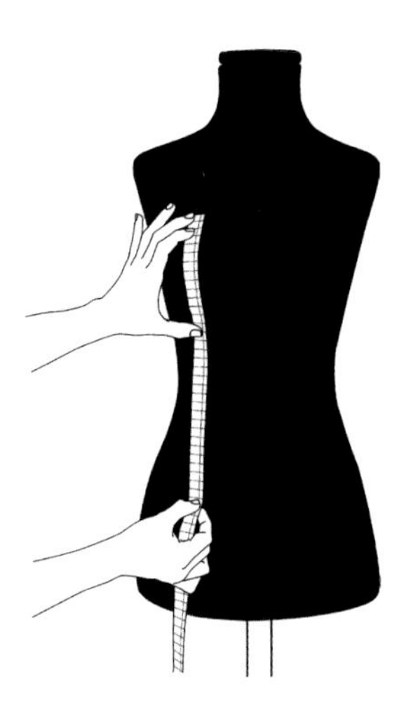

2

Measure the length of the piece that you want to pleat. For this project, we will measure the width, which includes from the neckline to 2 inches (5 cm) below the waist, and the length, which goes from the center front to the side. You should always multiply the width of the fabric to use by three, since pleating it will make it more narrow. This can be seen in the other ruffle and pleating projects.

3

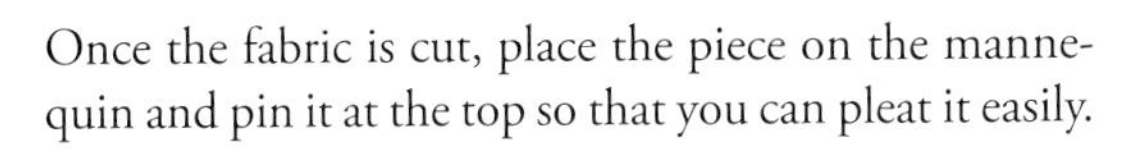

Once the fabric is cut, place the piece on the mannequin and pin it at the top so that you can pleat it easily.

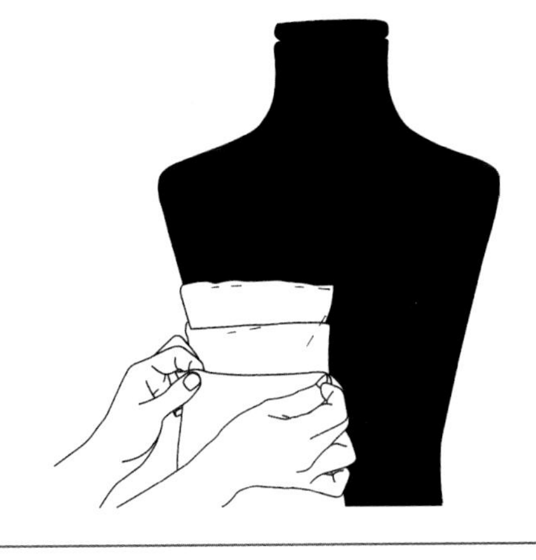

4

Begin pleating the material upward and, when you have made the first pleat, pin it so that it is held firmly.

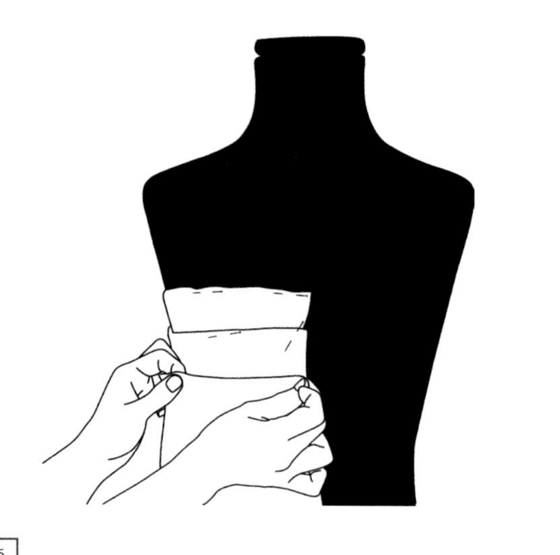

Repeat the process for the second pleat and pin it.

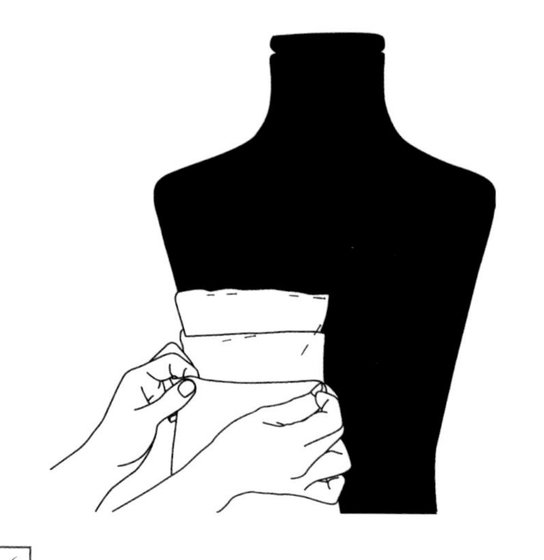

Continue pleating the rest of the piece, playing with the pleats. Try making some different from others, adjusting them to the shape of the mannequin. By not pleating too accurately you will give the project an artisanal, handmade look.

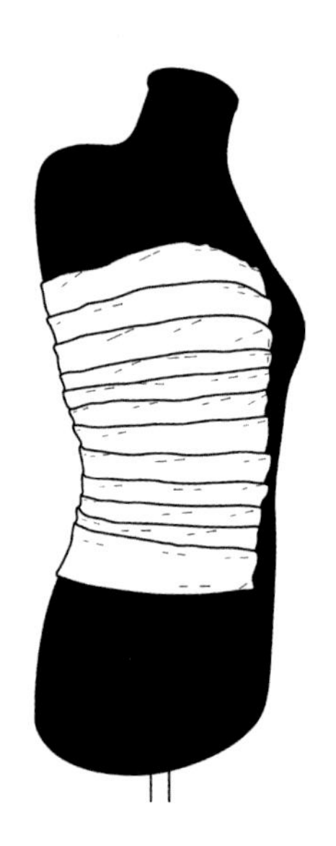

Once the whole piece is pleated on the mannequin, even with the pins still in place, it should resemble a perfectly modeled and personalized bodice. It should hug the curves of the chest and waist in a suggestive and feminine manner.

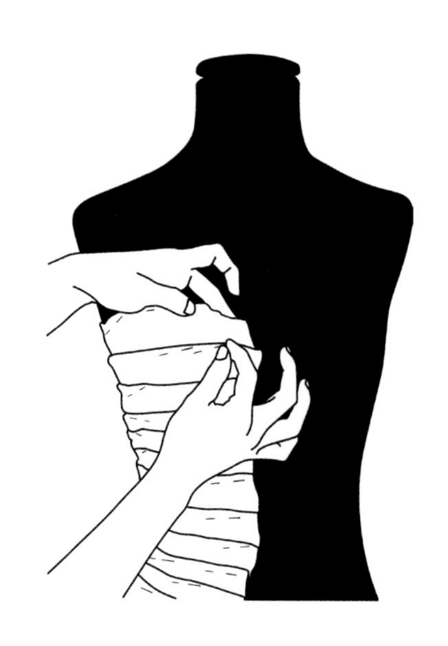

Carefully separate the piece from the mannequin, removing the pins one by one. Now use the sewing machine to add a tack to each end to secure it.

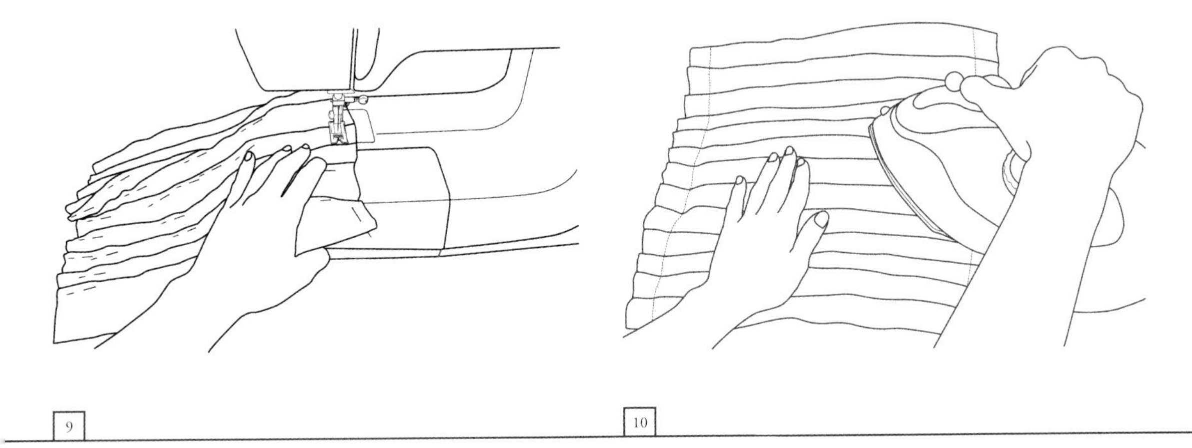

9

Straight stitch the ends to fix the pleats where they begin.

10

Now, you should remove any remaining pins and iron the pleats carefully. Make sure to maintain the shapes of the pleats, setting each fold well.

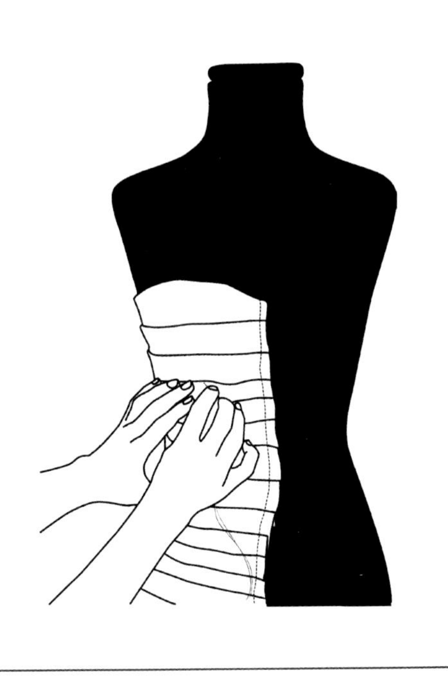

11

Place the piece back on the mannequin and, with needle and thread, make small hidden stitches between the pleats to ensure that they do not come undone. Remember that it is important to hide each one of these stitches.

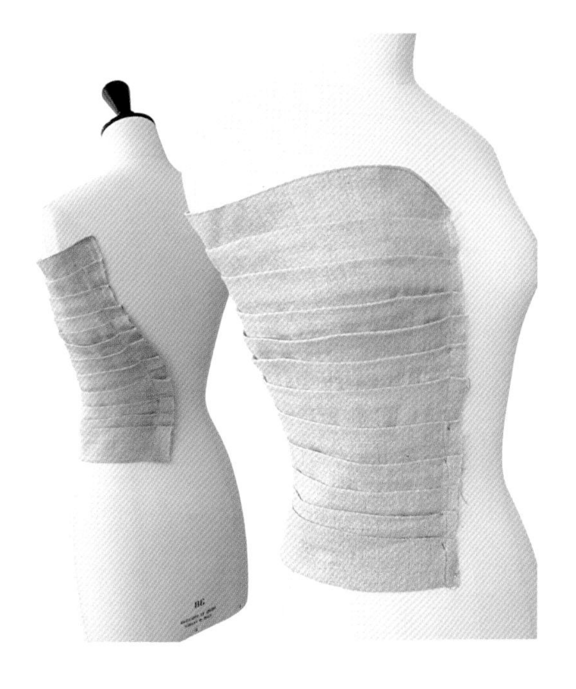

If you follow these guidelines and apply this technique to the pieces of fabric that you want to pleat, you will achieve an artisanal look. You will enjoy discovering, step by step, how fun and inspiring it is to work on a mannequin.

OVERLAPPING DIAMOND FANTASY

This project has a storybook look, full of fantasy and imagination. We will add diamond shapes to a skirt to create a garment that is fit for princesses, fairies and the like.

1

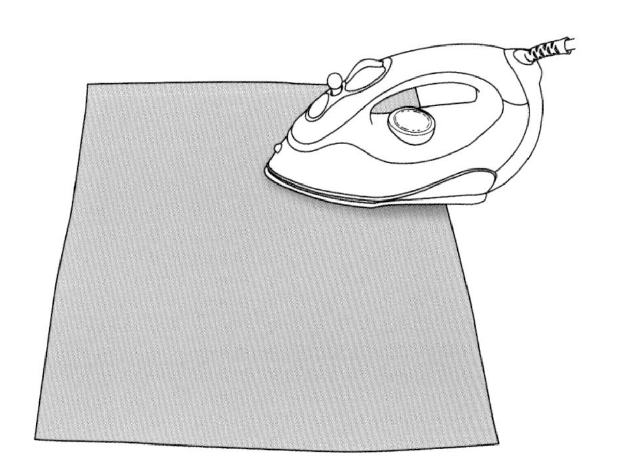

2

This project consists of creating additional volume from diamond-shaped pieces of fabric sewn onto a garment. For this reason, it is advisable to sew straight onto the garment with the aid of a mannequin.

Cut and iron a section of the fabric that will be used. Ideally you should choose a stiff fabric, such as organza, to obtain the desired effect.

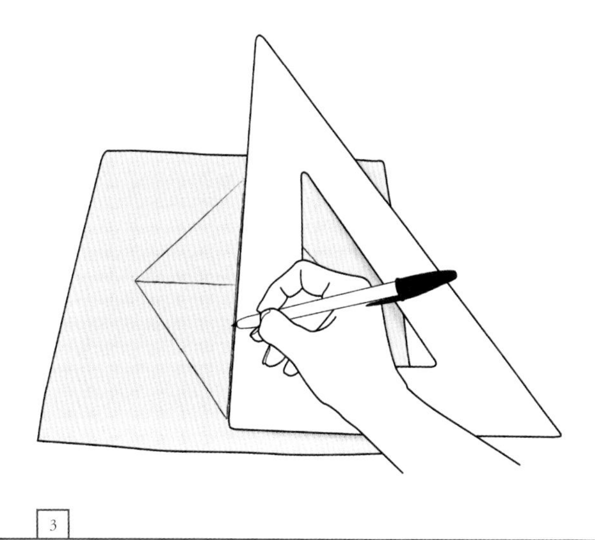

3

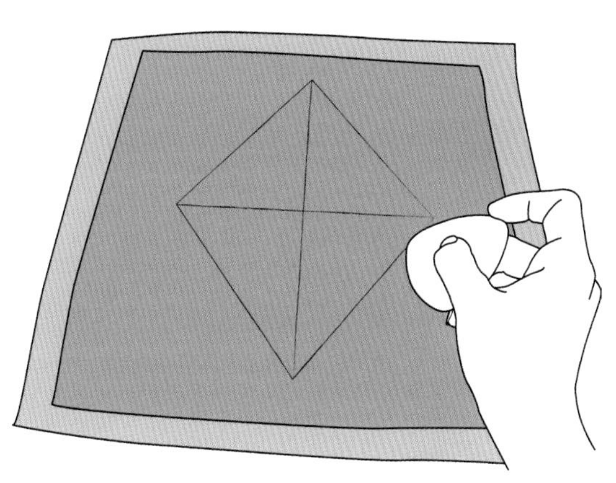

4

Use a ruler and dark-colored pen to draw a diamond shape measuring 8 inches (20 cm) high and 6 inches (16 cm) wide on brown paper or pattern card. This shape will be your pattern.

Place the fabric over the card. Since the fabric is translucent and thin, it will be easy to mark out the diamond onto the fabric with tailor's chalk.

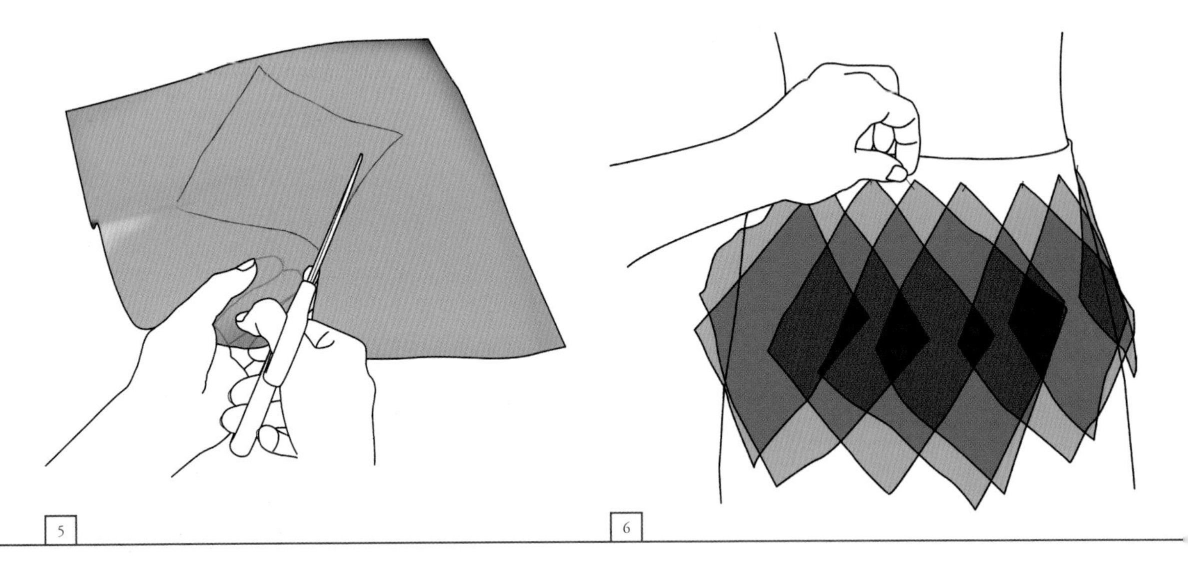

Now that the diamond is drawn on the fabric, cut it out using scissors. Calculate the number of diamond shapes you will need to cover the surface of the chosen garment, then draw them and cut them out.

Once you have cut all the diamond shapes out, begin to pin them onto the mannequin. Place them in lines, trying to alternate them so that the first overlaps the second, the third overlaps the second and the fourth and so on. When you finish the first line, begin the second line 2 inches (5 cm) away from the first.

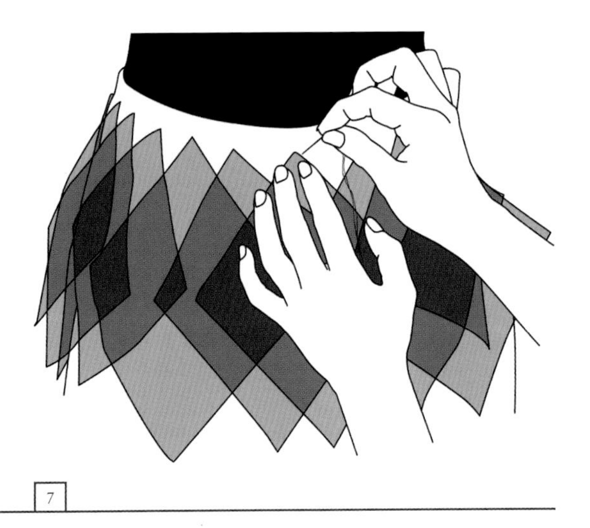

Once you have pinned all the diamond shapes to the garment, attach them by hand with strong, decisive stitches. The first line will always leave gaps between the points of the diamonds, so you should cover this area with fabric; for example, if you use the project on a skirt, this space will be covered by the waistband.

SNAKE SCALES

The outcome of this project will be a finish that resembles the scaly skin of reptiles and fish. The arrangement of the fabric scales is similar to that found in nature, creating a garment that is reminiscent of the ocean and its wild inhabitants.

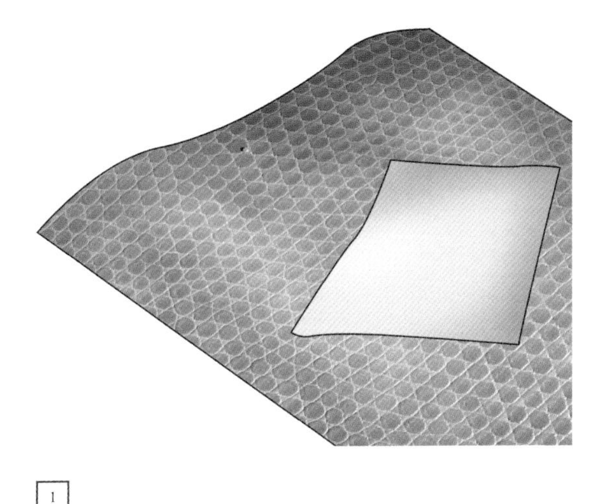

1

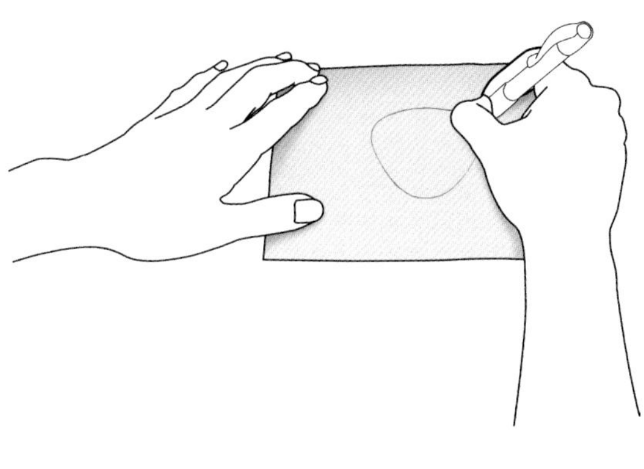

2

Cut the section of fabric that you are going to use. For this project, the most suitable material is a synthetic leather to simulate the appearance of reptile skin. You will also need brown paper or pattern card.

On the pattern card, draw a triangular shape with rounded corners, a bit like a scale.

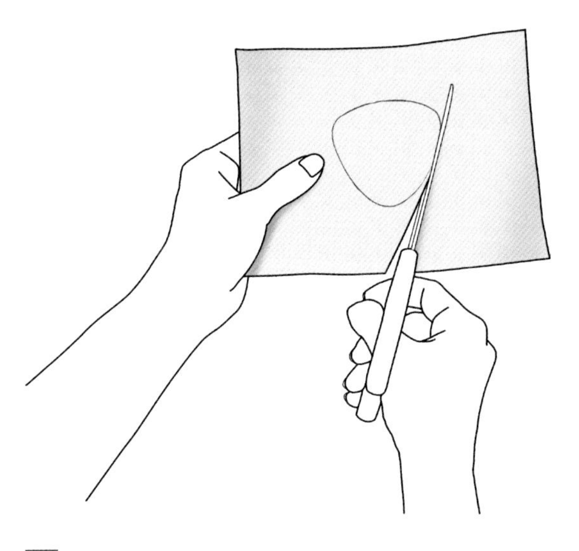

3

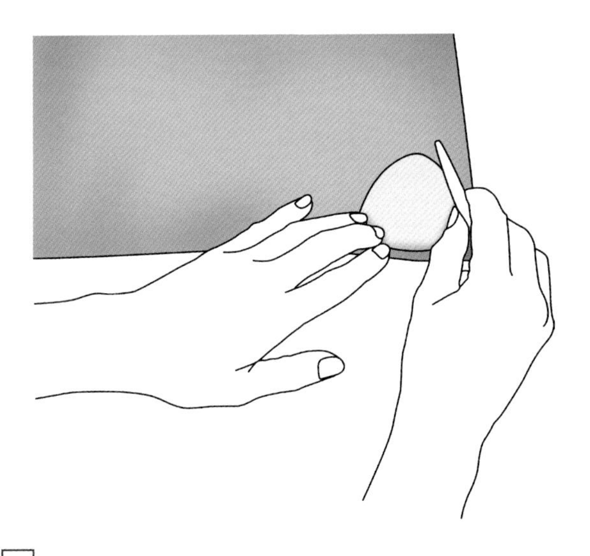

4

Use scissors to cut out this shape, which you are going to use as a pattern.

Place the scale pattern on the wrong side of the piece of fabric and mark the outline with tailor's chalk.

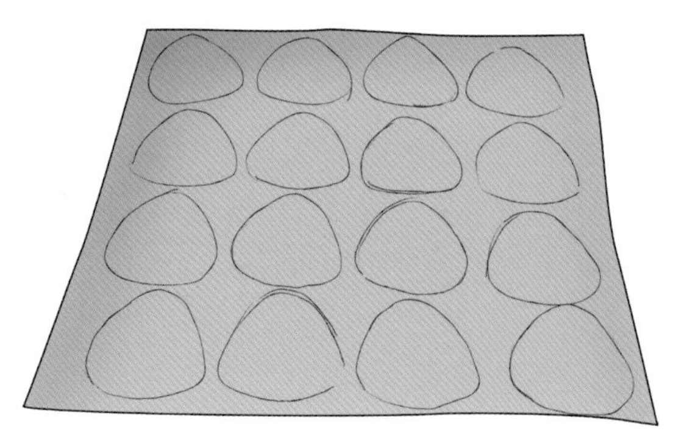

5

Repeat the process over the entire surface of the fabric until you have as many scales as you need to make the desired garment or to cover the area that you want to decorate.

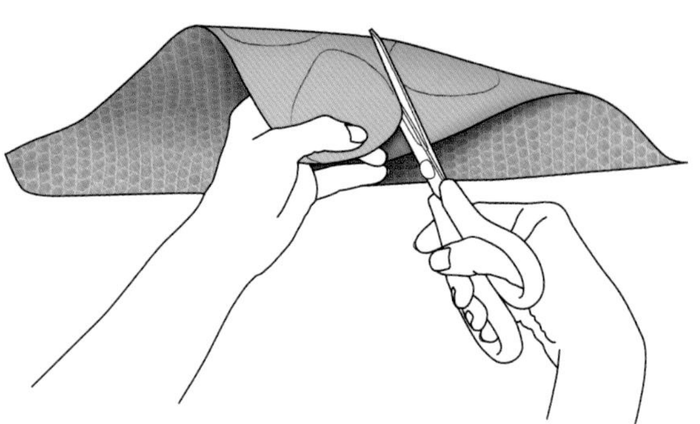

6

Trim carefully around the marked shapes.

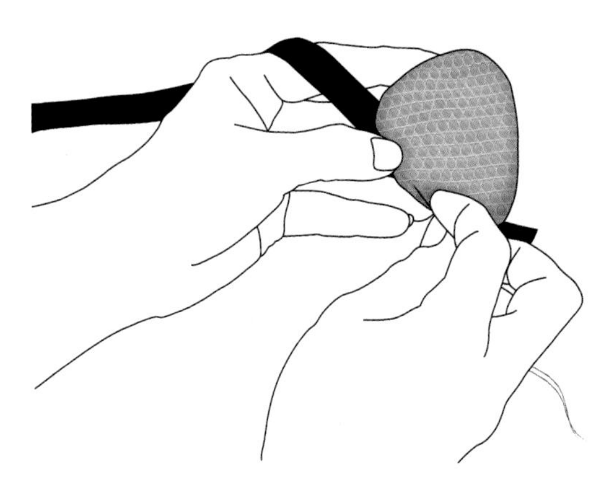

7

Tack a row of scales positioned with their points down on a 1.2-inch-wide (3 cm) satin ribbon, joining the lateral edges without overlapping them.

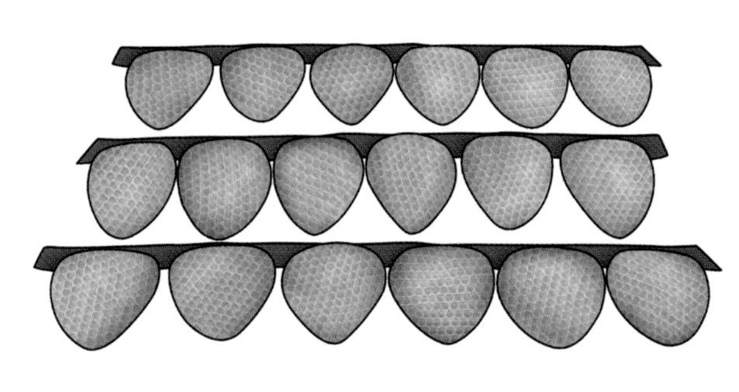

8

Repeat the same process with at least five ribbons of the same length to obtain the desired effect, always bearing in mind the garment you are making (you will probably need a lot more).

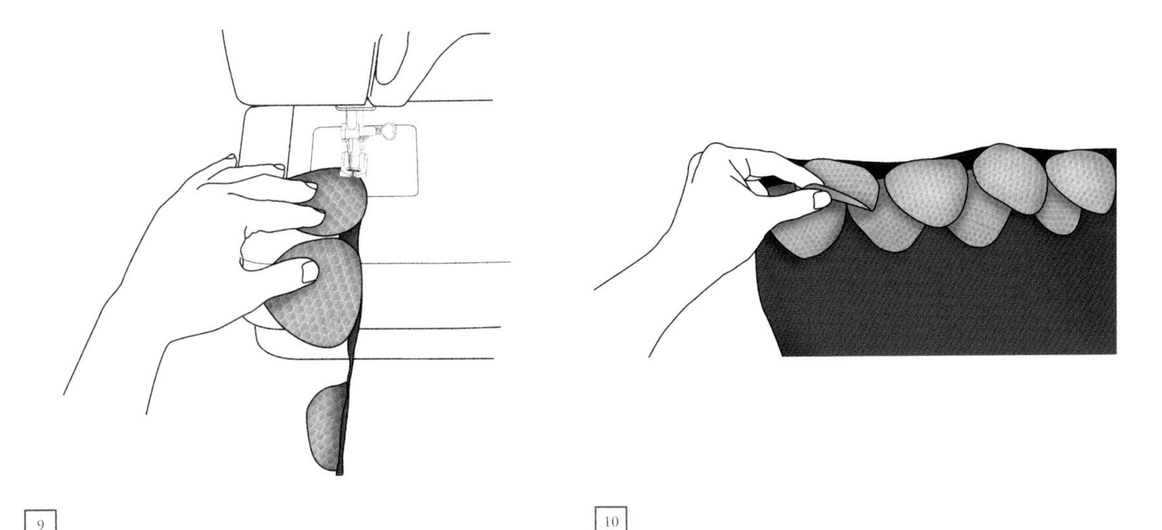

When you have tacked the scales, straight stitch the strips with the sewing machine to attach them permanently.

Once you have made the necessary strips, sew them onto a fabric base or directly onto the garment. They should be sewn in parallel lines, close enough so that the scales from each line overlap the ones beneath them. This way you will not have any gaps that would leave the fabric visible, allowing you to obtain the desired effect.

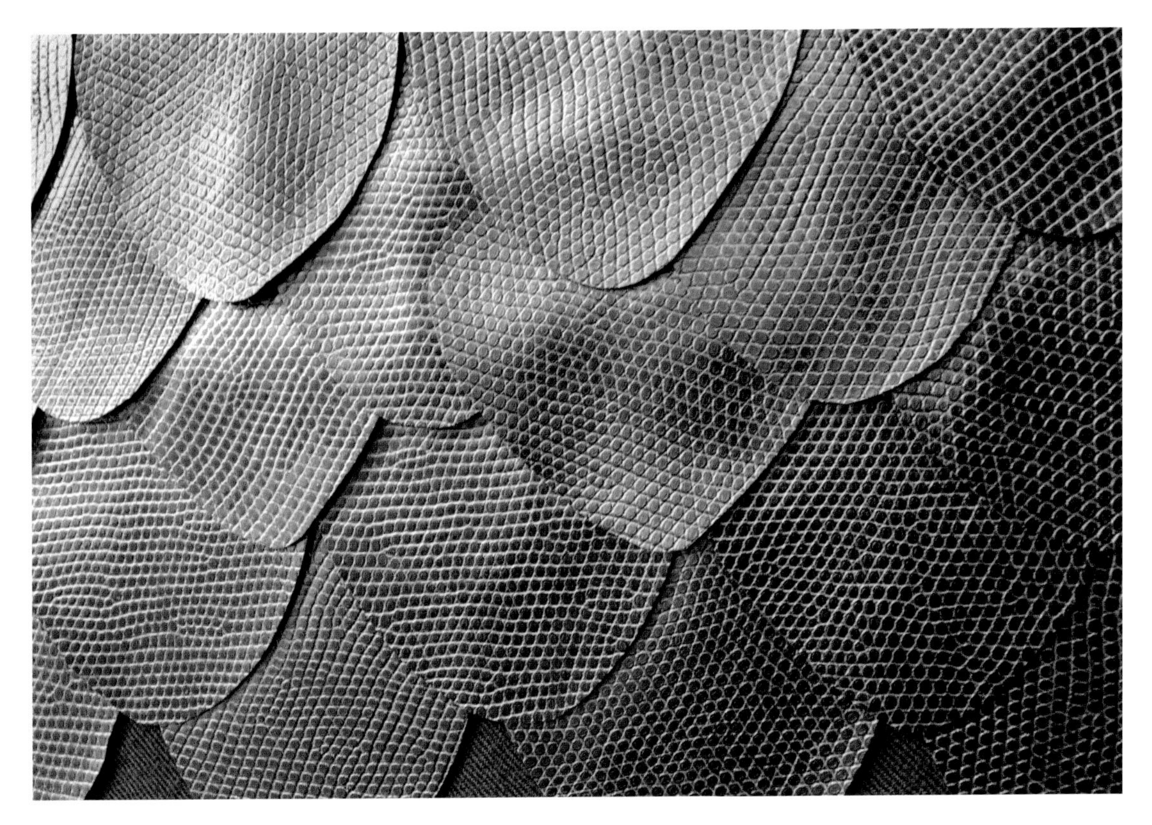

SHIRT COLLAR

Starting with a plain shirt collar, we can use shirring and a satin ribbon to create a collar with a childlike touch, reminiscent of school uniforms.

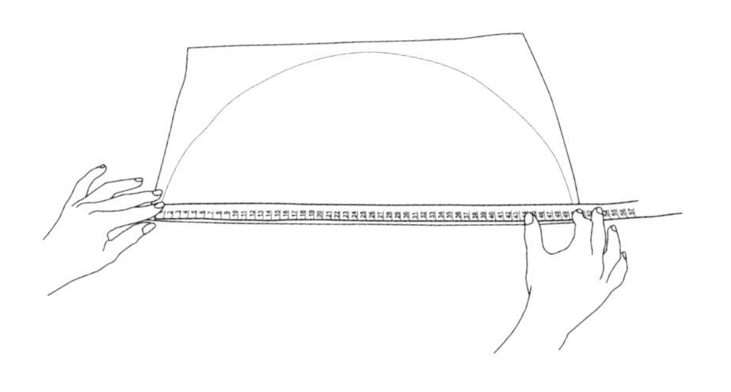

1

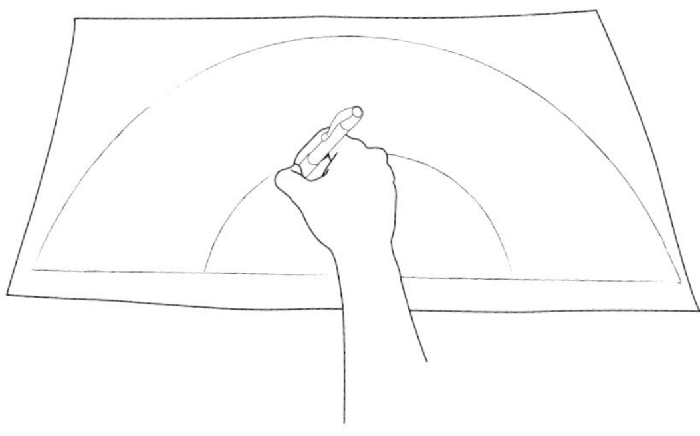

2

On a piece of brown paper or cardboard paper for patternmaking, draw with pencil and ruler a straight line about 20 inches (49 cm) long. Then use this line as a diameter and trace a semicircle arcing above it. The measurements that we will work with will create a medium-size shirt collar.

Use a pencil to make two new marks at 5 inches (13 cm) from each end of the line, so that they are separated by 9 inches (23 cm). This will allow you to make another semicircle with a diameter of 9 inches (23 cm) within the first one. From the same starting line, you have drawn two semicircles that form a sort of arch.

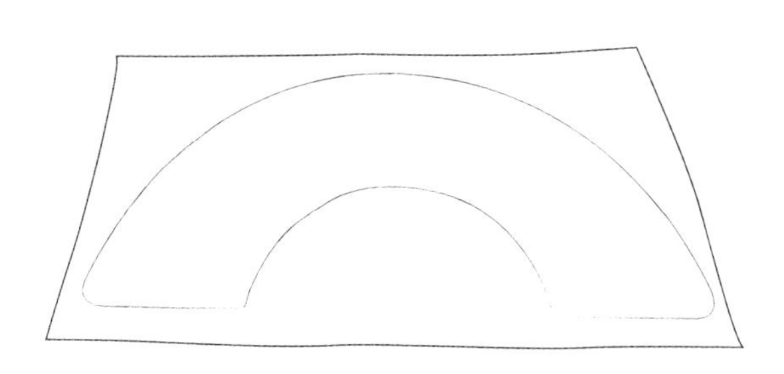

3

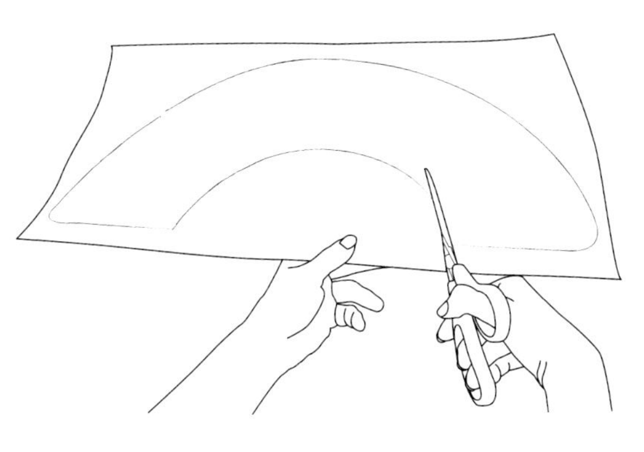

4

Erase the section of the line that forms the diameter of the inner semicircle. Also round any sharp edges.

You can see how the pattern is taking the shape of an open neck. Cut all the way around it with scissors.

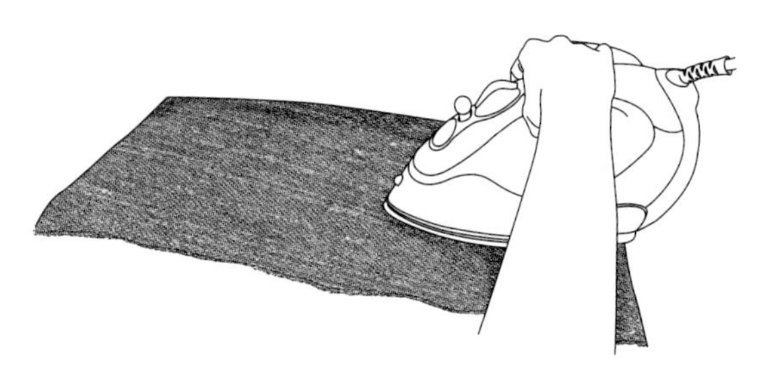

5

Cut and iron the fabric that you are going to use, a denim cotton fabric is ideal if the collar will be used to create a casual look. Remember, if you want to give more body to the piece, you can interline one of the two sections of fabric.

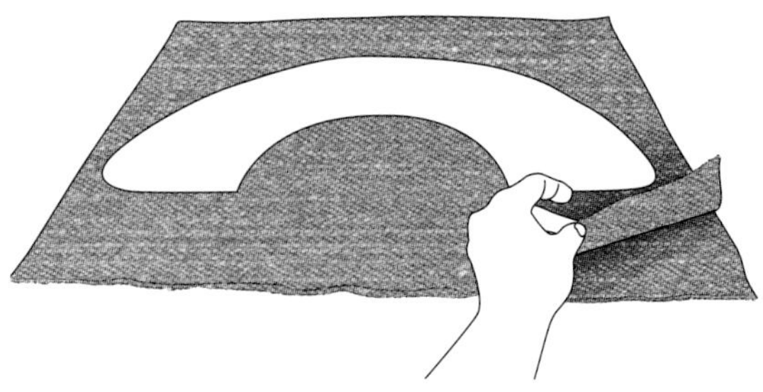

6

Place the two pieces of fabric over one another, under the neck pattern.

7

Mark its outline with tailor's chalk.

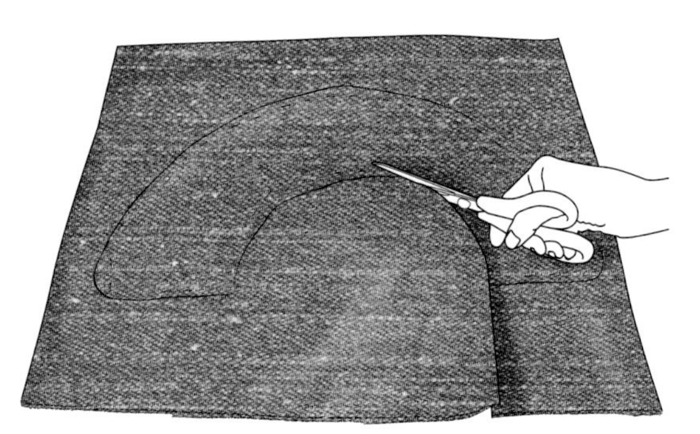

8

Pin the two sections of fabric inside the marks and cut along the chalked line with scissors.

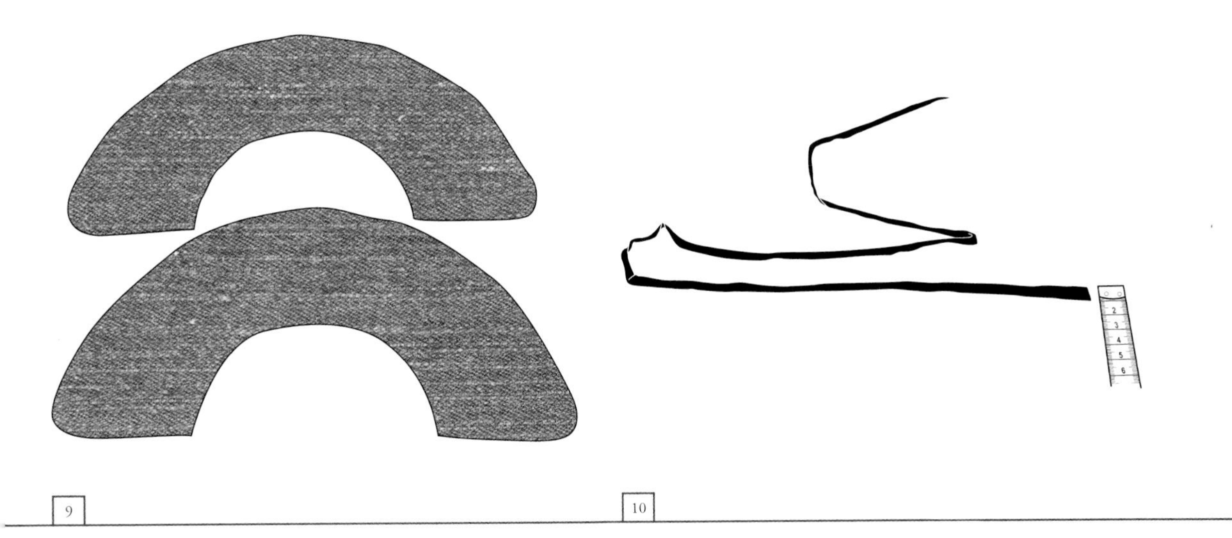

9

You will now have two identical neck pieces.

10

To tie the collar in a decorative manner, use a satin ribbon 0.4 inches (1 cm) wide.

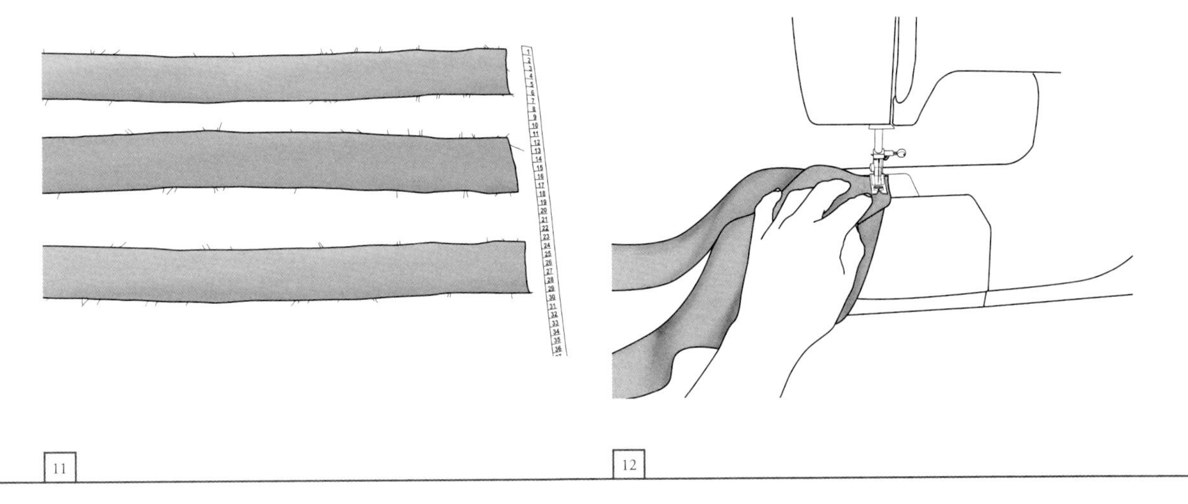

11

Cut three strips of thin fabric, such as silk gauze or muslin, in a color that contrasts with the neck piece. These strips should be 2.5 inches (6 cm) wide by 3 feet (1 m) long.

12

With the sewing machine, link the strips at their ends with final stitching to get a single strip that is 10 feet (3 m) long.

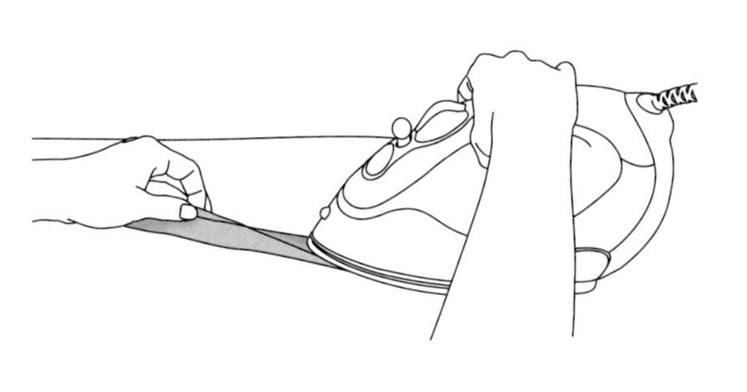

13

Fold and iron the resulting strip through the center, so that its width is reduced to 1.2 inches (3 cm).

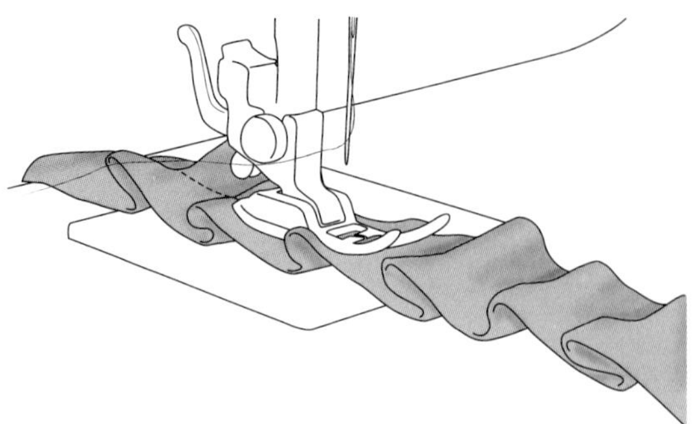

14

Now, with the sewing machine, stitch the folded strip center and, at the same time, pinch the fabric to create small pleats that are about 0.8 inches (2 cm). Once completed, these folds create a zigzag shape.

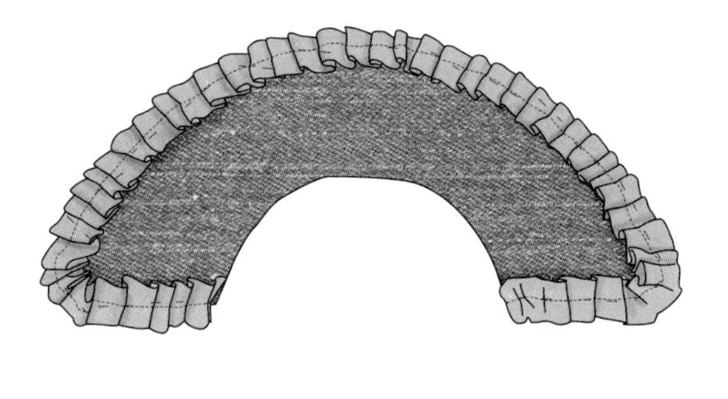

15

Now take the neck piece, place the fabric right side upward and pin on the folded strip.

16

Using thread in a different color, tack the folded strip to the neck piece.

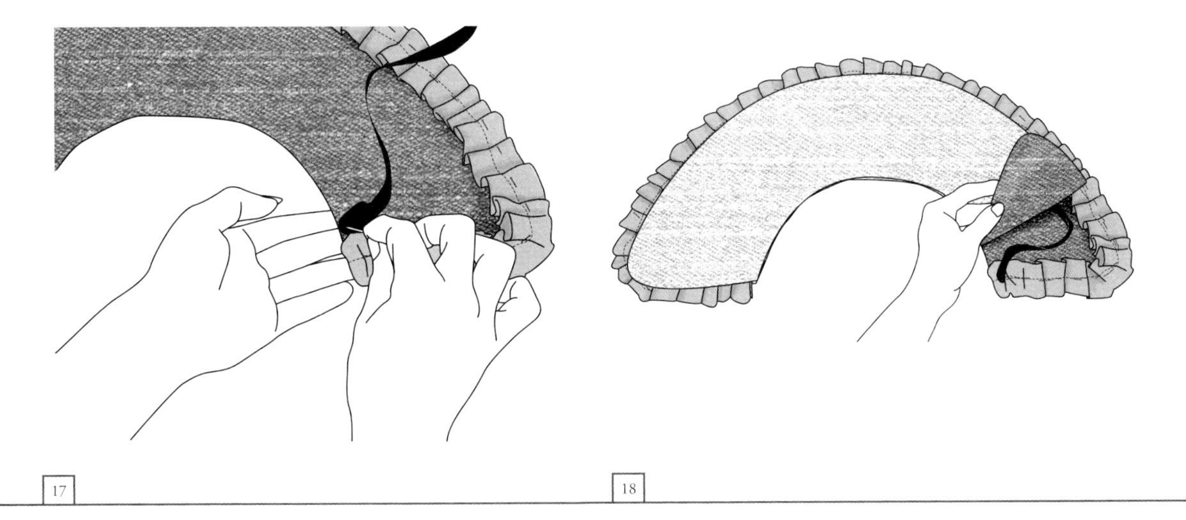

17

18

Also tack the ends of the satin ribbon to avoid the pieces sliding when the collar is closed.

Make sure that the strips do not fall out of the contour of the neck piece as you put the other fabric piece on top, leaving the wrong side of the fabric facing up (the two right sides are on the inside).

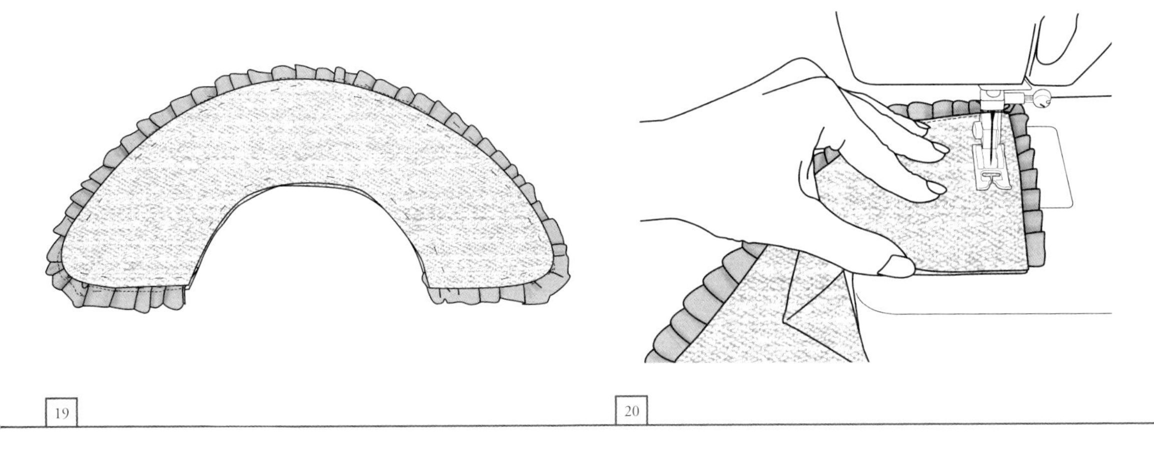

19

20

Pin both pieces together carefully, making sure to match the contours.

With the sewing machine, sew the two pieces with a short stitch. The stitches should be approximately 0.2 inches (0.5 cm) from the edge and should be as neat as possible. Leave about 2 inches (5 cm) to use when turning the piece the right way out.

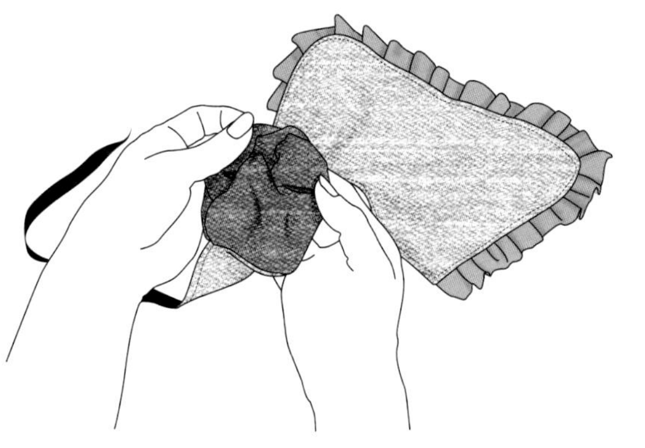

21

Cut the remaining basting so that only the final sewing is left visible. Turn the piece the right way out using the 2 inches (5 cm) that you left without stitches.

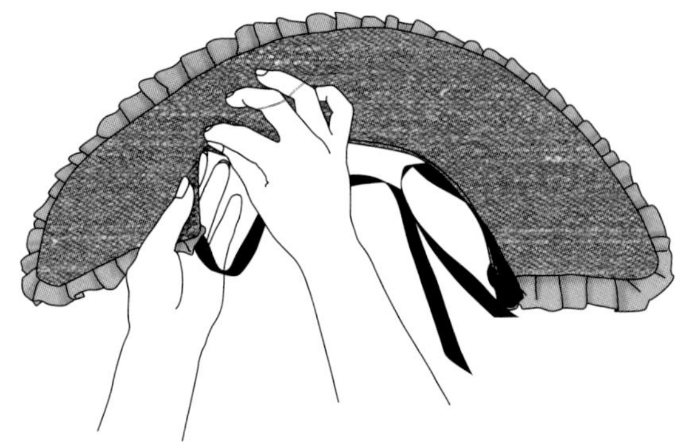

22

Sew with invisible stitching the 2-inch (5 cm) area so that the piece is fully closed.

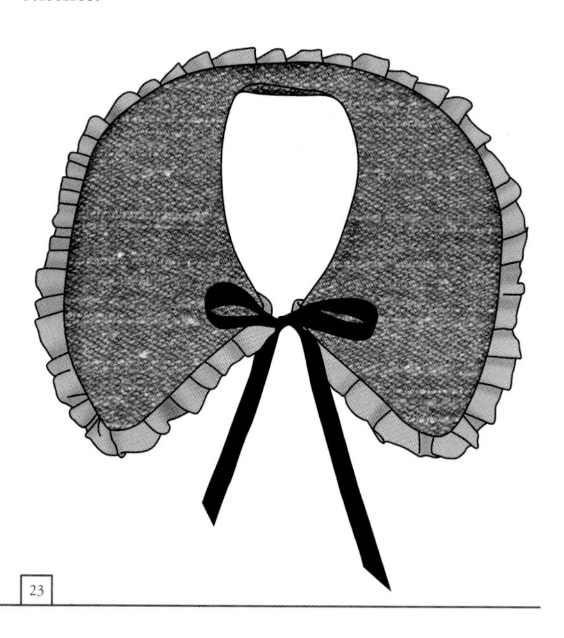

23

Tie the satin ribbon in a bow to join the piece at the front.

Look at the final result — an original shirt collar that can be decorated with embroidered beads and studs. You can try this project with fabrics of varying colors and textures to suit any occasion.

GLOSSARY

Bias cut: A way of cutting fabric on a diagonal, which makes the garment fit the body much more closely.

Brown paper: Brown paper, or kraft paper, is a strong paper that is often used for packaging and making patterns in dressmaking.

Crêpe de Chine: A silky, lightweight and rugged fabric that is very fine without being translucent. It can be made with 100 percent silk or with acetate, viscose rayon or even polyester. It is characterized by its wonderful fall and is generally used to make ladies' dresses, shirts and scarves.

Cup: An object made with rigid material that completely covers and supports the breast. It is mostly used with revealing necklines and in garments such as bikinis and bras, in order to reinforce the area. It can be bought in almost all sizes.

Draping: After gathering the fabric at a given point, this technique permits you to shape various pleats from that point.

Fabric weight: Fabrics are categorized as light, medium or heavy. Manufacturers categorize fabrics by their weight, independently of their composition.

Fraying: Removing threads from the edge of the fabric to achieve an effect similar to a fringe, but made from the fabric's own threads.

Freeing seams: Moving seams toward one side or the other after they have been sewn. This is usually done to avoid them being visible on the garment because they are raised, or so that they do not mark the fabric when ironed.

Gathering: Folding the fabric in small parallel folds. This technique can be performed by hand or by machine, but in general the latter helps to give a more uniform look.

Georgette: Light semitransparent fabric, generally with a matte finish. Like most fabrics, it was originally made of silk but nowadays many synthetic variations are available.

Godet: A French term used for the triangular piece of fabric added to a garment to give it fullness.

Hem: A fold or finish that is usually done at the edges of a garment to finish it.

Hemstitch: Tiny stitches that can be made either by hand, with a diagonal stitch from back to front, or by machine, making a tiny fold and applying the smallest zigzags possible on your machine. In both cases it is used as a finish.

Kapok: This is a very light, water resistant, cotton-like material used for filling jackets, pillows, cushions and more. It is also used to add volume and to create padded effects on smaller items.

Lace ribbon: Synthetic or silk ribbon that is sold in different widths and mostly used for giving a garment a delicate touch. It is often found in lingerie and baby clothes.

Long stitch: Consecutive straight stitches with space between them. When done by machine, setting number three or four is usually used. When the tension of the thread is decreased slightly, the stitches are ideal for gathering.

Manila paper: Silk paper that is used to create sewing patterns especially for pleats, as it can withstand the heat of the iron and its texture is very flexible and thin.

Muslin: Very fine translucent fabric from India. Originally made from silk, and then cotton, muslins today are often made of polyester because of its low price.

Notches: Small cuts, made on the outside edge of the seam allowance, that are used to create curves in fabric. They get their name from marks made on the pattern as an assembly guide.

Organdy: Very similar to organza, but usually finer. Organdy is made from cotton and finished using the same method as organza, which is ideal for starched sections of dresses.

Organza: A fine, transparent material that is characterized by its rigidity. This rigidity is created by a chemical treatment and does not disappear after being washed. It is used mainly for making entire garments, usually ceremonial, as well as for finishes, antique collars and other decorative touches.

Pattern card: A thicker type of kraft paper.

Pintucks: Small folds in the fabric that are stitched very near the fold's edge. Due to their small size, they seem to have been folded around a pin. Their purpose is mainly aesthetic.

Presser foot for sewing leather: The presser foot on sewing machines holds the fabric firmly while you sew. Several different types can be used, depending on the project. The presser foot for sewing leather consists of a wheel that runs the leather through it as it is being sewed, making sewing curves and straight lines easy.

Round pliers: Pliers with cylindrical or tapered tips, mostly used to bend wire, but can also be used to make chains.

Rustic (or raw) fabric: A finish that is used mainly on silk. It has a somewhat rough texture, ideal for creating contrast when combined with finer materials.

Satin ribbon: A dressmaking ribbon, usually made from synthetic material. It is available in standard widths and is sold in men's clothing stores.

Set of beads: Small set of beads prepared for embroidery on fabric. These beads are usually brightly colored and come in a variety of different sizes and shapes.

Silk chiffon: This material is virtually identical to muslin, except it is lighter and more airy.

Silk satin: A compact and shiny fabric with thicker threads that are hidden during manufacture, giving it a delicate yet rigid look.

Starch spray: Liquid chemical preparation in a powder spray that is used when ironing clothes to achieve a similar finish to starching — it gives the fabric a certain stiffness and eliminates creases.

Straight stitch: Simple, straight, consecutive stitches, used especially in final seams and finishing edges. In most modern sewing machines, this stitch is controlled with setting number one or two.

Suede/suedette: Suede is usually made from the inside of lamb skin and has a fine, soft texture. It is used in leatherwork to make garments as well as accessories and even footwear. Suedette is a finer, synthetic version with a velvety look.

Synthetic leather: Usually plastic, this material imitates natural leather. These days, the similarity to natural leather has been perfected and most types of skins have a synthetic version available.

Tacking: Used to temporarily join layers of fabric, especially to prevent movement while the garment is being tried on. It is done by hand with large stitches that are removed at the final sewing.

Tube: Name for the semi-cylindrical form that the fabric takes on when it has been gathered.

Tulle: The king of delicate fabrics, these days it is used for making all kinds of garments but is generally used for delicate veils and accessories. Whether silk or other fibers are used, it is made on a base of crossed threads. It is one of the prettiest and most valued fabrics.

Wire: Iron, copper or brass wire is used in sewing to provide rigidity and reinforce certain parts of the garment.

Zigzag stitch: A type of sewing machine stitch in a zigzag shape, generally used for finishing seams and for seams that need some slack, since its unusual shape allows them to yield slightly.